THE AUTOBIOGRAPH
OF SCIENCE
EDITED BY
FOREST RAY MOULTON
AND
JUSTUS J. SCHIFFERES

THE GREAT TRIUMPHS of science, in all fields, throughout all time, are recorded here in the original words of those who achieved them. Each of the one hundred selections is the best thing a man ever said or wrote about the most important thing he ever did or thought. Together with introductory notes by the editors these masterpieces form a complete life story of science on the march from the Egyptians to Einstein, from alchemy to aerodynamics.

Good science makes good reading, as this unique anthology proves. Hippocrates on medicine, Leonardo da Vinci on flight, Newton on gravitation, Harvey on blood circulation, Benjamin Franklin on electricity, Darwin on natural selection, Curie on radium, Freud on psychoanalysis— such epics of science are lucid, dramatic, and filled with warmly autobiographical touches. The thrill and excitement of vital new discoveries can be experienced here at first hand, and the combination of readability and reliability makes this a book for layman and scientific student alike.

A glance at the table of contents inside will reveal the brilliant selection the editors have made covering all sciences: medicine, biology, chemistry, physics, astronomy, optics, botany, genetics, anthropology, geology, aeronautics, psychology, as well as many related studies. Both editors are distinguished in the field of

(Continued on back flap)

4622-45

plays have been produced in Minneapolis, Chicago, and New York. He now heads Science Publications Council.

THE AUTOBIOGRAPHY
OF
SCIENCE

THE
AUTOBIOGRAPHY
OF
SCIENCE

EDITED BY

FOREST RAY MOULTON

AND

JUSTUS J. SCHIFFERES

DOUBLEDAY, DORAN AND COMPANY, INC.

Garden City 1945 New York

A SCIENCE PUBLICATIONS COUNCIL BOOK

PRINTED IN THE UNITED STATES
AT
THE COUNTRY LIFE PRESS, GARDEN CITY, N. Y.

To
ANNA SCHIFFERES
whom we affectionately
call
QUEEN ANNE

Preface

> But what is the life of a literary or scientific man, and where are we to find the history of it? In his works. Newton and Euler are their own best biographers.—HENRY HUNTER, D.D., in Preface to "The Letters of Euler": London, 1802.

SCIENCE, born in antiquity, has grown up to dominate the twentieth century. Like Atlas of old, this new giant carries civilization poised on his shoulders. There is no need to rehearse here the "miracles" of modern science and its offspring, technology. They abound everywhere—in metal, plastics, drugs, and statistics concerning increased length of life. The companion volume to this book is not another book but a museum, as variegated and endless as the products of civilization itself. We should not, however, confuse the spawn of science with the spirit of science.

At the mention of the word "science" many otherwise well-educated people are prompted to one of two quite irrational reactions. They bow down or they run away. It is one of the many purposes of "The Autobiography of Science" to prove to the general reader not only that he can understand but also that he will enjoy the literature of science written by its greatest masters. No single definition of science has ever been accepted. We describe science simply as the sum of the things and thoughts of its practitioners.

They are a motley company, including artists, tax collectors, clergymen, lawyers, brewers, army officers, apothecaries, patent-office clerks, dandies, *bons vivants,* recluses, explorers, diplomats, lens grinders, child prodigies, university professors, alchemists, astrologers, cranks, and fanatics. But all the great scientists have one thing in common: each snatched from the subtle motions of nature one irrevocable secret; each caught one feather of the plumage of the Great White Bird that symbolizes everlasting truth.

"The Autobiography of Science" is their story. Though welded together with brief introductory commentaries to orient the reader through the centuries, "The Autobiography of Science" is fundamentally an anthology of the key passages from the master works of all sciences. The selections are in general arranged in chronological sequence by periods. Occasionally the time order has been violated to permit grouping by topics, and some attempt has been made to keep the biological sciences and the physical sciences together within periods. Often dramatic and exciting and always alive, this is the life story of science in the original words of the men who made it.

For the most part they are simple words, easy to understand and follow in their context. Of the 100 scientists whose works are quoted in this volume, there are fewer than a dozen (actually less than 5 per cent of the whole book) whose writing could be classed as hard or even slow reading.[1] It is also our impression that there are fewer than 100 unusual scientific words among the more than 250,000 words in this volume. In only one instance, Einstein, have we felt it incumbent to provide a key to vocabulary and that principally because a discussion of the theory of relativity employs old and common words with new and unaccustomed meanings.

The great scientists have proved amazingly adept at communicating their great truths to their fellow men. Often they have vaulted over apparent difficulties in language and vocabulary by appeal to common, human example, familiar in connotation. For example, in expounding the laws of motion, as abstruse a subject as one could select, Isaac Newton does not hesitate to drive home his point by use of homely example, thus: "If you press a stone with your finger, the finger is also pressed by the stone. If a horse draws a stone tied to a rope, the horse (if I may say so) will be equally drawn back towards the stone."

Many of the passages in this anthology partake of the highest qualities of literary style. Present-day "third-person," "passive-voice" fashion in scientific communications notwithstanding, the science masters of the ages, speaking in the first person, unequivocally illustrate that "the literature of power" and "the literature of knowledge"—De Quincey's phrases—can be one. Good science makes good reading.

In both the choice of eminent scientists represented and the selection of specific passages from their works, we have been guided chiefly by two criteria: first, importance as "turning points" in the history of science, and second, readability. We have tried to locate the best thing a man ever said or wrote about the most important thing he ever did or thought. We have given greatest consideration to those men whose work seemed to chart the main stream of the development of scientific thought. Our original outline contained three hundred names. We gathered or noted enough material to fill a dozen books. No anthology is ever complete, nor can every selection be justified to every critic. We ask that this book be judged on what is in it rather than on what is left out.

[1]Parts of Copernicus, Galileo, Newton, Dalton, Maxwell, Gibbs, Einstein, Planck, Bohr, Schroedinger, De Broglie, Heisenberg.

We have our own regrets at the omission, for example, of such great figures in the history of science as Celsus and Varro in antiquity; the Arabs who preserved science during the Middle Ages; astronomers like Johannes Kepler, Tycho Brahe, Pierre Simon de Laplace, Thomas Chamberlin, and the Herschels; mathematicians like Euclid, Leibnitz, Euler, Gauss, Bishop Berkeley, and Sir William Hamilton; physicians whose pens were dipped in poet's ink: Ronald Ross, S. Weir Mitchell, and Oliver Goldsmith; biometricians like Quételet and Karl Pearson; men of healing such as William Withering, Robert Koch, Paul Ehrlich, Gerhard Domagk, Minot, Murphy and Whipple, Fleming and Florey, Banting and Best; and finally, such trenchant modern interpreters of science as Eddington, Jeans, Hogben, and the Haldanes.

Figuratively speaking, we have attempted to plan an itinerary through the history of science which would enable the reader to behold for himself all the great monuments and "points of interest" which a literary tour, necessarily limited in space, might encompass. Quite definitely we do not claim to have drawn a detailed map of the whole continent of science across which such a road must lead. Instead of rushing the reader through an excessive number of short, disjointed passages from a multitude of authors, we have in most cases endeavored to quote passages long enough to give the substance as well as the occasion of the great ideas in science. Now well accepted, many of these ideas—evolution, psychoanalysis, radioactivity, and the revolution of the earth about the sun— were revolutionary and startling when first enunciated.

Both to preserve the substance of these landmarks of scientific literature and to follow as straight a highway as possible through the winding and often crisscrossed paths of scientific thought, we have limited ourselves to the science of the Western world, excluded the "social sciences," and discarded developments in favor of beginnings. In placing emphasis on origins rather than results, we have, for example, chosen to illuminate the chronicle of electricity with Gilbert, Franklin, and Faraday rather than its later-day wizards, Edison, Pupin, and Steinmetz. In reading passages from the "fathers" of the various sciences, we hope that others may share with us the recaptured thrill of being present at the birth of great, glistening new ideas.

Our difficulties in selecting the men and the passages that finally appear in this volume were multiplied not only by the interrelationships between the sciences but also by the fact that many of the great scientists were polymaths who, like the many-sided Leonardo da Vinci, succeeded brilliantly in many fields. We will cite a single representative example of our difficulty, for in so doing we can further display the method by which we actually carried out our task of selection.

Hermann von Helmholtz (1821–94) was admittedly a most eminent and versatile scientist. While still a young man, he brilliantly demonstrated the doctrine of the conservation of energy. Later he invented the ophthalmoscope for observing the retina of the eye. He was at the same time investigating problems in physiological optics, which together with other manifold experiments on the mechanism of hearing and the sensations of tone laid the foundations of experimental psychology. Intermittently he made stirring addresses in defense of academic freedom. With such a plethora, what should we pick?

The famous memoir on the conservation of energy was ruled out not only because it is too abstrusely mathematical but also because we were already convinced that James Prescott Joule's delightful paper on "Matter, Living Force, and Heat" would give the reader the substance of this great concept in clearer, more picturesque language—and we did not wish to repeat. Physiological optics was a tempting subject, but we had already given considerable space to optics in the passages from Roger Bacon, Newton, Huygens, De Broglie, and Schroedinger. The invention of the ophthalmoscope was a great event. "Helmholtz has unfolded a new world to us!" exclaimed one of his colleagues. But recourse to Helmholtz' original paper confirmed the suspicion that a dull description of a physical object rarely suggests the importance of the thing itself. As for the addresses on academic freedom in German universities, they are pitiably outmoded. We were left with "The Sensations of Tone as a Physiologic Basis for the Theory of Music." But here was plenty of meat! This long, 330,000-word book is a fundamental work, a turning point in the history of experimental psychology.

Except for a short passage on acoustics in Vitruvius, the Roman architect, we had nowhere else covered the subject of sound. It is part of our general plan to demonstrate or infer the relationships of science to other arts of civilized man: literature, painting, sculpture, cookery, medicine, and philosophy. With Helmholtz we could suggest a fundamental relationship between science and music. Furthermore, we could reveal that science is a pathway to aesthetics in general. Always we sought after such "overtones" in our selections.

Why the specific passages, which happen to come from the first and last chapters? Judged from a literary standpoint, both are well written and excellently translated from the original German. They are rich in colorful words and apt metaphors; they are well organized. Even when taken from their context and shortened by the omission of a few sentences and paragraphs, they have structure. Like a satisfying essay, each passage—the one a simple introductory exposition, the other a provocative summary—purveys a complete idea. Then, from the scientific point of view, we felt that the substance of these passages offers an accurate introduction to the theory of sound, an important topic in physics. Finally, the passage on "sensations of tone in general" supplies the best simple description that we could find of wave motion, a subject of highest significance in other branches of physics. Such interrelatedness more than justified our selection, we concluded. This in general was our method.

We have earlier anthologists of science, notably Allan R. Cullimore, William Dampier-Whetham, Logan Clendening, W. S. Knickerbocker, Frederick Houk Law, Harlow Shapley, and W. F. Magie, to thank for directing us to a few pieces that we might not otherwise have considered and for confirming our judgment concerning others.

That science has always spoken an international language "The Autobiography of Science" confirms. Fewer than half—only forty-five— of the selections in this volume were originally written in English. The original texts of the others, as noted separately in the bibliographic note accompanying each selection, are in French, Italian, German, Greek, Latin, Dutch, Danish, Hebrew, and hieroglyphics. We wish to express our grateful appreciation to the many scholars and historians of science, as well as the learned societies, whose labors and interest have made good English translations available to us. Only one new translation is offered (Cuvier). It is our earnest hope that this book may play some part in extending interest in the history of science beyond the small circle of graduate schools and specialized societies and carry it forward into the minds of men and women at home and at work and to young people in elementary and secondary schools and in colleges. We think science can be studied as a *cultural* subject.

In preparing our texts for publication we have kept the general reader rather than the specialist primarily in mind. With a few exceptions (for the sake of literary charm) the final editing of the texts has been in a style according to the best current American usage. We have not hesitated to modernize spelling or punctuation and break up long paragraphs into shorter ones wherever such practice gave promise of saving the reader from discouragement at queer words or unaccustomed orthography.

Because many of our passages are excerpts from much longer works and since we were trying to present the gist of what each scientist had to say in the briefest space, we have sometimes had to emend the texts by omissions of sentences, paragraphs, or whole sections. Where these have been few, three points (. . .) have been used to indicate the omission. However, where they have been so frequent as to make the passage look strange in print, the repetition of the points has been given up entirely. In only one instance, Maxwell's paper on "A Dynamical Theory of the Electromagnetic Field," has a genuine "condensation" been attempted. Elsewhere any words inserted by us have been set in brackets [ ]. The reader may be certain that the autobiography of science is authentic.

There are no mathematical formulas in this book and only a few statistical tables. If it be therefore affirmed that we have given the reader science with mathematics left out, an error comparable to serving a Thanksgiving dinner without turkey, we must reply that it is only mathematical notation and symbolism that have been omitted. From Archimedes to Einstein we have included whatever mathematical reasoning and theory was germane to our theme. To have included extensive passages on mathematics in its own symbolic language, we felt, would be as inconsiderate of the general reader as reprinting our texts in their original foreign languages. If precedent be necessary, we lean upon Laplace and Faraday. Helmholtz said of Faraday: "It is indeed remarkable in the highest degree to observe how, by a kind of intuition, without using a single formula, he found out a number of comprehensive theorems which can only be proved by the highest powers of mathematical analysis."

There are six ways to read this book: as a storybook, a history book, a textbook, a reference book, a source book, or a chronicle. Taste and previous interests may guide the reader to those authors and passages which he will first savor, but it is our hope that in their proper order every passage will prove both interesting and illuminating.

In conclusion, we hope that this book will introduce many readers to the history of science and orient them in it; that it will give them a firsthand, original account of the substance of great scientific thinking; that it will suggest the sweep, scope, and international brilliance of scientific development; that it will give them a basis for discriminating between true and pseudo science; and finally, best of all, that it will provide an accurate, intimate, living knowledge of the great men and women of science, some insight into their characters, some sense of the true nature of their work. We shall be pleased if the reader, whether scientist or layman, finds "The Autobiography of Science" a continuing source of entertainment and education, a book to read, to enjoy, to quote, and to own.

Our most grateful appreciation goes to Richard E. Scammon, distinguished service professor at the University of Minnesota, who gave unstintingly of his time and great fund of learning that this work in the history of science might be carried forward.

F. R. MOULTON
JUSTUS J. SCHIFFERES

January, 1945

Contents

VI SCIENCE WEDS PROGRESS: In the Early Nineteenth
    Century 286

    Nineteenth-Century Chemists
    LIEBIG, WÖHLER, DAVY, VAN'T HOFF, ARRHENIUS, KEKULÉ,
    MENDELYEEV, PERKIN, BAEYER, AND NOBEL 286
        Up to Aspirin and Dynamite 286

    "The Mutual Relation of Electricity, Magnetism, and Motion"
    MICHAEL FARADAY (1791–1867) 288
        Notes from His Diary 290

    More Electricity of the Same Kind
    JOSEPH HENRY (1797–1878) 291
        Induced Electrical Currents 292

    Conservation of Energy
    JAMES PRESCOTT JOULE (1818–89) 292
        "On Matter, Living Force, and Heat" 293
        Memoir on the Mechanical Equivalent of Heat . . . 298

    A New Method of Diagnosis
    RENÉ LAËNNEC (1781–1826) 299
        The Invention of the Stethoscope 300

    A Classic of Epidemiology: "On Cholera"
    JOHN SNOW (1813–58) 302
        The Broad Street Pump 303
        The Prevention of Cholera 307

    How We Digest Our Food: The Scientific Account
    WILLIAM BEAUMONT (1785–1853) 309
        "Experiments and Observations on the Gastric Juice and
        the Physiology of Digestion" 310

    The Great Argument Against Needless Deaths in Childbirth
    OLIVER WENDELL HOLMES (1809–94) 312
        "The Contagiousness of Puerperal Fever" 313

    Anesthesia! The Conquest of Pain
    CRAWFORD LONG (1815–78) 320
        An Affidavit Concerning the First Administration of a
        Surgical Anesthetic 321

Introduction

SCIENCE YESTERDAY, TODAY, AND TOMORROW

SCIENCE is so much a part of the life and thoughts of the world that it is difficult to withdraw enough from its immediate influence to survey its long history, evaluate its current importance, or speculate profitably on its future. In some respects the history of science resembles a flowing river. Its beginnings, like those of the mighty Amazon, lie beyond the farthest horizons of the known. As rivulets join successively into larger and larger streams, finally becoming irresistible floods, so the elementary and isolated first elements of various branches of science progressively combine and develop into such great syntheses of experience and reasoning as the law of gravitation, the electromagnetic theory of radiation, and the principle of the conservation of energy.

The beginnings of science were in simple things—the regular succession of day and night, the recurrence of the seasons, the repetitious phases of the moon, the sprouting of plants, the unfolding of blossoms, the maturing of seeds, the coming and going of the winds, the rains, and the storms. It was from observations of such phenomena and reflections on their meaning that science was born. These phenomena did not occur so frequently as to be commonplace nor so rarely that their recurrence passed unnoticed. It was the repetitions that attracted attention and stimulated more careful observations. The month was defined by the cyclic recurrence of the phases of the moon, and the days of the week were named after the seven known wandering celestial bodies in the sky.

More than twenty centuries before the beginning of the Christian Era observations of the rising and setting of Venus were being accurately recorded in Babylon, and twenty-five hundred years ago the times of eclipses were being successfully predicted from laws of their repetitions which had been derived from many centuries of careful observations. The orderliness of nature was being established even though that order was often ascribed to the intervention of gods and goddesses. The interval of incubation before the arrival of this stage when science in a sense was born was undoubtedly many times longer than that which has since elapsed.

Science from the beginning traveled along both speculative and practical paths. Of the former, theories of the creation of the earth were among the most generally invented. They were important in the development of science because they are expressions of a general desire of the human mind to know what is the "cause" of things. That desire, refined and clarified, becomes a fixed purpose to know the antecedents of every existing set of conditions, which is one of the essentials of the scientific method. When this desire is turned toward less formidable problems than the origin of the physical universe, it often leads to results of great practical value. For this reason speculations about a creation of the earth, and "the stars also," may be gratefully forgiven.

Since centuries of observations are necessary to determine the period of the recurrence of similar eclipses of the moon, it is obvious that so far as astronomy is concerned it had its beginnings back beyond the limits of recorded history. Similarly it would be an error to assume that the wisdom in the Hippocratic Oath was distilled in a shorter period from the varied experiences of physicians dealing with the sick and dying, and with one another. To suppose that the laws for human relations contained in the Code of Hammurabi, or in Aristotle's principle of the continuity of organs and qualities in living organisms, or the sanitary rules of Moses, or the axioms and logical structures of Euclid, sprang, phoenixlike, from the mind of one man would be almost as naïve as the ancient theories of creation. Instead of originating in and coming forth full grown from the individual who first cast them in permanent form, such sayings, weighted with wisdom, were more like a stream bursting into the open from a thousand unknown sources. To change the figure of speech, modern man has much to learn by attending the records left by rare spirits who, standing on the shoulders of their predecessors, as Newton said he did, saw farther and more clearly and put their visions in words that time and fate fortunately have not destroyed.

Science did not originate at only one time or place or among only one people or under any particular form of government or religion, nor was it permanently recorded in only one language or by one race. Moses led his people out from Egyptian slavery, Hippocrates practiced the arts of healing in a small island south of Greece, and Archimedes was drawing geometrical figures in Sicilian sand when Roman soldiers struck him down. Copernicus in tragic Poland and Galileo in historic Italy, using astronomical observations made by Babylonians and Greeks two thousand years earlier, proved the heliocentric theory of the planetary system, and in doing so took man from his proud place at the center of creation and relegated him to the surface of a little body revolving around the sun. Lucretius and Pliny were from proud Rome; Harvey and Bacon and Newton and Darwin from England; Huygens and Van Leeuwenhoek from Holland; Descartes and Pascal and Cuvier and Pasteur from France; Lyell and Clerk Maxwell from Scotland; Lord Kelvin from Ireland; Mendel and Freud from Austria; Linnaeus and Arrhenius from Sweden; Mme. Curie, as well as Copernicus, from Poland; Von Humboldt, and Liebig and Wöhler and Einstein from Germany; Mendelyeev from Russia; Bohr from Denmark; Maeterlinck from Belgium; Rutherford from New Zealand; Osler from Canada; and Franklin and Henry and Langley from the United States. These names are a few from the many which must appear in any autobiography of science. If the list were more nearly complete and suitable quotations available, names would appear also of men who lived and learned in Crete, in Persia, in Assyria, in Babylonia, in Sumeria, in India, and in China.

The limitations of the mind are such that it has been found advantageous to divide human history into periods characterized by the use of tools, or by wealth or military power, or by culture or form of government. There were, for example, the Stone Age and the Age of Bronze, the age of the Old Kingdom in Egypt, the Golden Age of Greece, the Dark Ages in Europe, the Elizabethan Period in England and the Colonial Period in North America. Such terms are partly descriptive of the times and countries to which they are applied, but only partly descriptive. For Rome at the summit of her power was decaying most rapidly in her heart; and in the long night of the Dark Ages in Europe the great Library and School of Translation was established at Bagdad (c. 856), the House of Science in Cairo (995), a school of medicine in Salerno (1077) and another at Bologna (1156); students began gathering at Oxford (1167), paper was produced in Spain (1189), the University of Paris was chartered (1200), the *"Opus Magnus"* was written by Roger Bacon (1214–92?), University College at Oxford was founded (1249), Peterhouse College, Cambridge, was established (1284), spectacles were invented (1289), the University of Vienna was opened (1364), and printing from movable type was first practiced (c. 1450).

Instead of dividing the history of science into fixed periods of time it has been thought advantageous in collating an autobiography of science to present it under such general subdivisions as "Science Is Born," "Science Sleeps," "Science Reawakens," et cetera, because they are partly descriptive phrases that provide something concrete in universal human experience on which to fasten the attention. Yet, like the changes going on in living organisms, in which new cells are always being formed and old ones are always being eliminated, new ideas in science are always being born and old ones are always dying and being abandoned. But the definite and explicit titles for the major subdivisions of this book, even though incomplete and perhaps oversimplified, are better than attempts at more precise historical characterization.

It is clearly impossible to consider individually the innumerable and widely different currents of science which exist today. It would be difficult even to separate them into fairly distinct classes on the basis of their subject matter or of the methods by which they are advanced. There are, however, two somewhat different, but not wholly distinct, aspects of science that may be used, generally, to separate its vast river into two parts. One part consists of the technological applications which within a few decades have made greater changes in the physical environment of man than had taken place in all earlier human history. The other consists of the formulation of the so-called laws of nature which describe how natural phenomena succeed one another. One is concerned with the practical usefulness of science; the other is interested in it as art. The one is grandeur in the world; the other is glory in the heart.

Long centuries ago our intellectual ancestors in the valleys of the Euphrates and the Nile, and on the hills of Greece, looked up into the starry sky at night and saw majestic beauty there. The relatively changeless stars spoke of order above a chaotic world. Among them wandered the moon, and more leisurely Aurora and Hesperus, the morning and the evening stars, always changing as the seasons ran through their cycles, even while dynasties rose and passed away. In a period dominated by mythology and superstition, and when kings were creating hanging gardens in Babylon and building wonders of the world, a few rare spirits in various lands were observing and recording and transmitting down the centuries the order in the heavens, the music of the spheres. That order, found first in motions of celestial bodies, was discerned with greater difficulty in the complicated conditions which exist on the earth below. Yet gradually observations of such recurring phenomena as the succession of the seasons, the flowing and ebbing of the tides, the cycles of living organisms, each reproducing its own kind, suggested convincingly that order is universal. With even the partial acceptance of this conclusion, perhaps the most momentous in human history, superstitions began to lose their terrors and the stream of science was well under way.

Celestial phenomena are so largely cyclical that observers of the heavenly bodies might have concluded that fixed cycles are the only expressions of order and therefore the only basis for science. But the mind recoils from believing in endless repetition, for eventually it becomes as monotonous as stagnation. Among the Greeks there were discussions of primeval elements, and universal law and adumbrations of evolution. The Roman Lucretius in *"De Rerum Natura"* declared that all things change. As rendered into stately verse by Hallock, he said:

> *No single thing abides; but all things flow.*
> *Fragment to fragment clings—the things thus grow*
> *Until we know them and name them. By degrees*
> *They melt, and are no more the things we know.*

All things change, but not in a chaotic, haphazard manner. The order which exists at this instant will be transformed into that which will exist in the next in an *orderly* way capable of understanding and description. This is the essence of the doctrine of evolution, and it applies not only to the motions of the planets and the stars in the sky, where it started, but also to everything that takes place on this earth, including the myriad steps from the amoeba to man. In ancient days heroes slew the dragons that terrified men; science is destroying the more dreadful superstitions that have darkened human lives.

THE AUTOBIOGRAPHY
OF
SCIENCE

I SCIENCE IS BORN: In Antiquity

"In the Beginning, God . . ."

THE BOOK OF GENESIS, CHAPTER I

No SCIENTIFIC EXPLANATION of the existence of the universe and the flesh-and-blood men who do the explaining has superseded the first four words of the Bible. Science does not tell *why* we and the universe about us exist at all. It has cautiously offered to explain *how* the world arrived at its present physical state; and over these details men have quarreled. For many centuries after their promulgation, some time after 1500 B.C., the opening verses of the first of the five books of Moses gave what the wisest men of those times considered the most reasonable and hence the most scientific account of creation.

Hebrew was the language in which Genesis and other historical books of the Bible were compiled in Babylon twenty-five hundred years ago. Greek translations were made about 150 B.C. The English text given here is a slightly modernized rendering of the most famous English version, the King James Bible of the seventeenth century.

THE STORY OF CREATION

In THE BEGINNING God created the heaven and the earth.

And the earth was without form, and void; and darkness was upon the face of the deep. And the Spirit of God moved upon the face of the waters.

And God said, Let there be light: and there was light.

And God saw the light, that it was good: and God divided the light from the darkness.

And God called the light Day, and the darkness he called Night. And the evening and the morning were the first day.

And God said, Let there be a firmament in the midst of the waters, and let it divide the waters from the waters.

And God made the firmament, and divided the waters which were under the firmament from the waters which were above the firmament: and it was so.

And God called the firmament Heaven. And the evening and the morning were the second day.

And God said, Let the waters under the heaven be gathered together unto one place, and let the dry land appear: and it was so.

And God called the dry land Earth; and the gathering together of the waters called he Seas: and God saw that it was good.

And God said, Let the earth bring forth grass, the herb yielding seed, and the fruit tree yielding fruit after his kind, whose seed is in itself, upon the earth: and it was so.

And the earth brought forth grass, and herb yielding seed after his kind, and the tree yielding fruit, whose seed was in itself, after his kind: and God saw that it was good.

And the evening and the morning were the third day.

And God said, Let there be lights in the firmament of the heaven to divide the day from the night; and let them be for signs, and for seasons, and for days, and years:

And let them be for lights in the firmament of the heaven to give light upon the earth: and it was so.

And God made two great lights; the greater light to rule the day, and the lesser light to rule the night: he made the stars also.

And God set them in the firmament of the heaven to give light upon the earth.

And to rule over the day and over the night, and to divide the light from the darkness: and God saw that it was good.

And the evening and the morning were the fourth day.

And God said, Let the waters bring forth abundantly the moving creature that hath life, and fowl that may fly above the earth and in the open firmament of heaven.

And God created great whales, and every living creature that moveth, which the waters brought forth abundantly, after their kind, and every winged fowl after his kind: and God saw that it was good.

And God blessed them, saying, Be fruitful, and multiply, and fill the waters in the seas, and let fowl multiply in the earth.

And the evening and the morning were the fifth day.

And God said, Let the earth bring forth the living creature after his kind, cattle, and creeping thing, and beast of the earth after his kind: and it was so.

And God made the beast of the earth after his kind, and cattle after their kind, and everything that creepeth upon the earth after his kind: and God saw that it was good.

And God said, Let us make man in our image, after our likeness: and let them have dominion over the fish of the sea, and over the fowl of the air, and over the cattle, and over all the earth, and over every creeping thing that creepeth upon the earth.

So God created man in his own image, in the image of God created he him; male and female created he them.

And God blessed them, and God said unto them, Be fruitful, and multiply, and replenish the earth, and subdue it: and have dominion over the fish of the sea, and over the fowl of the air, and over every living thing that moveth upon the earth.

And God said, Behold, I have given you every herb bearing seed, which is upon the face of all the earth, and every tree, in the which is the fruit of a tree yielding seed; to you it shall be for meat.

And to every beast of the earth, and to every fowl of the air, and to every thing that creepeth upon the earth, wherein there is life, I have given every green herb for meat: and it was so.

And God saw everything that he had made, and, behold, it was very good. And the evening and the morning were the sixth day.

The Hieroglyphic Record

EGYPTIAN PAPYRI

To MANY MODERNS science remains only a better form of magic. Yet the leisured priests of ancient Egypt, practicing medicine and astronomy back in the Pyramid Age (3000–2475 B.C.), had already begun to take the fundamental scientific step of objectively recording accurate observations. The records, preserved on papyri (paper made from reeds), were only rediscovered in the nineteenth century. To relieve their parishioners of mankind's immemorial ills (for example, indigestion), the priests prescribed prayers against demons to be taken with potions—a standard method of magic—but they also wrote down reasonably accurate case histories for further study.

Hieroglyphics, or picture writing, was the "language" in which the priestly wisdom was preserved. The case of the broken nose appears in the Edwin Smith Surgical Papyrus whose English version (University of Chicago Press) was turned by Chicago's renowned Egyptologist, J. H. Breasted. He calls this five-thousand-year-old treatise on surgery "the earliest document in the history of science." "Advertisement for a Remedy" is from the Ebers Papyrus, the English version by Ebbell, as edited by Logan Clendening in "A Source Book of Medical History" (Paul B. Hoeber–Harper & Brothers, 1942).

ADVERTISEMENT FOR A REMEDY

HERE IS the great remedy. Come, thou who expellest evil things in this my stomach and drives them out from these my limbs! Horus and Seth have been conducted to the big palace at Heliopolis, where they consulted over the connection between Seth's testicles with Horus, and Horus shall get well like one who is on earth. He who drinks this shall be cured like these gods who are above. . . . These words should be said when drinking a remedy. Really excellent, proven many times!

HOW TO SET A BROKEN NOSE

IF THOU examinest a man having a break in the column of his nose, his nose being disfigured, and a [depression] being in it, while the swelling that is on it protrudes, [and] he had discharged blood from both his nostrils, thou shouldst say concerning him: "One having a break in the column of his nose. An ailment which I will treat."

Thou shouldst cleanse [it] for him [with] two plugs of linen. Thou shouldst place two [other] plugs of linen saturated with grease in the inside of his two nostrils. Thou shouldst put [him] at his mooring stakes until the swelling is drawn out. Thou shouldst apply for him stiff rolls of linen by which his nose is held fast. Thou shouldst treat him afterward [with] lint, every day until he recovers.

The Father of Medicine

HIPPOCRATES (460?-377? B.C.)

TODAY'S PHYSICIANS still take the Hippocratic Oath, the pledge of ethical responsibility to patients and teachers. It was laid down by Hippocrates, the "father of medicine," when he practiced and taught a truly scientific medicine among the snake-infested temples of Aesculapius—actually sanitariums—on the Greek island of Cos in the Aegean Sea sometime during the fourth and fifth centuries B.C. Hippocrates' great contribution was the concept that disease is caused by natural agents and not by supernatural demons. He also demonstrated that the diagnosis of specific diseases and the prognosis (opinion as to the outcome) should be made by observing the sequence of symptoms. He left many complete case histories, such as that of childbirth fever, from which a modern physician can still make a "retrospective diagnosis." The "Hippocratic collection" of writings contains eighty-seven treatises, including the aphorisms quoted here, attributed to the master (but not all written by him).

Greek was the language which Hippocrates spoke. The English translations of all pieces given here (except the Oath) were made by Francis Adams and published by the Sydenham Society in 1847. The Oath was translated by Ludwig Edelstein, and published in 1943 in Supplement No. 1 to the "Bulletin of the History of Medicine" (Johns Hopkins Press).

THE HIPPOCRATIC OATH

I SWEAR by Apollo Physician and Aesculapius and Hygeia and Panacea and all the gods and goddesses, making them my witnesses, that I will fulfill according to my ability and judgment this oath and this covenant:

To hold him who has taught me this art as equal to my parents and to live my life in partnership with him, and if he is in need of money to give him a share of mine, and to regard his offspring as equal to my brothers in male lineage and to teach them this art—if they desire to learn it— without fee and covenant; to give a share of precepts and oral instruction and all the other learning to my sons and to the sons of him who has instructed me and to pupils who have signed the covenant and have taken an oath according to the medical law, but to no one else.

I will apply dietetic measures for the benefit of the sick according to my ability and judgment; I will keep them from harm and injustice.

I will neither give a deadly drug to anybody if asked for it, nor will I make a suggestion to this effect. Similarly I will not give to a woman an abortive remedy. In purity and holiness I will guard my life and my art.

I will not use the knife, not even on sufferers from stone, but will withdraw in favor of such men as are engaged in this work.

Whatever houses I may visit, I will come for the benefit of the sick, remaining free of all intentional injustice, of all mischief and in particular of sexual relations with both female and male persons, be they free or slaves.

What I may see or hear in the course of the treatment or even outside of the treatment in regard to the life of men, which on no account one must spread abroad, I will keep to myself, holding such things shameful to be spoken about.

If I fulfill this oath and do not violate it, may it be granted to me to enjoy life and art, being honored with fame among all men for all time to come; if I transgress it and swear falsely, may the opposite of all this be my lot.

THE APHORISMS OF HIPPOCRATES

LIFE IS SHORT, and the Art long; the occasion fleeting; experience fallacious, and judgment difficult. The physician must not only be prepared to do what is right himself, but also to make the patient, the attendants, and externals co-operate.

¶A slender and restricted diet is always dangerous in chronic diseases, and also in acute diseases, where it is not requisite. And again, a diet brought to the extreme point of attenuation is dangerous; and repletion, when in the extreme, is also dangerous.

¶Old persons endure fasting most easily; next, adults; young persons not nearly so well; and most especially infants, and of them such as are of a particularly lively spirit.

¶In whatever disease sleep is laborious, it is a deadly symptom; but if sleep does good, it is not deadly.

¶Both sleep and insomnolency, when immoderate, are bad.

¶It is better that a fever succeed to a convulsion, than a convulsion to a fever.

¶Persons who are naturally very fat are apt to die earlier than those who are slender.

¶In every movement of the body, whenever one begins to endure pain, it will be relieved by rest.

¶Phthisis [tuberculosis] most commonly occurs between the ages of eighteen and thirty-five years.

¶In persons who cough up frothy blood, the discharge of it comes from the lungs.

¶Sneezing coming on, in the case of a person afflicted with hiccup, removes the hiccup.

¶In acute diseases, complicated with fever, a moaning respiration is bad.

¶Persons are most subject to apoplexy between the ages of forty and sixty.

¶In acute diseases, coldness of the extremities is bad.

¶A chill supervening on a sweat is not good.

¶Those diseases which medicines do not cure, iron [surgery?] cures; those which iron cannot cure, fire cures; and those which fire cannot cure are to be reckoned wholly incurable.

PROGNOSIS: THE FACE THAT TOKENS DEATH
(THE HIPPOCRATIC FACIES)

I

IT APPEARS to me a most excellent thing for the physician to cultivate prognosis; for by foreseeing and foretelling, in the presence of the sick, the present, the past, and the future, and explaining the omissions which patients have been guilty of, he will be the more readily believed to be acquainted with the circumstances of the sick; so that men will have confidence to intrust themselves to such a physician. And he will manage the cure best who has foreseen what is to happen from the present state of matters. For it is impossible to make all the sick well; this, indeed, would have been better than to be able to foretell what is going to happen; but since men die, some even before calling the physician, from the violence of the disease, and some die immediately after calling him, having lived, perhaps, only one day or a little longer, and before the physician could bring his art to counteract the disease, it therefore becomes necessary to know the nature of such affections, how far they are above the powers of the constitution; and, moreover, if there be anything divine in the diseases, and to learn a foreknowledge of this also. Thus a man will be the more esteemed to be a good physician, for he will be the better able to treat those aright who can be saved, from having long anticipated everything; and by seeing and announcing beforehand those who will live and those who will die, he will thus escape censure.

II

He should observe thus in acute diseases; first, the countenance of the patient, if it be like itself, for this is the best of all; whereas the most opposite to it is the worst, such as the following: a sharp nose, hollow eyes, collapsed temples; the ears cold, contracted, and their lobes turned out; the skin about the forehead being rough, distended, and parched; the color of the whole face being green, black, livid, or lead-colored.[1] If the countenance be such at the commencement of the disease, and if this cannot be accounted for from the other symptoms, inquiry must be made whether the patient has long wanted sleep; whether his bowels have been very loose; and whether he has suffered from want of food; and if any of these causes be confessed to, the danger is to be reckoned so far less; and it becomes obvious, in the course of a day and a night, whether or not the appearance of the countenance proceed from these causes. But if none of these be said to exist, and if the symptoms do not subside in the aforesaid time, it is to be known for certain that death is at hand. And, also, if the disease be in a more advanced stage either on the third or fourth day, and the countenance be such, the same inquiries as formerly directed are to be made, and the other symptoms are to be noted, those in the whole countenance, those on the body, and those in the eyes; for if they shun the light, or weep involuntarily, or squint, or if the one be less than the other, or if the white of them be red, livid, or has black veins in it; if there be a gum upon the eyes, if they are restless, protruding, or are become very hollow; and if the countenance be squalid and dark, or the color of the whole face be changed—all these are to be reckoned bad and fatal symptoms. The physician should also observe the appearance of the eyes from below the eyelids in sleep; for when a portion of the white appears owing to the eyelids not being

[1] The Hippocratic facies.

closed together, and when this is connected with diarrhea or purgation from medicine, or when the patient does not sleep thus from habit, it is to be reckoned an unfavorable and very deadly symptom; but if the eyelid be contracted, livid, or pale, or also the lip, or nose, along with some of the other symptoms, one may know for certain that death is close at hand. It is a mortal symptom also, when the lips are relaxed, pendent, cold, and blanched.

A CASE OF CHILDBIRTH FEVER

THE WIFE of Epicrates, who was lodged at the house of Archigetes, being near the term of delivery, was seized with a violent rigor, and, as was said, she did not become heated; next day the same. On the third, she was delivered of a daughter, and everything went on properly. On the day following her delivery she was seized with acute fever, pain in the cardiac region of the stomach, and in the genital parts. Having had a suppository, was in so far relieved; pain in the head, neck, loins; no sleep; alvine discharges scanty, bilious, thin, and unmixed; urine thin and blackish. Toward the night of the sixth day from the time she was seized with the fever, became delirious. On the seventh, all the symptoms exacerbated; insomnolency, delirium, thirst; stools bilious and high-colored. On the eighth, had a rigor; slept more. On the ninth, the same. On the tenth, her limbs painfully affected; pain again of the cardiac region of the stomach; heaviness of the head; no delirium; slept more; bowels constipated. On the eleventh, passed urine of a better color and, having an abundant sediment, felt lighter. On the fourteenth, had a rigor; acute fever. On the fifteenth, had a copious vomiting of bilious and yellow matters; sweated; fever gone; at night acute fever; urine thick, sediment white. On the seventeenth, an exacerbation; night uncomfortable; no sleep; delirium. On the eighteenth, thirsty; tongue parched; no sleep; much delirium; legs painfully affected. About the twentieth, in the morning, had a slight rigor; was comatose; slept tranquilly; had slight vomiting of bilious and black matters; towards night deafness. About the twenty-first, weight generally in the left side, with pain; slight cough; urine thick, muddy, and reddish; when allowed to stand, had no sediment; in other respects felt lighter; fever not gone; fauces painful from the commencement, and red; uvula retracted; defluxion remained acrid, pungent, and saltish throughout. About the twenty-seventh, free of fever; sediment in the urine; pain in the side.

About the thirty-first was attacked with fever, bilious diarrhea; slight bilious vomiting on the fortieth. Had a complete crisis, and was freed from the fever on the eighteenth day.

The Founder of Biology

ARISTOTLE (384–322 B.C.)

PUPIL OF PLATO, tutor of Alexander the Great, philosopher of Athens in its Golden Age, Aristotle was one of the Greeks who "began nearly everything of which the modern world makes its boast." Though "science" once went by the name of "natural philosophy," Aristotle's reputation as a philosopher has overshadowed his originality as a scientist. Yet he is one of the true founders of modern biology, as his discussion of the principle of continuity reveals, and was a potent pioneer of the scientific method that looks to systematic investigation of facts for its inspiration. It was not Aristotle's fault that his name became a bludgeon of authority among the Schoolmen of the Middle Ages or that his voluminous works on logic, metaphysics, ethics, politics, and rhetoric as well as natural science endured, with all their errors, to stifle fresh scientific observation and experiment.

Greek was the language in which Aristotle wrote the "History of Animals," which includes the present passage. D'Arcy Wentworth Thompson made the English translation, published in 1910 in "The Works of Aristotle," edited by J. A. Smith and W. D. Ross (Oxford, England: Clarendon Press).

"HISTORY OF ANIMALS": THE PRINCIPLE OF CONTINUITY

WE HAVE now discussed the physical characteristics of animals and their methods of generation. Their habits and their modes of living vary according to their character and their food.

In the great majority of animals there are traces of psychical qualities or attitudes, which qualities are more markedly differentiated in the case of human beings. For just as we pointed out resemblances in the physical organs, so in a number of animals we observe gentleness or fierceness, mildness or cross temper, courage or timidity, fear or confidence, high spirit or low cunning, and with regard to intelligence, something equivalent to sagacity. Some of these qualities in man, as compared with the corresponding qualities in animals, differ only quantitatively: that is to say, a man has more or less of this quality, and an animal has more or less of some other; other qualities in man are represented by analogous and not identical qualities: for instance, just as in man we find knowledge, wisdom, and sagacity, so in certain animals there exists some other natural potentiality akin to these. The truth of this statement will be the more clearly apprehended if we have regard to the phenomena of childhood: for in children may be observed the traces and seeds of what will one day be settled psychological habits, though psychologically a child hardly differs for the time being from an animal; so that one is quite justified in saying that, as regards man and animals, certain psychical qualities are identical with one another, whilst others resemble, and others are analogous to, each other.

Nature proceeds little by little from things lifeless to animal life in such a way that it is impossible to determine the exact line of demarcation, nor on which side thereof an intermediate form should lie. Thus, next after lifeless things in the upward scale comes the plant, and of plants one will differ from another as to its amount of apparent vitality; and, in a word, the whole genus of plants, whilst it is devoid of life as compared with an animal, is endowed with life as compared with other corporeal entities. Indeed, as we just remarked, there is observed in plants a continuous scale of ascent toward the animal. So, in the sea, there are certain objects concerning which one would be at a loss to determine whether they be animal or vegetable. For instance, certain of these objects are fairly rooted, and in several cases perish if detached; thus the pinna is rooted to a particular spot, and the solen (or razor shell) cannot survive withdrawal from its burrow. Indeed, broadly speaking, the entire genus of testaceans have a resemblance to vegetables, if they be contrasted with such animals as are capable of progression.

In regard to sensibility, some animals give no indication whatsoever of it, whilst others indicate it but indistinctly. Further, the substance of some of these intermediate creatures is fleshlike, as is the case with the so-called tethya (or ascidians) and the acalephae (or sea anemones); but the sponge is in every respect like a vegetable. And so throughout the entire animal scale there is a graduated differentiation in amount of vitality and in capacity for motion.

A similar statement holds good with regard to habits of life. Thus of

plants that spring from seed the one function seems to be the reproduction of their own particular species, and the sphere of action with certain animals is similarly limited. The faculty of reproduction, then, is common to all alike. If sensibility be superadded, then their lives will differ from one another in respect to sexual intercourse through the varying amount of pleasure derived therefrom, and also in regard to modes of parturition and ways of rearing their young. Some animals, like plants, simply procreate their own species at definite seasons; other animals busy themselves also in procuring food for their young, and after they are reared quit them and have no further dealings with them; other animals are more intelligent and endowed with memory, and they live with their offspring for a longer period and on a more social footing.

The life of animals, then, may be divided into two acts—procreation and feeding; for on these two acts all their interests and life concentrate. Their food depends chiefly on the substance of which they are severally constituted; for the source of their growth in all cases will be this substance. And whatsoever is in conformity with nature is pleasant, and all animals pursue pleasure in keeping with their nature.

The Idea of Big Numbers

ARCHIMEDES (287?–212 B.C.)

WE KNOW that one scientist may be worth ten thousand soldiers. The ancient Romans found it out when they attacked Syracuse in Sicily, in 212 B.C., only to have their ships fired by burning glasses, smashed by stones from short- and long-range catapults, pulled out of the water and overturned by iron-beaked cranes. All these fearful engines of war, not to mention such useful machines of peace as the water screw for irrigating land and pumping mines, the cogwheel and pulley for launching ships, were the inventions of an "absent-minded" mathematician, Archimedes, who considered them "mere diversions of geometry at play." Whether or not he ran naked from his bath shouting, "Eureka [I have found it]," upon discovering that cunning goldsmiths had defrauded his relative, King Gelon of Syracuse, by substituting silver for gold in the King's crown, the fact remains that he did work out the laws of floating bodies and fluid displacement ("Archimedes principle") upon which the disclosure of such fraud depended. Among the other primarily mathematical, but later practical, problems which engaged his interest were the laws of the lever ("Give me a place to stand and I will move the earth") and the theory of big numbers, more important in a billion-dollar modern world than when Archimedes anciently discussed it in "The Sand Reckoner."

Greek was the language in which Archimedes wrote, and from which Sir Thomas Heath made the present English translation published in 1897 in "The Works of Archimedes" (Cambridge University Press).

"THE SAND RECKONER"

THERE ARE SOME, King Gelon, who think that the number of the sand is infinite in multitude; and I mean by the sand not only that which exists about Syracuse and the rest of Sicily but also that which is found in every region whether inhabited or uninhabited. Again there are some who, without regarding it as infinite, yet think that no number has been named which is great enough to exceed its multitude. And it is clear that they who hold this view, if they imagined a mass made up of sand in other respects as large as the mass of the earth, including in it all the seas and the hollows of the earth filled up to a height equal to that of the highest of the mountains, would be many times further still from recognizing that any number could be expressed which exceeded the multitude of the sand so taken. But I will try to show you by means of geometrical proofs, which you will be able to follow, that, of the numbers named by me and given in the work which I sent to Zeuxippus, some exceed not only the number of the mass of sand equal in magnitude to the earth filled up in the way described, but also that of a mass equal in magnitude to the universe.

Now you are aware that "universe" is the name given by most astronomers to the sphere whose center is the center of the earth and whose radius is equal to the straight line between the center of the sun and the center of the earth. This is the common account, as you have heard from astronomers. But Aristarchus of Samos brought out a book consisting of some hypotheses, in which the premises lead to the result that the universe is many times greater than that now so called. His hypotheses are that the fixed stars and the sun remain unmoved, that the earth revolves about the sun in the circumference of a circle, the sun lying in the middle of the orbit, and that the sphere of the fixed stars, situated about the same center as the sun, is so great that the circle in which he supposes the earth to revolve bears such a proportion to the distance of the fixed stars as the center of the sphere bears to its surface. Now it is easy to see that this is impossible; for, since the center of the sphere has no magnitude, we cannot conceive it to bear any ratio whatever to the surface of the sphere. We must, however, take Aristarchus to mean this: since we conceive the earth to be, as it were, the center of the universe, the ratio which the earth bears to what we describe as the "universe" is the same as the ratio which the sphere containing the circle in which he supposes the earth to revolve bears to the sphere of the fixed stars. For he adapts the proof of his results to a hypothesis of this kind, and in particular he appears to suppose the magnitude of the sphere in which he represents the earth as moving to be equal to what we call the "universe."

I say then that, even if a sphere were made up of the sand, as great as Aristarchus supposes the sphere of the fixed stars to be, I shall still prove that, of the numbers named in the *Principles,* some exceed in multitude the number of the sand which is equal in magnitude to the sphere referred to, provided that the following assumptions be made.

1. *The perimeter of the earth is about 3,000,000 stadia*[1] *and not greater.*

It is true that some have tried, as you are of course aware, to prove that the said perimeter is about 300,000 stadia. But I go further and, putting the magnitude of the earth at ten times the size that my predecessors thought it, I suppose its perimeter to be about 3,000,000 stadia and not greater.

2. *The diameter of the earth is greater than the diameter of the moon, and the diameter of the sun is greater than the diameter of the earth.*

In this assumption I follow most of the earlier astronomers.

3. *The diameter of the sun is about thirty times the diameter of the moon and not greater.*

It is true that, of the earlier astronomers, Eudoxus declared it to be about nine times as great, and Pheidias, my father, twelve times, while Aristarchus tried to prove that the diameter of the sun is greater than eighteen times but less than twenty times the diameter of the moon. But I go even further than Aristarchus, in order that the truth of my proposition may be established beyond dispute, and I suppose the diameter of the sun to be about thirty times that of the moon and not greater.

---

[1]Stadium: Greek unit of distance equal to 606.9 English feet (185 meters), which was the length of a track used for footraces. A more recent determination sets it at about 488 feet. ("Isis," 28, 493, 1938.)

4. *The diameter of the sun is greater than the side of the chiliagon*[2] *inscribed in the greatest circle in the [sphere of the] universe.*

I make this assumption because Aristarchus discovered that the sun appeared to be about 1/720th part of the circle of the zodiac, and I myself tried . . . to find experimentally the angle subtended by the sun and having its vertex at the eye. . . .

I conceive that these things, King Gelon, will appear incredible to the great majority of people who have not studied mathematics, but that to those who are conversant therewith and have given thought to the question of the distances and sizes of the earth the sun and moon and the whole universe the proof will carry conviction. And it was for this reason that I thought the subject would not be inappropriate for your consideration.

"Of the Nature of Things"

LUCRETIUS (98–55 B.C.)

EXPANDING scientific knowledge often changes the meaning of scientific words. Today we speak hopefully of "atom smashing"; yet the Greek scientist and philosopher, Democritus (460?–370? B.C.), who first formulated an atomic theory, chose the word *a-tom* (not divisible) to signify a fundamental particle of matter so firm and small that it could not be further divided or smashed. The speculations of Democritus ("atoms . . . must a little swerve"), once pointed, now outmoded, have been preserved and sharpened in the magnificent poetry of Lucretius, Epicurean philosopher and Roman contemporary of Cicero and Julius Caesar.

Latin was the tongue in which Titus Lucretius Carus composed six books of poetry, "Of the Nature of Things" (*"De Rerum Natura"*), addressed to C. Memmius Gemellus, Roman praetor in 58 B.C. The metrical English translation given here is by the modern American poet, William Ellery Leonard. It is reprinted with permission of the publishers of Everyman's Library (Dutton and Dent).

[2]Chiliagon: a polygon with 1000 equal sides, inscribed in a circle.

CHARACTER OF THE ATOMS

Bodies, again,
Are partly primal germs of things, and partly
Unions deriving from the primal germs.
And those which are the primal germs of things
No power can quench; for in the end they conquer
By their own solidness; though hard it be
To think that aught in things has solid frame . . .
There are, then, certain bodies, possessed of power
To vary forever the empty and the full;
And these can nor be sundered from without
By beats and blows, nor from within be torn
By penetration, nor be overthrown
By any assault soever through the world . . .
So primal germs have solid singleness,
Nor otherwise could they have been conserved
Through aeons and infinity of time
For the replenishment of wasted worlds. . . .
Since nature hath inviolably decreed
What each can do, what each can never do;
Since naught is changed, but all things so abide
That ever the variegated birds reveal
The spots or stripes peculiar to their kind,
Spring after spring: thus surely all that is
Must be composed of matter immutable. . . .
For if the primal germs in any wise
Were open to conquest and to change, 'twould be
Uncertain also what could come to birth
And what could not, and by what law to each
Its scope prescribed, its boundary stone that clings
So deep in Time. Nor could the generations
Kind after kind so often reproduce
The nature, habits, motions, ways of life,
Of their progenitors. . . .

ATOMIC MOTIONS

Now come: I will untangle for thy steps
Now by what motions the begetting bodies

Of the world-stuff beget the varied world,
And then forever resolve it when begot . . .
For far beneath the ken of senses lies
The nature of those ultimates of the world;
And so, since those themselves thou canst not see,
Their motion also must they veil from men—
For mark, indeed, how things we *can* see, oft
Yet hide their motions, when afar from us
Along the distant landscape . . .
The atoms, as their own weight bears them down
Plumb through the void, at scarce determined times,
In scarce determined places, from their course
Decline a little—call it, so to speak,
Mere changèd trend. For were it not their wont
Thuswise to swerve, down would they fall, each one,
Like drops of rain, through the unbottomed void;
And then collisions ne'er could be nor blows
Among the primal elements; and thus
Nature would never have created aught. . . .

                                        And so I say,
The atoms must a little swerve at times—
But only the least, lest we should seem to feign
Motions oblique, and fact refute us there. . . .
The sum of things there is no power can change,
For naught exists outside, to which can flee
Out of the world matter of any kind,
Nor forth from which a fresh supply can spring,
Break in upon the founded world, and change
Whole nature of things, and turn their motions about.

The Origin of Money: Economics Repeats Itself

PLINY (A.D. 23–79)

MANY a scientist has been killed by pursuing his intellectual curiosity, but none more spectacularly than Pliny the Elder. This indefatigable Roman scholar was overcurious about the nature of volcanoes. He tarried too long too close to the eruption of Vesuvius that buried the city of Pompeii in A.D. 79 and he was suffocated by sulphur fumes. In turn soldier, lawyer, governor of provinces, and adviser to the Roman court, he found time to compose (his nephew, Pliny the Younger, tells us) thirty-seven books on natural history ("*Historia Naturalis*") and as many more—now lost—on military tactics (for example, "On the Use of the Dart by Cavalry"), rhetoric, and history by dictating day and night, at home and abroad, to a corps of trailing secretaries who took down his words in shorthand. His writings have served as an encyclopedic mine of classical information, however inaccurate, on the natural sciences.

Latin was the tongue in which Pliny dictated. The English translation, by John Bostock and H. T. Riley, appeared in "The Natural History of Pliny," Vol. IV (London: Henry G. Bohn, 1857).

"THE NATURAL HISTORY OF METALS"

METALS

WE ARE NOW about to speak of metals, of actual wealth, the standard of comparative value, objects for which we diligently search, within the earth, in numerous ways. In one place, for instance, we undermine it for the purpose of obtaining riches, to supply the exigencies of life, searching for either gold or silver, electrum or copper. In another place, to satisfy the requirements of luxury, our researches extend to gems and pigments, with which to adorn our fingers and the walls of our houses; while in a third place we gratify our rash propensities by a search for iron, which, amid wars and carnage, is deemed more acceptable even than gold. We trace out all the veins of the earth, and yet, living upon it, undermined as it is beneath our feet, are astonished that it should occasionally cleave asunder or tremble: as though, forsooth, these signs could be any other than expressions of the indignation felt by our sacred parent! We penetrate into her entrails and seek for treasures as though each spot we tread upon were not sufficiently bounteous and fertile for us! . . .

GOLD

Gold is dug out of the earth, and, in close proximity to it, chrysocolla. . . . It was not enough for us to have discovered one bane for the human race, but we must set a value too upon the very humors of gold. While avarice, too, was on the search for silver, it congratulated itself upon the discovery of minium, and devised a use to be made of this red earth.

Alas for the prodigal inventions of man! In how many ways have we augmented the value of things! In addition to the standard value of these metals, the art of painting lends its aid, and we have rendered gold and silver still more costly by the art of chasing them. Man has learned how to challenge both nature and art to become the incitements to vice! His very cups he has delighted to engrave with libidinous subjects, and he takes pleasure in drinking from vessels of obscene form. But in lapse of time the metals passed out of fashion, and men began to make no account of them; gold and silver, in fact, became too common. From this same earth we have extracted vessels of murrhine and vases of crystal, objects the very fragility of which is considered to enhance their value. In fact, it has come to be looked upon as proof of opulence, and as quite the glory of luxury, to possess that which may be irremediably destroyed in an instant. Nor was even this enough; we now drink from out of a mass of gems, and we set our goblets with smaragdi; we take delight in possessing the wealth of India, as the promoter of intoxication, and gold is now nothing more than a mere accessory.

WHAT WAS THE FIRST RECOMMENDATION OF GOLD

Would that gold could have been banished forever from the earth, accursed by universal report, as some of the most celebrated writers have expressed themselves, reviled by the reproaches of the best of men, and looked upon as discovered only for the ruin of mankind. How much more happy the age when things themselves were bartered for one another; as was the case in the times of the Trojan War, if we are to believe what Homer says. For, in this way, in my opinion, was commerce then carried on for the supply of the necessaries of life. Some, he tells us, would make their purchases by bartering oxhides, and others by bartering iron or the spoil which they had taken from the enemy: and yet he himself, already an admirer of gold, was so far aware of the relative value of things that Glaucus, he informs us, exchanged his arms of gold, valued at one hundred oxen, for those of Diomedes, which were worth but nine. Proceeding upon the same system of barter, many of the fines imposed by ancient laws, at Rome even, were levied in cattle [and not in money].

THE ORIGIN OF GOLD RINGS

The worst crime against mankind was committed by him who was the first to put a ring upon his fingers: and yet we are not informed, by tradition, who it was that first did so. For as to all the stories told about

Prometheus, I look upon them as utterly fabulous, although I am aware that the ancients used to represent him with a ring of iron: it was their intention, however, to signify a chain thereby, and not an ornament. As to the ring of Midas, which, upon the collet being turned inwards, con-ferred invisibility upon the wearer, who is there that must not admit, perforce, that this story is even still more fabulous? It was the hand, and a sinister hand, too, in every sense, that first brought gold into such high repute: not a Roman hand, however, for upon that it was the practice to wear a ring of iron only, and solely as an indication of warlike prowess. . . .

THE VALUE OF COPPER AND OF COINED MONEY HAS BEEN CHANGED

The next crime committed against the welfare of mankind was on the part of him who was the first to coin a denarius of gold, a crime the author of which is equally unknown. The Roman people made no use of impressed silver even before the period of the defeat of King Pyrrhus. The *as* of copper weighed exactly one libra; and hence it is that we still use the terms *libella* and *dupondius*. Hence it is, too, that fines and penalties are inflicted under the name of *aes grave,* and that the words still used in keeping accounts are *expensa, impendia,* and *dependere.* Hence, too, the word *stipendium,* meaning the pay of the soldiers, which is nothing more than *stipis pondera;* and from the same source those other words, *dispensators* and *libripendes.* It is also from this circum-stance that in sales of slaves, at the present day even, the formality of using the balance is introduced.

King Servius was the first to make an impress upon copper. Before his time, according to Timaeus, at Rome the raw metal only was used. The form of a sheep was the first figure impressed upon money, and to this fact it owes its name, *pecunia.* The highest figure at which one man's property was assessed in the reign of that king was one hundred and twenty thousand asses, and consequently that amount of property was considered the standard of the first class.

Silver was not impressed with a mark until the year of the City 485, the year of the consulship of Q. Ogulnius and C. Fabius, five years be-fore the First Punic War; at which time it was ordained that the value of the denarius should be ten librae of copper, that of the quinarius five librae, and that of the sestertius two librae and a half. The weight, how-ever, of the libra of copper was diminished during the First Punic War, the republic not having means to meet its expenditure: in consequence of which, an ordinance was made that the as should in future be struck of two ounces weight. By this contrivance a saving of five sixths was effected, and the public debt was liquidated. The impression upon these copper coins was a two-faced Janus on one side, and the beak of a ship of war on the other: the *triens,* however, and the *quadrans,* bore the impression of a ship. The quadrans, too, had, previously to this, been called *teruncius,* as being three *unciae* in weight. At a later period again, when Hannibal was pressing hard upon Rome, in the dictatorship of Q. Fabius Maximus, asses of one ounce weight were struck, and it was ordained that the value of the denarius should be sixteen asses, that of the quinarius eight asses, and that of the sestertius four asses; by which last reduction of the weight of the as the republic made a clear gain of one half. Still, however, so far as the pay of the soldiers is concerned, one denarius has always been given for every ten asses. The impressions upon the coins of silver were two-horse and four-horse chariots, and hence it is that they received the names of *bigati* and *quadrigati.*

Shortly after, in accordance with the law of Papirius, asses were coined weighing half an ounce only. Livius Drusus, when tribune of the people, alloyed the silver with one eighth part of copper. The coin that is known at the present day as the *victoriatus* was first struck in accordance with the Clodian Law: before which period, a coin of this name was imported from Illyricum, but was only looked upon as an article of merchandise. The impression upon it is a figure of Victory, and hence its name.

The first golden coin was struck sixty-two years after that of silver, the scruple of gold being valued at twenty sesterces; a computation which gave, according to the value of the sesterce then in use, nine hundred sesterces to each libra of gold. In later times, again, an ordinance was made, that denarii of gold should be struck, at the rate of forty denarii to each libra of gold; after which period, the emperors gradually curtailed the weight of the golden denarius, until at last, in the reign of Nero, it was coined at the rate of forty-five to the libra. . . .

How Gold Is Found

Gold is found in our own part of the world; not to mention the gold extracted from the earth in India by the ants, and in Scythia by the griffins. Among us it is procured in three different ways; the first of which is in the shape of dust, found in running streams, the Tagus in

Spain, for instance, the Padus in Italy, the Hebrus in Thracia, the Pactolus in Asia, and the Ganges in India; indeed, there is no gold found in a more perfect state than this, thoroughly polished as it is by the continual attrition of the current.

A second mode of obtaining gold is by sinking shafts or seeking it among the debris of mountains. The persons in search of gold in the first place remove the *segutilum,* such being the name of the earth which gives indication of the presence of gold. This done, a bed is made, the sand of which is washed, and, according to the residue found after washing, a conjecture is formed as to the richness of the vein. Sometimes, indeed, gold is found at once in the surface earth, a success, however, but rarely experienced. Recently, for instance, in the reign of Nero, a vein was discovered in Dalmatia which yielded daily as much as fifty pounds" weight of gold. The gold that is thus found in the surface crust is known as *talutium,* in cases where there is auriferous earth beneath. The mountains of Spain, in other respects arid and sterile, and productive of nothing whatever, are thus constrained by man to be fertile, in supplying him with this precious commodity. . . .

The third method of obtaining gold surpasses the labors of the giants even: by the aid of galleries driven to a long distance, mountains are excavated by the light of torches, the duration of which forms the set times for work, the workmen never seeing the light of day for many months together. These mines are known as *arrugiae;* and not unfrequently clefts are formed on a sudden, the earth sinks in, and the workmen are crushed beneath; so that it would really appear less rash to go in search of pearls and purples at the bottom of the sea, so much more dangerous to ourselves have we made the earth than the water! Hence it is that in this kind of mining arches are left at frequent intervals for the purpose of supporting the weight of the mountain above. In mining either by shaft or by gallery, barriers of silex are met with, which have to be driven asunder by the aid of fire and vinegar; or more frequently, as this method fills the galleries with suffocating vapors and smoke, to be broken to pieces with bruising machines shod with pieces of iron weighing one hundred and fifty pounds: which done, the fragments are carried out on the workmen's shoulders, night and day, each man passing them on to his neighbor in the dark, it being only those at the pit's mouth that ever see the light. In cases where the bed of silex appears too thick to admit of being penetrated, the miner traces along the sides of it, and so turns it. And yet, after all, the labor entailed by this silex is looked upon as comparatively easy, there being an earth—

a kind of potter's clay mixed with gravel, *gangadia* by name, which it is almost impossible to overcome. This earth has to be attacked with iron wedges and hammers like those previously mentioned, and it is generally considered that there is nothing more stubborn in existence —except indeed the greed for gold, which is the most stubborn of all things.

When these operations are all completed, beginning at the last, they cut away the wooden pillars at the point where they support the roof: the coming downfall gives warning, which is instantly perceived by the sentinel, and by him only, who is set to watch upon a peak of the same mountain. By voice as well as by signals, he orders the workmen to be immediately summoned from their labors, and at the same moment takes to flight himself. The mountain, rent to pieces, is cleft asunder, hurling its debris to a distance with a crash which it is impossible for the human imagination to conceive; and from the midst of a cloud of dust, of a density quite incredible, the victorious miners gaze upon this downfall of nature. Nor yet even then are they sure of gold, nor indeed were they by any means certain that there was any to be found when they first began to excavate, it being quite sufficient, as an inducement to undergo such perils and to incur such vast expense, to entertain the hope that they shall obtain what they so eagerly desire. . . .

Asturia, Gallacia, and Lusitania furnish in this manner, yearly, according to some authorities, twenty thousand pounds' weight of gold, the produce of Asturia forming the major part. Indeed, there is no part of the world that for centuries has maintained such a continuous fertility in gold. I have already mentioned that by an ancient decree of the Senate the soil of Italy has been protected from these researches; otherwise there would be no land more fertile in metals. There is extant also a censorial law relative to the gold mines of Victumulae, in the territory of Vercellae, by which the farmers of the revenue were forbidden to employ more than five thousand men at the works. . . .

"Concerning Architecture"

VITRUVIUS (A.D. First Century)

STILL STANDING for modern eyes to see and marvel, the cathedrals of the Middle Ages and the palaces of the Renaissance remain in debt to

Vitruvius, Roman architect and engineer of the Augustan age. Partly original, partly a compilation of earlier, especially Greek, sources, his ten volumes on architecture, building, and building materials became the only influential guide and standard textbook for the "master builders" and artists of the next sixteen centuries. That he dealt with and partly solved a peculiarly twentieth-century problem in theater acoustics will be appreciated by anyone who attended the showings of the earlier "talking" motion pictures in halls and theaters built for "silent" films.

Latin was the language of the original "Vitruvius: The Ten Books on Architecture" ("De Architectura"), parts of whose English translation, by Morris Hicky Morgan, are given here.

THE ORIGIN OF BUILDING . . . THE LOG CABIN

IT WAS the discovery of fire that originally gave rise to the coming together of men, to the deliberative assembly, and to social intercourse. And so, as they kept coming together in greater numbers into one place, finding themselves naturally gifted beyond the other animals in not being obliged to walk with faces to the ground, but upright and gazing upon the splendor of the starry firmament, and also in being able to do with ease whatever they chose with their hands and fingers, they began in that first assembly to construct shelters. Some made them of green boughs, others dug caves on mountainsides, and some, in imitation of the nests of swallows and the way they built, made places of refuge out of mud and twigs. Next, by observing the shelters of others and adding new details to their own inceptions, they constructed better and better kinds of huts as time went on.

And since they were of an imitative and teachable nature, they would daily point out to each other the results of their building, boasting of the novelties in it; and thus, with their natural gifts sharpened by emulation, their standards improved daily. At first they set up forked stakes connected by twigs and covered these walls with mud. Others made walls of lumps of dried mud, covering them with reed and leaves to keep out the rain and the heat. Finding that such roofs could not stand the rain during the storms of winter, they built them with peaks daubed with mud, the roofs sloping and projecting so as to carry off the rain water.

That houses originated as I have written above we can see for ourselves from the buildings that are to this day constructed of like materials by foreign tribes: for instance, in Gaul, Spain, Portugal, and Aquitaine, roofed with oak shingles or thatched. Among the Colchians in Pontus, where there are forests in plenty, they lay down entire trees flat on the ground to the right and the left, leaving between them a space to suit the length of the trees, and then place above these another pair of trees, resting on the ends of the former and at right angles with them. These four trees enclose the space for the dwelling. Then upon these they place sticks of timber one after the other on the four sides, crossing each other at the angles, and so, proceeding with their walls of trees laid perpendicularly above the lowest, they build up high towers. The interstices which are left on account of the thickness of the building material are stopped up with chips and mud. As for the roofs, by cutting away the ends of the crossbeams and making them converge gradually as they lay them across, they bring them up to the top from the four sides in the shape of a pyramid. They cover it with leaves and mud, and thus construct the roofs of their towers in a rude form of the "tortoise" style.

On the other hand, the Phrygians, who live in an open country, have no forests and consequently lack timber. They therefore select a natural hillock, run a trench through the middle of it, dig passages, and extend the interior space as widely as the site admits. Over it they build a pyramidal roof of logs fastened together, and this they cover with reeds and brushwood, heaping up very high mounds of earth above their dwellings. Thus their fashion in houses makes their winters very warm and their summers very cool. Some construct hovels with roofs of rushes from the swamps. Among other nations, also, in some places there are huts of the same or a similar method of construction. Likewise at Marseille we can see roofs without tiles, made of earth mixed with straw. In Athens on the Areopagus there is to this day a relic of antiquity with a mud roof. The hut of Romulus on the Capitol is a significant reminder of the fashions of old times, and likewise the thatched roofs of temples on the Citadel.

From such specimens we can draw our inferences with regard to the devices used in the buildings of antiquity and conclude that they were similar.

Furthermore, as men made progress by becoming daily more expert in building and as their ingenuity was increased by their dexterity so that from habit they attained to considerable skill, their intelligence was enlarged by their industry until the more proficient adopted the trade of carpenters. From these early beginnings and from the fact that nature had not only endowed the human race with senses like the rest of the animals but had also equipped their minds with the powers of thought and understanding, thus putting all other animals under their sway, they next gradually advanced from the construction of buildings to the other arts and sciences, and so passed from a rude and barbarous mode of life to civilization and refinement.

Then, taking courage and looking forward from the standpoint of higher ideas born of the multiplication of the arts, they gave up huts and began to build houses with foundations, having brick or stone walls and roofs of timber and tiles; next, observation and application led them from fluctuating and indefinite conceptions to definite rules of symmetry. Perceiving that nature had been lavish in the bestowal of timber and bountiful in stores of building material, they treated this like careful nurses, and, thus developing the refinements of life, embellished them with luxuries.

THEATER ACOUSTICS

VOICE IS a flowing breath of air, perceptible to the hearing by contact. It moves in an endless number of circular rounds like the innumerably increasing circular waves which appear when a stone is thrown into smooth water, and which keep on spreading indefinitely from the center unless interrupted by narrow limits or by some obstruction which prevents such waves from reaching their end in due formation. When they are interrupted by obstructions, the first waves, flowing back, break up the formation of those which follow.

In the same manner the voice executes its movements in concentric circles; but while in the case of water the circles move horizontally on a plane surface, the voice not only proceeds horizontally but also ascends vertically by regular stages. Therefore, as in the case of the waves formed in the water, so it is in the case of the voice: the first wave, when there is no obstruction to interrupt it, does not break up the second or the following waves, but they all reach the ears of the lowest and highest spectators without an echo.

Hence the ancient architects [i.e., the Greeks], following in the footsteps of nature, perfected the ascending rows of seats in theaters from their investigations of the ascending voice, and by means of the canonical theory of the mathematicians and that of the musicians, endeavored to make every voice uttered on the stage come with greater clearness and sweetness to the ears of the audience. For just as musical instruments are brought to perfection of clearness in the sound of their strings by means of bronze plates or horn sounding boards, so the ancients devised methods of increasing the power of the voice in theaters through the application of the science of harmony. . . .

In accordance with the foregoing investigations on mathematical principles, let bronze vessels be made, proportionate to the size of the theater, and let them be so fashioned that, when touched, they may produce with one another the notes of the fourth, the fifth, and so on up to the double octave. Then, having constructed niches in between the seats of the theater, let the vessels be arranged in them, in accordance with musical laws, in such a way that they nowhere touch the wall, but have a clear space all round them and room over their tops. . . . On this principle of arrangement the voice, uttered from the stage as from a center and spreading and striking against the cavities of the different vessels as it comes in contact with them, will be increased in clearness of sound and will wake a harmonious note in unison with itself. . . .

Somebody will perhaps say that many theaters are built every year in Rome and that in them no attention at all is paid to these principles; but he will be in error, from the fact that all our public theaters made of wood contain a great deal of boarding, which must be resonant. . . . But when theaters are built of solid materials like masonry, stone, or marble, which cannot be resonant, then the principles of the resonator must be applied.

If, however, it is asked in what theater these vessels have been employed, we cannot point to any in Rome itself, but only to certain districts of Italy and in a good many Greek states. We have also the evidence of Lucius Mummius, who, after destroying the theater in Corinth, brought its bronze vessels to Rome and made a dedicatory offering at the temple of Luna with the money obtained from the sale of them. Besides, many skillful architects, in constructing theaters in small towns, have, for lack of means, taken large jars made of clay, but similarly resonant, and have produced very advantageous results by arranging them on the principles described.

The Classical Authority in Medicine

GALEN (A.D. 130–201)

GREAT SCIENTIFIC authorities often begin at humble tasks. The undisputed medical authority for thirteen centuries (until Vesalius), encyclopedic author of over one hundred extant medical treatises, whose translation into Arabic preserved much of the classical knowledge of medicine throughout the so-called "Dark Ages" of Europe, foremost medical practitioner at Rome during the heyday of the empire, personal physician to the Emperor Marcus Aurelius (whom he first treated for a simple stomach upset), Galen nevertheless began his professional career as surgeon to the gladiators at Pergamum, his native town in Asia Minor. A jealous missionary in the cause of the common-sense doctrines of his "ancient master," Hippocrates, Galen dissected—apes if not men—and learned anatomy and clinical medicine from personal observation and experience, not from the speculative systems of contemporary schools of medical thought.

Greek was the language in which Galen originally wrote. His works were never published in English until the present century. The English translations given here were made by Arthur J. Brock, M.D., published in 1929 in "Greek Medicine" (London: J. M. Dent & Sons, Ltd., New York: E. P. Dutton & Co., Inc.).

ON THE DISSECTION OF APES

WHAT TENT POLES are to tents, and walls to houses, so to animals is their bony structure; the other parts adapt themselves to this and change with it. Thus, if an animal's cranium is round, its brain must be the same; or, again, if it is oblong, then the animal's brain must also be oblong. If the jaws are small, and the face as a whole roundish, the muscles of these parts will also necessarily be small; and similarly, if the jaws are prominent, the animal's face as a whole will be long, as also the facial muscles. Consequently also the monkey is of all animals the likest to man in its viscera, muscles, arteries, veins, and nerves, because it is so also in the form of its bones. From the nature of these it walks on two legs, uses its front limbs as hands, has the flattest breastbone of all quadrupeds, collarbones like those of a man, a round face, and a short neck. And these being similar, the muscles cannot be different; for they are extended on the outside of the bones in such a manner that they resemble them in size and form. To the muscles, again, correspond the arteries, veins, and nerves; so these, being similar, must correspond to the bones. . . .

First of all, then, I would ask you to make yourself well acquainted with the human bones, and not to look on this as a matter of secondary importance. Nor must you merely read the subject up in one of these books which are called by some "Osteology," by others "The Skeleton," and by others simply "On Bones," as is my own book; which, by the way, I am certain is better than any previously written, both as regards the exactitude of its matter and the brevity and clearness of its explanations. Make it your earnest business, then, not only to learn exactly from the book the appearance of each of the bones, but to become yourself by the use of your own eyes an eager firsthand observer of human osteology.

At Alexandria this is very easy, since the physicians in that country accompany the instruction they give to their students with opportunities for personal inspection. Hence you must try to get to Alexandria for this reason alone, if for no other. But if you cannot manage this, still it is not impossible to obtain a view of human bones. Personally I have very often had a chance to do this where tombs or monuments have become broken up. On one occasion a river, having risen to the level of a grave which had been carelessly constructed a few months previously, easily disintegrated this; then by the force of its current it swept right over the dead man's body, of which the flesh had already putrefied, while the bones were still closely attached to one another. This it carried away downstream for the distance of a league, till, coming to a lakelike stretch with sloping banks, it here deposited the corpse. And here the latter lay ready for inspection, just as though prepared by a doctor for his pupil's lesson.

Once also I examined the skeleton of a robber, lying on a mountainside a short distance from the road. This man had been killed by some traveler whom he had attacked, but who had been too quick for him. None of the inhabitants of the district would bury him; but in their detestation of him they were delighted when his body was eaten by birds of prey; the latter, in fact, devoured the flesh in two days and left the skeleton ready, as it were, for anyone who cared to enjoy an anatomical demonstration.

As regards yourself, then, even if you do not have the luck to see anything like this, still you can dissect an ape, and learn each of the bones from it, by carefully removing the flesh. For this purpose you must choose the apes which most resemble man. . . .

Thus if you should also later meet with a human skeleton, you would easily recognize and remember everything. . . . When apes are not available, one should be prepared to dissect the bodies of other animals, distinguishing at once in what ways they differ from apes.

THE LADY AND THE DANCER

I was called in to see a woman who was stated to be sleepless at night and to lie tossing about from one position into another. Finding she had no fever, I made a detailed inquiry into everything that had happened to her, especially considering such factors as we know to cause insomnia. But she either answered little or nothing at all, as if to show that it was useless to question her. Finally she turned away, hiding herself completely by throwing the bedclothes over her whole body, and laying her head on another small pillow, as if desiring sleep.

After leaving I came to the conclusion that she was suffering from one of two things: either from a melancholy dependent on black bile, or else trouble about something she was unwilling to confess. I therefore deferred till the next day a closer investigation of this. Further, on first arriving I was told by her attendant maid that she could not at present be seen; and on returning a second time, I was told the same again. So I went yet a third time, but the attendant asked me to go away, as she did not want her mistress disturbed. Having learned, however, that when I left she had washed and taken food in her customary manner, I came back the next day, and in a private conversation with the maid on one subject and another I found out exactly what was worrying the patient. And this I discovered by chance.

After I had diagnosed that there was no bodily trouble, and that the woman was suffering from some mental uneasiness, it happened that, at the very time I was examining her, this was confirmed. Somebody came from the theater and said he had seen Pylades dancing. Then both her expression and the color of her face changed. Seeing this, I applied my hand to her wrist and noticed that her pulse had suddenly become extremely irregular (*anomalous*). This kind of pulse indicates that the mind is disturbed; thus it occurs also in people who are disputing over any subject. So on the next day I said to one of my followers that, when I paid my visit to the woman, he was to come a little later and announce to me, "Morphus is dancing today." When he said this, I found that the pulse was unaffected. Similarly also on the next day, when I had an announcement made about the third member of the troupe, the pulse remained unchanged as before. On the fourth evening I kept very careful watch when it was announced that Pylades was dancing, and I noticed that the pulse was very much disturbed. Thus I found out that the woman was in love with Pylades, and by careful watch on the succeeding days my discovery was confirmed.

Similarly, too, I diagnosed the case of a slave who administered the household of another wealthy man, and who sickened in the same way. He was concerned about having to give an account of his expenses, in which he knew that there was a considerable sum wanting; the thought of this kept him awake, and he grew thin with anxiety. I first told his master that there was nothing physically wrong with the old man, and advised an investigation to be made as to whether he feared his master was about to ask an account of the sums he had entrusted to him, and for this reason was worried, knowing that a considerable amount would be found wanting. The master told me I had made a good suggestion, so in order to make the diagnosis certain, I advised him to do as follows: he was to tell the slave to give him back all the money he had in hand, lest, in the event of his sudden death, it should be lost, owing to the administration passing into the hands of some other servant whom he did not know, for there would be no use asking for an account from such an one. And when the master said this to him, he felt sure he would not be questioned. So he ceased to worry, and by the third day had regained his natural physical condition.

Now what was it that escaped the notice of previous physicians when examining the aforesaid woman and the aforesaid slave? For such discoveries are made by common inductions (*epilogisms*) if one has even the smallest acquaintance with medical science. I suppose it is because they have no clear conception (*diagnosis*) of how the body tends to be affected by mental conditions. Possibly also they do not know that the pulse is altered by quarrels and alarms which suddenly disturb the mind.

THE EMPEROR'S BELLYACHE

WHAT HAPPENED in the case of the Emperor [Marcus Aurelius] himself
was really wonderful. His own opinion and that of the physicians of
his entourage who had gone abroad with him was that some febrile
paroxysm had begun. But they all proved wrong both on the second
and third day, in the morning and at the third hour. He had on the
preceding day taken a draught of bitter aloes at the first hour, and then
some theriac, as was his daily custom. Next he took some food about
the sixth hour, washed at sunset, and had a small meal. During the
whole night there ensued colicky pains with intestinal evacuations. This
made him feverish, and when his attendant physicians observed this,
they gave orders that he should be kept quiet; then they prescribed
slop diet at the ninth hour. After this I was myself also summoned to
come and sleep in the palace. Then, when the lamps were newly lit, a
messenger came to call me at the Emperor's bidding. Three doctors had
been observing him since about daybreak, and two of them feeling his
pulse, and they all considered this the beginning of a febrile attack. I
stood by, however, without saying anything; so the Emperor, looking
at me first, asked why, when the others felt his pulse, I alone did not
do so. I said to him, "Two of these gentlemen have already done this,
and probably when they were abroad with you they already learned by
experience the characteristics of your pulse; hence I expect they will be
better able to judge its present condition [diathesis]." On my saying
this he bade me also feel his pulse. It seemed to me that, taking his
age and constitution into account, the pulse was far from indicating
the beginning of a febrile attack. I declared that this was no onset of
fever, but that his stomach was overloaded by the food he had taken,
which had turned to phlegm prior to ejection.

My diagnosis seemed praiseworthy to the Emperor, and he repeated
three times in succession: "That's it. It is just what you say. I feel I have
taken too much cold food." And he asked what was to be done. I answered what I knew, and said to him: "If it were anyone else who was
in this state, I should follow my custom and give him wine sprinkled
with pepper. But in the case of kings like yourself, physicians are in
the habit of giving safer remedies; hence it will be enough to apply
over your stomach some wool impregnated with warm spikenard ointment." The Emperor said that in any case when his stomach was out

of order he was in the habit of applying warm spikenard ointment enveloped in purple wool. So he gave orders to Pitholaus to do this, and to let me go. When this application had been made, and his feet thoroughly heated by rubbing with the warm hand, he asked for some Sabine wine, sprinkled pepper in it, and drank. He then declared to Pitholaus that he had "one physician, and he was a perfect gentleman." Further, as you know, he keeps constantly saying about me that I am "first among the physicians and alone among the philosophers." For he had already had experience of many who were not only mercenary, but also quarrelsome, conceited, selfish, and malicious. . . .

"*The Great Work*" *of Medieval Science*

ROGER BACON (1214?–1294)

EMBEDDED in the superstitions of the thirteenth century, any man who knew gunpowder, handled the furnaces, alembics, and other instruments of an alchemical "elaboratory," prophesied "horseless carriages" and ships moved without sails or oars, could easily stand accused of practicing "black arts" (i.e., magic) and writing heresy punishable by imprisonment. Such was the fate of Roger Bacon, the English-born Franciscan of Oxford. Yet his *"Opus Majus"* ("Great Work"), ordered by and delivered to Pope Clement IV in 1267, but not published for five hundred years, reveals clearly that this learned and traveled friar, pupil of the great Bishop of Lincoln, Robert Grosseteste, dealt with "magic," not to practice but to expose "the mad acts of magicians" by the true test of "experimental science." He was no sorcerer who looked upon mathematics as "the alphabet of all philosophy" and studied optics for the "sweetness" and "nobility" of "this very beautiful science."

Latin was the language in which Bacon composed his *"Opus Majus,"* a summary of then-known physical science from Latin, Greek, and Arabic sources. The English translation, by Robert Belle Burke, is from "The Opus Majus of Roger Bacon," published in 1928 (Philadelphia: University of Pennsylvania Press).

THE USEFULNESS OF MATHEMATICS, "THE ALPHABET OF PHILOSOPHY"

WHAT HAS BEEN SHOWN as regards mathematics as a whole through authority can now be shown likewise by reason. And I make this statement, in the first place, because other sciences use mathematical examples, but examples are given to make clear the subjects treated by the sciences; wherefore ignorance of the examples involves an ignorance of the subjects for the understanding of which the examples are adduced.

For since change in natural objects is not found without some augmentation and diminution nor do these latter take place without change; Aristotle was not able to make clear without complications the difference between augmentation and change by any natural example, because augmentation and diminution go together always with change in some way; wherefore he gave the mathematical example of the rectangle which, augmented by a gnomon, increases in magnitude and is not altered in shape. This example cannot be understood before the twenty-second proposition of the sixth book of the Elements. For in that proposition of the sixth book it is proved that a smaller rectangle is similar in every particular to a larger one and therefore a smaller one is not altered in shape, although it becomes larger by the addition of the gnomon.

Secondly, because comprehension of mathematical truths is innate, as it were, in us. For a small boy, as Tullius states in the first book of the Tusculan Disputations, when questioned by Socrates on geometrical truths, replied as though he had learned geometry. And this experiment has been tried in many cases, and does not hold in other sciences, as will appear more clearly from what follows. Wherefore since this knowledge is almost innate, and as it were precedes discovery and learning, or at least is less in need of them than other sciences, it will be first among sciences and will precede others disposing us toward them; since what is innate or almost so disposes toward what is acquired.

Thirdly, because this science of all the parts of philosophy was the earliest discovered. For this was first discovered at the beginning of the human race. Since it was discovered before the Flood and then later by the sons of Adam, and by Noah and his sons, as is clear from the prologue to the Construction of the Astrolabe according to Ptolemy, and from Albumazar in the larger introduction to astronomy, and from the first book of the Antiquities, and this is true as regards all its parts, geometry, arithmetic, music, astronomy. But this would not have been the case except for the fact that this science is earlier than the others and naturally precedes them. Hence it is clear that it should be studied first, that through it we may advance to all the later sciences.

CONCERNING OPTICS, "THIS VERY BEAUTIFUL SCIENCE"

HAVING EXPLAINED the fundamental principles of wisdom, both sacred and human, which are found in the tongues from which the sciences of the Latins have been translated, and likewise in mathematics, I now wish to discuss some principles which belong to optics. If the consideration just mentioned is noble and pleasing, the one in hand is far nobler and more pleasing, since we take especial delight in vision, and light and color have an especial beauty beyond the other things that are brought to our senses, and not only does beauty shine forth, but advantage and a greater necessity appear.

For Aristotle says in the first book of the Metaphysics that vision alone reveals the differences of things; since by means of it we search out experimental knowledge of all things that are in the heavens and in the earth. For those things that are in the heavenly bodies are studied by visual instruments, as Ptolemy and the other astronomers teach. So also are those things that are generated in the air, like comets, rainbows, and the like. For their altitude above the horizon, their size, form, number, and all things that are in them, are verified by the methods of viewing them with instruments. Our experience of things here in the earth we owe to vision, because a blind man can have no experience worthy of the name concerning this world.

Hearing causes us to believe because we believe our teachers, but we cannot try out what we learn except through vision. If, moreover, we should adduce taste and touch and smell, we assume a knowledge belonging to beasts. For brutes are busied with the things pertaining to taste and touch, and exercise their sense of smell because of taste and touch, but the things are of little value, few in number, and common to us and to brutes concerning which these senses give verification, and therefore they do not rise to the rank of human wisdom.

But because of necessity, utility, and difficulty, sciences are formed, since art has to do with the difficult and with the good, as Aristotle says in the second book of the Ethics. For if what is sought is easy, there is no need for the formation of a science. Likewise although a matter be difficult yet not useful, no science is developed concerning it, because the labor would be foolish and vain. Also unless a subject were very useful and possessed many excellent truths, it does not require the formation of a separate science, but it suffices that this subject be treated in some particular book or chapter along with other matters in general science. But concerning vision alone is a separate science formed among philosophers, namely, optics, and not concerning any other sense. Wherefore there must be a special utility in our knowledge through vision which is not found in the other senses.

What I have now touched upon in general I wish to show in particular by disclosing the basic principles of this very beautiful science. It is possible that some other science may be more useful, but no other science has so much sweetness and beauty of utility. Therefore it is the flower of the whole of philosophy and through it, and not without it, can the other sciences be known. We must note, moreover, that Aristotle first treated this science, of which he says in the second book of the Physics that the subject is placed under another head. He also mentions it in his book on Sense and the Sensible, and has proved Democritus in error, because he did not name refractions and reflections of vision with reference to the optic and concave visual nerves. This book has been translated into Latin. After him Alhazen treats the subject more fully in a book which is extant. Alkindi also has arranged some data more fully, likewise authors of books on vision and mirrors.

EXPERIMENTAL SCIENCE

SINCE this experimental science is wholly unknown to the rank and file of students, I am therefore unable to convince people of its utility unless at the same time I disclose its excellence and its proper signification. This science alone, therefore, knows how to test perfectly what can be done by nature, what by the effort of art, what by trickery, what the incantations, conjurations, invocations, deprecations, sacrifices that belong to magic mean and dream of, and what is in them, so that all falsity may be removed and the truth alone of art and nature may be retained. This science alone teaches us how to view the mad acts of magicians, that they may be not ratified but shunned, just as logic considers sophistical reasoning.

This science has three leading characteristics with respect to other sciences. The first is that it investigates by experiment the notable conclusions of all those sciences. For the other sciences know how to discover their principles by experiments, but their conclusions are reached by reasoning drawn from the principles discovered. But if they should have a particular and complete experience of their own conclusions, they must have it with the aid of this noble science. For it is true that mathematics has general experiments as regards its conclusions in its figures and calculations, which also are applied to all sciences and to this kind of experiment, because no science can be known without mathematics. But if we give our attention to particular and complete experiments and such as are attested wholly by the proper method, we must employ the principles of this science which is called experimental. I give as an example the rainbow and phenomena connected with it, of which nature are the circle around the sun and the stars, the streak [*virga*] also lying at the side of the sun or of a star, which is apparent to the eye in a straight line, and is called by Aristotle in the third book of the Meteorologics a perpendicular, but by Seneca a streak, and the circle is called a corona, phenomena which frequently have the colors of the rainbow. The natural philosopher discusses these phenomena, and the writer on perspective has much to add pertaining to the mode of vision that is necessary in this case. But neither Aristotle nor Avicenna in their Natural Histories has given us a knowledge of phenomena of this kind, nor has Seneca, who composed a special book on them. But experimental science attests them.

The "Black Death" Disrupts Life and Learning

GUY DE CHAULIAC (1300?-1370?)

THE MODERN WORLD has not completely recovered from the profound sociological changes (especially the relationship between capital and labor) produced by the epidemics of "black death" (bubonic plague) that decimated Europe in the fourteenth and fifteenth centuries. Medical science was then helpless against it; prince and pauper took it; serf and scholar died; commerce failed and learning languished. One, among many accounts (such as the opening of Boccaccio's "Decameron"), was left by a great French physician and surgeon, Guy de Chauliac, who served three popes during the "Babylonian captivity" of the papacy at Avignon. De Chauliac's reputation rests upon his "Great Surgery" (*"Grande Chirurgie"*), considered an influential and authoritative work for three centuries after its translation into French in 1592.

Latin was the language in which De Chauliac originally wrote his great work. The English translation given here is from an 1890 French edition, edited by E. Nicaise, and is quoted from "The Black Death and Men of Learning" by A. M. Campbell (Columbia University Press, 1931).

THE PLAGUE OF 1348 AT AVIGNON

THE GREAT MORTALITY appeared at Avignon in January 1348, when I was in the service of Pope Clement VI. It was of two kinds. The first lasted two months, with continued fever and spitting of blood, and people died of it in three days. The second was all the rest of the time, also with continuous fever, and with tumors in the external parts, chiefly the armpits and groin; and people died in five days. It was so contagious, especially that accompanied by spitting of blood, that not only by staying together, but even by looking at one another, people caught it, with the result that men died without attendants and were buried without priests. The father did not visit his son, nor the son his father. Charity was dead and hope crushed.

I call it great, because it covered the whole world, or lacked little of doing so. For it began in the East and, thus casting its darts against the world, passed through our region toward the West. It was so great that it left scarcely a fourth part of the people. And I say that it was such that its like has never been heard tell of before; of the pestilences in the past that we read of, none was so great as this. For those covered only one region, this the whole world; those could be treated in some way, this in none.

For this reason it was useless and shameful for the doctors, the more so as they dared not visit the sick, for fear of being infected. And when they did visit them, they did hardly anything for them and were paid nothing; for all the sick died, except some few at the last who escaped, the buboes being ripened.

Many were in doubt about the cause of this great mortality. In some places they thought that the Jews had poisoned the world: and so they killed them. In others, that it was the poor deformed: and they drove them out. In others, that it was the nobles: and they feared to go abroad. Finally they reached the point where they kept guards in the cities and villages, and permitted the entry of no one who was not well known. And if powders or unguents were found on anyone the owners, for fear that they were poisons, were forced to swallow them. . . .

And I, to avoid infamy, dared not absent myself, but with continual fear preserved myself as best I could by means of [certain] remedies. Notwithstanding this, toward the end of the mortality I fell into a continuous fever, with a tumor in the groin. I was ill for nearly six weeks, and was in such great danger that all my associates thought that I would die; but the tumor being ripened, and treated . . . , I escaped by the will of God.

Doctors Merryman, Diet, and Quiet

THE REGIMEN OF SALERNO

Once the name of Salerno, a health resort on the west coast of Italy just south of Naples, reached the ears of the world because it was the site of one of the most famous medical schools connected with a medieval university. Among its distinguished teachers were Gariopontus, Petrus Clericus, Benvenuto Graefo, Aegidius Carbolenis, Rolando Capelluti, and Roger of Parma. The "Regimen of Salerno" was a Latin poem, first printed in 1484, but composed anonymously some time earlier, setting forth popular rules for hygiene and medical care.

The *Latin* original, very much longer, was translated into English in 1608 by Sir John Harington, Elizabethan courtier and author whose own contribution to sanitary science was the invention of the water closet. The verses given here are a modernization of his translation.

THE RULES OF HYGIENE IN POETRY

The Salerno School doth by these lines impart
All health to England's King, and doth advise
From care his head to keep, from wrath his heart;
Drink not much wine, sup light and soon arise,
When meat is gone, long sitting breedeth smart:
And afternoon still waking keep your eyes.
When moved you find yourself to Nature's needs,
Forbear them not, for that much danger breeds—
Use three physicians still: first, Doctor Diet,
Next Doctor Merryman and Doctor Quiet.

Rise early in the morn, and straight remember
With water cold to wash your hands and eyes;

In gentle fashion stretching every member,
And to refresh your brain whenas you rise,
In heat, in cold, in July and December.
Both comb your head and rub your teeth likewise;
If bled you have, keep cool; if bath'd, keep warm;
If dined, to stand or walk will do no harm. . . .
A King that cannot rule himself in diet,
Will hardly rule his realm in peace and quiet.

III SCIENCE REAWAKENS: In the Renaissance

Aviation Flutters in the Leaves of an Artist's "Notebooks"

LEONARDO DA VINCI (1452–1519)

WHEN THE LIGHTS of learning came on again over all Europe, ignited after long dark ages by the rediscovery of the works of the ancient Greeks, kindled by the invention of printing and fanned by voyages of discovery into new worlds, the flamboyant torches of the Italian Renaissance not only illuminated a gorgeous new art and literature but awakened also the spirit of inquiry into those phases of human thought and invention which, grown great, have become the grist of modern science.

No man better exemplifies the seething curiosity of the extravagant age of the rebirth of learning than the bearded, keen-sighted, sure-handed Florentine giant of intellect. Painter, sculptor, architect, engineer, and scientist, Leonardo da Vinci is more famed perhaps as an artist than as a scientist. Among the best known of his paintings are "The Last Supper," "The Annunciation," and the "Mona Lisa."

If his scientific work had been published instead of being left for centuries in the five thousand scribbled and half-sketched leaves of his "Notebooks," his scientific reputation might be even greater than it is. A true pioneer of science, Da Vinci foreshadowed many of the most notable discoveries of later scientists: Galileo, Harvey, Newton, and Langley, to name but a few. Despite the difficulties of the wretched Florentine dialect and the reversed mirror-image writing to which Da Vinci was addicted, scholars have done yeoman service in making Da Vinci's thoughts available in modern languages, including English. And so great and subtle was his mind that every reworking of his material uncovers new and useful observations.

His "Notebooks" reveal accurate observation and incisive, almost prophetic, thinking on many subjects: natural and mechanical flight— the dream of aviation; the lever, the wheel, the axle, freely falling bodies, and other subjects of mechanics, that "paradise of the mathematical sciences"; astronomy and optics; anatomy and physiology; hydraulics and even fossils. He made accurate anatomical drawings, illustrating the geometrically correct proportions of the body. Many sketches illustrated points for his friends; he himself had the artist's eye for proportion and perspective.

Much has been made of his unfinished sketches and notes as tokens of frustration. A more probable explanation is to be had by recognizing that Da Vinci was primarily an experimenter, restlessly pricked on by a truly scientific curiosity. The unfinished pieces were simply notes to organize and jog his thinking processes. When he was satisfied with the thought in his own mind he had no further interest or use for the paper scaffolding and did not bother to complete it. "While Nature begins with the cause and ends with the experiment," he said, "we must nevertheless pursue the opposite plan, beginning with the experiment and by means of it investigating the cause."

Da Vinci was not the first of the artists of the Renaissance to accept and further closer relationships between mathematics and architecture, geometry and painting, medicine and art. This trend had begun almost a century and a half before this time with the painter and architect, Giotto. Artists were soon admitted to the picture section (*membrum pictum*) of the medical guilds.

Da Vinci was born in Tuscany, the natural son of a Florentine notary. At fourteen he came to Florence as a protégé of Lorenzo the Magnificent. Later he went to Milan, under the protection of Ludovico Sforza; thence to Mantua, Venice, and back to Florence. When he needed a job he usually played upon his skill as an engineer or artist, not upon his interest in science. He served as military engineer to Cesare Borgia and as court painter to Louis XII and Francis I of France; constructed the Martesana Canal and was architect of the Milan Cathedral.

Italian—Florentine dialect—was the language in which Da Vinci wrote. The English translations given here are from "The Notebooks of Leonardo da Vinci," arranged and translated by Edward MacCurdy, and published by Reynal & Hitchcock, Inc., in 1938.

ON NATURAL AND MECHANICAL FLIGHT: AVIATION'S DREAM

A BIRD IS an instrument working according to mathematical law, which instrument it is within the capacity of man to reproduce with all its movements, but not with a corresponding degree of strength, though it is deficient only in the power of maintaining equilibrium. We may therefore say that such an instrument constructed by man is lacking in nothing except the life of the bird, and this life must needs be supplied from that of man.

The life which resides in the bird's members will without doubt better conform to their needs than will that of man, which is separated from them, and especially in the almost imperceptible movements which preserve equilibrium. But since we see that the bird is equipped for many obvious varieties of movements, we are able from this experience to declare that the most rudimentary of these movements will be capable of being comprehended by man's understanding; and that he will to a great extent be able to provide against the destruction of that instrument of which he has himself become the living principle and the propeller.

The slanting descent of birds made against the wind will always be made beneath the wind, and their reflex movement will be made upon the wind.

But if this falling movement is made to the east when the wind is blowing from the north, then the north wing will remain under the wind and it will do the same in the reflex movement, wherefore at the end of this reflex movement the bird will find itself with its front to the north.

And if the bird descends to the south while the wind is blowing from the north it will make this descent upon the wind, and its reflex movement will be below the wind; but this is a vexed question which shall be discussed in its proper place, for here it would seem that it could not make the reflex movement.

When the bird makes its reflex movement facing and upon the wind it will rise much more than its natural impetus requires, seeing that it is also helped by the wind which enters underneath it and plays the part of a wedge. But when it is at the end of its ascent it will have used up its impetus and therefore will depend upon the help of the wind, which as it strikes it on the breast would throw it over if it were not that it lowers the right or left wing, for this will cause it to turn to the right or left, dropping down in a half circle.

The bird maintains itself in the air by imperceptible balancing when near to the mountains or lofty ocean crags; it does this by means of the curves of the winds which, as they strike against these projections, being forced to preserve their first impetus, bend their straight course toward the sky with divers revolutions, at the beginning of which the birds come to a stop with their wings open, receiving underneath themselves the continual buffetings of the reflex courses of the winds, and by the angle of their bodies acquiring as much weight against the wind as the wind makes force against this weight. And so by such a condition of equilibrium the bird proceeds to employ the smallest beginnings of every variety of power that can be produced.

The man in a flying machine has to be free from the waist upward in order to be able to balance himself as he does in a boat, so that his center of gravity and that of his machine may oscillate and change where necessity requires through a change in the center of its resistance.

The movement of the [man-made] bird ought always to be above the clouds so that the wing may not be wetted, and in order to survey more country and to escape the danger caused by the revolutions of the winds among the mountain defiles which are always full of gusts and eddies of winds. And if, moreover, the bird should be overturned you will have plenty of time to turn it back again, following the instructions I have given, before it falls down again to the ground.

If the point of the wing is struck by the wind and the wind enters underneath the point the bird will then find itself liable to be overturned unless it employs one of two remedies; that is, either it suddenly enters with this point under the wind or lowers the opposite wing from the middle forward.

The [mechanical] bird I have described ought to be able by the help of the wind to rise to a great height, and this will prove to be its safety; since even if all the above-mentioned revolutions were to befall it, it would still have time to regain a condition of equilibrium; provided that its various parts have a great power of resistance, so that they can safely withstand the fury and violence of the descent, by the aid of the defenses which I have mentioned; and its joints should be made of strong tanned hide, and sewn with cords of strong raw silk. And let no one encumber himself with iron bands, for these are very soon broken at the joints or else they become worn out, and consequently it is well not to encumber oneself with them.

THE PARACHUTE

If a man have a tent made of linen of which the apertures have all been stopped up, and it be twelve braccia across [over twenty-five feet] and twelve in depth, he will be able to throw himself down from any height without sustaining any injury.

ANATOMICAL STUDIES

ARM AND FOREARM

You will first have these bones sawn lengthwise and then across, so that one can see where the bones are thick or thin; then represent them whole and disjoined, as here above, but from four aspects in order that one can understand their true shape; then proceed to clothe them by degrees with their nerves, veins, and muscles.

HANDS AND WINGS

No movement either of the hand or the fingers is produced by the muscles above the elbow; and so it is with birds, and it is for this reason that they are so powerful, because all the muscles which lower the wings spring from the breast and these have in themselves a greater weight than that of all the rest of the bird.

MUSCLES USED IN BREATHING

These muscles have a voluntary and an involuntary movement, seeing that they are those which open and shut the lung. When they open they suspend their function, which is to contract, for the ribs which at first were drawn up and compressed by the contracting of these muscles then remain at liberty and resume their natural distance as the breast expands. And since there is no vacuum in nature the lung which touches the ribs from within must necessarily follow their expansion; and the lung therefore, opening like a pair of bellows, draws in the air in order to fill the space so formed.

The intestines. As to these you will understand their windings well if you inflate them. And remember that after you have made them from four aspects thus arranged you then make them from four other aspects, expanded in such a way that from their spaces and openings you can understand the whole, that is, the variations of their thicknesses.

EMBRYOLOGY ANTICIPATED

The plant never springs from the ramification, for at first the plant exists before this ramification, and the heart exists before the veins.

All the veins and arteries proceed from the heart; and the reason is that the maximum thickness that is found in these veins and arteries is at the junction that they make with the heart; and the farther away they are from the heart the thinner they become, and they are divided into more minute ramifications. And if you should say that the veins start in the protuberance of the liver because they have their ramifications in this protuberance, just as the roots of plants have in the earth, the reply to this comparison is that plants do not have their origin in their roots, but that the roots and the other ramifications have their origin in the lower part of these plants, which is between the air and the earth; and all the parts of the plant above and below are always less than this part which borders upon the earth; therefore it is evident that the whole plant has its origin from the thickness, and, in consequence, the veins have their origin in the heart where is their greatest thickness; never can any plant be found which has its origin in the points of its roots or other ramifications; and the example of this is seen in the growing of the peach, which proceeds from its nut, as is shown above.

Metallurgy in a Sculptor's Autobiography

BENVENUTO CELLINI (1500–71)

Through his classic "Autobiography" Cellini's personal life as profligate lover, duelist, and artist in gold and bronze has become almost as well known as his statues and jewelry are famed. Like many other artists of the Italian Renaissance, Cellini was half artisan, a metalworker as seriously concerned as his contemporary, Agricola, with the texture, structure, composition of his materials. Many passages in the famous autobiography, such as the one given here, are penetrating treatises on metallurgy. What the scientists called "the laws of nature" are here disguised as "the rules of art"—to be scrupulously regarded even by spendthrifts of passion and coin. It is interesting that this pioneer metallurgist was most seriously concerned with a phase of the science that has become increasingly important in providing the modern era with rapid transportation and better shelter: namely, alloys of two or more metals.

Italian was the language in which Cellini disclosed himself. The English translation is by John Addington Symonds. The footnotes are his.

CASTING A STATUE

[Benvenuto is about to cast in bronze a statue of Perseus ordered by Cosimo de' Medici.]

ACCORDINGLY I strengthened my heart, and with all the forces of my body and my purse, employing what little money still remained to me, I set to work. First I provided myself with several loads of pine wood from the forests of Serristori, in the neighborhood of Montelupo. While these were on their way, I clothed my Perseus with the clay which I had prepared many months beforehand, in order that it might be duly seasoned. After making its clay tunic (for that is the term used in this art) and properly arming it and fencing it with iron girders, I began to draw the wax out by means of a slow fire. This melted and issued through numerous air vents I had made; for the more there are of these the better will the mold fill. When I had finished drawing off the wax, I constructed a funnel-shaped furnace all around the model of my Perseus.[1] It was built of bricks, so interlaced, the one above the other, that numerous apertures were left for the fire to exhale at. Then I began to lay on wood by degrees, and kept it burning two whole days and nights. At length, when all the wax was gone, and the mold was well baked, I set to work at digging the pit in which to sink it. This I performed with scrupulous regard to all the rules of art. When I had finished that part of my work, I raised the mold by windlasses and stout ropes to a perpendicular position, and, suspending it with the greatest care one cubit above the level of the furnace, so that it hung exactly above the middle of the pit, I next lowered it gently down into the very bottom of the furnace and had it firmly placed with every possible precaution for its safety. When this delicate operation was accomplished, I began to bank it up with the earth I had excavated; and, ever as the earth grew higher, I introduced its proper air vents, which were little tubes of earthenware, such as folk use for drains and suchlike purposes.[2] At length I

---

[1] This furnace, called *manica*, was like a grain hopper, so that the mold could stand upright in it as in a cup. The word "manica" is the same as our "manuch," an antique form of sleeve.

[2] These air vents, or *sfiatatoi*, were introduced into the outer mold, which Cellini calls the *tonaca*, or clay tunic laid upon the original model of baked clay and wax. They served the double purpose of drawing off the wax, whereby a space was left for the molten bronze to enter, and also of facilitating the penetration of this molten metal by allowing a free escape of air and gas from the outer mold.

felt sure that it was admirably fixed and that the filling in of the pit and the placing of the air vents had been properly performed. I also could see that my work people understood my method, which differed very considerably from that of all the other masters in the trade. Feeling confident, then, that I could rely upon them, I next turned to my furnace, which I had filled with numerous pigs of copper and other bronze stuff. The pieces were piled according to the laws of art; that is to say, so resting one upon the other that the flames could play freely through them, in order that the metal might heat and liquefy the sooner. At last I called out heartily to set the furnace going. The logs of pine were heaped in, and, what with the unctuous resin of the wood and the good draft I had given, my furnace worked so well that I was obliged to rush from side to side to keep it going. The labor was more than I could stand; yet I forced myself to strain every nerve and muscle. To increase my anxieties, the workshop took fire, and we were afraid lest the roof should fall upon our heads; while, from the garden, such a storm of wind and rain kept blowing in that it perceptibly cooled the furnace.

Battling thus with all these untoward circumstances for several hours, and exerting myself beyond even the measure of my powerful constitution, I could at last bear up no longer, and a sudden fever,[3] of the utmost possible intensity, attacked me. I felt absolutely obliged to go and fling myself upon my bed. Sorely against my will having to drag myself away from the spot, I turned to my assistants, about ten or more in all, what with master founders, hand workers, country fellows, and my own special journeymen, among whom was Bernardino Mannellini, of Mugello, my apprentice through several years. To him in particular I spoke: "Look, my dear Bernardino, that you observe the rules which I have taught you; do your best with all dispatch, for the metal will soon be fused. You cannot go wrong; these honest men will get the channels ready; you will easily be able to drive back the two plugs with this pair of iron crooks; and I am sure that my mold will fill miraculously. I feel more ill than I ever did in all my life, and verily believe that it will kill me before a few hours are over."[4] Thus, with despair at heart, I left them and betook myself to bed.

[3] *Una febbre efimera*. Literally, a fever of one day's duration.

[4] Some technical terms require explanation in this sentence. The canals or channels were sluices for carrying the molten metal from the furnace into the mold. The *mandriani*, which I have translated by "iron crooks," were poles fitted at the end with curved irons, by which the openings of the furnace, plugs, or, in Italian *spine,* could be partially or wholly driven back, so as to let the molten metal flow through the channels into the mold. When the

No sooner had I got to bed than I ordered my serving-maids to carry food and wine for all the men into the workshop; at the same time I cried: "I shall not be alive tomorrow." They tried to encourage me, arguing that my illness would pass over, since it came from excessive fatigue. In this way I spent two hours battling with the fever, which steadily increased, and calling out continually: "I feel that I am dying." My housekeeper, who was named Mona Fiore da Castel del Rio, a very notable manager and no less warmhearted, kept chiding me for my discouragement; but, on the other hand, she paid me every kind attention which was possible. However, the sight of my physical pain and moral dejection so affected her that, in spite of that brave heart of hers, she could not refrain from shedding tears; and yet, so far as she was able, she took good care I should not see them. While I was thus terribly afflicted, I beheld the figure of a man enter my chamber, twisted in his body into the form of a capital S. He raised a lamentable, doleful voice, like one who announces their last hour to men condemned to die upon the scaffold, and spoke these words: "O Benvenuto! Your statue is spoiled, and there is no hope whatever of saving it." No sooner had I heard the shriek of that wretch than I gave a howl which might have been heard from the sphere of flame. Jumping from my bed, I seized my clothes and began to dress. The maids, and my lad, and everyone who came around to help me, got kicks or blows of the fist, while I kept crying out in lamentation: "Ah! Traitors! Enviers! This is an act of treason, done by malice prepense! But I swear by God that I will sift it to the bottom, and before I die will leave such witness to the world of what I can do as shall make a score of mortals marvel."

When I had got my clothes on, I strode with soul bent on mischief toward the workshop; there I beheld the men, whom I had left erewhile in such high spirits, standing stupefied and downcast. I began at once and spoke: "Up with you! Attend to me! Since you have not been able or willing to obey the directions I gave you, obey me now that I am with you to conduct my work in person. Let no one contradict me, for in cases like this we need the aid of hand and hearing, not of advice."

When I had uttered these words, a certain Maestro Alessandro Lastricati broke silence and said: "Look you, Benvenuto, you are going to at-

metal reached the mold, it entered in a red-hot stream between the *tonaca,* or outside mold, and the *anima,* or inner block, filling up exactly the space which had previously been occupied by the wax extracted by a method of slow burning alluded to above. I believe that the process is known as casting *à cire perdue.* The *forma,* or mold, consisted of two pieces: one hollow (*la tonaca*), which gave shape to the bronze; one solid and rounded (*la anima*), which stood at a short interval within the former and regulated the influx of the metal.

tempt an enterprise which the laws of art do not sanction and which cannot succeed."

I turned upon him with such fury and so full of mischief that he and all the rest of them exclaimed with one voice: "On then! Give orders! We will obey your least commands, so long as life is left in us." I believe they spoke thus feelingly because they thought I must fall shortly dead upon the ground. I went immediately to inspect the furnace and found that the metal was all curdled; an accident which we express by "being caked." I told two of the hands to cross the road and fetch from the house of the butcher Capretta a load of young oak wood, which had lain dry for above a year; this wood had been previously offered me by Mme. Ginevra, wife of the said Capretta. So soon as the first armfuls arrived, I began to fill the grate beneath the furnace.[5] Now oak wood of that kind heats more powerfully than any other sort of tree; and for this reason, where a slow fire is wanted, as in the case of gun foundry, alder or pine is preferred. Accordingly, when the logs took fire, oh! how the cake began to stir beneath that awful heat, to glow and sparkle in a blaze! At the same time I kept stirring up the channels and sent men upon the roof to stop the conflagration, which had gathered force from the increased combustion in the furnace; also I caused boards, carpets, and other hangings to be set up against the garden, in order to protect us from the violence of the rain.

When I had thus provided against these several disasters, I roared out first to one man and then to another: "Bring this thing here! Take that thing there!" At this crisis, when the whole gang saw the cake was on the point of melting, they did my bidding, each fellow working with the strength of three. I then ordered half a pig of pewter to be brought, which weighed about sixty pounds, and flung it into the middle of the cake inside the furnace. By this means, and by piling on wood and stirring now with pokers and now with iron rods, the curdled mass rapidly began to liquefy. Then, knowing I had brought the dead to life again, against the firm opinion of those ignoramuses, I felt such vigor fill my veins that all those pains of fever, all those fears of death, were quite forgotten.

All of a sudden an explosion took place, attended by a tremendous flash of flame, as though a thunderbolt had formed and been discharged amongst us. Unwonted and appalling terror astonished everyone, and me more even than the rest. When the din was over and the dazzling

[5]The Italian is *bracciaiuola,* a pit below the grating, which receives the ashes from the furnace.

light extinguished, we began to look each other in the face. Then I discovered that the cap of the furnace had blown up, and the bronze was bubbling over from its source beneath. So I had the mouths of my mold immediately opened, and at the same time drove in the two plugs which kept back the molten metal. But I noticed that it did not flow as rapidly as usual, the reason being probably that the fierce heat of the fire we kindled had consumed its base alloy. Accordingly I sent for all my pewter platters, porringers, and dishes, to the number of some two hundred pieces, and had a portion of them cast, one by one, into the channels, the rest into the furnace. This expedient succeeded, and everyone could now perceive that my bronze was in most perfect liquefaction, and my mold was filling; whereupon they all with heartiness and happy cheer assisted and obeyed my bidding, while I, now here, now there, gave orders, helped with my own hands, and cried aloud: "O God! Thou that by Thy immeasurable power didst rise from the dead, and in Thy glory didst ascend to heaven!" . . . Even thus in a moment my mold was filled; and seeing my work finished, I fell upon my knees and with all my heart gave thanks to God.

From Alchemy toward Chemistry

PARACELSUS (THEOPHRASTUS BOMBASTUS VON HOHENHEIM) (1493?-1541)

A SHADY FIGURE in the shadows where medieval alchemy was gradually being transformed into modern chemistry wandered this bombastic, unorthodox Swiss physician. He was born Theophrastus Bombastus von Hohenheim, in the Tyrolean village of Einsiedeln. Later he chose to call himself Phillipus Aureolus Paracelsus, after Celsus, Roman physician of the second century A.D., whose works on medicine, published in 1478, were then held of the highest authority. In the obscure language of an alchemical quack, of which the passage given here is a fair sample, Paracelsus concealed much original scientific thinking, especially on metallurgy, miners' diseases, and the use of metals (for example, mercury) in the treatment of disease. Not until almost a century after its use in medicine had been established by Morton and Long did anyone guess that Paracelsus' obscure "receipt" for "extract of vitriol" actually yielded anesthetic ether.

Latin was the original language of the "Hermetic and Alchemical Writings of Paracelsus," translated by Arthur Edward Waite and published in London in 1894. These passages are from *"Coelum Philosophorum"* ("Heaven of Philosophy") which deals with "The Science and Nature of Alchemy, and What Opinion Should Be Formed Thereof."

THE RECEIPTS OF ALCHEMY

THE PREFACE

YOU WHO ARE SKILLED in alchemy, and as many others as promise yourselves great riches or chiefly desire to make gold and silver, which alchemy in different ways promises and teaches; equally, too, you who willingly undergo toil and vexations, and wish not to be freed from them until you have attained your rewards and the fulfillment of the promises made to you: experience teaches this every day, that out of thousands of you not even one accomplishes his desire. Is this a failure of nature or of art? I say no; but it is rather the fault of fate, or of the unskillfulness of the operator. . . .

HOW TO MAKE GOLD AND SILVER (Sol and Luna)

What, then, shall we say about the receipts of alchemy, and about the diversity of its vessels and instruments? These are furnaces, glasses, jars, waters, oils, limes, sulphurs, salts, saltpeters, alums, vitriols, chrysocollae, copper greens, atraments, auripigments, fel vitri, ceruse, red earth, thucia, wax, lutum sapientiae, pounded glass, verdigris, soot, crocus of Mars, soap, crystal, arsenic, antimony, minium, elixir, lazarium, gold leaf, salt niter, sal ammoniac, calamine stone, magnesia, bolus armenus, and many other things. Moreover, [what shall we say] concerning preparations, putrefactions, digestions, probations, solutions, cementings, filtrations, reverberations, calcinations, graduations, rectifications, amalgamations, purgations, et cetera, with these alchemical books are crammed. Then, again, concerning herbs, roots, seeds, woods, stones, animals, worms, bone dust, snail shells, other shells, and pitch. These and the like, whereof there are some very farfetched in alchemy, are mere incumbrances of work; since even if Sol and Luna could be made by them they rather hinder and delay than further one's purpose. But it is not from these—to say the truth—that the art of making Sol and Luna is to be learned. So, then, all these things should be passed by, because they have no effect with the five metals, so far as Sol and Luna are concerned. Someone may ask, "What, then, is this short and easy way, which involves no difficulty, and yet whereby Sol and Luna can be made?" Our answer is: this has been fully and openly explained in the Seven Canons. It would be lost labor should one seek further to instruct one who does not understand these. It would be impossible to convince such a person that these matters could be so easily understood, but in an occult rather than in an open sense.

The art is this: after you have made heaven, or the sphere of Saturn, with its life to run over the earth, place it on all the planets, or such, one or more, as you wish, so that the portion of Luna may be the smallest. Let all run, until heaven, or Saturn, has entirely disappeared. Then all those planets will remain dead with their old corruptible bodies, having meanwhile obtained another new, perfect, and incorruptible body.

That body is the spirit of heaven. From it these planets again receive a body and life, and live as before. Take this body from the life and the earth. Keep it. It is Sol and Luna. Here you have the art altogether, clear and entire. If you do not yet understand it, or are not practiced therein, it is well. It is better that it should be kept concealed, and not made public.

"On Metals"

AGRICOLA (GEORG BAUER) (1494–1555)

EX-PRESIDENT of the United States Herbert Hoover, by profession a mining engineer, and his wife, Lou Henry Hoover, translated from the Latin and published in 1912 the passages here quoted from the enduring classic work on mining and metallurgy written four centuries before by a scholarly Saxon physician and miner, Georg Bauer, surnamed Agricola. His work "On Metals" ("*De Re Metallica*") originally published in the sixteenth century (1530? or 1556?) carried far beyond Pliny the available knowledge of mining and metallurgy, geology and medicine.

Latin in the original, the Hoovers' translation originally appeared in the London "Mining Journal."

WHAT A MINING ENGINEER MUST KNOW

MANY PERSONS hold the opinion that the metal industries are fortuitous and that the occupation is one of sordid toil, and altogether a kind of business requiring not so much skill as labor. But as for myself, when I reflect carefully upon its special points one by one, it appears to be far otherwise. For a miner must have the greatest skill in his work, that he may know first of all what mountain or hill, what valley or plain, can be prospected most profitably, or what he should leave alone; moreover, he must understand the veins, stringers, and seams in the rocks. Then he must be thoroughly familiar with the many and varied species of earths, juices, gems, stones, marbles, rocks, metals, and compounds. He must also have a complete knowledge of the method of making all underground works. Lastly, there are the various systems of assaying substances and of preparing them for smelting; and here again there are many altogether diverse methods. For there is one method for gold and silver, another for copper, another for quicksilver, another for iron, another for lead, and even tin and bismuth are treated differently from lead. Although the evaporation of juices is an art apparently quite distinct from metallurgy, yet they ought not to be considered separately, inasmuch as these juices are also often dug out of the ground solidified, or they are produced from certain kinds of earth, and stones which the miners dig up, and some of the juices are not themselves devoid of metals. Again, their treatment is not simple, since there is one method for common salt, another for soda, another for alum, another for vitriol, another for sulphur, and another for bitumen.

Furthermore, there are many arts and sciences of which a miner should not be ignorant. First there is philosophy, that he may discern the origin, cause, and nature of subterranean things; for then he will be able to dig out the veins easily and advantageously, and to obtain more abundant results from his mining. Secondly, there is medicine, that he may be able to look after his diggers and other workmen, that they do not meet with those diseases to which they are more liable than workmen in other occupations, or if they do meet with them, that he himself may be able to heal them or may see that the doctors do so. Thirdly follows astronomy, that he may know the divisions of the heavens and from them judge the direction of the veins. Fourthly, there is the science of surveying, that he may be able to estimate how deep a shaft should be sunk to reach the tunnel which is being driven to it and to determine the limits and boundaries in these workings, especially in depth. Fifthly, his knowledge of arithmetical science should be such that he may calculate the cost to be incurred in the machinery and the working of the mine. Sixthly, his learning must comprise architecture, that he himself may construct the various machines and timberwork required underground, or that he may be able to explain the method of the construction to others. Next, he must have knowledge of drawing, that he can draw plans of his machinery. Lastly, there is the law, especially that dealing with metals, that he may claim his own rights, that he may undertake the duty of giving others his opinion on legal matters, that he may not take another man's property and so make trouble for himself, and that he may fulfill his obligations to others according to the law.

It is therefore necessary that those who take an interest in the methods and precepts of mining and metallurgy should read these and others of our books studiously and diligently; or on every point they should consult expert mining people, though they will discover few who are skilled in the whole art. As a rule one man understands only the methods of mining, another possesses the knowledge of washing, another is experienced in the art of smelting, another has the knowledge of measuring the hidden parts of the earth, another is skillful in the art of making machines, and finally, another is learned in mining law. But as for us, though we may not have perfected the whole art of discovery and preparation of metals, at least we can be of great assistance to persons studious in its acquisition.

SMELTING IRON

VERY GOOD IRON ore is smelted in a furnace almost like the cupellation furnace. The hearth is three and a half feet high, and five feet long and wide; in the center of it is a crucible a foot deep and one and a half feet wide, but it may be deeper or shallower, wider or narrower, according to whether more or less ore is to be made into iron. A certain quantity of iron ore is given to the master, out of which he may smelt either much or little iron. He, being about to expend his skill and labor on this matter, first throws charcoal into the crucible and sprinkles over it an iron shovelful of crushed iron ore mixed with unslaked lime. Then he repeatedly throws on charcoal and sprinkles it with ore, and continues this until he has slowly built up a heap; it melts when the charcoal has been kindled and the fire violently stimulated by the blast of the bellows, which are skillfully fixed in a pipe. He is able to complete this work sometimes in eight hours, sometimes in ten, and again sometimes in twelve. In order that the heat of the fire should not burn his face, he covers it entirely with a cap, in which, however, there are holes through which he may see and breathe. At the side of the hearth is a bar which he raises as often as is necessary, when the bellows blow too violent a blast, or when he adds more ore and charcoal. He also uses the bar to draw off the slags or to open or close the gates of the sluice, through which the waters flow down onto the wheel which turns the axle that compresses the bellows. In this sensible way iron is melted out and a mass weighing two or three *centumpondia* may be made, providing the iron ore was rich. When this is done the master opens the slag vent with the tapping bar, and when all has run out he allows the iron mass to cool. Afterward he and his assistant stir the iron with the bar, and then in order to chip off the slag which had until then adhered to it and to condense and flatten it, they take it down from the furnace to the floor, and beat it with large wooden mallets having slender handles five feet long. Thereupon it is immediately placed on the anvil and repeatedly beaten by the large iron hammer that is raised by the cams of an axle turned by a water wheel. Not long afterward it is taken up with tongs and placed under the same hammer, and cut up with a sharp iron into four, five, or six pieces, according to whether it is large or small. These pieces, after they have been reheated in the blacksmith's forge and again placed on the anvil, are shaped by the smith into square bars or into plowshares or tires, but mainly into bars. Four, six, or eight of these bars weigh one fifth of a centumpondium, and from these they make various implements. During the blows from the hammer by which it is shaped by the smith, a youth pours water with a ladle onto the glowing iron, and this is why the blows make such a loud sound that they may be heard a long distance from the works. The masses, if they remain and settle in the crucible of the furnace in which the iron is smelted, become hard iron which can only be hammered with difficulty, and from these they make the iron-shod heads for the stamps, and suchlike very hard articles.

The Revolution in Astronomy

NICOLAUS COPERNICUS (1473-1543)

No ONE COULD TELL, simply by observation with the naked eye, that the earth and the planets revolve about the sun. Others had speculated, Copernicus *proved* by Titanic calculation that the heliocentric hypothesis was the simplest and most satisfying explanation of the observed revolutions of the heavenly bodies. His "new astronomy," upsetting the long accepted but more complicated astronomical system of Ptolemy, Alexandrian Greek astronomer of the second century A.D., was summed up in one of the great scientific books of all time, "The Revolutions of the Heavenly Bodies" (*"De Revolutionibus Orbium Coelestium"*). The first copies, it is said, reached him on his deathbed in 1543. Given here is Copernicus' own original outline or sketch (*"Commentariolus"*) of the great work written sometime after 1520 and circulated only as a letter.

By birth (at Thorn on the Vistula) and by residence (at Frauenburg), Copernicus was a Pole; by profession, a cleric (appointed canon of the cathedral by his considerate maternal uncle, the Bishop of Ermland); by training at the famed Italian universities of Bologna, Padua, and Rome, a canon lawyer and a physician; by inclination—in spite of poor eyesight —a portrait painter, an astronomer, and a mathematician. After his death Copernicus' heliocentric doctrine, carried forward by Tycho Brahe, John Kepler, Galileo, and others, ran afoul of the authority of the Catholic Church, racked by Luther's Reformation. But *"De Revolutionibus"* is dedicated to the Pope.

Kepler (1571-1630), like Copernicus, was a great theorist and mathematician and formulated the celebrated three "laws of planetary motion"; namely:

1. The planet describes an ellipse, the sun being in one focus.

2. The straight line joining the planet to the sun sweeps out equal areas in equal intervals of time.

3. The squares of the periodic times of any two planets are to each other exactly as the cubes of their median distances.

Kepler's life was a constant struggle against poverty. At times he cast horoscopes to eke out a living. "Mother Astronomy," he said, "would surely have to suffer hunger if the daughter Astrology did not earn their bread."

Less a theorist, more a scanner of the heavens, was Kepler's one-time employer, Tycho Brahe (1546–1601), a Dane whose regally opulent astronomical observatory—Uraniborg, the Castle of the Heavens—with the best instruments of the time, including a ten-foot quadrant with a brass scale reading to fractions of a minute, permitted the extravagant Tycho to make for twenty years a "magnificent series of observations, far transcending in accuracy and extent anything that had been accomplished by his predecessors." Brahe's observations, Kepler's mathematics, and Galileo's telescope established Copernicus' theory.

Latin was the language of Copernicus' *"Commentariolus."* The English translation, by Edward Rosen, was first published in "Three Copernican Treatises" (Columbia University Press, 1939).

HYPOTHESIS ON HEAVENLY MOTIONS: A PRELIMINARY OUTLINE OF THE THEORY THAT THE EARTH MOVES AROUND THE SUN

OUR ANCESTORS assumed, I observe, a large number of celestial spheres for this reason especially, to explain the apparent motion of the planets by the principle of regularity. For they thought it altogether absurd that a heavenly body, which is a perfect sphere, should not always move uniformly. They saw that by connecting and combining regular motions in various ways they could make any body appear to move to any position.

Callippus and Eudoxus, who endeavored to solve the problem by the use of concentric spheres, were unable to account for all the planetary movements; they had to explain not merely the apparent revolutions of the planets but also the fact that these bodies appear to us sometimes to mount higher in the heavens, sometimes to descend; and this fact is incompatible with the principle of concentricity. Therefore it seemed better to employ eccentrics and epicycles, a system which most scholars finally accepted.

Yet the planetary theories of Ptolemy and most other astronomers, although consistent with the numerical data, seemed likewise to present no small difficulty. For these theories were not adequate unless certain equants were also conceived; it then appeared that a planet moved with uniform velocity neither on its deferent nor about the center of its epicycle. Hence a system of this sort seemed neither sufficiently absolute nor sufficiently pleasing to the mind.

Having become aware of these defects, I often considered whether there could perhaps be found a more reasonable arrangement of circles, from which every apparent inequality would be derived and in which everything would move uniformly about its proper center, as the rule of absolute motion requires. After I had addressed myself to this very difficult and almost insoluble problem, the suggestion at length came to me how it could be solved with fewer and much simpler constructions than were formerly used, if some assumptions (which are called axioms) were granted me. They follow in this order.

ASSUMPTIONS

1. There is no one center of all the celestial circles or spheres.
2. The center of the earth is not the center of the universe, but only of gravity and of the lunar sphere.
3. All the spheres revolve about the sun as their mid-point, and therefore the sun is the center of the universe.
4. The ratio of the earth's distance from the sun to the height of the firmament is so much smaller than the ratio of the earth's radius to its distance from the sun that the distance from the earth to the sun is imperceptible in comparison with the height of the firmament.
5. Whatever motion appears in the firmament arises not from any motion of the firmament but from the earth's motion. The earth together with its circumjacent elements performs a complete rotation on its fixed poles in a daily motion, while the firmament and highest heaven abide unchanged.
6. What appear to us as motions of the sun arise not from its motion but from the motion of the earth and our sphere, with which we revolve about the sun like any other planet. The earth has, then, more than one motion.
7. The apparent retrograde and direct motion of the planets arises not from their motion but from the earth's. The motion of the earth alone, therefore, suffices to explain so many apparent inequalities in the heavens.

Having set forth these assumptions, I shall endeavor briefly to show how uniformity of the motions can be saved in a systematic way. However, I have thought it well, for the sake of brevity, to omit from this sketch mathematical demonstrations, reserving these for my larger work. But in the explanation of the circles I shall set down here the lengths of the radii; and from these the reader who is not unacquainted with mathematics will readily perceive how closely this arrangement of circles agrees with the numerical data and observations.

Accordingly, let no one suppose that I have gratuitously asserted, with the Pythagoreans, the motion of the earth; strong proof will be found in my exposition of the circles. For the principal arguments by which the natural philosophers attempt to establish the immobility of the earth rest for the most part on the appearances; it is particularly such arguments that collapse here, since I treat the earth's immobility as due to an appearance.

The Order of the Spheres

The celestial spheres are arranged in the following order. The highest is the immovable sphere of the fixed stars, which contains and gives position to all things. Beneath it is Saturn, which Jupiter follows, then Mars. Below Mars is the sphere on which we revolve; then Venus; last is Mercury. The lunar sphere revolves about the center of the earth and moves with the earth like an epicycle. In the same order also one planet surpasses another in speed of revolution, according as they trace greater or smaller circles. Thus Saturn completes its revolution in thirty years, Jupiter in twelve, Mars in two and one half, and the earth in one year, Venus in nine months, Mercury in three.

The Apparent Motions of the Sun

The earth has three motions. First, it revolves annually in a great circle about the sun in the order of the signs, always describing equal arcs in equal times; the distance from the center of the circle to the center of the sun is one twenty-fifth of the radius of the circle. The radius is assumed to have a length imperceptible in comparison with the height of the firmament; consequently the sun appears to revolve with this motion, as if the earth lay in the center of the universe. However, this appearance is caused by the motion not of the sun but of the earth, so that, for example, when the earth is in the sign of Capricornus, the sun is seen diametrically opposite in Cancer, and so on. On account of the previously mentioned distance of the sun from the center of the circle, this apparent motion of the sun is not uniform, the maximum inequality being two and one sixth degrees.

The line drawn from the sun through the center of the circle is invariably directed toward a point of the firmament about ten degrees west of the more brilliant of the two bright stars in the head of Gemini; therefore when the earth is opposite this point, and the center of the circle lies between them, the sun is seen at its greatest distance from the earth. In this circle, then, the earth revolves together with whatever else is included within the lunar sphere.

The second motion, which is peculiar to the earth, is the daily rotation on the poles in the order of the signs; that is, from west to east. On account of this rotation the entire universe appears to revolve with enormous speed. Thus does the earth rotate together with its circumjacent waters and encircling atmosphere.

The third is the motion in declination. For the axis of the daily rotation is not parallel to the axis of the great circle, but is inclined to it at an angle that intercepts a portion of a circumference, in our time about twenty-three and one half degrees. Therefore, while the center of the earth always remains in the plane of the ecliptic—that is, in the circumference of the great circle—the poles of the earth rotate, both of them describing small circles about centers equidistant from the axis of the great circle. The period of this motion is not quite a year and is nearly equal to the annual revolution on the great circle. But the axis of the great circle is invariably directed toward the points of the firmament which are called the poles of the ecliptic. In like manner the motion in declination, combined with the annual motion in their joint effect upon the poles of the daily rotation, would keep these poles constantly fixed at the same points of the heavens, if the periods of both motions were exactly equal. Now with the long passage of time it has become clear that this inclination of the earth to the firmament changes. Hence it is the common opinion that the firmament has several motions in conformity with a law not yet sufficiently understood. But the motion of the earth can explain all these changes in a less surprising way. . . .

EQUAL MOTION SHOULD BE MEASURED NOT BY THE EQUINOXES BUT BY THE FIXED STARS

Since the equinoxes and the other cardinal points of the universe shift considerably, whoever attempts to derive from them the equal length of the annual revolution necessarily falls into error. Different determinations of this length were made in different ages on the basis of many observations. Hipparchus computed it as 365¼ days, and Albategnius the Chaldean as 365 days, 5 hours, 46 minutes, that is, 13⅗ minutes or 13⅓ minutes less than Ptolemy. Hispalensis increased Albategnius' estimate by the twentieth part of an hour, since he determined the tropical year as 365 days, 5 hours, 49 minutes.

Lest these differences should seem to have arisen from errors of observation, let me say that if anyone will study the details carefully he will find that the discrepancy has always corresponded to the motion of the equinoxes. For when the cardinal points moved one degree in one hundred years, as they were found to be moving in the age of Ptolemy, the length of the year was then what Ptolemy stated it to be. When, however, in the following centuries they moved with greater rapidity, being opposed to lesser motions, the year became shorter; and this decrease corresponded to the increase in precession. For the annual motion was completed in a shorter time on account of the more rapid recurrence of the equinoxes. Therefore the derivation of the equal length of the year from the fixed stars is more accurate. I used Spica Virginis and found that the year has always been 365 days, 6 hours, and about 10 minutes, which is also the estimate of the ancient Egyptians. The same method must be employed also with the other motions of the planets, as shown by their apsides, by the fixed laws of their motion in the firmament, and by heaven itself with true testimony.

Stargazer and Father of Mechanics

GALILEO GALILEI (1564–1642)

IN 1492, Columbus discovered a new world; in 1610 another Italian, her greatest scientist, Galileo, uncovered a new heaven, whose depths are yet incompletely explored. Training his self-constructed telescope through the clear night sky, the Florentine mathematician was the first man to look upon the true face of the moon, the first to discover overhead far greater myriads of stars than had been dreamed in any philosophy. Here was the long-sought message of the stars, set forth in "The Sidereal Messenger"; here the visible confirmation of his valiantly championed Copernican astronomy, at last made plain for any Inquisitor at Rome, who dared, to see.

To celestial sight the persecuted "knight militant of science" added terrestrial insight, equally disquieting to churchmen who hugged the errors of Aristotle. Awakened by his youthful observation of the pendulum-swaying lamps in the cathedral of Pisa, convinced by his carefully planned experiments with stones of different weights falling in equal times from the top of her leaning tower, it was Galileo who first clearly perceived and expressed the fundamental law of the two "new sciences" which he founded, dynamics and ballistics; namely, that it is *change* of motion, not motion itself, that requires application of an external force. What happens when that force is gravity itself was the problem reserved for Newton to solve in detail.

Italian was Galileo's usual language. The English translation of "The Sidereal Messenger" (from Latin, however) is by Edward Stafford Carlos (1880). The passages from "Dialogues Concerning Two New Sciences" were translated by Henry Crew and Alfonso de Salvio, published under that title in 1914 by the Macmillan Company, reissued in 1939 by the Editorial Board of Northwestern Universities Studies.

THE
SIDEREAL MESSENGER

unfolding great and marvelous sights,
and proposing them to the attention of everyone,
but especially philosophers and astronomers,

being such as have been observed by

GALILEO GALILEI

a gentleman of Florence,
Professor of Mathematics in the University of Padua,

with the aid of a

TELESCOPE

lately invented by him,

Respecting the Moon's Surface, an innumerable number
of Fixed Stars, the Milky Way, and Nebulous Stars,
but especially respecting Four Planets which revolve round the Planet Jupiter at different
distances and in different periodic times,
with amazing velocity, and which, after
remaining unknown to everyone up to
this day, the Author recently discovered, and determined to name
the

MEDICEAN STARS

Venice 1610.

INTRODUCTION

IN THE PRESENT small treatise I set forth some matters of great interest for all observers of natural phenomena to look at and consider. They are of great interest, I think, first, from their intrinsic excellence; secondly, from their absolute novelty; and lastly, also on account of the instrument by the aid of which they have been presented to my apprehension.

The number of the fixed stars which observers have been able to see without artificial powers of sight up to this day can be counted. It is therefore decidedly a great feat to add to their number, and to set distinctly before the eyes other stars in myriads, which have never been seen before, and which surpass the old, previously known stars in number more than ten times.

Again, it is a most beautiful and delightful sight to behold the body of the moon, which is distant from us nearly sixty semidiameters of the earth, as near as if it was at a distance of only two of the same measures; so that the diameter of this same moon appears about thirty times larger, its surface about nine hundred times, and its solid mass nearly twenty-seven thousand times larger than when it is viewed only with the naked eye: and consequently anyone may know with the certainty that is due to the use of our senses that the moon certainly does not possess a smooth and polished surface, but one rough and uneven, and, just like the face of the earth itself, is everywhere full of vast protuberances, deep chasms, and sinuosities.

Then to have got rid of disputes about the Galaxy, or Milky Way, and to have made its nature clear to the very senses, not to say to the understanding, seems by no means a matter which ought to be considered of slight importance. In addition to this, to point out, as with one's finger, the nature of those stars which every one of the astronomers up to this time has called *nebulous,* and to demonstrate that it is very different from what has hitherto been believed, will be pleasant, and very fine. But that which will excite the greatest astonishment by far, and which indeed especially moved me to call the attention of all astronomers and philosophers, is this, namely, that I have discovered four planets, neither known nor observed by any one of the astronomers before my time, which have their orbits round a certain bright star, one of those previously known, like Venus and Mercury round the sun, and are sometimes in front of it, sometimes behind it, though they never depart from it beyond certain limits. All which facts were discovered and observed a few days ago by the help of a telescope devised by me, through God's grace first enlightening my mind.

Perchance other discoveries still more excellent will be made from time to time by me or other observers, with the assistance of a similar instrument, so I will first briefly record its shape and preparation, as well as the occasion of its being devised, and then I will give an account of the observations made by me.

Galileo's Account of the Invention of His Telescope

About ten months ago a report reached my ears that a Dutchman[1] had constructed a telescope, by the aid of which visible objects, although at a great distance from the eye of the observer, were seen distinctly as if near; and some proofs of its most wonderful performances were reported, which some gave credence to, but others contradicted. A few days after, I received confirmation of the report in a letter written from Paris by a noble Frenchman, Jacques Badovere, which finally determined me to give myself up first to inquire into the principle of the telescope, and then to consider the means by which I might compass the invention of a similar instrument, which after a little while I succeeded in doing, through deep study of the theory of refraction; and I prepared a tube, at first of lead, in the ends of which I fitted two glass lenses, both plane on one side, but on the other side one spherically convex and the other concave. Then, bringing my eye to the concave lens, I saw objects satisfactorily large and near, for they appeared one third of the distance off and nine times larger than when they are seen with the natural eye alone. I shortly afterward constructed another telescope with more nicety, which magnified objects more than sixty times. At length, by sparing neither labor nor expense, I succeeded in constructing for myself an instrument so superior that objects seen through it appear magnified nearly a thousand times, and more than thirty times nearer than if viewed by the natural powers of sight alone.

Galileo's First Observations with His Telescope

It would be altogether a waste of time to enumerate the number and importance of the benefits which this instrument may be expected to confer, when used by land or sea. But without paying attention to its

[1]Hans Lippershey.

use for terrestrial objects, I betook myself to observations of the heavenly bodies; and first of all I viewed the moon as near as if it was scarcely two semidiameters of the earth distant. After the moon, I frequently observed other heavenly bodies, both fixed stars and planets, with incredible delight; and, when I saw their very great number, I began to consider about a method by which I might be able to measure their distances apart, and at length I found one. And here it is fitting that all who intend to turn their attention to observations of this kind should receive certain cautions. For, in the first place, it is absolutely necessary for them to prepare a most perfect telescope, one which will show very bright objects distinct and free from any mistiness, and will magnify them at least four hundred times, for then it will show them as if only one twentieth of their distance off. For unless the instrument be of such power, it will be in vain to attempt to view all the things which have been seen by me in the heavens, or which will be enumerated hereafter.

METHOD OF DETERMINING THE MAGNIFYING POWER OF THE TELESCOPE

But in order that anyone may be a little more certain about the magnifying power of his instrument he shall fashion two circles, or two square pieces of paper, one of which is four hundred times greater than the other, but that will be when the diameter of the greater is twenty times the length of the diameter of the other. Then he shall view from a distance simultaneously both surfaces, fixed on the same wall, the smaller with one eye applied to the telescope, and the larger with the other eye unassisted: for that may be done without inconvenience at one and the same instant with both eyes open. Then both figures will appear of the same size, if the instrument magnifies objects in the desired proportion. . . .

Now let me review the observations made by me during the two months just past, again inviting the attention of all who are eager for true philosophy to the beginnings which led to the sight of most important phenomena.

THE MOON. RUGGEDNESS OF ITS SURFACE. EXISTENCE OF LUNAR MOUNTAINS AND VALLEYS

Let me first speak of the surface of the moon, which is turned toward us. For the sake of being understood more easily I distinguish two parts in it, which I call respectively the brighter and the darker. The brighter part seems to surround and pervade the whole hemisphere; but the darker part, like a sort of cloud, discolors the moon's surface and makes it appear covered with spots. Now these spots, as they are somewhat dark and of considerable size, are plain to everyone, and every age has seen them, wherefore I shall call them *great* or *ancient* spots, to distinguish them from other spots, smaller in size, but so thickly scattered that they sprinkle the whole surface of the moon, but especially the brighter portion of it. These spots have never been observed by anyone before me; and from my observations of them, often repeated, I have been led to that opinion which I have expressed, namely, that I feel sure that the surface of the moon is not perfectly smooth, free from inequalities, and exactly spherical, as a large school of philosophers considers with regard to the moon and the other heavenly bodies, but that, on the contrary, it is full of inequalities, uneven, full of hollows and protuberances, just like the surface of the earth itself, which is varied everywhere by lofty mountains and deep valleys.

The appearances from which we may gather these conclusions are of the following nature. On the fourth or fifth day after new moon, when the moon presents itself to us with bright horns, the boundary which divides the part in shadow from the enlightened part does not extend continuously in an ellipse, as would happen in the case of a perfectly spherical body, but it is marked out by an irregular, uneven, and very wavy line . . . for several bright excrescences, as they may be called, extend beyond the boundary of light and shadow into the dark part, and on the other hand pieces of shadow encroach upon the light—nay, even a great quantity of small blackish spots, altogether separated from the dark part, sprinkle everywhere almost the whole space which is at the time flooded with the sun's light, with the exception of that part alone which is occupied by the great and ancient spots. I have noticed that the small spots just mentioned have this common characteristic always and in every case, that they have the dark part toward the sun's position, and on the side away from the sun they have brighter boundaries, as if they were crowned with shining summits.

Now we have an appearance quite similar on the earth about sunrise, when we behold the valleys, not yet flooded with light, but the mountains surrounding them on the side opposite to the sun already ablaze with the splendor of his beams; and just as the shadows in the hollows of the earth diminish in size as the sun rises higher, so also these spots on the moon lose their blackness as the illuminated part grows larger and larger. Again, not only are the boundaries of light and shadow in the moon seen to be uneven and sinuous, but—and this produces still greater astonishment—there appear very many bright points within the darkened portion of the moon, altogether divided and broken off from the illuminated tract, and separated from it by no inconsiderable interval, which, after a little while, gradually increase in size and brightness, and after an hour or two become joined onto the rest of the main portion, now become somewhat larger; but in the meantime others, one here and another there, shooting up as if growing, are lighted up within the shaded portion, increase in size, and at last are linked onto the same luminous surface, now still more extended. . . .

Now is it not the case on the earth before sunrise that, while the level plain is still in shadow, the peaks of the most lofty mountains are illuminated by the sun's rays? After a little while does not the light spread further, while the middle and larger parts of those mountains are becoming illuminated; and at length, when the sun has risen, do not the illuminated parts of the plains and hills join together? The grandeur, however, of such prominences and depressions in the moon seems to surpass both in magnitude and extent the ruggedness of the earth's surface, as I shall hereafter show. .. . .

STARS. THEIR APPEARANCE IN THE TELESCOPE

Hitherto I have spoken of the observations which I have made concerning the moon's body; now I will briefly announce the phenomena which have been, as yet, seen by me with reference to the fixed stars. And first of all the following fact is worthy of consideration. The stars, fixed as well as erratic, when seen with a telescope, by no means appear to be increased in magnitude in the same proportion as other objects, and the moon herself, gain increase of size; but in the case of the stars such an increase appears much less, so that you may consider that a telescope, which (for the sake of illustration) is powerful enough to magnify other objects a hundred times, will scarcely render the stars magnified four or five times. But the reason of this is as follows. When stars are viewed with our natural eyesight they do not present themselves to us of their bare, real size, but beaming with a certain vividness, and fringed with sparkling rays, especially when the night is far advanced; and from this circumstance they appear much larger than they would if they were stripped of those adventitious fringes, for the angle which they subtend at the eye is determined not by the primary disk of the star but by the brightness which so widely surrounds it. . . . A telescope . . . removes from the stars their adventitious and accidental splendors before it enlarges their true disks (if indeed they are of that shape), and so they seem less magnified than other objects, for a star of the fifth or sixth magnitude seen through a telescope is shown as of the first magnitude only.

The difference between the appearance of the planets and the fixed stars seems also deserving of notice. The planets present their disks perfectly round, just as if described with a pair of compasses, and appear as so many little moons, completely illuminated and of a globular shape; but the fixed stars do not look to the naked eye bounded by a circular circumference, but rather like blazes of light, shooting out beams on all sides and very sparkling, and with a telescope they appear of the same shape as when they are viewed by simply looking at them, but so much larger that a star of the fifth or sixth magnitude seems to equal Sirius, the largest of all the fixed stars.

TELESCOPIC STARS: THEIR INFINITE MULTITUDE

As Examples, Orion's Belt and Sword and the Pleiades Are Described as Seen by Galileo

But beyond the stars of the sixth magnitude you will behold through the telescope a host of other stars, which escape the unassisted sight, so numerous as to be almost beyond belief, for you may see more than six other differences of magnitude, and the largest of these, which I may call stars of the seventh magnitude, or of the first magnitude of invisible stars, appear with the aid of the telescope larger and brighter than stars of the second magnitude seen with the unassisted sight. But in order that you may see one or two proofs of the inconceivable manner in which they are crowded together, I have determined to make out a case against two star clusters, that from them as a specimen you may decide about the rest.

As my first example I had determined to depict the entire constellation of Orion, but I was overwhelmed by the vast quantity of stars and by want of time, and so I have deferred attempting this to another occasion, for there are adjacent to or scattered among the old stars more than five hundred new stars within the limits of one or two degrees. For this reason I have selected the three stars in Orion's Belt and the six in his Sword, which have been long well-known groups, and I have added

eighty other stars recently discovered in their vicinity, and I have preserved as exactly as possible the intervals between them. The well-known
or old stars, for the sake of distinction, I have depicted of larger size, and
I have outlined them with a double line; the others, invisible to the

FIG. I. ORION'S BELT AND SWORD

naked eye, I have marked smaller and with one line only. I have also preserved the differences of magnitude as much as I could. As a second
example I have depicted the six stars of the constellation Taurus, called
the Pleiades (I say *six* intentionally, since the seventh is scarcely ever
visible), a group of stars which is enclosed in the heavens within very
narrow precincts. Near these there lie more than forty others invisible
to the naked eye, no one of which is more than half a degree off any
of the aforesaid six; of these I have noticed only thirty-six in my diagram.

I have preserved their intervals, magnitudes, and the distinction between the old and the new stars, just as in the case of the constellation Orion.

FIG. 2. PLEIADES

THE MILKY WAY CONSISTS ENTIRELY OF STARS IN COUNTLESS NUMBERS AND OF VARIOUS MAGNITUDES

The next object which I have observed is the essence or substance of the Milky Way. By the aid of a telescope anyone may behold this in a manner which so distinctly appeals to the senses that all the disputes which have tormented philosophers through so many ages are exploded at once by the irrefragable evidence of our eyes, and we are freed from wordy disputes upon this subject, for the Galaxy is nothing else but a mass of innumerable stars planted together in clusters. Upon whatever part of it you direct the telescope, straightway a vast crowd of stars presents itself to view; many of them are tolerably large and extremely bright, but the number of small ones is quite beyond determination. . . .

DISCOVERY OF JUPITER'S SATELLITES, JANUARY 7, 1610: RECORD OF GALILEO'S OBSERVATIONS DURING TWO MONTHS

I have now finished my brief account of the observations which I have thus far made with regard to the moon, the fixed stars, and the Galaxy. There remains the matter, which seems to me to deserve to be considered the most important in this work, namely, that I should disclose and publish to the world the occasion of discovering and observing four *planets,* never seen from the very beginning of the world up to our own times, their positions, and the observations made during the last two months about their movements and their changes of magnitude; and I summon all astronomers to apply themselves to examine and determine their periodic times, which it has not been permitted me to achieve up to this day, owing to the restriction of my time. I give them warning, however, again, so that they may not approach such an inquiry to no purpose, that they will want a very accurate telescope, and such as I have described in the beginning of this account.

On the seventh day of January in the present year, 1610, in the first hour of the following night, when I was viewing the constellations of the heavens through a telescope, the planet Jupiter presented itself to my view, and as I had prepared for myself a very excellent instrument, I noticed a circumstance which I had never been able to notice before, owing to want of power in my other telescope, namely, that three little stars, small but very bright, were near the planet; and although I believed them to belong to the number of the fixed stars, yet they made me somewhat wonder, because they seemed to be arranged exactly in a straight line, parallel to the ecliptic, and to be brighter than the rest of the stars equal to them in magnitude. The position of them with reference to one another and to Jupiter was as follows.

Ori.   *   *   O   *   Occ.

FIG. 3.

On the east side there were two stars, and a single one toward the west. The star which was furthest toward the east, and the western star, appeared rather larger than the third.

I scarcely troubled at all about the distance between them and Jupiter, for, as I have already said, at first I believed them to be fixed stars; but when on January 8, led by some fatality, I turned again to look at the same part of the heavens, I found a very different state of things, for there were three little stars all west of Jupiter, and nearer together than on the previous night, and they were separated from one another by equal intervals, as the accompanying figure shows.

Ori.   O   *   *   *   Occ.

FIG. 4.

At this point, although I had not turned my thoughts at all upon the approximation of the stars to one another, yet my surprise began to be excited, how Jupiter could one day be found to the east of all the aforesaid fixed stars when the day before it had been west of two of them; and forthwith I became afraid lest the planet might have moved differently from the calculation of astronomers, and so had passed those stars by its own proper motion. I therefore waited for the next night with the most intense longing, but I was disappointed of my hope, for the sky was covered with clouds in every direction.

But on January 10 the stars appeared in the following position with regard to Jupiter, the third, as I thought, being hidden by the planet. They were situated just as before, exactly in the same straight line with Jupiter, and along the Zodiac.

Ori.   *   *   O   **Occ.**

FIG. 5.

When I had seen these phenomena, as I knew that corresponding changes of position could not by any means belong to Jupiter, and as, moreover, I perceived that the stars which I saw had always been the same, for there were no others either in front or behind, within a great distance, along the Zodiac—at length, changing from doubt into surprise, I discovered that the interchange of position which I saw belonged not to Jupiter but to the stars to which my attention had been drawn, and I thought therefore that they ought to be observed henceforward with more attention and precision.

Accordingly, on January 11 I saw an arrangement of the following kind,

Ori.   *   *   O   **Occ.**

FIG. 6.

namely, only two stars to the east of Jupiter, the nearer of which was distant from Jupiter three times as far as from the star further to the east; and the star furthest to the east was nearly twice as large as the other one; whereas on the previous night they had appeared nearly of equal magnitude. I therefore concluded, and decided unhesitatingly, that there are three stars in the heavens moving about Jupiter, as Venus and Mercury round the sun; which at length was established as clear as daylight by numerous other subsequent observations. These observations also established that there are not only three but four erratic sidereal bodies performing their revolutions round Jupiter, observations of whose changes of position made with more exactness on succeeding nights the following account will supply. I have measured also the intervals between them with the telescope in the manner already explained. Besides this, I have given the times of observation, especially when several were made in the same night, for the revolutions of these planets are so

swift that an observer may generally get differences of position every
hour.

January 12. At the first hour of the next night I saw these heavenly
bodies arranged in this manner.

Ori.   *   *O   *   **Occ.**

FIG. 7.

The satellite farthest to the east was greater than the satellite farthest
to the west; but both were very conspicuous and bright; the distance of
each one from Jupiter was two minutes. A third satellite, certainly not
in view before, began to appear at the third hour: it nearly touched
Jupiter on the east side, and was exceedingly small. They were all arranged in the same straight line, along the ecliptic.

January 13. For the first time four satellites were in view in the following position with regard to Jupiter.

Ori.   *   O ***   **Occ.**

FIG. 8.

There were three to the west and one to the east; they made a straight
line nearly, but the middle satellite of those to the west deviated a little
from the straight line toward the north. The satellite farthest to the east
was at a distance of 2' from Jupiter; there were intervals of 1' only
between Jupiter and the nearest satellite, and between the satellites themselves, west of Jupiter. All the satellites appeared of the same size, and
though small they were very brilliant and far outshone the fixed stars
of the same magnitude.

January 14. The weather was cloudy. . . .

These are my observations upon the four Medicean planets, recently
discovered for the first time by me; and although it is not yet permitted
me to deduce by calculation from these observations the orbits of these
bodies, yet I may be allowed to make some statements, based upon them,
well worthy of attention.

DEDUCTIONS FROM THE PREVIOUS OBSERVATIONS CONCERNING THE ORBITS AND
PERIODS OF JUPITER'S SATELLITES

And, in the first place, since they are sometimes behind, sometimes
before Jupiter, at like distances, and withdraw from this planet toward
the east and toward the west only within very narrow limits of divergence,

and since they accompany this planet alike when its motion is retrograde and direct, it can be a matter of doubt to no one that they perform their revolutions about this planet, while at the same time they all accomplish together orbits of twelve years' length about the center of the world. Moreover, they revolve in unequal circles, which is evidently the conclusion to be drawn from the fact that I have never been permitted to see two satellites in conjunction when their distance from Jupiter was great, whereas near Jupiter two, three, and sometimes all four have been found closely packed together. Moreover, it may be detected that the revolutions of the satellites which describe the smallest circles round Jupiter are the most rapid, for the satellites nearest to Jupiter are often to be seen in the east, when the day before they have appeared in the west, and contrariwise. Also the satellite moving in the greatest orbit seems to me, after carefully weighing the occasions of its returning to positions previously noticed, to have a periodic time of half a month.

Besides, we have a notable and splendid argument to remove the scruples of those who can tolerate the revolution of the planets round the sun in the Copernican system, yet are so disturbed by the motion of one moon about the earth, while both accomplish an orbit of a year's length about the sun, that they consider that this theory of the universe must be upset as impossible: for now we have not one planet only revolving about another, while both traverse a vast orbit about the sun, but our sense of sight presents to us four satellites circling about Jupiter, like the moon about the earth, while the whole system travels over a mighty orbit about the sun in the space of twelve years.

"DIALOGUES CONCERNING TWO NEW SCIENCES" (MECHANICS AND BALLISTICS)

INTERLOCUTORS: SALVIATI, SAGREDO, AND SIMPLICIO

Salviati: The constant activity which you Venetians display in your famous arsenal suggests to the studious mind a large field for investigation, especially that part of the work which involves mechanics; for in this department all types of instruments and machines are constantly being constructed by many artisans, among whom there must be some who, partly by inherited experience and partly by their own observations, have become highly expert and clever in explanation.

Sagredo: You are quite right. Indeed, I myself, being curious by nature, frequently visit this place for the mere pleasure of observing the work of those who, on account of their superiority over other artisans, we call "first-rank men." . . .

The Speed of Light

Salviati: We observe that other combustions and resolutions are accompanied by motion, and that, the most rapid; note the action of lightning and of powder as used in mines and petards; note also how the charcoal flame, mixed as it is with heavy and impure vapors, increases its power to liquefy metals whenever quickened by a pair of bellows. Hence I do not understand how the action of light, although very pure, can be devoid of motion and that of the swiftest type.

Sagredo: But of what kind and how great must we consider this speed of light to be? Is it instantaneous or momentary or does it, like other motions, require time? Can we not decide this by experiment?

Simplicio: Everyday experience shows that the propagation of light is instantaneous; for when we see a piece of artillery fired, at great distance, the flash reaches our eyes without lapse of time; but the sound reaches the ear only after a noticeable interval.

Sagredo: Well, Simplicio, the only thing I am able to infer from this familiar bit of experience is that sound, in reaching our ear, travels more slowly than light; it does not inform me whether the coming of the light is instantaneous or whether, although extremely rapid, it still occupies time. An observation of this kind tells us nothing more than one in which it is claimed that "as soon as the sun reaches the horizon its light reaches our eyes"; but who will assure me that these rays had not reached this limit earlier than they reached our vision?

Salviati: The small conclusiveness of these and other similar observations once led me to devise a method by which one might accurately ascertain whether illumination, i.e., the propagation of light, is really instantaneous. The fact that the speed of sound is as high as it is assures us that the motion of light cannot fail to be extraordinarily swift. The experiment which I devised was as follows.

Let each of two persons take a light contained in a lantern, or other receptacle, such that by the interposition of the hand the one can shut off or admit the light to the vision of the other. Next let them stand opposite each other at a distance of a few cubits and practice until they acquire such skill in uncovering and occulting their lights that the instant one sees the light of his companion he will uncover his own. After a few trials the response will be so prompt that without sensible error the uncovering of one light is immediately followed by the uncovering of the other, so that as soon as one exposes his light he will instantly see that of the other. Having acquired skill at this short distance, let the two experimenters, equipped as before, take up positions separated by a distance of two or three miles and let them perform the same experiment at night, noting carefully whether the exposures and occultations occur in the same manner as at short distances; if they do, we may safely conclude that the propagation of light is instantaneous; but if time is required at a distance of three miles which, considering the going of one light and the coming of the other, really amounts to six, then the delay ought to be easily observable. If the experiment is to be made at still greater distances, say eight or ten miles, telescopes may be employed, each observer adjusting one for himself at the place where he is to make the experiment at night; then, although the lights are not large and are therefore invisible to the naked eye at so great a distance, they can readily be covered and uncovered, since by aid of the telescopes, once adjusted and fixed, they will become easily visible.

Sagredo: This experiment strikes me as a clever and reliable invention. But tell us what you conclude from the results.

Salviati: In fact I have tried the experiment only at a short distance, less than a mile, from which I have not been able to ascertain with certainty whether the appearance of the opposite light was instantaneous or not; but if not instantaneous it is extraordinarily rapid—I should call it momentary; and for the present I should compare it to motion which we see in the lightning flash between clouds eight or ten miles distant from us. We see the beginning of this light—I might say its head and source— located at a particular place among the clouds; but it immediately spreads to the surrounding ones, which seems to be an argument that at least some time is required for propagation; for if the illumination were instantaneous and not gradual, we should not be able to distinguish its origin—its center, so to speak—from its outlying portions. What a sea we are gradually slipping into without knowing it! With vacua and infinities and indivisibles and instantaneous motions, shall we ever be able, even by means of a thousand discussions, to reach dry land?

Sagredo: Really these matters lie far beyond our grasp. Just think, when we seek the infinite among numbers we find it in unity; that which is ever divisible is derived from indivisibles; the vacuum is found inseparably connected with the plenum; indeed the views commonly held concerning the nature of these matters are so reversed that even the circumference of a circle turns out to be an infinite straight line. . . .

HOW FAST DOES A STONE FALL?

Simplicio: Your discussion is really admirable; yet I do not find it easy to believe that a bird shot falls as swiftly as a cannon ball.

Salviati: Why not say a grain of sand as rapidly as a grindstone? But, Simplicio, I trust you will not follow the example of many others who divert the discussion from its main intent and fasten upon some statement of mine which lacks a hairsbreadth of the truth and, under this hair, hide the fault of another which is as big as a ship's cable. Aristotle says that "an iron ball of one hundred pounds falling from a height of one hundred cubits reaches the ground before a one-pound ball has fallen a single cubit."

I say that they arrive at the same time.

You find, on making the experiment, that the larger outstrips the smaller by two fingerbreadths, that is, when the larger has reached the ground, the other is short of it by two fingerbreadths; now you would not hide behind these two fingers the ninety-nine cubits of Aristotle, nor would you mention my small error and at the same time pass over in silence his very large one. Aristotle declares that bodies of different weights, in the same medium, travel (insofar as their motion depends upon gravity) with speeds which are proportional to their weights; this he illustrates by use of bodies in which it is possible to perceive the pure and unadulterated effect of gravity, eliminating other considerations, for example, figure as being of small importance influences which are greatly dependent upon the medium which modifies the single effect of gravity alone. Thus we observe that gold, the densest of all substances, when beaten out into a very thin leaf, goes floating through the air; the same thing happens with stone when ground into a very fine powder. But if you wish to maintain the general proposition you will have to show that the same ratio of speeds is preserved in the case of all heavy bodies, and that a stone of twenty pounds moves ten times as rapidly as one of two; but I claim that this is false and that, if they fall from a height of fifty or a hundred cubits, they will reach the earth at the same moment.

Simplicio: Perhaps the result would be different if the fall took place not from a few cubits but from some thousands of cubits.

Salviati: If this were what Aristotle meant you would burden him with another error which would amount to a falsehood; because, since there is no such sheer height available on earth, it is clear that Aristotle could not have made the experiment; yet he wishes to give us the impression of his having performed it when he speaks of such an effect as one which we see.

Simplicio: In fact, Aristotle does not employ this principle, but uses the other one which is not, I believe, subject to these same difficulties.

Salviati: But the one is as false as the other; and I am surprised that you yourself do not see the fallacy and that you do not perceive that if it were true that, in media of different densities and different resistances, such as water and air, one and the same body moved in air more rapidly than in water, in proportion as the density of water is greater than that of air, then it would follow that any body which falls through air ought also to fall through water. But this conclusion is false inasmuch as many bodies which descend in air not only do not descend in water but actually rise.

Simplicio: I do not understand the necessity of your inference; and in addition I will say that Aristotle discusses only those bodies which fall in both media, not those which fall in air but rise in water.

Salviati: The arguments which you advance for the philosopher are such as he himself would have certainly avoided so as not to aggravate his first mistake. . . .

ENVY

Simplicio: The previous experiments, in my opinion, left something to be desired: but now I am fully satisfied.

Salviati: The facts set forth by me up to this point and, in particular, the one which shows that difference of weight, even when very great, is without effect in changing the speed of falling bodies, so that as far as weight is concerned they all fall with equal speed: this idea is, I say, so new, and at first glance so remote from fact, that if we do not have the means of making it just as clear as sunlight it had better not be mentioned; but, having once allowed it to pass my lips, I must neglect no experiment or argument to establish it.

Sagredo: Not only this but also many other of your views are so far removed from the commonly accepted opinions and doctrines that if you were to publish them you would stir up a large number of antagonists; for human nature is such that men do not look with favor upon discoveries—either of truth or fallacy—in their own field, when made by others than themselves. They call him an innovator of doctrine, an unpleasant title, by which they hope to cut those knots which they cannot untie, and by subterranean mines they seek to destroy structures which patient artisans have built with customary tools. But as for ourselves who have no such thoughts, the experiments and arguments which you have thus far adduced are fully satisfactory.

A GIANT'S BONES

Salviati: From what has already been demonstrated you can plainly see the impossibility of increasing the size of structures to vast dimensions either in art or in nature; likewise the impossibility of building ships, palaces, or temples of enormous size in such a way that their oars, yards, beams, iron bolts, and, in short, all their other parts will hold together; nor can nature produce trees of extraordinary size because the branches would break down under their own weight; so also it would be impossible to build up the bony structures of men, horses, or other animals so as to hold together and perform their normal functions if these animals were to be increased enormously in height; for this increase in height can be accomplished only by employing a material which is harder and stronger than usual, or by enlarging the size of the bones, thus changing their shape until the form and appearance of the animals suggest a monstrosity. This is perhaps what our wise poet had in mind when he says, in describing a huge giant:

> *Impossible it is to reckon his height*
> *So beyond measure is his size.*[1]

To illustrate briefly, I have sketched a bone whose natural length has been increased three times and whose thickness has been multi-

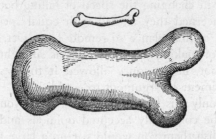

plied until, for a correspondingly large animal, it would perform the same function which the small bone performs for its small animal. From the figures here shown you can see how out of proportion the enlarged bone appears. Clearly then, if one wishes to maintain in a great giant the same proportion of limb as that found in an ordinary man, ne

[1] Ariosto's "Orlando Furioso," XVII, 30 (Trans.).

must either find a harder and stronger material for making the bones, or he must admit a diminution of strength in comparison with men of medium stature; for, if his height be increased inordinately, he will fall and be crushed under his own weight. Whereas, if the size of a body be diminished, the strength of that body is not diminished in the same proportion; indeed, the smaller the body the greater its relative strength. Thus a small dog could probably carry on his back two or three dogs of his own size; but I believe that a horse could not carry even one of his own size.

Simplicio: This may be so; but I am led to doubt it on account of the enormous size reached by certain fish, such as the whale, which, I understand, is ten times as large as an elephant; yet they all support themselves.

Salviati: Your question, Simplicio, suggests another principle, one which had hitherto escaped my attention and which enables giants and other animals of vast size to support themselves and to move about as well as smaller animals do. This result may be secured either by increasing the strength of the bones and other parts intended to carry not only their weight but also the superincumbent load; or, keeping the proportions of the bony structure constant, the skeleton will hold together in the same manner or even more easily, provided one diminishes, in the proper proportion, the weight of the bony material, of the flesh, and of anything else which the skeleton has to carry. It is this second principle which is employed by nature in the structure of fish, making their bones and muscles not merely light but entirely devoid of weight.

Simplicio: The trend of your argument, Salviati, is evident. Since fish live in water, which on account of its density or, as others would say, heaviness diminishes the weight of bodies immersed in it, you mean to say that, for this reason, the bodies of fish will be devoid of weight and will be supported without injury to their bones. But this is not all; for although the remainder of the body of the fish may be without weight, there can be no question but that their bones have weight. Take the case of a whale's rib, having the dimensions of a beam; who can deny its great weight or its tendency to go to the bottom when placed in water? One would, therefore, hardly expect these great masses to sustain themselves.

Salviati: A very shrewd objection! And now, in reply, tell me whether you have ever seen fish stand motionless at will under water, neither descending to the bottom nor rising to the top, without the exertion of force by swimming?

Simplicio: This is a well-known phenomenon.

Salviati: The fact, then, that fish are able to remain motionless underwater is a conclusive reason for thinking that the material of their bodies has the same specific gravity as that of water; accordingly, if in their make-up there are certain parts which are heavier than water there must be others which are lighter, for otherwise they would not produce equilibrium.

Hence, if the bones are heavier, it is necessary that the muscles or other constituents of the body should be lighter in order that their buoyancy may counterbalance the weight of the bones. In aquatic animals, therefore, circumstances are just reversed from what they are with land animals, inasmuch as, in the latter, the bones sustain not only their own weight but also that of the flesh, while in the former it is the flesh which supports not only its own weight but also that of the bones. We must, therefore, cease to wonder why these enormously large animals inhabit the water rather than the land, that is to say, the air.

Simplicio: I am convinced and I only wish to add that what we call land animals ought really to be called air animals, seeing that they live in the air, are surrounded by air, and breathe air.

Sagredo: I have enjoyed Simplicio's discussion, including both the question raised and its answer. Moreover I can easily understand that one of these giant fish, if pulled ashore, would not perhaps sustain itself for any great length of time but would be crushed under its own mass as soon as the connections between the bones gave way.

Salviati: I am inclined to your opinion; and, indeed, I almost think that the same thing would happen in the case of a very big ship which floats on the sea without going to pieces under its load of merchandise and armament, but which on dry land and in air would probably fall apart.

CHANGE OF POSITION

[The author himself, Galileo, is speaking here.]

My purpose is to set forth a very new science dealing with a very ancient subject. There is, in nature, perhaps nothing older than motion, concerning which the books written by philosophers are neither few nor small; nevertheless I have discovered by experiment some properties of it which are worth knowing and which have not hitherto been either observed or demonstrated. Some superficial observations have been made, as, for instance, that the free motion of a heavy falling body is continuously accelerated; but to just what extent this acceleration occurs has not yet been announced; for, so far as I know, no one has yet pointed out that the distances traversed, during equal intervals of time, by a body falling from rest stand to one another in the same ratio as the odd numbers beginning with unity.

It has been observed that missiles and projectiles describe a curved path of some sort; however, no one has pointed out the fact that this path is a parabola. But this and other facts, not few in number or less worth knowing, I have succeeded in proving; and what I consider more important, there have been opened up to this vast and most excellent science, of which my work is merely the beginning, ways and means by which other minds more acute than mine will explore its remote corners.

The first part [of our discussion] deals with motion which is steady or uniform; the second treats of motion as we find it accelerated in nature; the third deals with the so-called violent motions and with projectiles.

UNIFORM MOTION: In dealing with steady or uniform motion we need a single definition which I give as follows:

DEFINITION: By steady or uniform motion, I mean one in which the distances traversed by the moving particle during any equal intervals of time are themselves equal.

THE ROLLING BALL EXPERIMENT

Salviati: A piece of wooden molding or scantling, about twelve cubits long, half a cubit wide, and three fingerbreadths thick, was taken; on its edge was cut a channel a little more than one finger in breadth; having made this groove very straight, smooth, and polished, and having lined it with parchment, also as smooth and polished as possible, we rolled along it a hard, smooth, and very round bronze ball. Having placed this board in a sloping position, by lifting one end some one or two cubits above the other, we rolled the ball, as I was just saying, along the channel, noting, in a manner presently to be described, the time required to make the descent. We repeated this experiment more than once in order to measure the time with an accuracy such that the deviation between two observations never exceeded one tenth of a pulse beat. Having performed this operation and having assured ourselves of its reliability, we now rolled the ball only one quarter the length of the channel; and having measured the time of its descent, we found it precisely one half of the former. Next we tried other distances, comparing the time for the whole length with that for the half, or with that for two thirds, or indeed for any fraction; in such experiments, repeated a full hundred times, we always found that the spaces traversed were to each other as the squares of the times, and this was true for all inclinations of the plane, i.e., of the channel, along which we rolled the ball. We also observed that the times of descent for various inclinations of the plane bore to one another precisely that ratio which, as we shall see later, the author had predicted and demonstrated for them.

For the measurement of time we employed a large vessel of water placed in an elevated position; to the bottom of this vessel was soldered a pipe of small diameter giving a thin jet of water, which we collected in a small glass during the time of each descent, whether for the whole length of the channel or for a part of its length; the water thus collected was weighed, after each descent, on a very accurate balance; the differences and ratios of these weights gave us the differences and ratios of the times, and this with such accuracy that although the operation was repeated many, many times, there was no appreciable discrepancy in the results.

Simplicio: I would like to have been present at these experiments; but feeling confidence in the care with which you performed them, and in the fidelity with which you relate them, I am satisfied and accept them as true and valid.

The Father of Epidemiology

GIROLAMO FRACASTORO (1478?–1553)

THE "father of modern epidemiology" gave the name "syphilis" to the disease which first flared in his time and country and has malingered everywhere since. In an elegant Latin poem, the least scientific but most renowned of his many original writings on medicine, epidemiology, geography, geology, and optics (he first hinted at the telescope), Fracastoro chose the name "Syphilis" (Hog Lover) for the mythical shepherd lad of the western isles, whence the disease was conjectured to have sprung. This quiet-mannered physician of the "academic" period of the Italian Renaissance, once a fellow student with Copernicus at Padua, perceived more clearly than anyone for the next three centuries that epidemics in communities are the result of infections in individuals. Discounting the influence of "miasmic air," he thought of "essential seeds" of infection and suggested three true routes of contagion: (1) by contact with the sick; (2) through their intimate belongings (*fomites*); and (3) by something—which we now know are germs— conveyed at a distance.

Latin was the language of Fracastoro's poem, *"Syphilis, Sive de Morbo Gallico"* ("Syphilis, or the French Disease"), first published in 1530. The metrical English translation, by William Van Wyck, was printed in 1934 (Los Angeles: Primavera Press).

"THE SINISTER SHEPHERD"—SYPHILIS

THE strangest plague returned to sear the world.
Infecting Europe's breast, the scourge was hurled
From Lybian cities to the Black Sea's wave.
When warring France would march on Italy,
It took her name. I consecrate my rhymes
To this unbidden guest of twenty climes. . . .

O Muse, reveal to me what seed has grown
This evil that for long remained unknown!
Till Spanish sailors made the west their goal,
And plowed the seas to find another pole,
Adding to this world a new universe.
Did these men bring to us this latent curse? . . .
Hiding its origin, this evil thing
Sprawls over Europe. . . .

This pestilence's savage voice I hear,
And wandering to our houses, will it sow
In tender virgin breasts a wicked seed,
Hatched from a poison that no vice has wrought.
And from its evil clutches none is freed.
It is at home in hovel and the court,
Its symptoms never twice the same, indeed. . . .

The epidemic bursting, very soon,
Shutting her disk four times, a frightened moon

Showed by the signs that she would manifest
That this new evil would become a pest.
Within the body, long its ferment rests,
To nourish at some hidden source of breasts.
Then suddenly, beneath a languor's weight,
The victim creeps about in fearful state,
The heart defective and the slightest strain
Tiring the limbs, while energies remain
All sapped. A gloomy eye and saddened face
Of sickly pallor bend to this disgrace,
And soon a vicious ulcer eats its way
Into the privates. And a vengeful sway
Takes cancerous possession to remain.
Extended to the groin is its fell bane. . . .

Soon is the body ulcerous and vile.
The face becomes within a little while
A mask of running pustules small and great.
A horny shell will glands well imitate.
Breaking and emptying an acrid humor,
From pus-corroded skin, pours every tumor.
And bloody ulcers deeply dig away,
Gnawing the tissues that they make their prey.
Then is man stripped until his piteous moans
Come from a skeleton of putrid bones.
The lips are torn to shreds for this vile ill,
And, ere the voice dies, it is harsh and shrill. . . .

Seek out the strongest remedies, nor fear
Fatigue, though it belabors somewhat drear.
And if you haste, success will crown your pains.
Then is the plague less harsh within your veins. . . .
Exile your mistress that a lonely bed
Shuns Venus and her altars and embraces.
And shun your love for all her tender graces,
Or for your lack of faith will she be dead. . . .

Touch not the truffle or the artichoke.
Leeks and cucumbers leave to other folk. . . .
All men concede that mercury's the best
Of agents that will cure a tainted breast.

"Science Belongs to Everyone"

CONRAD GESNER (1516–65)

THE DEVELOPMENT of the art of printing from movable type, generally credited to Johann Gutenberg (1397–1468) sometime before 1444, was of inestimable importance to the advance of science. Among other things it assured the freely international character of scientific knowledge, a distinction which has been only occasionally, and then temporarily, lost. One of the first, a century after the invention of printing, to assert that science belongs to everybody—as you may read in his letter to a distinguished but less generous contemporary botanist—was Conrad Gesner, a conscientious Swiss physician whom a Frenchman (Cuvier) called "the German Pliny." Ill-paid city physician of Zurich, where he died at his task of tending plague victims, Gesner probably made his living, one of the first, as a scientific writer and editor of the plethora of manuscripts, ancient and contemporary, going into type for the first time. His massive, five-volume, beautifully illustrated "History of Animals" ("*Historia Animalium*"), whose English version was Shakespeare's source book, marked the high spot in zoology between Aristotle and Linnaeus. It described and pictured every animal then known to Europe. Gesner also wrote on botany, medicine, linguistics, and mountain climbing. Lucky the library that has a copy of his *"Bibliotheca Universalis"* ("Universal Book Catalogue"), whose faithful record of the first century of printing has won Gesner the added title of "father of bibliography." His "Mithradates," comparing a hundred and thirty languages and containing the Lord's Prayer in twenty-two, is the foundation of the literary science of comparative linguistics.

German text of Gesner's letter to Fuchs, printed by Willy Ley, was translated into English by Thomas Fleming.

LETTER FROM AN EDITOR

FROM YOUR LETTER, my learned friend, I have noted with the greatest pleasure that you are well, and that you are working with great zeal on your history of plants in three parts. I was less pleased that you intend to keep me from treating the same material. In this matter, we should think more of the general advantage than of ourselves. "One man; nothing." This proverb is excellently applicable in this case; for the number of plants is endless, and on account of the difference of place and vicinity in which they grow the individual person cannot learn to know them exactly. But if each one makes known his observations for the general welfare, then, someday, one complete and comprehensive work can be completed from these initial steps. Whether this can already happen in our century, I dare not hope no matter how much I wish it.

It is your wish that others send their observations to you. I shall be glad if really many lovers of plants do that and by doing so aid your great and beautiful undertaking. I, too, would like to do that, if I had not already collected so much material, or if my opinions had been written in their final draft so that they could be of service to you. But the number of my observations has been jotted down on innumerable small leaves, rather than worked out in detail, and have been written in such a way that they can serve no one but myself. Moreover, at present, I have no time to write the final draft. And there is much more material in my mind than on my papers. Because since earliest childhood, I found my greatest delight in the study of plants; and being occupied with it will be my favorite inclination until the last breath of my life. Therefore, do not rob me of my freedom and delight of my life.

I do not know as yet when I shall publish something about plants, because I have not yet entirely completed my great work about the history of animals. But I promise you this, that if I ever write your name it shall be mentioned in the most respectful way. And if I am not of a similar opinion, I shall state my deviating opinion in simple or humble modesty. If I could see your pictures and descriptions of plants before publication, I would sincerely give you my opinion and I could perhaps suggest to you many corrections, especially concerning the names of plants. Surely you could offer me the same service, if you should see my collection, because in a science like botany there always remains plenty for us to learn.

Likewise, it has always been my opinion, and my wish, that really many scholars would treat the same material as I. Belon and Rondelet have written in France about mammals, birds, and fishes at the same time as myself, but they have mentioned me with respect in their works, and Rondelet has even furnished me with important contributions for my work. That is how far envy was from our minds. It is true that

Rondelet occasionally reprimands Belon and Hippolitus Romanus (however, without mentioning the names), but he does this justly, because he sent them very many contributions and they have not mentioned him with a single word. They have taken possession of his discoveries and have claimed them as their own, which betrays the greatest ingratitude; yes, the most ungrateful ambition. However, I have always respectfully mentioned those from whom I have received something, and that, to be sure, not only once, but as often as something occurs in my works for which I am indebted to another scholar. . . .

If this proposition pleases you, I am glad; and if it doesn't please you, I shall return to my original plan and not consider myself obligated by your work not to do what I consider good. Farewell.

ZURICH, *October 18, 1556.*

"I Dressed Him, God Healed Him"

AMBROISE PARÉ (1517?-1590)

As EVERY NOSEBLEED or cut finger recalls, the first problem in surgery is to control bleeding. The "father of modern surgery," once the most illustrious member of the barber-surgeons' guild of Paris, Ambroise Paré, solved this ancient problem by tying off all seriously bleeding veins and arteries with a ligature thread. A kind and pious army surgeon, he describes in the autobiographical passages here quoted from his "Journeys in Divers Places" how he came to forsake the cruel treatment of cauterizing gunshot wounds with boiling oil and used simple dressings instead. He served under five French sovereigns, from Francis I to Henry IV, wrote many books on surgery and obstetrics.

Latin was the language in which Paré wrote. The English translation, by the famous American medical historian, Francis R. Packard, appeared in his "Life and Times of Ambroise Paré" (New York: Paul B. Hoeber, 1921).

A SURGEON'S "JOURNEYS IN DIVERS PLACES"

MOREOVER, I will here show to my readers the towns and places where I have been enabled to learn the art of surgery, always the better to instruct the young surgeon.

And first in the year 1536 the great King François sent a great army to Turin to recover the cities and castles which had been taken by the Marquis de Guast, lieutenant general of the Emperor.

There Monsieur the Constable, then grand master, was lieutenant general of the army, and Monsieur de Montejan was colonel general of the infantry, to whom I was then surgeon. A great part of the army having arrived at the Pass of Suze, we found the enemy holding the passage and having made certain forts and trenches insomuch that to make them dislodge and quit the place, it was necessary to fight, where there were many killed and wounded, as many on one side as the other, but the enemy were constrained to retire and gain the castle, which was taken in part by Captain Le Rat, who climbed with many soldiers from his company on a little hill, from whence they fired directly on the enemy. He received a shot from an arquebus in the ankle of his right foot, wherewith he suddenly fell to the ground and then said, "Now the Rat is taken." I dressed him, and God healed him.

We thronged into the city and passed over the dead bodies and some that were not yet dead, hearing them cry under the feet of our horses, which made a great pity in my heart, and truly I repented that I had gone forth from Paris to see so pitiful a spectacle. Being in the city, I entered a stable thinking to lodge my horse and that of my man, where I found four dead soldiers and three who were propped against the wall, their faces wholly disfigured, and they neither saw, nor heard, nor spake, and their clothes yet flaming from the gunpowder which had burnt them. Beholding them with pity there came an old soldier who asked me if there was any means of curing them. I told him no. At once he approached them and cut their throats gently and without anger. Seeing this great cruelty, I said to him that he was a bad man. He answered me that he prayed God that when he should be in such a case, he might find someone who would do the same for him, to the end that he might not languish miserably.

And to return to our discourse, the enemy was summoned to surrender, which they did, and went forth, their lives only saved, and a white staff in their hands, but the greater part went to gain the Château de Villaine, where there were about two hundred Spaniards. Monsieur the Constable would not leave them in his rear in order to render the road free. The château is seated upon a little mountain, which gave great assurance to those within that we could not place the artillery so as to bear upon them. . . .

Now all the said soldiers at the château, seeing our men coming with a great fury, did all they could to defend themselves, and killed and wounded a great number of our soldiers with pikes, arquebuses, and stones, where the surgeons had much work cut out for them. Now I was at that time a fresh-water soldier, I had not yet seen wounds made by gunshot at the first dressing. It is true that I had read in Jean de Vigo, first book, "Of Wounds in General," Chapter Eight, that wounds made by firearms participate of venenosity, because of the powder, and for their cure he commands to cauterize them with oil of elder, scalding hot, in which should be mixed a little theriac and in order not to err before using the said oil, knowing that such a thing would bring great pain to the patient, I wished to know first, how the other surgeons did for the first dressing which was to apply the said oil as hot as possible, into the wound with tents and setons, of whom I took courage to do as they did. At last my oil lacked and I was constrained to apply in its place a digestive made of the yolks of eggs, oil of roses and turpentine. That night I could not sleep at my ease, fearing by lack of cauterization that I should find the wounded on whom I had failed to put the said oil dead or empoisoned, which made me rise very early to visit them, where beyond my hope, I found those upon whom I had put the digestive medicament feeling little pain, and their wounds without inflammation or swelling having rested fairly well throughout the night; the others to whom I had applied the said boiling oil, I found feverish, with great pain and swelling about their wounds. Then I resolved with myself never more to burn thus cruelly poor men wounded with gunshot.

Being at Turin, I found a surgeon who was famous above all for good treatment of gunshot wounds, into whose grace I found means to insinuate myself, to have the recipe which he called his balm, with which he treated gunshot wounds, and he made me court him for years before I could draw his recipe from him. At last by gifts and presents he gave it to me, which was to boil in oil of lilies, little puppies just born, with earthworms prepared with Venetian turpentine. Then I was joyful and my heart made glad, to have understood his remedy, which was like to that which I had obtained by chance.

See how I learned to treat wounds made by gunshot, not from books.

The Cornerstone of Modern Medicine

ANDREAS VESALIUS (1514–64)

THE FIRST MAN who really knew the human body in an exact and complete fashion was Andreas Vesalius. Truly the foundation of modern medicine was his great seven-volume work, "The Anatomy of the Human Body" (*"De Humani Corporis Fabrica"*), first published in 1543, the same year that greeted Copernicus' "Revolutions of the Heavenly Bodies." Vesalius was born in Brussels; studied—with dissatisfaction, as he relates in the introduction to "The Anatomy" given here—at Paris; became professor of anatomy at Padua, where he observed with his own eyes and dissected with his own hands, sometimes —tradition says—getting material by cutting down from their gibbets the hanged bodies of condemned criminals. The opposition of authorities, chiefly ecclesiastical, eventually drove him to Spain, where he served the Emperor Charles V, to whom "The Anatomy" is dedicated.

Latin is the language of the original. The English translation, by B. Farrington, was first published in the Proceedings of the Royal Society of Medicine for July 1932, pp. 1357–66.

THE PREFACE OF ANDREAS VESALIUS

to

His Own Books on the Anatomy of the Human Body

addressed to

The Most Great and Invincible Emperor

THE DIVINE CHARLES V

THOSE ENGAGED in the arts and sciences, Most Gracious Emperor Charles, find many serious obstacles to the exact study and successful application of them. In the first place, no slight inconvenience results from too great separation between branches of study which serve for the perfection of one art. But much worse is the mischievous distribution among different practitioners of the practical applications of the art. This has been carried so far that those who have set before themselves the attainment of an art embrace one part of it to the neglect of the rest, although they are intimately bound up with it and can by no means be separated from it. Such never achieve any notable result; they never attain their goal or succeed in basing their art upon a proper foundation.

I shall pass over all the other arts in silence and confine myself to a few remarks on that which presides over the health of mankind. This, of all the arts which the mind of man has discovered, is by far the most beneficial, necessary, abstruse, and laborious. But in bygone times, that is to say [in the West] after the Gothic deluge and [in the East] after the reign of Mansor at Bochara in Persia, under whom, as we know, the Arabs still lived as was right on terms of familiarity with the Greeks, medicine began to be sore distempered. Its primary instrument, the employment of the hand in healing, was so neglected that it was relegated to vulgar fellows with no instruction whatsoever in the branches of knowledge that subserve the art of medicine.

In ancient times there were three medical sects, to wit, the Dogmatic, the Empirical, and the Methodical, but the exponents of each of these embraced the whole of the art as the means to preserve health and war against disease. To this end they referred all that they individually thought necessary in their particular sects, and employed the service of a threefold aid to health: first, a theory of diet; secondly, the whole use of drugs; and thirdly, manual operation. This last, above the rest, nicely proves the saying that medicine is the addition of that which is defective and the removal of that which is in excess; as often as we resort to the art of medicine for the treatment of disease we have occasion to employ it; and time and experience have taught, by the benefits it has conferred, that it is the greatest aid to human health.

This triple manner of treatment was equally familiar to the doctors of each sect; and those who applied manual operation according to the nature of the affection expended no less care in training their hands than in establishing a theory of diet, or in learning to recognize and compound drugs. This, not to mention his other books, is clearly shown by those most perfect of the compositions of Hippocrates: "On the Function of the Doctor," "On Fractures of Bones," "On Dislocations of Joints and Similar Ailments." Nay, more, Galen, after Hippocrates the prince of medicine, in addition to the fact that he boasts from time to time that the care of the gladiators of Pergamum was entrusted to his sole charge, and that when age was now becoming a burden he was reluctant for the monkeys he had for dissection to be skinned by the help of slaves, frequently impresses on us his joy in manual dexterity and how zealously he, in common with the other doctors of Asia, employed it. Indeed, there is no one of the ancients who does not seem as solicitous to hand down to posterity the method of cure which is effected by the hand as those methods which depend on diet and drugs.

But it was especially after the ruin spread by the Goths, when all the sciences, which before had flourished gloriously and were practiced as was fitting, went to ruin, that more fashionable doctors, first in Italy, in imitation of the old Romans, despising the work of the hand, began to delegate to slaves the manual attentions which they judged needful for their patients, and themselves merely to stand over them like master builders. Then, when all the rest also who practiced the true art of healing gradually declined the unpleasant duties of their profession, without, however, abating any of their claim to money or honor, they quickly fell away from the standard of the doctors of old. Methods of cooking, and all the preparation of food for the sick, they left to nurses; compounding of drugs they left to the apothecaries; manual operation to barbers. Thus in course of time the art of healing has been so wretchedly rent asunder that certain doctors, advertising themselves under the name of physicians, have arrogated to themselves alone the prescription of drugs and diet for obscure diseases, and have relegated the rest of medicine to those whom they call surgeons and scarcely regard as slaves, disgracefully banishing from themselves the chief and most ancient branch of the medical art, and that which principally (if indeed there be any other) bases itself upon the investigation of nature. Yet among the Indians today it is the kings that chiefly exercise this [surgical] art; the Persians hand it down as an obligatory inheritance to their children, as formerly did the whole family of the Asclepiads; the Thracians, with many other nations, cultivate and honor it above other arts, to the neglect almost of that part of the art [the prescription of drugs] which formerly many proscribed from the state, as devised for the deception and destruction of men; for it, refusing the aid of nature, gives no deep relief, but rather, endeavoring to help nature while it is in any case overwrought by the effort to cast off the disease, it often destroys it quite and utterly distracts it from its normal function. Consequently it is to it in particular we owe the fact that so many scoffs are wont to be cast at doctors, and this most holy art is made a mock, though all the time one part of it, which those trained in liberal studies allow basely to be torn from them, could adorn it forever with peculiar praise.

For when Homer, that wellspring of genius, declares that a man that is a doctor is better than a host, and together with all the poets of Greece celebrates Podalyrius and Machaon, truly these divine sons of Aesculapius are thus praised not for the reason that they banished a touch of fever or other ailments which nature usually cures, unaided, and without the assistance of the doctor more easily than with his aid, nor because they pandered to the appetites of men in obscure and desperate affections, but because they devoted themselves in particular to the cure of dislocations, fractures, bruises, wounds, and other breaches of continuity, and to fluxions of blood, and because they freed the noble warriors of Agamemnon from javelins, darts, and other evils of that kind, which wars particularly occasion, and which always demand the careful attention of the doctor.

But it was not at all my purpose to set one instrument of medicine above the rest, since the triple art of healing, as it is called, cannot at all be disunited and wrenched asunder, but belongs in its entirety to the same practitioner; and for the due attainment of this triple art, all the parts of medicine have been established and prepared on an equal footing, so that the individual parts are brought into use with a success proportioned to the degree in which one combines the cumulative force of all. How rarely indeed a disease occurs which does not at once require the triple manner of treatment; that is to say, a proper diet must be prescribed, some service must be rendered by medicine, and some by the hand. Therefore the tyros in this art must by every means be exhorted to follow the Greeks in despising the whisperings of those physicians (save the mark!), and, as the fundamental nature and rational basis of the art prescribes, to apply their hands also to the treatment, lest they should rend the body of medicine and make of it a force destructive of the common life of man.

And they must be urged to this with all the greater earnestness because men today who have had an irreproachable training in the art are seen to abstain from the use of the hand as from the plague, and for this very reason, lest they should be slandered by the masters of the profession as barbers before the ignorant mob, and should henceforth lack equal gain and honor with those less than half doctors, losing their standing both with the uneducated commonalty and with princes. For it is indeed above all other things the wide prevalence of this hateful error that prevents us even in our age from taking up the healing art as a whole, makes us confine ourselves merely to the treatment of internal complaints, and, if I may utter the blunt truth once for all, causes us, to the great detriment of mankind, to study to be healers only in a very limited degree.

For when, in the first place, the whole compounding of drugs was handed over to the apothecaries, then the doctors promptly lost the knowledge of simple medicines which is absolutely essential to them; and they became responsible for the fact that the druggists' shops were filled with barbarous terms and false remedies, and also that so many elegant compositions of the ancients were lost to us, several of which have not yet come to light; and, finally, they prepared an endless task for the learned men, not only of our own age, but for those who preceded it by some years, who devoted themselves with indefatigable zeal to research in simple medicines; so much so that they may be regarded as having gone far to restore the knowledge of them to its former brilliance.

But this perverse distribution of the instruments of healing among a variety of craftsmen inflicted a much more odious shipwreck and a far more cruel blow upon the chief branch of natural philosophy [anatomy], to which, since it comprises the natural history of man and should rightly be regarded as the firm foundation of the whole art of medicine and its essential preliminary, Hippocrates and Plato attached so much importance that they did not hesitate to put it first among the parts of medicine. For though originally it was the prime object of the doctors' care, and though they strained every nerve to acquire it, it finally began to perish miserably when the doctors themselves, by resigning manual operations to others, ruined anatomy. For when the doctors supposed that only the care of internal complaints concerned them, considering a mere knowledge of the viscera as more than enough for them, they neglected the structure of the bones and muscles, as well as of the nerves, veins, and arteries which run through bones and muscles, as of no importance for them. And further, when the whole conduct of manual operations was entrusted to barbers, not only did doctors lose the true knowledge of the viscera, but the practice of dissection soon died out, doubtless for the reason that the doctors did not attempt to operate, while those to whom the manual skill was resigned were too ignorant to read the writings of the teachers of anatomy.

It is thus utterly impossible for this class of men to preserve for us a difficult art which they have acquired only mechanically. And equally inevitably this deplorable dismemberment of the art of healing has introduced into our schools the detestable procedure now in vogue, that one man should carry out the dissection of the human body, and another give the description of the parts. These latter are perched up aloft in a pulpit like jackdaws, and with a notable air of disdain they drone out information about facts they have never approached at first hand, but which they merely commit to memory from the books of others, or of which they have descriptions before their eyes; the former are so ignorant of languages that they are unable to explain their dissections to the onlookers and botch what ought to be exhibited in accordance with the instruction of the physician, who never applies his hand to the dissection, and contemptuously steers the ship out of the manual, as the saying goes. Thus everything is wrongly taught, days are wasted in absurd questions, and in the confusion less is offered to the onlooker than a butcher in his stall could teach a doctor. I omit all mention of those schools in which there is scarcely even a thought of opening a human body to exhibit its structure. So far had ancient medicine fallen some years ago from its pristine glory.

But when medicine in the great blessedness of this age, which the gods will to entrust to the wise guidance of your divine power, had, together with all studies, begun to live again and to lift its head up from its utter darkness (so much so, indeed, that it might without fear of contradiction be regarded in some academies as having well-nigh recovered its ancient brilliance); and when there was nothing of which the need was now so urgently felt as the resurrection of the science of anatomy, then I, challenged by the example of so many eminent men, insofar as I could and with what means I could command, thought I should lend my aid. And lest, when all others for the sake of our common studies were engaged in some attempt and with such great success, I alone should be idle, or lest I should fall below the level of my forebears, doctors to be sure not unknown to fame, I thought that this branch of natural philosophy should be recalled from the dead, so that if it did not achieve with us a greater perfection than at any other place or time among the old teachers of anatomy, it might at least reach such a point that one could with confidence assert that our modern science of anatomy was equal to that of old, and that in this age anatomy was unique both in the level to which it had sunk and in the completeness of its subsequent restoration.

But this effort could by no manner of means have succeeded if, when I was studying medicine at Paris, I had not myself applied my hand to this business, but had acquiesced in the casual and superficial display to me and my fellow students by certain barbers of a few organs at one or two public dissections. For in such a perfunctory manner was anatomy then treated in the place where we have lived to see medicine happily reborn that I myself, having trained myself without guidance in the dissection of brute creatures, at the third dissection at which it was my fortune ever to be present (this, as was the custom there, was concerned exclusively or principally with the viscera), led on by the encouragement of my fellow students and teachers, performed in public a more thorough dissection than was wont to be done. Later I attempted a second dissection, my purpose being to exhibit the muscles of the hand together with a more accurate dissection of the viscera. For except for eight muscles of the abdomen, disgracefully mangled and in the wrong order, no one (I speak the simple truth) ever demonstrated to me any single muscle, or any single bone, much less the network of nerves, veins, and arteries.

Subsequently at Louvain, where I had to return on account of the disturbance of war, because during eighteen years the doctors there had not even dreamed of anatomy, and in order that I might help the students of that academy, and that I myself might acquire greater skill in a matter both obscure and in my judgment of prime importance for the whole of medicine, I did somewhat more accurately than at Paris expound the whole structure of the human body in the course of dissecting, with the result that the younger teachers of that academy now appear to spend great and very serious study in acquiring a knowledge of the parts of man, clearly understanding what invaluable material for philosophizing is presented to them from this knowledge. Furthermore at Padua, in the most famous gymnasium of the whole world, I had been charged with the teaching of surgical medicine five years by the illustrious Senate of Venice, which is far the most liberal in the endowment of the higher branches of learning. And since the carrying out of anatomical inquiry is of importance for surgical medicine, I devoted much effort to the investigation of the structure of man, and so directed my inquiries, and, exploding the ridiculous fashion of the schools, so taught the subject that we could not find in my procedure anything that fell short of the tradition of the ancients.

However, the supineness of the medical profession has seen to it only too well that the writings of Eudemus, Herophilus, Marinus, Andreas, Lycus, and other princes of anatomy should not be preserved to us, since not even a fragment of any page has survived of all those famous writers whom Galen mentions, to the number of more than twenty, in his second commentary to the book of Hippocrates on "The Nature of Man." Nay, even of his own anatomical writings scarcely the half has been saved from destruction. But those who followed Galen, among whom I place Oribasius, Theophilus, the Arabs, and all our own writers whom I have read to date, all of them (and they must pardon me for saying this), if they handed on anything worth reading, borrowed it from him. And, believe me, the careful reader will discover that there is nothing they were further from attempting than the dissection of bodies. They placed an absolute trust in I know not what quality of the writing of their chief, and in the neglect of dissection of the rest, and shamefully reduced Galen to convenient summaries, never departing from him by so much as the breadth of a nail, that is, supposing they succeed in arriving at his meaning. Nay, they place it in the forefront of their books that their own writings are pieced together from the teachings of Galen, and that all that is theirs is his. And so completely have all surrendered to his authority that no doctor has been found to declare that in the anatomical books of Galen even the slightest error has ever been found, much less could now be found; though all the time (apart from the fact that Galen frequently corrects himself, and in later books, after acquiring more experience, removes oversights that he had committed in earlier books, and sometimes teaches contradictory views) it is quite clear to us, from the revival of the art of dissection, from a painstaking perusal of the works of Galen, and from a restoration of them in several places, of which we have no reason to be ashamed, that Galen himself never dissected a human body lately dead. Nay, more, deceived by his monkeys (although it is admitted that human bodies dried, and prepared as it were for an inspection of the bones, did come under his observation), he frequently wrongly controverts the ancient doctors who had trained themselves by dissecting human corpses.

And again, how many false observations you will find him to have made even on his monkeys. I shall say nothing about the astonishing fact that in the manifold and infinite divergences of the organs of the human body from those of the monkey Galen hardly noticed anything except in the fingers and the bend of the knee—which he would certainly have passed over with the rest, if they had not been obvious to him without dissection. But at the moment I do not propose to criticize the false statements of Galen, easily the foremost among the teachers of anatomy; and much less would I wish to be regarded now in the beginning as disloyal to the author of all good things and lacking in respect for his authority. For I am not unaware how the medical profession (in this so different from the followers of Aristotle) are wont to be upset when in more than two hundred instances, in the conduct of the single course of anatomy I now exhibit in the schools, they see that Galen has failed to give a true description of the interrelation, use, and function of the parts of man—how they scowl at times, and examine every inch of the dissection in their determination to defend him. Yet they too, drawn by the love of truth, gradually abandon that attitude and, growing less emphatic, begin to put faith in their own not ineffectual sight and powers of reason rather than in the writings of Galen. These true paradoxes, won not by slavish reliance on the efforts of others, nor supported merely by masses of authorities, they eagerly communicate in their correspondence to their friends; they exhort them so earnestly and so friendly-wise to examine them for themselves, and to come at last to a true knowledge of anatomy, that there is ground for hope that anatomy will ere long be cultivated in all our academies as it was of old in Alexandria.

And that the muses might the more smile upon this hope, I have, so far as in me lay, and in addition to my other publications on this subject—which certain plagiarists, thinking me far away from Germany, have put out there as their own—made a completely fresh arrangement in seven books of my information about the parts of the human body in the order in which I am wont to lay the same before that learned assembly in this city, as well as at Bologna and at Pisa. Thus those present at the dissections will have a record of what was there demonstrated, and will be able to expound anatomy to others with less trouble. And also the books will be by no means useless to those who have no opportunity for personal examination, for they relate with sufficient fullness the number, position, shape, substance, connection with other parts, use and function of each part of the human body, together with many similar facts which we are wont to unravel during dissection concerning the nature of the parts, and also the method of dissection applicable to dead and living animals. Moreover, the books contain representations of all the parts inserted in the text of the discourse, in such a way that they place before the eyes of the student of nature's works, as it were, a dissected corpse.

Thus in the first book I have described the nature of all bones and cartilages, which, since the other parts are supported by them, and must be described in accordance with them, are the first to be known by students of anatomy. The second book treats of the ligaments by which bones and cartilages are linked one with another, and then the muscles that affect the movements that depend upon our will. The third comprises the close network of veins which carry to the muscles and bones and the other parts the ordinary blood by which they are nourished, and of arteries which control the mixture of innate heat and vital spirit. The fourth treats of the branches not only of the nerves which convey the animal spirit to the muscles, but of all the other nerves as well. The fifth explains the structure of the organs that subserve nutrition effected through food and drink; and furthermore, on account of the proximity of their position, it contains also the instruments designed by the Most High Creator for the propagation of the species. The sixth is devoted to the heart, the *fomes* of the vital faculty, and the parts that subserve it. The seventh describes the harmony between the structure of the brain and the organs of sense, without, however, repeating from the fourth book the description of the network of nerves arising from the brain. . . .

But here there comes into my mind the judgment of certain men who vehemently condemn the practice of setting before the eyes of students, as we do with the parts of plants, delineations, be they never so accurate, of the parts of the human body. These, they say, ought to be learned not by pictures but by careful dissection and examination of the things themselves. As if, forsooth, my object in adding to the text of my discourse images of the parts, which are most faithful, and which I wish could be free from the risk of being spoiled by the printers, was that students should rely upon them and refrain from dissecting bodies; whereas my practice has rather been to encourage students of medicine in every way I could to perform dissections with their own hands. Assuredly, if the practice of the ancients had lasted down to our day, namely, to train boys at home in carrying out dissections, just as in making their letters and in reading, I would gladly consent to our dispensing not only with pictures but with all commentaries. For the ancients only began to write about dissection when they decided that honor demanded that they should communicate the art not only to their children but to strangers whom they respected for their virtue. For, as soon as boys were no longer trained in dissection, the inevitable consequence at once followed that they learned anatomy less well, since the training had been abolished with which they had been wont to begin in youth. So much so that when the art had deserted the family of the Asclepiads, and had been now for many centuries on the decline, books were needed to preserve a complete view of it. Yet how greatly pictures aid the understanding of these things, and how much more accurately they put the things before the eyes than even the clearest language, nobody can have failed to experience in geometry and the other mathematical disciplines.

But, however that may be, I have done my best to this single end, namely, in an equally recondite and laborious matter, to aid as many as possible, and truly and completely to describe the structure of the human body—which is built up not of some ten or twelve parts (as seems to those who give it a passing glance) but of some thousands of different parts—and to bring to students of medicine a substantial contribution toward the understanding of those books of Galen treating of this branch of learning, which of all his writings most require the assistance of a teacher.

Moreover, I am aware [first] how little authority my efforts will carry by reason of my youth (I am still in my twenty-eighth year); and [secondly] how little, on account of the frequency with which I draw attention to the falsity of Galen's pronouncements, I shall be sheltered from the attacks of those who have not—as I have done in the schools of Italy—applied themselves earnestly to anatomy, and who, being now old men devoured by envy at the true discoveries of youths, will be ashamed, together with all the other sectaries of Galen, that they have been hitherto so purblind, failing to notice what I now set forth, yet arrogating to themselves a mighty reputation in the art—[I know, I say, how little authority my efforts will carry] unless they come forth auspiciously into the light, commended by the great patronage of some divine power. And, inasmuch as it cannot be more safely sheltered or more splendidly adorned than by the imperishable name of the Divine Charles, the Most Great and Invincible Emperor, I beseech Your Majesty to allow this useful work of mine, which on many accounts and for many reasons is dangerous to itself, to circulate for a short time under Your Majesty's auspices, glory, and patronage, until through experience of the facts, through judgment which matures with time, and through learning, I may make the fruit of my toil worthy of the Most High and Best Prince, or may offer another gift worthy of acceptance on another subject chosen from our art.

PADUA, *August 1*, A.D. *1542.*

The Key to Modern Physiology

WILLIAM HARVEY (1578–1657)

HARVEY's scientific reputation—"the greatest name in English medicine" —was made by the simple arithmetical demonstration that the blood moves, "as it were, in a circle," that is, circulates, through the body. If we consider the great quantity of blood that is thrown out every minute by the heart (approximately two ounces times seventy-two beats), he asked, where can it go unless it circulates? This clinching argument was set forth in his great work, *"De Motu Cordis"* ("On the Motion of the Heart"), 1628, quoted here. Harvey is also known as "the father of embryology," the first man after Aristotle to work out the development of the chicken from the egg.

William was one of the five brothers Harvey who made a fortune in the "Turkey trade," importing and exporting. Student of Fabricius at Padua, where he was president of the English "nation" (that is, fraternity), Harvey got his M.D. in 1602. He returned to England to become, successively, physician to St. Bart's—St. Bartholomew's Hospital, London; physician to Kings James I and Charles I; and president of the Royal College of Physicians, which he endowed. One of his official duties was the examination of witches; but, a humane and sensible doctor, he never found or reported signs (burns) of intercourse with the devil. A matter-of-fact Cavalier, he is reported to have sat reading quietly under a hedge while the battle of Edgehill, against Cromwell's Puritans, raged near by.

Latin is the language of Harvey's slender classic, whose complete title is *"Exercitatio Anatomica de Motu Cordis et Sanguinibus in Animalibus"* ("Anatomical Essay on the Motion of the Heart and Blood in Animals"). The English translation, by Robert Willis, was published by the Sydenham Society in 1847.

"ON THE MOTION OF THE HEART AND THE CIRCULATION OF THE BLOOD"

The Author's Motives for Writing

WHEN I FIRST GAVE my mind to vivisections, as a means of discovering the motions and uses of the heart, and sought to discover these from actual inspection, and not from the writings of others, I found the task so truly arduous, so full of difficulties, that I was almost tempted to think, with Fracastorius, that the motion of the heart was only to be comprehended by God. . . .

Of the Motions of the Heart, as Seen in the Dissection of Living Animals

In the first place, then, when the chest of a living animal is laid open and the capsule that immediately surrounds the heart is slit up or removed, the organ is seen now to move, now to be at rest; there is a time when it moves, and a time when it is motionless.

These things are more obvious in the colder animals, such as toads, frogs, serpents, small fishes, crabs, shrimps, snails, and shellfish. They also become more distinct in warm-blooded animals, such as the dog and hog, if they be attentively noted when the heart begins to flag, to move more slowly, and, as it were, to die: the movements then become slower and rarer, the pauses longer, by which it is made much easier to perceive and unravel what the motions really are, and how they are performed. In the pause, as in death, the heart is soft, flaccid, exhausted, lying, as it were, at rest.

In the motion, and interval in which this is accomplished, three principal circumstances are to be noted:

1. That the heart is erected, and rises upward to a point, so that at this time it strikes against the breast and the pulse is felt externally.

2. That it is everywhere contracted, but more especially toward the sides, so that it looks narrower, relatively longer, more drawn together. The heart of an eel taken out of the body of the animal and placed upon the table or the hand shows these particulars; but the same things are manifest in the hearts of small fishes and of those colder animals where the organ is more conical or elongated.

3. The heart, being grasped in the hand, is felt to become harder during its action. Now this hardness proceeds from tension, precisely as when the forearm is grasped, its tendons are perceived to become tense and resilient when the fingers are moved.

4. It may further be observed in fishes, and the colder-blooded animals, such as frogs, serpents, et cetera, that the heart when it moves becomes of a paler color; when quiescent, of a deeper blood-red color.

From these particulars it appeared evident to me that the motion of the heart consists in a certain universal tension—both contraction in the line of its fibers and constriction in every sense. It becomes erect, hard, and of diminished size during its action; the motion is plainly of the same nature as that of the muscles when they contract in the line of their sinews and fibers; for the muscles, when in action, acquire vigor and tenseness, and from soft become hard, prominent, and thickened: in the same manner the heart.

We are therefore authorized to conclude that the heart, at the moment of its action, is at once constricted on all sides, rendered thicker in its parietes[1] and smaller in its ventricles, and so made apt to project or expel its charge of blood. This, indeed, is made sufficiently manifest by the fourth observation preceding, in which we have seen that the heart, by squeezing out the blood it contains, becomes paler, and then, when it sinks into repose and the ventricle is filled anew with blood, that the deeper crimson color returns. But no one need remain in doubt of the fact, for if the ventricle be pierced the blood will be seen to be forcibly projected outward upon each motion or pulsation when the heart is tense.

These things, therefore, happen together or at the same instant: the tension of the heart, the pulse of its apex, which is felt externally by its striking against the chest, the thickening of its parietes, and the forcible expulsion of the blood it contains by the constriction of its ventricles.

Hence the very opposite of the opinions commonly received appears to be true; inasmuch as it is generally believed that, when the heart strikes the breast and the pulse is felt without, the heart is dilated in its ventricles and is filled with blood; but the contrary of this is the fact, and the heart, when it contracts (and the shock is given), is emptied. Whence the motion which is generally regarded as the diastole of the heart is in truth its systole. And in like manner the intrinsic motion of the heart is not the diastole but the systole; neither is it in the diastole that the heart grows firm and tense, but in the systole, for then only, when tense, is it moved and made vigorous. . . .

[1]Muscular walls of the heart.

OF THE MOTION, ACTION, AND OFFICE OF THE HEART

From these and other observations of the like kind I am persuaded it will be found that the motion of the heart is as follows.

First of all, the auricle contracts, and in the course of its contraction throws the blood (which it contains in ample quantity as the head of the veins, the storehouse, and cistern of the blood) into the ventricle, which, being filled, the heart raises itself straightway, makes all its fibers tense, contracts the ventricles, and performs a beat, by which beat it immediately sends the blood supplied to it by the auricle into the arteries; the right ventricle sending its charge into the lungs by the vessel which is called vena arteriosa, but which, in structure and function, and all things else, is an artery; the left ventricle sending its charge into the aorta, and through this by the arteries to the body at large.

These two motions, one of the ventricles, another of the auricles, take place consecutively, but in such a manner that there is a kind of harmony or rhythm preserved between them, the two concurring in such wise that but one motion is apparent, especially in the warmer-blooded animals, in which the movements in question are rapid. Nor is this for any other reason than it is in a piece of machinery, in which, though one wheel gives motion to another, yet all the wheels seem to move simultaneously; or in that mechanical contrivance which is adapted to firearms, where, the trigger being touched, down comes the flint, strikes against the steel, elicits a spark, which, falling among the powder, it is ignited, upon which the flame extends, enters the barrel, causes the explosion, propels the ball, and the mark is attained—all of which incidents, by reason of the celerity with which they happen, seem to take place in the twinkling of an eye. So also in deglutition: by the elevation of the root of the tongue and the compression of the mouth, the food or drink is pushed into the fauces, the larynx is closed by its own muscles, and the epiglottis, while the pharynx, raised and opened by its muscles no otherwise than is a sac that is to be filled, is lifted up, and its mouth dilated; upon which, the mouthful being received, it is forced downward by the transverse muscles, and then carried farther by the longitudinal ones. Yet are all these motions, though executed by different and distinct organs, performed harmoniously, and in such order that they seem to constitute but a single motion and act, which we call deglutition. . . .

Even so does it come to pass with the motions and action of the heart, which constitute a kind of deglutition, a transfusion of the blood from the veins to the arteries. And if anyone, bearing these things in mind, will carefully watch the motions of the heart in the body of a living animal, he will perceive not only all the particulars I have mentioned, viz., the heart becoming erect, and making one continuous motion with its auricles; but farther, a certain obscure undulation and lateral inclination in the direction of the axis of the right ventricle (the organ), twisting itself slightly in performing its work. And indeed everyone may see, when a horse drinks, that the water is drawn in and transmitted to the stomach at each movement of the throat, the motion being accompanied with a sound and yielding a pulse both to the ear and the touch; in the same way it is with each motion of the heart, when there is the delivery of a quantity of blood from the veins to the arteries, that a pulse takes place and can be heard within the chest. . . .

OF THE QUANTITY OF BLOOD PASSING THROUGH THE HEART FROM THE VEINS TO THE ARTERIES; AND OF THE CIRCULAR MOTION OF THE BLOOD

Thus far I have spoken of the passage of the blood from the veins into the arteries, and of the manner in which it is transmitted and distributed by the action of the heart; points to which some, moved either by the authority of Galen or Columbus, or the reasonings of others, will give in their adhesion. But what remains to be said upon the quantity and source of the blood which thus passes is of so novel and unheard-of character that I not only fear injury to myself from the envy of a few, but I tremble lest I have mankind at large for my enemies, so much does wont and custom, that become as another nature, and doctrine once sown and that has struck deep root, and respect for antiquity influence all men. Still the die is cast, and my trust is in my love of truth and the candor that inheres in cultivated minds. And sooth to say, when I surveyed my mass of evidence, whether derived from vivisections, and my various reflections on them, or from the ventricles of the heart and the vessels that enter into and issue from them, the symmetry and size of these conduits—for nature, doing nothing in vain, would never have given them so large a relative size without a purpose—or from the arrangement and intimate structure of the valves in particular, and of the other parts of the heart in general, with many things besides, I frequently and seriously bethought me, and long revolved in my mind, what might be the quantity of blood which was transmitted, in how short a time its passage might be effected, and the like; and not finding it possible that this could be supplied by the juices of the ingested aliment without the veins on the one hand becoming drained, and the arteries on the other getting ruptured through the excessive charge of blood, unless the blood should somehow find its way from the arteries into the veins, and so return to the right side of the heart; I began to think whether there might not be *a motion, as it were, in a circle.* Now this I afterwards found to be true; and I finally saw that the blood, forced by the action of the left ventricle into the arteries, was distributed to the body at large, and its several parts, in the same manner as it is sent through the lungs, impelled by the right ventricle into the pulmonary artery, and that it then passed through the veins and along the vena cava, and so round to the left ventricle in the manner already indicated. Which motion we may be allowed to call circular, in the same way as Aristotle says that the air and the rain emulate the circular motion of the superior bodies; for the moist earth, warmed by the sun, evaporates; the vapors, drawn upward, are condensed and, descending in the form of rain, moisten the earth again; and by this arrangement are generations of living things produced; and in like manner, too, are tempests and meteors engendered by the circular motion, and by the approach and recession of the sun. . . .

THAT THERE IS A CIRCULATION OF THE BLOOD IS CONFIRMED FROM THE FIRST PROPOSITION

But lest anyone should say that we give them words only, and make mere specious assertions without any foundation, and desire to innovate without sufficient cause, three points present themselves for confirmation, which being stated, I conceive that the truth I contend for will follow necessarily, and appear as a thing obvious to all. First, the blood is incessantly transmitted by the action of the heart from the vena cava to the arteries in such quantity that it cannot be supplied from the ingesta, and in such wise that the whole mass must very quickly pass through the organ. Second, the blood under the influence of the arterial pulse enters and is impelled in a continuous, equable, and incessant stream through every part and member of the body, in much larger quantity than were sufficient for nutrition, or than the whole mass of fluids could supply. Third, the veins in like manner return this blood incessantly to the heart from all parts and members of the body. These points proved, I conceive it will be manifest that the blood circulates, revolves, propelled and then returning, from the heart to the extremities, from the extremities to the heart, and thus that it performs a kind of circular motion.

Let us assume either arbitrarily or from experiment the quantity of blood which the left ventricle of the heart will contain when distended to be, say, two ounces, three ounces, one ounce and a half—in the dead body I have found it to hold upwards of two ounces. Let us assume further how much less the heart will hold in the contracted than in the dilated state; and how much blood it will project into the aorta upon each contraction (and all the world allows that with the systole something is always projected, a necessary consequence demonstrated in the third chapter, and obvious from the structure of the valves); and let us suppose as approaching the truth that the fourth, or fifth, or sixth, or even but the eighth part of its charge is thrown into the artery at each contraction; this would give either half an ounce, or three drams, or one dram of blood as propelled by the heart at each pulse into the aorta; which quantity, by reason of the valves at the root of the vessel, can by no means return into the ventricle. Now, in the course of half an hour, the heart will have made more than one thousand beats, in some as many as two, three, and even four thousand. Multiplying the number of drams propelled by the number of pulses, we shall have either one thousand half ounces, or one thousand times three drams, or a like proportional quantity of blood, according to the amount which we assume as propelled with each stroke of the heart, sent from this organ into the artery; a larger quantity in every case than is contained in the whole body! In the same way, in the sheep or dog, say that but a single scruple of blood passes with each stroke of the heart, in one half hour we should have one thousand scruples, or about three pounds and a half of blood injected into the aorta; but the body of neither animal contains above four pounds of blood, a fact which I have myself ascertained in the case of the sheep.

Upon this supposition, therefore, assumed merely as a ground for reasoning, we see the whole mass of blood passing through the heart, from the veins to the arteries, and in like manner through the lungs.

But let it be said that this does not take place in half an hour, but in an hour, or even in a day; anyway, it is still manifest that more blood passes through the heart in consequence of its action than can either be supplied by the whole of the ingesta, or than can be contained in the veins at the same moment.

Nor can it be allowed that the heart in contracting sometimes propels and sometimes does not propel, or at the most propels but very little, a mere nothing, or an imaginary something: all this, indeed, has already been refuted; and is, besides, contrary both to sense and reason. For if it be a necessary effect of the dilatation of the heart that its ventricles become filled with blood, it is equally so that, contracting, these cavities should expel their contents; and this not in any trifling measure, seeing that neither are the conduits small nor the contractions few in number, but frequent, and always in some certain proportion, whether it be a third, or a sixth, or an eighth, to the total capacity of the ventricles, so that a like proportion received with each stroke of the heart, the capacity of the ventricle contracted always bearing a certain relation to the capacity of the ventricle when dilated. And since, in dilating, the ventricles cannot be supposed to get filled with nothing, or with an imaginary something; so in contracting they never expel nothing or aught imaginary, but always a certain something, viz., blood, in proportion to the amount of the contraction. Whence it is to be inferred that if at one stroke the heart in man, the ox, or the sheep ejects but a single dram of blood, and there are one thousand strokes in half an hour, in this interval there will have been ten pounds five ounces expelled: were there with each stroke two drams expelled, the quantity would of course amount to twenty pounds and ten ounces; were there half an ounce, the quantity would come to forty-one pounds and eight ounces; and were there one ounce, it would be as much as eighty-three pounds and four ounces; the whole of which, in the course of one half hour, would have been transfused from the veins to the arteries. The actual quantity of blood expelled at each stroke of the heart, and the circumstances under which it is either greater or less than ordinary, I leave for particular determination afterward, from numerous observations which I have made on the subject.

Meantime this much I know, and would here proclaim to all, that the blood is transfused at one time in larger, at another in smaller quantity; and that the circuit of the blood is accomplished now more rapidly, now more slowly, according to the temperament, age, et cetera, of the individual, to external and internal circumstances, to naturals and non-naturals—sleep, rest, food, exercise, affections of the mind, and the like. But indeed, supposing even the smallest quantity of blood to be passed through the heart and the lungs with each pulsation, a vastly greater amount would still be thrown into the arteries and whole body than could by any possibility be supplied by the food consumed; in short it could be furnished in no other way than by making a circuit and returning.

This truth, indeed, presents itself obviously before us when we consider what happens in the dissection of living animals; the great artery need not be divided, but a very small branch only (as Galen even proves in regard to man), to have the whole of the blood in the body, as well that of the veins as of the arteries, drained away in the course of no long time—some half hour or less. Butchers are well aware of the fact and can bear witness to it; for, cutting the throat of an ox and so dividing the vessels of the neck, in less than a quarter of an hour they have all the vessels bloodless—the whole mass of blood has escaped. The same thing also occasionally occurs with great rapidity in performing amputations and removing tumors in the human subject.

Nor would this argument lose any of its force did anyone say that in killing animals in the shambles, and performing amputations, the blood escaped in equal, if not perchance in larger quantity, by the veins than by the arteries. The contrary of this statement, indeed, is certainly the truth; the veins, in fact, collapsing, and being without any propelling power, and further, because of the impediment of the valves, as I shall show immediately, pour out but very little blood; while the arteries spout it forth with force abundantly, impetuously, and as if it were propelled by a syringe. And then the experiment is easily tried of leaving the vein untouched, and only dividing the artery in the neck of a sheep or dog, when it will be seen with what force, in what abundance, and how quickly the whole blood in the body, of the veins as well as of the arteries, is emptied. But the arteries receive blood from the veins in no other way than by transmission through the heart, as we have already seen; so that if the aorta be tied at the base of the heart, and the carotid or any other artery be opened, no one will now be surprised to find it empty, and the veins only replete with blood. . . .

The First Words About Electricity

WILLIAM GILBERT (1540–1603)

WHY DOES a compass needle point north, but not true north? The answer to this question, which mystified the mariners of Queen Elizabeth's day, is now known to every schoolboy who has worked out the simple but fundamental experiment in magnetism and electricity here described in the words of the Queen's personal physician, William Gilbert of Colchester, sometimes called "the father of electricity." In "Magnetism and Magnetic Bodies" (*"De Magnete, Magneticisque Corporibus"*), the first great scientific work published in England (1600), Gilbert, president of the Royal College of Physicians, invented the word "electricity" (from the Greek, "amber," which, rubbed, became electrified), noted the dip as well as the direction of the magnetic needle, and concluded after a series of experiments which Francis Bacon praised as models of the experimental method that the earth itself was a gigantic magnet whose magnetic poles do not quite coincide with its geographic poles.

Before Gilbert the one man who had scientifically studied the loadstone and the action of the magnetic needle, which, in the form of the mariner's compass, introduced from the East, had opened the Age of Discovery to European navigators, was a French crusader, Peter the Stranger, whose "Letter on Magnetism" (*"Epistola de Magnete"*), appearing in 1269, has been described as "one of the main landmarks in the history of science" (George Sarton).

Latin was the language of Gilbert's work. The English translation, by P. Fleury Mottelay, was published in 1893.

"ON MAGNETISM AND MAGNETIC BODIES": AN EASY EXPERIMENT

THE LOADSTONE POSSESSES PARTS DIFFERING IN THEIR NATURAL POWERS, AND HAS POLES CONSPICUOUS FOR THEIR PROPERTIES

THE MANY QUALITIES exhibited by the loadstone itself, qualities hitherto recognized yet not well investigated, are to be pointed out in the first place, to the end the student may understand the powers of the loadstone and of iron, and not be confused through want of knowledge at the threshold of the arguments and demonstrations. In the heavens astronomers give to each moving sphere two poles; thus do we find two natural poles of excelling importance even in our terrestrial globe, constant points related to the movement of its daily revolution, to wit, one pole pointing to Arctos (Ursa) and the north; the other looking toward the opposite part of the heavens. In like manner the loadstone has from nature its two poles, a northern and a southern; fixed, definite points in the stone, which are the primary termini of the movements and effects, and the limits and regulators of the several actions and properties. It is to be understood, however, that not from a mathematical point does the force of the stone emanate, but from the parts themselves; and all these parts in the whole —while they belong to the whole—the nearer they are to the poles of the stone the stronger virtues do they acquire and pour out on other bodies.

These poles look toward the poles of the earth, and move toward them, and are subject to them.

The magnetic poles may be found in every loadstone, whether strong and powerful (male, as the term was in antiquity) or faint, weak, and female; whether its shape is due to design or to chance, and whether it be long, or flat, or foursquare, or three-cornered, or polished; whether it be rough, broken off, or unpolished: the loadstone ever has and ever shows its poles. . . .

ONE LOADSTONE APPEARS TO ATTRACT ANOTHER IN THE NATURAL POSITION; BUT IN THE OPPOSITE POSITION REPELS IT AND BRINGS IT TO RIGHTS

First we have to describe in popular language the potent and familiar properties of the stone; afterward, very many subtle properties, as yet recondite and unknown, being involved in obscurities, are to be unfolded; and the causes of all these (nature's secrets being unlocked) are in their place to be demonstrated in fitting words and with the aid of apparatus. The fact is trite and familiar that the loadstone attracts iron; in the same way, too, one loadstone attracts another. Take the stone on which you have designated the poles, N. and S., and put it in its vessel so that it may float; let the poles lie just in the plane of the horizon, or at least in a plane not very oblique to it; take in your hand another stone the poles of which are also known, and hold it so that its south pole shall lie toward the north pole of the floating stone, and near it alongside; the floating loadstone will straightway follow the other (provided it be within the range and dominion of its powers), nor does it cease to move nor does it quit the other till it clings to it, unless by moving your hand away you manage skillfully to prevent the conjunction.

In like manner, if you oppose the north pole of the stone in your hand to the south pole of the floating one, they come together and follow each other. For opposite poles attract opposite poles. But now, if in the same way you present N. to N. or S. to S., one stone repels the other; and as though a helmsman were bearing on the rudder it is off like a vessel making all sail, nor stands nor stays as long as the other stone pursues. One stone also will range the other, turn the other around, bring it to right about and make it come to agreement with itself. But when the two come together and are conjoined in nature's order, they cohere firmly.

For example, if you present the north pole of the stone in your hand to the Tropic of Capricorn (for so we may distinguish with mathematical circles the round stone or terrella, just as we do the globe itself) or to any point between the Equator and the South Pole: immediately the floating stone turns round and so places itself that its south pole touches the north pole of the other and is most closely joined to it. In the same way you will get like effect at the other side of the Equator by presenting pole to pole; and thus by art and contrivance we exhibit attraction and repulsion, and motion in a circle toward the concordant position, and the same movements to avoid hostile meetings. Furthermore, in one same stone we are thus able to demonstrate all this: but also we are able to show how the selfsame part of one stone may by division become either

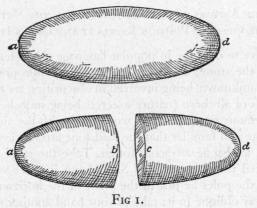

FIG I.

north or south. Take the oblong stone *ad* (Fig. 1) in which *a* is the north pole and *d* the south. Cut the stone in two equal parts, and put part *a* in a vessel and let it float in water.

You will find that *a,* the north point, will turn to the south as before; and in like manner the point *d* will move to the north, in the divided stone, as before division. But *b* and *c,* before connected, now separated from each other, are not what they were before. *B* is now south while *c* is north. *B* attracts *c,* longing for union and for restoration of the original continuity. They are two stones made out of one, and on that account, the *c* of one turning toward the *b* of the other, they are mutually attracted, and, being freed from all impediments and from their own weight, borne as they are on the surface of the water, they come together and into conjunction.

But if you bring the part or point *a* up to *c* of the other, they repel one another and turn away; for by such a position of the parts nature is crossed and the form of the stone is perverted: but nature observes strictly the laws it has imposed upon bodies: hence the flight of one part from the undue position of the other, and hence the discord unless everything is arranged exactly according to nature. And nature will not suffer an unjust and inequitable peace, or agreement, but makes war and employs force to make bodies acquiesce fairly and justly. Hence, when rightly arranged, the parts attract each other, i.e., both stones, the weaker and the stronger, come together and with all their might tend to union: a fact manifest in all loadstones, and not, as Pliny supposed, only in those from Ethiopia.

The Ethiopic stones, if strong, and those brought from China, which are all powerful stones, show the effect most quickly and most plainly, attract with most force in the parts nighest the pole, and keep turning till pole looks straight on pole. The pole of a stone has strongest attraction for that part of another stone which answers to it (the *adverse,* as it is called); e.g., the north pole of one has strongest attraction for, has the most vigorous pull on, the south part of another; so, too, it attracts iron more powerfully, and iron clings to it more firmly, whether previously magnetized or not. Thus it has been settled by nature, not without reason, that the parts nigher the pole shall have the greatest attractive force; and that in the pole itself shall be the seat, the throne, as it were, of a high and splendid power; and that magnetic bodies brought near thereto shall be attracted most powerfully and relinquished with most reluctance. So, too, the poles are readiest to spurn and drive away what is presented to them amiss, and what is inconformable and foreign.

IV SCIENCE GROWS UP:
In the Seventeenth and Early Eighteenth Centuries

"*Nature Is Commanded Only by Being Obeyed*"

FRANCIS BACON (1561–1626)

TRUE OR FALSE? This question applies equally to a scientific hypothesis or the statements of a witness in a court of law. Out of a lawyer's deep concern with the "rules of evidence," Francis Bacon, Lord Verulam, elaborated the basic philosophy of modern science: test everything by experiment, accept nothing that cannot be corroborated by experience. Bacon made no experiments himself; but his rigorous dismissal of hearsay testimony and his trenchant insistence on objective experimental evidence swept away the cobwebs of vague philosophical speculation that might have shuttered the true "advancement of learning." His book of this title was published in 1605; in it as well as in "The New Atlantis" ("*Novum Organum*"), 1620, he urged the systematic cultivation of natural science by the experimental method. But he recognized the "subtlety of nature" and knew that she could be "commanded only by being obeyed."

Bacon's legal career was serpentined with intrigue: once friend, he became prosecutor of Elizabeth's favorite, Lord Essex; Lord Chancellor of England, he confessed himself guilty of bribery and corruption, only to be pardoned by the King, James I, whom he, as commissioner to Scotland, had helped enthrone. Concise master of style, his prose, like Shakespeare's poetry, set the enduring tone and character of the English language and early demonstrated that science and literature can be one.

English was Bacon's native tongue, but he often wrote the same thing in both Latin and English so that it is difficult to say which is the original, which the translation. "Selected Aphorisms" and "On Invention," quoted here, are from the Spedding, Ellis, and Heath edition. "Francis Bacon Thought" appears in J. M. Robertson's edition of "The Philosophical Works of Francis Bacon" (London: George Routledge & Sons. New York: E. P. Dutton & Co., Inc., 1905).

"SUBTLETY OF NATURE" AND OTHER SELECTED APHORISMS

CONCERNING
THE INTERPRETATION OF NATURE AND THE KINGDOM OF MAN

(From *"Novum Organum"*)

I

MAN, being the servant and interpreter of Nature, can do and understand so much and so much only as he has observed in fact or in thought of the course of nature: beyond this he neither knows anything nor can do anything.

II

Neither the naked hand nor the understanding left to itself can effect much. It is by instruments and helps that the work is done, which are as much wanted for the understanding as for the hand. And as the instruments of the hand either give motion or guide it, so the instruments of the mind supply either suggestions for the understanding or cautions.

III

Human knowledge and human power meet in one; for where the cause is not known the effect cannot be produced. Nature to be commanded must be obeyed; and that which in contemplation is as the cause is in operation as the rule.

IV

Towards the effecting of works, all that man can do is to put together or put asunder natural bodies. The rest is done by nature working within.

VII

The productions of the mind and hand seem very numerous in books and manufactures. But all this variety lies in an exquisite subtlety and derivations from a few things already known; not in the number of axioms.

VIII

Moreover the works already known are due to chance and experiment rather than to sciences; for the sciences we now possess are merely systems for the nice ordering and setting forth of things already invented; not methods of invention or directions for new works.

IX

The cause and root of nearly all evils in the sciences is this—that while we falsely admire and extol the powers of the human mind we neglect to seek for its true helps.

X

The subtlety of nature is greater many times over than the subtlety of the senses and understanding; so that all those specious meditations, speculations, and glosses in which men indulge are quite from the purpose,[1] only there is no one by to observe it.

XIX

There are and can be only two ways of searching into and discovering truth. The one flies from the senses and particulars to the most general axioms, and from these principles, the truth of which it takes for settled and immovable, proceeds to judgment and to the discovery of middle axioms. And this way is now in fashion. The other derives axioms from the senses and particulars, rising by a gradual and unbroken ascent, so that it arrives at the most general axioms last of all. This is the true way, but as yet untried.

XX

The understanding left to itself takes the same course (namely, the former) which it takes in accordance with logical order. For the mind longs to spring up to positions of higher generality, that it may find rest there; and so after a little while wearies of experiment. But this evil is increased by logic, because of the order and solemnity of its disputations.

XXII

Both ways set out from the senses and particulars, and rest in the highest generalities; but the difference between them is infinite. For the one just glances at experiment and particulars in passing, the other dwells

[1] Literally, "are a thing insane." The meaning appears to be that these speculations, being founded upon such an inadequate conception of the case, must necessarily be so wide of the truth that they would seem like mere madness if we could only compare them with it: like the aim of a man blindfolded to bystanders looking on.

duly and orderly among them. The one, again, begins at once by establishing certain abstract and useless generalities, the other rises by gradual steps to that which is prior and better known in the order of nature.

XXIV

It cannot be that axioms established by argumentation should avail for the discovery of new works; since the subtlety of nature is greater many times over than the subtlety of argument. But axioms duly and orderly formed from particulars easily discover the way of new particulars, and thus render sciences active.

XXV

The axioms now in use, having been suggested by a scanty and manipular experience and a few particulars of most general occurrence, are made for the most part just large enough to fit and take these in: and therefore it is no wonder if they do not lead to new particulars. And if some opposite instance, not observed or not known before, chance to come in the way, the axiom is rescued and preserved by some frivolous distinction; whereas the truer course would be to correct the axiom itself.

XXVI

The conclusions of human reason as ordinarily applied in matter of nature, I call for the sake of distinction *Anticipations of Nature* (as a thing rash or premature). That reason which is elicited from facts by a just and methodical process, I call *Interpretation of Nature*.

XXVII

Anticipations are a ground sufficiently firm for consent; for even if men went mad all after the same fashion, they might agree one with another well enough.

XXVIII

For the winning of assent, indeed, anticipations are far more powerful than interpretations; because being collected from a few instances, and those for the most part of familiar occurrence, they straightway touch the understanding and fill the imagination; whereas interpretations on the other hand, being gathered here and there from very various and widely dispersed facts, cannot suddenly strike the understanding; and therefore they must needs, in respect of the opinions of the time, seem harsh and out of tune; much as the mysteries of faith do.

XXX

Though all the wits of all the ages should meet together and combine and transmit their labours, yet will no great progress ever be made in science by means of anticipations; because radical errors in the first concoction of the mind are not to be cured by the excellence of functions and remedies subsequent.

XXXI

It is idle to expect any great advancement in science from the superinducing and engrafting of new things upon old. We must begin anew from the very foundations, unless we would revolve for ever in a circle with mean and contemptible progress.

XXXII

The honour of the ancient authors, and indeed of all, remains untouched; since the comparison I challenge is not of wits or faculties, but of ways and methods, and the part I take upon myself is not that of a judge, but a guide.

XXXVII

One method of delivery alone remains to us; which is simply this: we must lead men to the particulars themselves, and their series and order; while men on their side must force themselves for a while to lay their notions by and begin to familiarize themselves with facts.

XXXVIII

The idols and false notions which are now in possession of the human understanding, and have taken deep root therein, not only so beset men's minds that truth can hardly find entrance, but even after entrance obtained, they will again in the very instauration[2] of the sciences meet and trouble us, unless men being forewarned of the danger fortify themselves as far as may be against their assaults.

XXXIX

There are four classes of Idols which beset men's minds. To these for distinction's sake I have assigned names,—calling the first class *Idols of*

[2]Renewal; restoration after decay.

the Tribe; the second, *Idols of the Cave;* the third, *Idols of the Market-place;* the fourth, *Idols of the Theatre.*

XLI

The *Idols of the Tribe* have their foundation in human nature itself, and in the tribe or race of men. For it is a false assertion that the sense of man is the measure of things. On the contrary, all perceptions as well of the sense as of the mind are according to the measure of the individual and not according to the measure of the universe. And the human understanding is like a false mirror, which, receiving rays irregularly, distorts and discolours the nature of things by mingling its own nature with it.

XLIX

The human understanding is no dry light, but receives an infusion from the will and affections; whence proceed sciences which may be called "sciences as one would." For what a man had rather were true he more readily believes. . . .

LI

The human understanding is of its own nature prone to abstractions and gives a substance and reality to things which are fleeting. But to resolve nature into abstractions is less to our purpose than to dissect her into parts; as did the school of Democritus, which went further into nature than the rest. Matter rather than forms should be the object of our attention, its configurations and changes of configuration, and simple action, and law of action or motion; for forms are figments of the human mind, unless you will call those laws of action forms.

LII

Such then are the idols which I call *Idols of the Tribe;* and which take their rise either from the homogeneity of the substance of the human spirit, or from its preoccupation, or from its narrowness, or from its restless motion, or from an infusion of the affections, or from the incompetency of the senses, or from the mode of impression.

LIII

The *Idols of the Cave* take their rise in the peculiar constitution, mental or bodily, of each individual; and also in education, habit, and accident. Of this kind there is a great number and variety; but I will instance those the pointing out of which contains the most important caution, and which have most effect in disturbing the clearness of the understanding.

LIV

Men become attached to certain particular sciences and speculations, either because they fancy themselves the authors and inventors thereof, or because they have bestowed the greatest pains upon them and become most habituated to them. But men of this kind, if they betake themselves to philosophy and contemplations of a general character, distort and colour them in obedience to their former fancies; a thing especially to be noticed in Aristotle, who made his natural philosophy a mere bond-servant to his logic, thereby rendering it contentious and well nigh useless. The race of chemists again out of a few experiments of the furnace have built up a fantastic philosophy, framed with reference to a few things; and Gilbert also, after he had employed himself most laboriously in the study and observation of the loadstone, proceeded at once to construct an entire system in accordance with his favourite subject.

LIX

But the *Idols of the Market-place* are the most troublesome of all: idols which have crept into the understanding through the alliances of words and names. For men believe that their reason governs words; but it is also true that words react on the understanding and this it is that has rendered philosophy and the sciences sophistical and inactive. Now words, being commonly framed and applied according to the capacity of the vulgar, follow those lines of division which are most obvious to the vulgar understanding. And whenever an understanding of greater acuteness or a more diligent observation would alter those lines to suit the true divisions of nature, words stand in the way and resist the change. Whence it comes to pass that the high and formal discussions of learned men end oftentimes in disputes about words and names; with which (according to the use and wisdom of the mathematicians) it would be more prudent to begin, and so by means of definitions reduce them to order. Yet even definitions cannot cure this evil in dealing with natural and material things; since the definitions themselves consist of words, and those words beget others: so that it is necessary to recur to individual instances, and those in due series and order; as I shall say presently when I come to the method and scheme for the formation of notions and axioms.

LXII

Idols of the Theatre, or of Systems, are many, and there can be and perhaps will be yet many more. For were it not that now for many ages men's minds have been busied with religion and theology; and were it not that civil governments, especially monarchies, have been averse to such novelties, even in matters speculative; so that men labour therein to the peril and harming of their fortunes,—not only unrewarded, but exposed also to contempt and envy; doubtless there would have arisen many other philosophical sects like to those which in great variety flourished once among the Greeks. For as on the phenomena of the heavens many hypotheses may be constructed, so likewise (and more also) many various dogmas may be set up and established on the phenomena of philosophy. And in the plays of this philosophical theatre you may observe the same thing which is found in the theatre of the poets, that stories invented for the stage are more compact and elegant, and more as one would wish them to be, than true stories out of history . . .

LXVIII

So much concerning the several classes of Idols, and their equipage: all of which must be renounced and put away with a fixed and solemn determination, and the understanding thoroughly freed and cleansed; the entrance into the kingdom of man, founded on the sciences, being not much other than the entrance into the kingdom of heaven, whereinto none may enter except as a little child.

"FRANCIS BACON THOUGHT THUS"[3]

(Ad Filios[4])

Pars Prima

1. FRANCIS BACON THOUGHT in this manner. The knowledge whereof the world is now possessed, especially that of nature, extendeth not to magnitude and certainty of works. The Physician pronounceth many diseases incurable, and faileth oft in the rest. The Alchemists wax old and die in hopes. The Magicians perform nothing that is permanent and profitable. The Mechanics take small light from natural philosophy, and do but spin

[3]Bacon is speaking of himself in the third person.
[4]This is written at the top of the page, in the left-hand corner, in Bacon's hand.

on their own little threads. Chance sometimes discovereth inventions; but that worketh not in years, but ages. So he saw well, that the inventions known are very unperfect; and that new are not like to be brought to light but in great length of time; and that those which are, came not to light by philosophy.

2. He thought also this state of knowledge was the worse, because men strive (against themselves) to save the credit of ignorance, and to satisfy themselves in this poverty. For the Physician, besides his cauteles[5] of practice, hath this general cautele of art, that he dischargeth the weakness of his art upon supposed impossibilities: neither can his art be condemned, when itself judgeth. That philosophy also, out of which the knowledge of physic, which now is in use, is hewed, receiveth certain positions and opinions, which (if they be well weighed) induce this persuasion, that no great works are to be expected from art, and the hand of man; as in particular that opinion, *that the heat of the sun and fire differ in kind;* and that other, *that Composition is the work of man, and Mixture is the work of nature,* and the like; all tending to the circumscription of man's power, and to artificial despair; killing in men, not only the comfort of[6] imagination but the industry of trial; only upon vain glory to have their art thought perfect, and that all is impossible that is not already found. The Alchemist dischargeth his art upon his own errors, either supposing a misunderstanding of the words of his authors, which maketh him listen after auricular traditions; or else a failing in the true proportions and scruples of practice, which maketh him renew infinitely his trials; and finding also that he lighteth upon some mean experiments and conclusions by the way, feedeth upon them, and magnifieth them to the most, and supplieth the rest in hopes. The Magician, when he findeth something (as he conceiveth) above nature effected, thinketh, when a breach is once made in nature, that it is all one to perform great things and small; not seeing that they are but subjects of a certain kind, wherein magic and superstition hath played in all times. The Mechanical person, if he can refine an invention, or put two or three observations or practices together in one, or couple things better with their use, or make the work in less or greater volume, taketh himself for an inventor. So he saw well, that men either persuade themselves of new inventions as of impossibilities; or else think they are already extant, but in secret and in few hands; or that they account of those little industries and additions, as of inventions: all of which turneth to the

[5]Artifices, tricks.

[6]*Of* is omitted in the MS.

averting of their minds from any just and constant labour to invent further in any quantity.

3. He thought also, when men did set before themselves the variety and perfection of works produced by mechanical arts, they are apt rather to admire the provisions of man, than to apprehend his wants; not considering, that the original inventions and conclusions of nature which are the life of all that variety, are not many nor deeply fetched; and that the rest is but the subtile and ruled motion of the instrument and hand; and that the shop therein is not unlike the library, which in such number of books containeth (for the far greater part) nothing but iterations, varied sometimes in form, but not new in substance. So he saw plainly, that opinion of store was a cause of want; and that both works and doctrines appear many and are few.

4. He thought also, that knowledge is uttered to men, in a form as if every thing were finished; for it is reduced into arts and methods, which in their divisions do seem to include all that may be. And how weakly soever the parts are filled, yet they carry the show and reason of a total; and thereby the writings of some received authors go for the very art: whereas antiquity used to deliver the knowledge which the mind of man had gathered, in observations, aphorisms, or short and dispersed sentences, or small tractates of some parts that they had diligently meditated and laboured; which did invite men, both to ponder that which was invented, and to add and supply further. But now sciences are delivered to be believed and accepted, and not to be examined and further discovered; and the succession is between master and disciple, and not between inventor and continuer or advanced: and therefore sciences stand at a stay, and have done for many ages, and that which is positive is fixed, and that which is question is kept question, so as the columns of no further proceeding are pitched. And therefore he saw plainly, men had cut themselves off from further invention; and that it is no marvel that that is not obtained, which hath not been attempted, but rather shut out and debarred.

5. He thought also, that knowledge is almost generally sought either for delight and satisfaction, or for gain and profession, or for credit and ornament, and that every one of these are as Atalanta's balls, which hinder the race of invention. For men are so far in these courses from seeking to increase the mass of knowledge, as of that mass which is they will take no more than will serve their turn: and if any one amongst so many seeketh knowledge for itself, yet he rather seeketh to know the variety of things, than to discern of the truth and causes of them; and if

his inquisition be yet more severe, yet it tendeth rather to judgment than to invention; and rather to discover truth in controversy than new matter; and if his heart be so large as he propoundeth to himself further discovery or invention, yet it is rather of new discourse and speculation of causes, than of effects and operations: and as for those that have so much in their mouths, action and use and practice and the referring of sciences thereunto, they mean it of application of that which is known, and not of a discovery of that which is unknown. So he saw plainly, that this mark, namely invention of further means to endow the condition and life of man with new powers or works, was almost never yet set up and resolved in man's intention and inquiry.

6. He thought also, that, amongst other knowledges, natural philosophy hath been the least followed and laboured. For since the Christian faith, the greatest number of wits have been employed, and the greatest helps and rewards have been converted upon divinity. And beforetime likewise, the greatest part of the studies of philosophers was consumed in moral philosophy, which was as the heathen divinity. And in both times a great part of the best wits betook themselves to law, pleadings, and causes of estate; especially in the time of the greatness of the Romans, who by reason of their large empire needed the service of all their able men for civil business. And the time amongst the Grecians in which natural philosophy seemed most to flourish, was but a short space; and that also rather abused in differing sects and conflicts of opinions, than profitably spent: since which time, natural philosophy was never any profession, nor never possessed any whole man, except perchance some monk in a cloister, or some gentleman in the country, and that very rarely; but became a science of passage, to season a little young and unripe wits, and to serve for an introduction to other arts, specially physic and the practical mathematics. So as he saw plainly, that natural philosophy hath been intended by few persons, and in them hath occupied the least part of their time, and that in the weakest of their age and judgment.

7. He thought also, how great opposition and prejudice natural philosophy had received by superstition, and the immoderate and blind zeal of religion; for he found that some of the Grecians which first gave the reason of thunder, had been condemned of impiety; and that the cosmographers which first discovered and described the roundness of the earth, and the consequence thereof touching the *Antipodes,* were not much otherwise censured by the ancient fathers of the Christian Church; and that the case is now much worse, in regard of the boldness of the

schoolmen and their dependances in the monasteries, who having made divinity into an art, have almost incorporated the contentious philosophy of Aristotle into the body of Christian religion. And generally he perceived in men of devout simplicity, this opinion, that the secrets of nature were the secrets of God and part of that glory whereinto the mind of man if it seek to press shall be oppressed; and that the desire in men to attain to so great and hidden knowledge, hath a resemblance with that temptation which caused the original fall: and on the other side in men of a devout policy, he noted an inclination to have the people depend upon God the more, when they are less acquainted with second causes; and to have no stirring in philosophy, lest it may lead to an innovation in divinity, or else should discover matter of further contradiction to divinity. But in this part resorting to the authority of the Scriptures, and holy examples, and to reason, he rested not satisfied alone, but much confirmed. For first he considered that the knowledge of nature, by the light whereof man discerned of every living creature, and imposed names according to their propriety, was not the occasion of the fall; but the moral knowledge of good and evil, affected to the end to depend no more upon God's commandments, but for man to direct himself; neither could he find in any Scripture, that the inquiry and science of man in any thing, under the mysteries of the Deity, is determined and restrained, but contrariwise allowed and provoked; for concerning all other knowledge the Scripture pronounceth, *That it is the glory of God to conceal, but it is the glory of man* (or of the king, for the king is but the excellency of man) *to invent;* and again, *The spirit of man is as the lamp of God, wherewith he searcheth every secret;* and again most effectually, *That God hath made all things beautiful and decent, according to the return of their seasons; also that he hath set the world in man's heart, and yet man cannot find out the work which God worketh from the beginning to the end;* shewing that the heart of man is a continent of that concave or capacity, wherein the content of the world (that is, all forms of the creatures and whatsoever is not God) may be placed or received; and complaining that through the variety of things and vicissitudes of times (which are but impediments and not impuissances) man cannot accomplish his invention. In precedent also he set before his eyes, that in those few memorials before the flood, the Scripture honoureth the name of the inventors of music and works in metal; that Moses had this addition of praise, that he was seen in all the learning of the Egyptians; that Solomon,[7] in his grant of wisdom from God, had contained as a

[7] So spelled in MS.

branch thereof, that knowledge whereby he wrote a natural history of all verdor, from the cedar to the moss, and of all that breatheth; that the book of Job, and many places of the prophets, have great aspersion of natural philosophy; that the Church in the bosom and lap thereof, in the greatest injuries of times, ever preserved (as holy relics) the books of philosophy and all heathen learning; and that when Gregory the bishop of Rome became adverse and unjust to the memory of heathen antiquity, it was censured for pusillanimity in him, and the honour thereof soon after restored, and his own memory almost persecuted by his successor Sabinian; and lastly in our times and ages of our fathers, when Luther and the divines of the Protestant Church on the one side, and the Jesuits on the other, have enterprised to reform, the one the doctrine, the other the discipline and manners of the Church of Rome, he saw well how both of them have awaked to their great honour and succour all human learning. And for reason, there cannot be a greater and more evident than this; that all knowledge and specially that of natural philosophy tendeth highly to the magnifying of the glory of God in his power, providence, and benefits; appearing and engraven in his works, which without this knowledge are beheld but as through a veil; for if the heavens in the body of them do declare the glory of God to the eye, much more do they in the rule and decrees of them declare it to the understanding. And another reason not inferior to this is, that the same natural philosophy principally amongst all other human knowledge doth give an excellent defence against both extremes of religion, superstition and infidelity; for both it freeth the mind from a number of weak fancies and imaginations, and it raiseth the mind to acknowledge that to God all things are possible: for to that purpose speaketh our Saviour in that first canon against heresies delivered upon the case of the resurrection, *You err, not knowing the Scriptures, nor the power of God;* teaching that there are but two fountains of heresy, not knowing the will of God revealed in the Scriptures, and not knowing the power of God revealed or at least made most sensible in his creatures. So as he saw well, that natural philosophy was of excellent use to the exaltation of the Divine Majesty; and that which is admirable, that being a remedy of superstition, it is nevertheless an help to faith. He saw likewise, that the former opinions to the prejudice thereof had no true ground; but must spring either out of mere ignorance, or out of an excess of devotion, to have divinity all in all, whereas it should be only above all (both which states of mind may be best pardoned); or else out of worse causes, namely out of envy, which is proud weakness and deserveth to be despised; or out of some mixture of imposture, to tell a lie for God's cause; or out of an impious diffidence, as if men should fear to discover some things in nature which might subvert faith. But still he saw well, howsoever these opinions are in right reason reproved, yet they leave not to be most effectual hindrances to natural philosophy and invention.

8. He thought also, that there wanted not great contrariety to the further discovery of sciences, in regard of the orders and customs of universities, and also in regard of common opinion. For in universities and colleges men's studies are almost confined to certain authors, from which if any dissenteth or propoundeth matter of redargution, it is enough to make him thought a person turbulent; whereas if it be well advised, there is a great difference to be made between matter contemplative and active. For in government change is suspected, though to the better; but it is natural to arts to be in perpetual agitation and growth; neither is the danger alike of new light, and of new motion or remove. And for vulgar and received opinions, nothing is more usual nor more usually complained of, than that it is imposed[8] for arrogancy and presumption for men to authorise themselves against antiquity and authors, towards whom envy is ceased, and reverence by time amortised; it not being considered what Aristotle himself did (upon whom the philosophy that now is chiefly dependeth); who came with a professed contradiction to all the world, and did put all his opinions upon his own authority and argument, and never so much as nameth an author but to confute and reprove him; and yet his success well fulfilled the observation of Him that said, *If a man come in his own name, him will you receive*. Men think likewise that if they should give themselves to the liberty of invention and travail of inquiry, that they shall light again upon some conceits and contemplations which have been formerly offered to the world, and have been put down by better, which have prevailed and brought them to oblivion; not seeing that howsoever the property and breeding of knowledges is in great and excellent wits, yet the estimation and price of them is in the multitude, or in the inclinations of princes and great persons meanly learned. So as those knowledges are like to be received and honoured, which have their foundation in the subtility or finest trial of common sense, or such as fill the imagination; and not such knowledge as is digged out of the hard mine of history and experience, and falleth out to be in some points as adverse to common sense or popular reason, as religion, or more. Which kind of knowledge, except it be delivered with strange advantages of eloquence and power, may be likely

[8] So in MS.: a miscopy, probably, for *imputed*.

to appear and disclose a little to the world and straight to vanish and shut again. So that time seemeth to be of the nature of a river or flood, that bringeth down to us that which is light and blown up, and sinketh and drowneth that which is solid and grave. So he saw well, that both in the state of religion, and in the administration of learning, and in common opinion, there were many and continual stops and traverses to the course of invention.

9. He thought also, that the invention of works and further possibility was prejudiced in a more special manner than that of speculative truth; for besides the impediments common to both, it hath by itself been notably hurt and discredited by the vain promises and pretences of Alchemy, Magic, Astrology, and such other arts, which (as they now pass) hold much more of imagination and belief than of sense and demonstration. But to use the poet's language, men ought to have remembered that although Ixion of a cloud in the likeness of Juno begat Centaurs and Chimaeras, yet Jupiter also of the true Juno begat Vulcan and Hebe. Neither is it just to deny credit to the greatness of the acts of Alexander, because the like or more strange have been feigned of an Amadis or an Arthur, or other fabulous worthies. But though this in true reason should be, and that men ought not to make a confusion of unbelief; yet he saw well it could not otherwise be in event, but that experience of untruth had made access to truth more difficult, and that the ignominy of vanity had abated all greatness of mind.

10. He thought also, there was found in the mind of man an affection naturally bred, and fortified and furthered by discourse and doctrine, which did pervert the true proceeding towards active and operative knowledge. This was a false estimation, that it should be as a diminution to the mind of man to be much conversant in experiences and particulars subject to sense and bound in matter, and which are laborious to search, ignoble to meditate, harsh to deliver, illiberal to practise, infinite as is supposed in number, and no ways accommodate to the glory of arts. This opinion or state of mind received much credit and strength by the school of Plato, who thinking that particulars rather revived the notions or excited the faculties of the mind, than merely informed; and having mingled his philosophy with superstition, which never favoureth the sense; extolleth too much the understanding of man in the inward light thereof. And again Aristotle's school, which giveth the due to the sense in assertion, denieth it in practice much more than that of Plato. For we see the schoolmen, Aristotle's succession, which were utterly ignorant of history, rested only upon agitation of wit; whereas Plato giveth good

example of inquiry by induction and view of particulars; though in such a wandering manner as is of no force or fruit. So that he saw well, that the supposition of the sufficiency of man's mind hath lost the means thereof.[9]

ON INVENTION

(From "The Advancement of Learning," Book II)

Invention is of two kinds, much differing; the one, of arts and sciences; and the other, of speech and arguments. The former of these I do report deficient; which seemeth to me to be such a deficience as if in the making of an inventory touching the estate of a defunct it should be set down *that there is no ready money*. For as money will fetch all other commodities, so this knowledge is that which should purchase all the rest. And like as the West Indies had never been discovered if the use of the mariner's needle had not been first discovered, though the one be vast regions and the other a small motion; so it cannot be found strange if sciences be no further discovered, if the art itself of invention and discovery hath been passed over.

That this part of knowledge is wanting, to my judgment standeth plainly confessed: for first, logic doth not pretend to invent sciences or the axioms of sciences, but passeth it over with a *cuique in sua arte credendum* [the knowledge that pertains to each art must be taken on trust from those that profess it]. And Celsus acknowledgeth it gravely, speaking of the empirical and dogmatical sects of physicians, *That medicines and cures were first found out, and then after the reasons and causes were discoursed; and not the causes first found out, and by light from them the medicines and cures discovered.*

[9]Here the MS. ends abruptly in the middle of the page. At the top is written in Bacon's hand: "The English as much as was parfited." The blank part of the last page seems to have formed the outside of a miscellaneous bundle, and bears the following docket, also in Bacon's hand, "Severall fragments of discourses."

Rules for Straight Thinking

RENÉ DESCARTES (1596–1650)

THE FRENCH PHILOSOPHER, mathematician, and soldier whose basic assertion was, "I think, therefore I am," did much of his best thinking while luxuriating dreamily in bed. There, for example, he caught the idea of analytic geometry, wedding algebraic equations and geometrical curves in a simple ceremony by plotting them on ruled paper according to a system of straight-line bases—now called Cartesian co-ordinates. Gifted with a sense of logic that enabled him to be wrong with confidence, Descartes attempted to explain the universe, in completely mechanical terms, as simply a gigantic machine which the Deity had constructed, set going, and found no occasion to bother with thereafter. Like Bacon, he argued that all knowledge had to be tested by experience and experiment. His "Discourse on Method," 1637, quoted here, contributed a great deal to the development of straight thinking along scientific lines.

French is the language of the original. The English translation, by John Veitch, is from Everyman's Library (Dutton and Dent).

"DISCOURSE ON METHOD"

GOOD SENSE is, of all things among men, the most equally distributed; for everyone thinks himself so abundantly provided with it that those even who are the most difficult to satisfy in everything else do not usually desire a larger measure of this quality than they already possess. And in this it is not likely that all are mistaken: the conviction is rather to be held as testifying that the power of judging aright and of distinguishing truth from error, which is properly what is called good sense or reason, is by nature equal in all men; and that the diversity of our opinions, consequently, does not arise from some being endowed with a larger share of reason than others, but solely from this, that we conduct our thoughts along different ways, and do not fix our attention on the same objects. For to be possessed of a vigorous mind is not enough; the prime requisite is rightly to apply it. The greatest minds, as they are capable of the highest excellences, are open likewise to the greatest aberrations; and those who travel very slowly may yet make far greater progress, provided they keep always to the straight road, than those who, while they run, forsake it.

For myself, I have never fancied my mind to be in any respect more perfect than those of the generality; on the contrary, I have often wished that I were equal to some others in promptitude of thought, or in clearness and distinctness of imagination, or in fullness and readiness of memory. . . .

I will not hesitate, however, to avow my belief that it has been my singular good fortune to have very early in life fallen in with certain tracks which have conducted me to considerations and maxims, of which I have formed a method that gives me the means, as I think, of gradually augmenting my knowledge, and of raising it by little and little to the highest point which the mediocrity of my talents and the brief duration of my life will permit me to reach. . . .

After all, it is possible I may be mistaken; and it is but a little copper and glass, perhaps, that I take for gold and diamonds. I know how very liable we are to delusion in what relates to ourselves, and also how much the judgments of our friends are to be suspected when given in our favor. But I shall endeavor in this discourse to describe the paths I have followed, and to delineate my life as in a picture, in order that each one may be able to judge of them for himself, and that in the general opinion entertained of them, as gathered from current report, I myself may have a new help toward instruction to be added to those I have been in the habit of employing.

My present design, then, is not to teach the method which each ought to follow for the right conduct of his reason, but solely to describe the way in which I have endeavored to conduct my own. They who set themselves to give precepts must of course regard themselves as possessed of greater skill than those to whom they prescribe; and if they err in the slightest particular they subject themselves to censure. But as this tract is put forth merely as a history, or, if you will, as a tale, in which, amid some examples worthy of imitation, there will be found, perhaps, as many more which it were advisable not to follow, I hope it will prove useful to some without being hurtful to any, and that my openness will find some favor with all.

From my childhood I have been familiar with letters; and as I was given to believe that by their help a clear and certain knowledge of all that is useful in life might be acquired, I was ardently desirous of instruction. But as soon as I had finished the entire course of study, at the close of which it is customary to be admitted into the order of the learned, I completely changed my opinion. For I found myself involved in so many doubts and errors that I was convinced I had advanced no farther in all my attempts at learning than the discovery at every turn of my own ignorance. And yet I was studying in one of the most celebrated schools in Europe, in which I thought there must be learned men, if such were anywhere to be found. I had been taught all that others learned there; and not contented with the sciences actually taught us, I had, in addition, read all the books that had fallen into my hands, treating of such branches as are esteemed the most curious and rare. I knew the judgment which others had formed of me; and I did not find that I was considered inferior to my fellows, although there were among them some who were already marked out to fill the places of our instructors. And, in fine, our age appeared to me as flourishing and as fertile in powerful minds as any preceding one. I was thus led to take the liberty of judging of all other men by myself, and of concluding that there was no science in existence that was of such a nature as I had previously been given to believe.

I still continued, however, to hold in esteem the studies of the schools. I was aware that the languages taught in them are necessary to the understanding of the writings of the ancients; that the grace of fable stirs the mind; that the memorable deeds of history elevate it; and, if read with discretion, aid in forming the judgment; that the perusal of all excellent books is, as it were, to interview with the noblest men of past ages, who have written them, and even a studied interview, in which are discovered to us only their choicest thoughts; that eloquence has incomparable force and beauty; that poesy has its ravishing graces and delights; that in the mathematics there are many refined discoveries eminently suited to gratify the inquisitive, as well as further all the arts and lessen the labor of man; that numerous highly useful precepts and exhortations to virtue are contained in treatises on morals; that theology points out the path to heaven; that philosophy affords the means of discoursing with an appearance of truth on all matters, and commands the admiration of the more simple; that jurisprudence, medicine, and the other sciences secure for their cultivators honors and riches; and, in fine, that it is useful to bestow some attention upon all, even upon those abounding the most in superstition and error, that we may be in a position to determine their real value and guard against being deceived.

But I believed that I had already given sufficient time to languages, and likewise to the reading of the writings of the ancients, to their histories and fables. For to hold converse with those of other ages and to travel are almost the same thing. . . .

I was especially delighted with the mathematics, on account of the certitude and evidence of their reasonings; but I had not as yet a precise knowledge of their true use; and thinking that they but contributed to the advancement of the mechanical arts, I was astonished that foundations, so strong and solid, should have had no loftier superstructure reared on them. On the other hand, I compared the disquisitions of the ancient moralists to very towering and magnificent palaces with no better foundation than sand and mud: they laud the virtues very highly and exhibit them as estimable far above anything on earth; but they give us no adequate criterion of virtue, and frequently that which they designate with so fine a name is but apathy, or pride, or despair, or parricide. . . .

Of philosophy I will say nothing, except that when I saw that it had been cultivated for many ages by the most distinguished men, and that yet there is not a single matter within its sphere which is not still in dispute, and nothing, therefore, which is above doubt, I did not presume to anticipate that my success would be greater in it than that of others; and further, when I considered the number of conflicting opinions touching a single matter that may be upheld by learned men, while there can be but one true, I reckoned as well-nigh false all that was only probable.

As to the other sciences, inasmuch as these borrow their principles from philosophy, I judged that no solid superstructures could be reared on foundations so infirm; and neither the honor nor the gain held out by them was sufficient to determine me to their cultivation: for I was not, thank heaven, in a condition which compelled me to make merchandise of science for the bettering of my fortune; and though I might not profess to scorn glory as a cynic, I yet made very slight account of that honor which I hoped to acquire only through fictitious titles. And, in fine, of false science I thought I knew the worth sufficiently to escape being deceived by the professions of an alchemist, the predictions of an astrologer, the impostures of a magician, or by the artifices and boasting of any of those who profess to know things of which they are ignorant.

For these reasons, as soon as my age permitted me to pass from under the control of my instructors, I entirely abandoned the study of letters and resolved no longer to seek any other science than the knowledge of myself, or of the great book of the world. I spent the remainder of my youth in traveling, in visiting courts and armies, in holding intercourse with men of different positions and ranks, in collecting varied experience, in proving myself in the different situations into which fortune threw me, and, above all, in making such reflection on the matter of my experience as to secure my improvement.

For it occurred to me that I should find much more truth in the reasonings of each individual with reference to the affairs in which he is personally interested, and the issue of which must presently punish him if he has judged amiss, than in those conducted by a man of letters in his study, regarding speculative matters that are of no practical moment, and followed by no consequences to himself, farther, perhaps, than that they foster his vanity the better the more remote they are from common sense; requiring, as they must in this case, the exercise of greater ingenuity and art to render them probable. In addition, I had always a most earnest desire to know how to distinguish the true from the false, in order that I might be able clearly to discriminate the right path in life and proceed in it with confidence.

It is true that, while busied only in considering the manners of other men, I found here, too, scarce any ground for settled conviction, and remarked hardly less contradiction among them than in the opinions of the philosophers. So that the greatest advantage I derived from the study consisted in this, that, observing many things which, however extravagant and ridiculous to our apprehension, are yet by common consent received and approved by other great nations, I learned to entertain too decided a belief in regard to nothing of the truth of which I had been persuaded merely by example and custom; and thus I gradually extricated myself from many errors powerful enough to darken our natural intelligence and incapacitate us in great measure from listening to reason. But after I had been occupied several years in thus studying the book of the world, and in essaying to gather some experience, I at length resolved to make myself an object of study and to employ all the powers of my mind in choosing the paths I ought to follow, an undertaking which was accompanied with greater success than it would have been had I never quitted my country or my books.

II

I was then in Germany, attracted thither by the wars in that country, which have not yet been brought to a termination; and as I was re-

turning to the Army from the coronation of the Emperor, the setting
in of winter arrested me in a locality where, as I found no society to
interest me, and was besides fortunately undisturbed by any cares or
passions, I remained the whole day in seclusion,[1] with full opportunity
to occupy my attention with my own thoughts. Of these one of the
very first that occurred to me was that there is seldom so much perfection in works composed of many separate parts, upon which different
hands had been employed, as in those completed by a single master.
Thus it is observable that the buildings which a single architect has
planned and executed are generally more elegant and commodious than
those which several have attempted to improve, by making old walls
serve for purposes for which they were not originally built. . . .

In the same way I thought that the sciences contained in books (such
of them, at least, as are made up of probable reasonings, without demonstrations), composed as they are of the opinions of many different
individuals massed together, are farther removed from truth than the
simple inferences which a man of good sense, using his natural and
unprejudiced judgment, draws respecting the matters of his experience. . . .

Hence it is that I cannot in any degree approve of those restless and
busy meddlers who, called neither by birth nor fortune to take part in
the management of public affairs, are yet always projecting reforms;
and if I thought that this tract contained aught which might justify
the suspicion that I was a victim of such folly, I would by no means
permit its publication. I have never contemplated anything higher than
the reformation of my own opinions and basing them on a foundation
wholly my own. And although my own satisfaction with my work has
led me to present here a draft of it, I do not by any means therefore
recommend to everyone else to make a similar attempt. . . .

But I had become aware, even so early as during my college life, that
no opinion, however absurd and incredible, can be imagined which has
not been maintained by some one of the philosophers; and afterwards
in the course of my travels I remarked that all those whose opinions
are decidedly repugnant to ours are not on that account barbarians and
savages, but on the contrary that many of these nations make an equally
good, if not a better, use of their reason than we do. I took into account
also the very different character which a person brought up from infancy in France or Germany exhibits from that which, with the same
mind originally, this individual would have possessed had he lived al-

---

[1]Literally, in a room heated by means of a stove.

ways among the Chinese or with savages, and the circumstance that in dress itself the fashion which pleased us ten years ago, and which may again, perhaps, be received into favor before ten years have gone, appears to us at this moment extravagant and ridiculous. I was thus led to infer that the ground of our opinions is far more custom and example than any certain knowledge. And, finally, although such be the ground of our opinions, I remarked that a plurality of suffrages is no guarantee of truth where it is at all of difficult discovery, as in such cases it is much more likely that it will be found by one than by many. I could, however, select from the crowd no one whose opinions seemed worthy of preference, and thus I found myself constrained, as it were, to use my own reason in the conduct of my life. . . .

Among the branches of philosophy I had, at an earlier period, given some attention to logic, and among those of the mathematics to geometrical analysis and algebra—three arts or sciences which ought, as I conceived, to contribute something to my design. But, on examination, I found that, as for logic, its syllogisms and the majority of its other precepts are of avail rather in the communication of what we already know, or even as the art of Lully, in speaking without judgment of things of which we are ignorant, than in the investigation of the unknown; and although this science contains indeed a number of correct and very excellent precepts, there are, nevertheless, so many others, and these either injurious or superfluous, mingled with the former, that it is almost quite as difficult to effect a severance of the true from the false as it is to extract a Diana or a Minerva from a rough block of marble.

Then as to the analysis of the ancients and the algebra of the moderns, besides that they embrace only matters highly abstract and, to appearance, of no use, the former is so exclusively restricted to the consideration of figures that it can exercise the understanding only on condition of greatly fatiguing the imagination; and in the latter there is so complete a subjection to certain rules and formulas that there results an art full of confusion and obscurity calculated to embarrass, instead of a science fitted to cultivate the mind. By these considerations I was induced to seek some other method which would comprise the advantages of the three and be exempt from their defects. And as a multitude of laws often only hampers justice, so that a state is best governed when, with few laws, these are rigidly administered; in like manner, instead of the great number of precepts of which logic is composed. I believe that the four following would prove perfectly sufficient for me, provided I took the firm and unwavering resolution never in a single instance to fail in observing them.

Four Rules for Straight Thinking

The *first* was never to accept anything for true which I did not clearly know to be such; that is to say, carefully to avoid precipitancy and prejudice, and to comprise nothing more in my judgment than what was presented to my mind so clearly and distinctly as to exclude all ground of doubt.

The *second,* to divide each of the difficulties under examination into as many parts as possible and as might be necessary for its adequate solution.

The *third,* to conduct my thoughts in such order that, by commencing with objects the simplest and easiest to know, I might ascend by little and little, and, as it were, step by step, to the knowledge of the more complex; assigning in thought a certain order even to those objects which in their own nature do not stand in a relation of antecedence and sequence.

And the *last,* in every case to make enumerations so complete, and reviews so general, that I might be assured that nothing was omitted.

The long chains of simple and easy reasonings by means of which geometers are accustomed to reach the conclusions of their most difficult demonstrations had led me to imagine that all things, to the knowledge of which man is competent, are mutually connected in the same way, and that there is nothing so far removed from us as to be beyond our reach, or so hidden that we cannot discover it, provided only we abstain from accepting the false for the true, and always preserve in our thoughts the order necessary for the deduction of one truth from another. And I had little difficulty in determining the objects with which it was necessary to commence, for I was already persuaded that it must be with the simplest and easiest to know, and, considering that of all those who have hitherto sought truth in the sciences, the mathematicians alone have been able to find any demonstrations, that is, any certain and evident reasons, I did not doubt but that such must have been the rule of their investigations.

I resolved to commence, therefore, with the examination of the simplest objects, not anticipating, however, from this any other advantage than that to be found in accustoming my mind to the love and nourishment of truth, and to a distaste for all such reasonings as were unsound. But I had no intention on that account of attempting to master all the particular sciences commonly denominated mathematics:

but observing that, however different their objects, they all agree in considering only the various relations or proportions subsisting among those objects, I thought it best for my purpose to consider these proportions in the most general form possible, without referring them to any objects in particular, except such as would most facilitate the knowledge of them, and without by any means restricting them to these, that afterwards I might thus be the better able to apply them to every other class of objects to which they are legitimately applicable. Perceiving further that in order to understand these relations I should sometimes have to consider them one by one, and sometimes only to bear them in mind, or embrace them in the aggregate, I thought that, in order the better to consider them individually, I should view them as subsisting between straight lines, than which I could find no objects more simple or capable of being more distinctly represented to my imagination and senses; and on the other hand, that in order to retain them in the memory, or embrace an aggregate of many, I should express them by certain characters the briefest possible. In this way I believed that I could borrow all that was best both in geometrical analysis and in algebra, and correct all the defects of the one by help of the other.

And, in point of fact, the accurate observance of these few precepts gave me, I take the liberty of saying, such ease in unraveling all the questions embraced in these two sciences that in the two or three months I devoted to their examination not only did I reach solutions of questions I had formerly deemed exceedingly difficult, but even as regards questions of the solution of which I continued ignorant I was enabled, as it appeared to me, to determine the means whereby, and the extent to which, a solution was possible; results attributable to the circumstance that I commenced with the simplest and most general truths, and that thus each truth discovered was a rule available in the discovery of subsequent ones. . . .

So that I might not remain irresolute in my actions, while my reason compelled me to suspend my judgment, and that I might not be prevented from living thenceforward in the greatest possible felicity, I formed a provisory code of morals, composed of three or four maxims, with which I am desirous to make you acquainted.

DESCARTES' CODE OF MORALS

The *first* was to obey the laws and customs of my country, adhering firmly to the faith in which, by the grace of God, I had been educated from my childhood, and regulating my conduct in every other matter according to the most moderate opinions, and the farthest removed from extremes, which should happen to be adopted in practice with general consent of the most judicious of those among whom I might be living. . . .

My *second* maxim was to be as firm and resolute in my actions as I was able, and not to adhere less steadfastly to the most doubtful opinions, when once adopted, than if they had been highly certain; imitating in this the example of travelers who, when they have lost their way in a forest, ought not to wander from side to side, far less remain in one place, but proceed constantly toward the same side in as straight a line as possible, without changing their direction for slight reasons, although perhaps it might be chance alone which at first determined the selection; for in this way, if they do not exactly reach the point they desire, they will come at least in the end to some place that will probably be preferable to the middle of a forest. In the same way, since in action it frequently happens that no delay is permissible, it is very certain that, when it is not in our power to determine what is true, we ought to act according to what is most probable; and even although we should not remark a greater probability in one opinion than in another, we ought notwithstanding to choose one or the other, and afterwards consider it, insofar as it relates to practice, as no longer dubious, but manifestly true and certain, since the reason by which our choice has been determined is itself possessed of these qualities. This principle was sufficient thenceforward to rid me of all those repentings and pangs of remorse that usually disturb the consciences of such feeble and uncertain minds as, destitute of any clear and determinate principle of choice, allow themselves one day to adopt a course of action as the best, which they abandon the next, as the opposite.

My *third* maxim was to endeavor always to conquer myself rather than fortune, and change my desires rather than the order of the world, and in general accustom myself to the persuasion that, except our own thoughts, there is nothing absolutely in our power; so that when we have done our best in respect of things external to us, all wherein we fail of success is to be held, as regards us, absolutely impossible: and this single principle seemed to me sufficient to prevent me from desiring for the future anything which I could not obtain, and thus render me contented; for since our will naturally seeks those objects alone which the understanding represents as in some way possible of attainment, it is plain that if we consider all external goods as equally beyond our power we shall no more regret the absence of such goods as seen due to our birth, when deprived of them without any fault of ours, than our not possessing the kingdoms of China or Mexico; and thus making, so to speak, a virtue of necessity, we shall no more desire health in disease, or freedom in imprisonment, than we now do bodies incorruptible as diamonds, or the wings of birds to fly with. But I confess there is need of prolonged discipline and frequently repeated meditation to accustom the mind to view all objects in this light. . . .

Having thus provided myself with these maxims, and having placed them in reserve along with the truths of faith, which have ever occupied the first place in my belief, I came to the conclusion that I might with freedom set about ridding myself of what remained of my opinions. And, inasmuch as I hoped to be better able successfully to accomplish this work by holding intercourse with mankind than by remaining longer shut up in the retirement where these thoughts had occurred to me, I betook me again to traveling before the winter was well ended. And during the nine subsequent years I did nothing but roam from one place to another, desirous of being a spectator rather than an actor in the plays exhibited on the theater of the world; and, as I made it my business in each matter to reflect particularly upon what might fairly be doubted and prove a source of error, I gradually rooted out from my mind all the errors which had hitherto crept into it.

Not that in this I imitated the skeptics who doubt only that they may doubt, and seek nothing beyond uncertainty itself; for, on the contrary, my design was singly to find ground of assurance and cast aside the loose earth and sand, that I might reach the rock or the clay. In this, as appears to me, I was successful enough; for, since I endeavored to discover the falsehood or incertitude of the propositions I examined, not by feeble conjectures, but by clear and certain reasonings, I met with nothing so doubtful as not to yield some conclusion of adequate certainty, although this were merely the inference, that the matter in question contained nothing certain. And, just as in pulling down an old house, we usually reserve the ruins to contribute toward the erection, so, in destroying such of my opinions as I judged to be ill founded, I made a variety of observations and acquired an amount of experience of which I availed myself in the establishment of more certain. And further, I continued to exercise myself in the method I had prescribed; for, besides taking care in general to conduct all my thoughts according to its rules, I reserved some hours from time to time which I expressly devoted to the employment of the method in the solution of mathematical difficulties, or even in the solution likewise of some questions belonging to other sciences, but which, by my having detached them from such principles of these sciences as were of inadequate certainty, were rendered almost mathematical.

A First Step in Meteorology

BLAISE PASCAL (1623-62)

THE "GREAT MORALIST," Blaise Pascal, was also a great scientist. His "Thoughts" ("*Pensées*") and "Letters"—in which he said, "Pardon the length of this letter; I have not time to write you a short one"—are gems of French literature. Yet the sincere Jansenist turned to the dice game and the trials of the gaming table to develop, after Cardan, an unscrupulous Italian mathematician, and with Fermat, a cryptic French attorney, the mathematical theory of probability upon which much of modern scientific thinking rests.

Current weather forecasting and present-day meteorology, upon which the fortunes of aerial warfare depend, could hardly have been born until someone had established what Pascal—with the help of his brother-in-law, F. Périer—proved in the "Great Experiment" on the Puy de Dôme; namely, the weight of the mass of the air. Here quoted is "the story of the great experiment," published posthumously in 1663. Employing Torricelli's recently invented barometer, Pascal slew forever the myth that "nature abhors a vacuum."

Pascal was a child prodigy; before he was eleven he had taught himself geometry, drawing figures with charcoal on the tiles of his playroom and giving his own names to the lines and curves which his doting father had forbidden him to study. A great mathematician, inventor of the adding (calculating) machine and the hydraulic press, Pascal has been honored by having a law (of fluid pressure), a triangle, and a mystic hexagram named after him.

French was the language which Pascal glorified. The English translation, by I. H. B. and A. G. H. Spiers, was published in "The Physical Treatises of Pascal" (Columbia University Press, 1937).

THE STORY OF THE GREAT EXPERIMENT ON THE WEIGHT OF THE MASS OF THE AIR

DEVISED BY MONSIEUR B. PASCAL

*in pursuance of the completion of the Treatise
promised in his shorter work on the Vacuum*

*And carried out by Monsieur F. P. on one of
the highest mountains in Auvergne, commonly
known as Le Puy de Dôme.*

THE MASS OF THE AIR HAS WEIGHT AND WITH THIS WEIGHT PRESSES UPON ALL THE BODIES IT SURROUNDS

IT IS no longer open to discussion that the air has weight. It is common knowledge that a balloon is heavier when inflated than when empty, which is proof enough. For if the air were light, the more the balloon was inflated the lighter the whole would be, since there would be more air in it. But since, on the contrary, when more air is put in, the whole becomes heavier, it follows that each part has a weight of its own, and consequently that the air has weight.

Whoever wishes for more elaborate proofs can find them in the writings of those who have devoted special treatises to the subject.

If it be objected that air is light when pure, but that the air that surrounds us is not pure, being mixed with vapor and impurities which alone give it weight, my answer is brief: I am not acquainted with "pure" air, and believe that it might be very difficult to find it. But throughout this treatise I am referring solely to the air such as we breathe, regardless of its component elements. Whether it be compound or simple, that is the body which I call the air, and which I declare to have weight. This cannot be denied, and I require nothing more for my further proof. . . .

If there were collected a great bulk of wool, say twenty or thirty fathoms high, this mass would be compressed by its own weight; the bottom layers would be far more compressed than the middle or top layers, because they are pressed by a greater quantity of wool. Similarly the mass of the air, which is a compressible and heavy body like wool, is compressed by its own weight, and the air at the bottom, in the lowlands, is far more compressed than the higher layers on the mountain tops, because it bears a greater load of air.

In the case of that bulk of wool, if a handful of it were taken from the bottom layer, compressed as it is, and lifted, in the same state of compression, to the middle of the mass, it would expand of its own accord; for it would then be nearer the top and subjected there to the pressure of a smaller quantity of wool. Similarly if a body of air, as found here below in its natural state of compression, were by some device transferred to a mountaintop, it would necessarily expand and come to the condition of the air around it on the mountain; for then it would bear a lesser weight of air than it did below. Hence if a balloon, only half inflated—not fully so, as they generally are—were carried up a mountain, it would necessarily be more inflated at the mountaintop, and would expand in the degree to which it was less burdened. The difference will be visible, provided the quantity of air along the mountain slope, from the pressure of which it is now relieved, has a weight great enough to cause a sensible effect.

THE STORY OF THE GREAT EXPERIMENT ON THE EQUILIBRIUM OF FLUIDS

At the time when I published my pamphlet entitled "New Experiments touching the Vacuum, et cetera," I used the phrase "Abhorrence of the Vacuum" because it was universally accepted and because I had not then any convincing evidences against it; but nevertheless sensed certain difficulties which made me doubt the truth of that conception. To clarify these doubts, I conceived at that very time the experiment here described, which I hoped would yield definite knowledge as a ground for my opinion. I have called it the Great Experiment on the Equilibrium of Fluids, because it is the most conclusive of all that can be made on this subject, inasmuch as it shows the equilibrium of air and quicksilver, which are, respectively, the lightest and the heaviest of all the fluids known in nature.

But since it was impossible to carry out this experiment here, in the city of Paris, and because there are very few places in France that are suitable for this purpose and the town of Clermont in Auvergne is one of the most convenient of these, I requested my brother-in-law, Monsieur Périer, counselor in the Court of Aids in Auvergne, to be so kind as to conduct it there. What my difficulties were and what the experiment is will be made clear by the accompanying letter concerning it which I wrote to him at the time.

COPY OF THE LETTER OF MONSIEUR PASCAL THE YOUNGER TO MONSIEUR PÉRIER,
NOVEMBER 15, 1647

Monsieur,

I should not break in upon the constant calls made on you by your official duties to submit to you considerations of physical science, were I not fully aware that they will be a refreshment to you in your hours of relaxation, and will be as entertaining to you as they would be burdensome to others. I hesitate the less to do this, also, because I know full well the delight you take in these pursuits. You will find here but a continuation of our former discussions concerning the vacuum. You know the views of the philosophers on this subject. They have all endorsed the principle that nature abhors a vacuum, and most of them have gone further and maintained that nature cannot admit of it and would perish sooner than suffer it. Thus opinions have been divided: some have been content to say only that nature abhors a vacuum, others have maintained that she could not tolerate it. I have tried in my pamphlet on the vacuum to refute the latter opinion, and I believe that the experiments recorded there suffice to show indubitably that nature can, and does, tolerate any amount of space empty of any of the substances that we are acquainted with, and that are perceptible to our senses. I am now engaged in testing the truth of the former statement, namely, that nature abhors a vacuum, and am trying to find experimental ways to show whether the effects ascribed to the abhorrence of a vacuum are really attributable to that abhorrence or to the weight and pressure of the air. . . .

To this end I have devised one that is in itself sufficient to give us the light we seek if it can be carried out with accuracy. This is to perform the usual experiment with a vacuum several times over in one day, with the same tube and with the same quicksilver, sometimes at the base and sometimes at the summit of a mountain at least five or six hundred fathoms high, in order to ascertain whether the height of the quicksilver suspended in the tube will be the same or different in the two situations. You see at once, doubtless, that such an experiment is decisive. If it happens that the height of the quicksilver is less at the top than at the base of the mountain (as I have many reasons to believe it is, although all who have studied the matter are of the opposite opinion), it follows of necessity that the weight and pressure of the air is the sole cause of this suspension of the quicksilver, and not the abhorrence of a vacuum: for it is quite certain that there is much more air that presses on the foot of the mountain than there is on its summit, and one cannot well say that nature abhors a vacuum more at the foot of the mountain than at its summit.

But since difficulty, as a rule, attends great achievement, I foresee much trouble in carrying out this plan, because for the purpose a very high mountain must be selected, in the vicinity of a town where a person may be found who is competent to bring to bear upon the task all the precision of measurement that it demands. If the mountain were very distant it would be difficult to carry to it the vessels, the quicksilver, the tubes, and many other necessary accessories, and to undertake the many laborious journeys that would be necessary in order to find upon these heights the suitably calm weather which is seldom to be met with there. And since it is as uncommon to find outside of Paris persons who have these qualifications as it is to find places that meet the conditions, I have been highly gratified by my good fortune in having on this occasion found both; for our town of Clermont is at the foot of the lofty Puy de Dôme, and I hope that you will be good enough to grant me the favor of conducting the experiment yourself. Being assured of this, I have encouraged all our interested Parisians to expect it, among others the Rev. Father Mersenne, who has already pledged himself by letters to Italy, Poland, Sweden, Holland, and elsewhere, to convey the result to the friends his great merit has won him in those countries. I say nothing about the means of performing the experiment, because I well know that you will omit none of the precautions necessary to carry it out with precision.

I would only beg of you to choose the earliest date you can, and to excuse the liberty I am taking, to which I am driven by my impatience to hear of the success of the experiment.

Monsieur,
Your very humble and very obedient servant,

PASCAL

M. Périer received this letter at Moulins, where he was discharging duties which forbade him full freedom of action. Anxious though he was to carry out the experiment at once, he was not at liberty to do so before the month of September last.

The reasons for this delay, the story of the experiment, and the precision with which he conducted it are made plain by the following letter with which he honored me.

COPY OF THE LETTER SENT BY MONSIEUR PÉRIER TO MONSIEUR PASCAL THE
YOUNGER, SEPTEMBER 22, 1648

Monsieur,
At last I have carried out the experiment you have so long wished for. I would have given you this satisfaction before now, but have been prevented both by the duties I have had to perform in Bourbonnais, and by the fact that ever since my return the Puy de Dôme, where the experiment is to be made, has been so wrapped in snow and fog that even in this season, which here is the finest of the year, there was hardly a day when one could see its summit, which is usually in the clouds and sometimes above them even while

the weather is clear in the plains. I was unable to adjust my own convenience to a favorable state of the weather before the nineteenth of this month. But my good fortune in performing the experiment on that day has amply repaid me for the slight vexation caused by so many unavoidable delays.

I send you herewith a complete and faithful account of it, in which you will find evidence of the painstaking care I bestowed upon the undertaking, which I thought it proper to carry out in the presence of a few men who are as learned as they are irreproachably honest, so that the sincerity of their testimony should leave no doubt as to the certainty of the experiment.

COPY OF THE ACCOUNT OF THE EXPERIMENT SUBMITTED BY MONSIEUR PÉRIER

The weather on Saturday last, the nineteenth of this month, was very unsettled. At about five o'clock in the morning, however, it seemed sufficiently clear; and since the summit of the Puy de Dôme was then visible, I decided to go there to make the attempt. To that end I notified several people of standing in this town of Clermont, who had asked me to let them know when I would make the ascent. Of this company some were clerics, others laymen. Among the clerics was the Very Rev. Father Bannier, one of the Minim Fathers of this city, who has on several occasions been "corrector" (that is, father superior), and Monsieur Mosnier, canon of the Cathedral Church of this city; among the laymen were Messieurs la Ville and Begon, councilors to the Court of Aids, and Monsieur la Porte, a doctor of medicine, practicing here. All these men are very able, not only in the practice of their professions, but also in every field of intellectual interest. It was a delight to have them with me in this fine work.

On that day, therefore, at eight o'clock in the morning, we started off all together for the garden of the Minim Fathers, which is almost the lowest spot in the town, and there began the experiment in this manner.

First, I poured into a vessel six pounds of quicksilver which I had rectified during the three days preceding; and having taken glass tubes of the same size, each four feet long and hermetically sealed at one end but open at the other, I placed them in the same vessel and carried out with each of them the usual vacuum experiment. Then, having set them up side by side without lifting them out of the vessel, I found that the quicksilver left in each of them stood at the same level, which was twenty-six inches and three and a half lines above the surface of the quicksilver in the vessel. I repeated this experiment twice at this same spot, in the same tubes, with the same quicksilver, and in the same vessel; and found in each case that the quicksilver in the two tubes stood at the same horizontal level, and at the same height as in the first trial.

That done, I fixed one of the tubes permanently in its vessel for continuous experiment. I marked on the glass the height of the quicksilver, and leaving that tube where it stood, I requested the Rev. Father Chastin, one of the brothers of the house, a man as pious as he is capable, and one who reasons very well upon these matters, to be so good as to observe from time to time all day any changes that might occur. With the other tube and a portion of the same quicksilver, I then proceeded with all these gentlemen to the top of the Puy de Dôme, some five hundred fathoms above the convent. There, after I had made the same experiments in the same way that I had made them at the Minims', we found that there remained in the tube a height of only twenty-three inches and two lines of quicksilver; whereas in the same tube, at the Minims', we had found a height of twenty-six inches and three and a half lines. Thus between the heights of the quicksilver in the two experiments there proved to be a difference of three inches one line and a half. We were so carried away with wonder and delight, and our surprise was so great, that we wished, for our own satisfaction, to repeat the experiment. So I carried it out with the greatest care five times more at different points on the summit of the mountain, once in the shelter of the little chapel that stands there, once in the open, once shielded from the wind, once in the wind, once in fine weather, once in the rain and fog which visited us occasionally. Each time I most carefully rid the tube of air; and in all these experiments we invariably found the same height of quicksilver. This was twenty-three inches, and two lines, which yields the same discrepancy of three inches, one line and a half in comparison with the twenty-six inches, three lines and a half which had been found at the Minims'. This satisfied us fully.

Later, on the way down at a spot called Lafon de l'Arbre, far above the Minims' but much farther below the top of the mountain, I repeated the same experiment, still with the same tube, the same quicksilver, and the same vessel, and there found that the height of the quicksilver left in the tube was twenty-five inches. I repeated it a second time at the same spot; and Monsieur Mosnier, one of those previously mentioned, having the curiosity to perform it himself, then did so again, at the same spot. All these experiments yielded the same height of twenty-five inches, which is one inch, three lines and a half less than that which we had found at the Minims', and one inch and ten lines more than we had just found at the top of the Puy de Dôme. It increased our satisfaction not a little to observe in this way that the height of the quicksilver diminished with the altitude of the site.

On my return to the Minims' I found that the [quicksilver in the] vessel I had left there in continuous operation was at the same height at which I had left it, that is, at twenty-six inches, three lines and a half; and the Rev. Father Chastin, who had remained there as observer, reported to us that no change had occurred during the whole day, although the weather had been very unsettled, now clear and still, now rainy, now very foggy, and now windy.

Here I repeated the experiment with the tube I had carried to the Puy de Dôme, but in the vessel in which the tube used for the continuous experiment was standing. I found that the quicksilver was at the same level in both tubes and exactly at the height of twenty-six inches, three lines and a half, at which it had stood that morning in this same tube, and as it had stood all day in the tube used for the continuous experiment.

I repeated it again a last time, not only in the same tube I had used on the Puy de Dôme, but also with the same quicksilver and in the same vessel that I had carried up the mountain; and again I found the quicksilver at the same height of twenty-six inches, three lines and a half which I had observed in the morning, and thus finally verified the certainty of our results. . . .

If you find any obscurities in this recital I shall be able in a few days to clear them up in conversation with you, since I am about to take a little trip to Paris, when I shall assure you that I am,

Monsieur,

Your very humble and very affectionate servant,

PÉRIER

This narrative cleared up all my difficulties and, I am free to say, afforded me great satisfaction. Seeing that a difference of twenty fathoms of altitude made a difference of two lines in the height of the quicksilver, and six or seven fathoms one of about half a line, facts which it was easy for me to verify in this city, I made the usual vacuum experiment on the top and at the base of the tower of St. Jacques de la Boucherie, which is some twenty-four or twenty-five fathoms high, and found a difference of more than two lines in the height of the quicksilver. I then repeated it in a private house ninety steps high, and found a clearly perceptible difference of half a line. These results are in perfect agreement with those given in M. Périer's narrative.

Any who care to do so, may, for themselves, confirm them at their pleasure.

CONSEQUENCES

From this experiment many inferences may be drawn, such as:

A method of ascertaining whether two places are at the same altitude, that is to say, equally distant from the center of the earth, or which of the two is the higher, however far apart they may be, even at antipodes—which would be impossible by any other means.

The unreliability of the thermometer in marking degrees of heat (which is not commonly recognized), as is shown by the fact that its liquid sometimes rises when the heat increases and sometimes, on the contrary, falls when the heat decreases, even though the thermometer be kept always in the same location.

Proof of the inequality of the pressure of the air, which, at the same degree of heat, is always greater in the lowest places.

The Speed and Character of Light

CHRISTIAN HUYGENS (1629-95)

EVERY TICK of a "grandfather's clock" pays tribute to the mathematical and mechanical ingenuity of the Dutch lens grinder, astronomer, and pioneer physicist, Christian Huygens, who first (1673) successfully devised a practical means of making a pendulum keep time—the pendulum clock. The importance of accurate time measurement in the development of scientific experiment cannot be overemphasized. Other crucial scientific problems to which he attended were the speed and nature of light, discussed in his "Treatise on Light" ("*Traité de la lumière*"), delivered before the French Academy, 1678, published 1690, and quoted here. In this slender book he first named "the ether," the "medium" through which light waves, radio waves, and cosmic rays all travel. We shall meet this troublesome "medium" again in the advanced works of Hertz and Maxwell. As an astronomer, working with his own powerful telescopes, he first discovered a satellite of Saturn and explained the nature of its rings.

The wave theory of light, first set forth by Huygens, was not accepted for over one hundred years; not until the optical work of Thomas Young (1773-1829), many-sided English physician who found the key to Egyptian hieroglyphics in the Rosetta stone, and the diffraction experiments of A. J. Fresnel (1788-1827), French physicist, revived Huygens' theory to explain "interference" of light rays. These men upset the "corpuscular" theory of light, which the authority of Isaac Newton upheld until their day. Nowadays (see Schroedinger) it appears that both Newton and Huygens were right.

French is the language of the original "Treatise on Light," for Huygens, born in The Hague, had accepted the invitation of Louis XIV to reside in Paris. The English translation by Silvanus P. Thompson was published in 1912 (London: Macmillan and Company).

WAVES IN THE ETHER: A NEW CHAPTER IN PHYSICS

I DO NOT FIND that anyone has yet given a probable explanation of the first and most notable phenomena of light, namely, why it is not propagated except in straight lines, and how visible rays, coming from an infinitude of diverse places, cross one another without hindering one another in any way. . . .

It is inconceivable to doubt that light consists in the motion of some sort of matter. For whether one considers its production, one sees that here upon the earth it is chiefly engendered by fire and flame which contain without doubt bodies that are in rapid motion, since they dissolve and melt many other bodies, even the most solid; or whether one considers its effects, one sees that when light is collected, as by concave mirrors, it has the property of burning as a fire does, that is to say, it disunites the particles of bodies. This is assuredly the mark of motion, at least in the true philosophy, in which one conceives the causes of all natural effects in terms of mechanical motions. This, in my opinion, we must necessarily do, or else renounce all hopes of ever comprehending anything in physics.

And as, according to this philosophy, one holds as certain that the sensation of sight is excited only by the impression of some movement of a kind of matter which acts on the nerves at the back of our eyes, there is here yet one reason more for believing that light consists in a movement of the matter which exists between us and the luminous body.

Further, when one considers the extreme speed with which light spreads on every side, and how, when it comes from different regions, even from those directly opposite, the rays traverse one another without hindrance, one may well understand that when we see a luminous object it cannot be by any transport of matter coming to us from this object, in the way in which a shot or an arrow traverses the air; for assuredly that would too greatly impugn these two properties of light, especially the second of them. It is then in some other way that light spreads; and that which can lead us to comprehend it is the knowledge which we have of the spreading of sound in the air.

We know that by means of the air, which is an invisible and impalpable body, sound spreads around the spot where it has been produced, by a movement which is passed on successively from one part of the air to another; and that the spreading of this movement, taking place equally rapidly on all sides, ought to form spherical surfaces ever enlarging and which strike our ears. Now there is no doubt at all that light also comes from the luminous body to our eyes by some movement impressed on the matter which is between the two; since, as we have already seen, it cannot be by the transport of a body which passes from one to the other. If, in addition, light takes time for its passage—which we are now going to examine—it will follow that this movement, impressed on the intervening matter, is successive; and consequently it spreads, as sound does, by spherical surfaces and waves: for I call them waves from their resemblance to those which are seen to be formed in water when a stone is thrown into it, and which present a successive spreading as circles, though these arise from another cause, and are only in a flat surface.

To see then whether the spreading of light takes time, let us consider first whether there are any facts of experience which can convince us to the contrary. As to those which can be made here on the earth, by striking lights at great distances, although they prove that light takes no sensible time to pass over these distances, one may say with good reason that they are too small, and that the only conclusion to be drawn from them is that the passage of light is extremely rapid . . . a hundred thousand times greater than that of sound.

But that which I employed only as a hypothesis has recently received great seemingness as an established truth by the ingenious proof of Mr. [Olaus] Römer [(1644–1710), Danish astronomer] which I am going here to relate, expecting him himself to give all that is needed for its confirmation. It is founded . . . upon celestial observations and proves not only that light takes time for its passage, but also demonstrates how much time it takes, and that its velocity is even at least six times greater than that which I have just stated.

For this he makes use of the eclipses suffered by the little planets which revolve around Jupiter, and which often enter his shadow.

The velocity of light is more than six hundred thousand times greater than that of sound. This, however, is quite another thing from being instantaneous, since there is all the difference between a finite thing and an infinite. Now the successive movement of light being confirmed in this way, it follows, as I have said, that it spreads by spherical waves, like the movement of sound. . . .

Now if one examines what this matter may be in which the movement coming from the luminous body is propagated, which I call ethereal matter, one will see that it is not the same that serves for the propagation of sound. For one finds that the latter is really that which we feel and which we breathe, and which, being removed from any place, still leaves there the other kind of matter that serves to convey light. This may be proved by shutting up a sounding body in a glass vessel from which the air is withdrawn by the machine which Mr. Boyle has given us, and with which he has performed so many beautiful experiments. But in doing this of which I speak care must be taken to place the sounding body on cotton or on feathers, in such a way that it cannot communicate its tremors either to the glass vessel which encloses it or to the machine; a precaution which has hitherto been neglected. For then, after having exhausted all the air, one hears no sound from the metal, though it is struck.

One sees here not only that our air, which does not penetrate through glass, is the matter by which sound spreads; but also that it is not the same air but another kind of matter in which light spreads; since if the air is removed from the vessel the light does not cease to traverse it as before.

And this last point is demonstrated even more clearly by the celebrated experiment of Torricelli, in which the tube of glass from which the quicksilver has withdrawn itself, remaining void of air, transmits light just the same as when air is in it. For this proves that a matter different from air exists in this tube, and that this matter must have penetrated the glass or the quicksilver, either one or the other, though they are both impenetrable to the air. And when, in the same experiment, one makes the vacuum after putting a little water above the quicksilver, one concludes equally that the said matter passes through glass or water, or through both. . . .

But the extreme velocity of light, and other properties which it has, cannot admit of such a propagation of motion, and I am about to show here the way in which I conceive it must occur. For this, it is needful to explain the property which hard bodies must possess to transmit movement from one to another.

When one takes a number of spheres of equal size, made of some very hard substance, and arranges them in a straight line, so that they touch one another, one finds, on striking with a similar sphere against the first of these spheres, that the motion passes as in an instant to the last of them, which separates itself from the row, without one's being able to perceive that the others have been stirred. And even that one which was used to strike remains motionless with them. Whence one sees that the movement passes with an extreme velocity which is the greater, the greater the hardness of the substance of the spheres.

But it is still certain that this progression of motion is not instantaneous, but successive, and therefore must take time. For if the movement, or the disposition to movement, if you will have it so, did not pass successively through all these spheres, they would all acquire the movement at the same time, and hence would all advance together; which does not happen. For the last one leaves the whole row and acquires the speed of the one which was pushed. Moreover there are experiments which demonstrate that all the bodies which we reckon of the hardest kind, such as quenched steel, glass, and agate, act as springs and bend somehow, not only when extended as rods but also when they are in the form of spheres or of other shapes. That is to say, they yield a little in themselves at the place where they are struck, and immediately regain their former figure. For I have found that on striking with a ball of glass or of agate against a large and quite thick piece of the same substance which had a flat surface, slightly soiled with breath or in some other way, there remained round marks, of smaller or larger size according as the blow had been weak or strong. This makes it evident that these substances yield where they meet, and spring back: and for this time must be required.

Now in applying this kind of movement to that which produces light there is nothing to hinder us from estimating the particles of the ether to be of a substance as nearly approaching to perfect hardness and possessing a springiness as prompt as we choose. It is not necessary to examine here the causes of this hardness, or of that springiness, the consideration of which would lead us too far from our subject. I will say, however, in passing that we may conceive that the particles of the ether, notwithstanding their smallness, are in turn composed of other parts and that their springiness consists in the very rapid movement of a subtle matter which penetrates them from every side and constrains their structure to assume such a disposition as to give to this fluid matter the most overt and easy passage possible. . . .

I have then shown in what manner one may conceive light to spread successively, by spherical waves, and how it is possible that this spreading is accomplished with as great a velocity as that which experiments and celestial observations demand. Whence it may be further remarked that although the particles are supposed to be in continual movement (for there are many reasons for this) the successive propagation of the waves cannot be hindered by this; because the propagation consists nowise in the transport of those particles but merely in a small agitation which they cannot help communicating to those surrounding, notwithstanding any movement which may act on them causing them to be changing positions among themselves.

Bacteriology Begins with the First of the Microbe Hunters

ANTON VAN LEEUWENHOEK (1632–1723)

"FIRST of the microbe hunters," "father of bacteriology and protozoology" (protozoa are another kind of tiny, usually single-celled animals to be seen under a microscope) are titles accorded to Anton van Leeuwenhoek, once shopkeeper and petty official of the picturesque city of Delft, in Holland. Grinding his own lenses and constructing his own jealously guarded microscopes, this keen-sighted, infinitely curious amateur naturalist was the first human being to see—in rain water (as told here) and on the "scum from the teeth"—the little living creatures which we now call microbes, bacteria, or germs. His microscopic adventures were indefatigably recorded (filling four quarto volumes) in rambling letters to the Royal Society of London, which unanimously elected him to membership in 1680. He repaid the honor by willing the Society twenty-six microscopes. Almost everything that Leeuwenhoek saw under his microscopes was new to the world. Most significant, perhaps, after microbes, were what he saw (1) in a tadpole's tail—the tiny capillary blood vessels, also seen by the Italian physiologist, Malpighi (1628–94), which solved the final mystery of the circulation of the blood; and (2) in human semen—spermatozoa, the male element.

Dutch was the only language Leeuwenhoek spoke or wrote. His letters to the Royal Society were translated for publication in the Society's famous "Philosophical Transactions."

"LITTLE ANIMALS IN RAIN WATER"

IN THE YEAR 1675 I discovered very small living creatures in rain water, which had stood but few days in a new earthen pot glazed blue within. This invited me to view this water with great attention, especially those little animals appearing to me ten thousand times less than those represented by Monsieur Swammerdam, and by him called water fleas, or water lice, which may be perceived in the water with the naked eye.

The first sort I several times observed to consist of five, six, seven, or eight clear globules without being able to discern any film that held them together, or contained them. When these animalcula or living atoms moved, they put forth two little horns, continually moving. The space between these two horns was flat, though the rest of the body was roundish, sharpening a little toward the end, where they had a tail, near four times the length of the whole body, of the thickness, by my microscope, of a spider's web; at the end of which appeared a globule of the size of one of those which made up the body. These little creatures, if they chanced to light on the least filament or string, or other particle, were entangled therein, extending their body in a long round and endeavoring to disentangle their tail. Their motion of extension and contraction continued awhile; and I have seen several thousands of these poor little creatures, within the space of a grain of gross sand, lie fast clustered together in a few filaments.

I also discovered a second sort, of an oval figure; and I imagined their head to stand on a sharp end. These were a little longer than the former. The inferior part of their body is flat, furnished with several extremely thin feet, which moved very nimbly. The upper part of the body was round, and had within eight, ten, or twelve globules, where they were very clear. These little animals sometimes changed their figure into a perfect round, especially when they came to lie on a dry place. Their body was also very flexible; for as soon as they struck against the smallest fibre or string their body was bent in, which bending presently jerked out again. When I put any of them on a dry place I observed that, changing themselves into a round, their body was raised pyramidalwise, with an extant point in the middle; and having lain thus a little while, with a motion of their feet, they burst asunder, and the globules were presently diffused and dissipated, so that I could not discern the least thing of any film, in which the globules had doubtless been enclosed; and at this time of their bursting asunder I was able to discover more globules than when they were alive.

I observed a third sort of little animals that were twice as long as broad, and to my eye eight times smaller than the first. Yes, I thought I discerned little feet, whereby they moved very briskly, both in round and straight line.

There was a fourth sort, which were so small that I was not able to give them any figure at all. These were a thousand times smaller than the eye of a large louse. These exceeded all the former in celerity. I have often observed them to stand still as it were on a point, and then turn themselves about with that swiftness, as we see a top turn round, the circumference they made being no larger than that of a grain of small sand, and then extending themselves straight forward, and by and by lying in a bending posture. I discovered also several other sorts of animals; these were generally made up of such soft parts, as the former, that they burst asunder as soon as they came to want water.

May 26, it rained hard; the rain growing less, I caused some of that rain water running down from the housetop to be gathered in a clean glass, after it had been washed two or three times with water. And in this I observed some few very small living creatures, and seeing them, I thought they might have been produced in the leaded gutters in some water that had remained there before.

I perceived in pure water, after some days, more of those animals, as also some that were somewhat larger. And I imagine that many thousands of these little creatures do not equal an ordinary grain of sand in bulk; and comparing them with a cheese mite, which may be seen to move with the naked eye, I make the proportion of one of these small water creatures to a cheese mite to be like that of a bee to a horse; for the circumference of one of these little animals in water is not so large as the thickness of a hair in a cheese mite.

In another quantity of rain water, exposed for some days to the air, I observed some thousands of them in a drop of water, which were of the smallest sort that I had seen hitherto. And in some time after I observed, besides the animals already noted, a sort of creatures that were eight times as large, of almost a round figure; and as those very small animalcula swam gently among each other, moving as gnats do in the air, so did these larger ones move far more swiftly, tumbling round as it were, and then making a sudden downfall.

In the waters of the river Maese I saw very small creatures of different kinds and colors, and so small that I could very hardly discern their figures; but the number of them was far less than those found in rain water. In the water of a very cold well in the autumn I discovered a very great number of living animals, very small, that were exceedingly clear, and a little larger than the smallest I ever saw. In sea water I observed at first a little blackish animal, looking as if it had been made up of two globules. This creature had a peculiar motion, resembling the skipping of a flea on white paper, so that it might very well be called a water flea; but it was far less than the eye of that little animal, which Dr. Swammerdam calls the water flea. I also discovered little creatures therein that were clear, of the same size with the former animal, but of an oval figure, having a serpentine motion. I further noticed a third sort, which were very slow in their motion; their body was of a mouse color, clear toward the oval point; and before the head and behind the body there stood out a sharp little point anglewise. This sort was a little larger. But there was yet a fourth somewhat longer than oval. Yet of all these sorts there were but a few of each. Some days after viewing this water I saw a hundred where before I had seen but one; but these were of another figure, and not only less, but they were also very clear, and of an oblong oval figure, only with this difference, that their heads ended sharper; and although they were a thousand times smaller than a small grain of sand, yet when they lay out of the water in a dry place they burst in pieces and spread into three or four very little globules, and into some aqueous matter, without any other parts appearing in them.

Having put about one third of an ounce of whole pepper in water, and it having lain about three weeks in the water, to which I had twice added some snow water, the other water being in great part exhaled, I discerned in it with great surprise an incredible number of little animals, of divers kinds, and among the rest, some that were three or four times as long as broad; but their whole thickness did not much exceed the hair of a louse. They had a very pretty motion, often tumbling about and sideways; and when the water was let to run off from them they turned round like a top; at first their body changed into an oval, and afterwards, when the circular motion ceased, they returned to their former length. The second sort of creatures discovered in this water were of a perfect oval figure, and they had no less pleasing or nimble a motion than the former; and these were in far greater numbers. There was a third sort, which exceeded the two former in number, and these had tails like those I had formerly observed in rain water. The fourth sort, which moved through the three former sorts, were incredibly small, so that I judged that if one hundred of them lay one by another they would not equal the length of a grain of coarse sand; and according to this estimate, one million of them could not equal the dimensions of a grain of such coarse sand. There was discovered a fifth sort, which had near the thickness of the former, but almost twice the length.

In snow water, which had been about three years in a glass bottle well stopped, I could discover no living creatures; and having poured some of it into a porcelain teacup, and put therein half an ounce of whole pepper, after some days I observed some animalcula, and those exceedingly small ones, whose body seemed to me twice as long as broad, but they moved very slowly, and often circularly. I observed also a vast multitude of oval-figured animalcula, to the number of eight thousand in a single drop.

The Primer of Vital Statistics

WILLIAM PETTY (1623–87)
AND
JOHN GRAUNT (1620–74)

DISPUTE HAS RAGED over the authorship, whether attributable to Graunt or to Petty, but never over the importance of the first book of its kind in any language: "Natural and Political Observations . . . on the Bills of Mortality," London, 1662. Begun with this slim book on what was then called "political arithmetic," vital statistics, in which every one of us is counted, has flourished to become the world-wide science upon whose counsel the great political decisions of nations must finally attend. Births, deaths, marriages, diseases—in short, the factors of population— are the raw material of vital statistics.

Captain John Graunt was a citizen of London and a fellow of the Royal Society, who, if nothing else, at least owned the "Bills of Mortality" upon which the famous observations were made.

Sir William Petty, one of the most penetrating and original minds in all science, was far better known to his contemporaries. A physician, reformer of the overloaded seventeenth century pharmacopoeia, and inventor of the horse-propelled military "tank," he went to Ireland as surgeon to Cromwell's army, and there completed in thirteen months the celebrated "Down Survey" of Irish lands forfeited in 1641. When Charles II was restored to the British throne in 1660 he, too, made Petty "Surveyor General" of Ireland, where the former Cromwellian immediately set up ironworks, opened mines and quarries, and established fisheries.

English, quaint seventeenth century style, is the original language of "Natural and Political Observations . . . on the Bills of Mortality."

NATURAL AND POLITICAL
OBSERVATIONS

Mentioned in a following INDEX
and Made upon the

BILLS OF MORTALITY

By

Captain JOHN GRAUNT,

Fellow of the Royal Society

With reference to the *Government, Religion,
Trade, Growth, Air, Diseases,* and the several
Changes of the said CITY

The Epistle Dedicatory

To the

RIGHT HONORABLE JOHN *Lord* ROBERTS
Baron of Truro, Lord Privy Seal,

and one of His Majesty's most Honorable
Privy Council

MY LORD,

Now having (I know not by what accident) engaged my thought upon the Bills of Mortality, and so far succeeded therein as to have reduced several great confused volumes into a few perspicuous tables, and abridged such observations as naturally flowed from them into a few succinct paragraphs, without any long series of multiloquious deductions, I have presumed to sacrifice these my small but first published labors unto your lordship, as unto whose benign acceptance of some others of my papers even the birth of these is due; hoping (if I may without vanity say it) they may be of as much use to persons in your lordship's place as they are of little or none to me, which is no more than the fairest diamonds are to the journeyman jeweler that works them, or the poor laborer that first digged them from the earth. For, with all humble submission to your lordship, I conceive:

That it doth not ill become a peer of the Parliament or member of His Majesty's Council to consider how few starve of the many that beg;

That the irreligious proposals of some to multiply people by polygamy is withal irrational and fruitless;

That the troublesome seclusions in the plague time are not a remedy to be purchased at vast inconveniences;

That the greatest plagues of the city are equally and quickly repaired from the country;

That the wasting of males by wars and colonies do not prejudice the due proportion between them and females;

That the opinions of plagues accompanying the entrance of kings is false and seditious;

That London, the metropolis of England, is perhaps a head too big for the body, and possibly too strong;

That this head grows three times as fast as the body unto which it belongs; that is, it doubles its people in a third part of the time;

That our parishes are now grown madly disproportionable;

That our temples are not suitable to our religion;

That the trade and very city of London removes westward;

That the walled city is but a fifth of the whole pile;

That the old streets are unfit for the present frequency of coaches;

That the passage of Ludgate is a throat too strait for the body;

That the fighting men about London are able to make three as great armies as can be of use in this island;

That the number of heads is such as hath certainly much deceived some of our senators in their appointments of poll money, et cetera.

Now, although your lordship's most excellent discourses have well informed me that your lordship is no stranger to these positions, yet because I knew not that your lordship had ever deduced them from the Bills of Mortality I hoped it might not be ungrateful to your lordship to see unto how much profit that one talent might be improved, besides the many curiosities concerning the waxing and waning of diseases, the relation between healthful and fruitful seasons, the difference between the city and the country air, et cetera. All which being new, to the best of my knowledge, and the whole pamphlet not two hours reading, I did make bold to trouble your lordship with a perusal of it, and by this humble dedication of it let your lordship and the world see the wisdom of our city, in appointing and keeping these accounts, and with how much affection and success, I am,

My Lord,

Your Lordship's most obedient,

and most faithful servant,

JOHN GRAUNT

BIRCHEN-LANE,
25 January, 1661/2

OF THE BILLS OF MORTALITY, THEIR BEGINNING AND PROGRESS

THE FIRST of the continued weekly Bills of Mortality extant at the Parish Clerk's Hall begins the twenty-ninth of December 1603, being the first year of King James's reign; since when a weekly account hath been kept there of burials and christenings. It is true there were bills before, viz., for the years 1592–94; but so interrupted since that I could not depend upon the sufficiency of them, rather relying upon those accounts which have been kept since in order, as to all the uses I shall make of them.

I believe that the rise of keeping these accounts was taken from the plague: for the said Bills (for ought appears) first began in the said year 1592, being a time of great mortality; and, after some disuse, were resumed again in the year 1603, after the great plague then happening likewise.

These Bills were printed and published not only every week on Thursdays but also a general account of the whole year was given in upon the Thursday before Christmas Day: which said general accounts have been presented in the several manners following, viz., from the year 1603 to the year 1624, inclusive. . . .

We have hitherto described the several steps whereby the Bills of

Mortality are come up to their present state; we come next to show how they are made and composed, which is in this manner, viz.: when anyone dies, then, either by tolling, or ringing of a bell, or by bespeaking of a grave of the sexton, the same is known to the searchers, corresponding with the said sexton.

The searchers hereupon (who are ancient matrons, sworn to their office) repair to the place where the dead corpse lies, and by view of the same, and by other inquiries, they examine by what disease or casualty the corpse died. Hereupon they make their report to the parish clerk, and he, every Tuesday night, carries in an account of all the burials and christenings happening that week to the clerk of the hall. On Wednesday the general account is made up and printed, and on Thursday published and dispersed to the several families who will pay four shillings per annum for them. . . .

Having premised these general advertisements, our first observation upon the casualties shall be that in twenty years there dying of all diseases and casualties 229,250, [yet] 71,124 died of the thrush, convulsion, rickets, teeth, and worms; and as abortives, chrisoms, infants, liver-grown, and overlaid; that is to say, that about one third of the whole died of those diseases, which we guess did all light upon children under four or five years old.

There died also of the smallpox, swine pox, and measles, and of worms without convulsions, 12,210, of which number we supposed likewise that about one half might be children under six years old. Now if we consider that sixteen [thousand] of the said 229,250 died of that extraordinary and grand casualty, the plague, we shall find that about thirty-six per centum of all quick conceptions died before six years old.

The second observation is that of the said 229,250 dying of all diseases, there died of acute diseases (the plague excepted) but about 50,000, or two ninths parts. The which proportion doth give a measure of the state and disposition of this climate and air as to health; these acute and epidemical diseases happening suddenly and vehemently upon the like corruptions and alterations in the air.

The third observation is that of the said 229,250 about seventy [thousand] died of chronical diseases, which shows (as I conceive) the state and disposition of the country (including as well its food as air) in reference to health, or rather to longevity. . . .

The fourth observation is that of the said 229,250 not 4000 died of outward griefs, as of cancers, fistulas, sores, ulcers, broken and bruised limbs, impostumes, itch, king's evil, leprosy, scald head, swine pox, wens, et cetera, viz., not one in sixty.

In the next place, whereas many persons live in great fear and apprehension of some of the more formidable and notorious diseases following, I shall only set down how many died of each: that the respective numbers, being compared with the total 229,250, those persons may the better understand the hazard they are in.

TABLE OF NOTORIOUS DISEASES		TABLE OF CASUALTIES	
Apoplexy	1306	Bleeding	69
Cut of the stone	38	Burned and scalded	125
Falling sickness	74	Drowned	829
Dead in the streets	243	Excessive drinking	2
Gout	134	Frighted	22
Headache	51	Grief	279
Jaundice	998	Hanged themselves	222
Lethargy	67	Killed by several accidents	1021
Leprosy	6	Murdered	86
Lunatic	158	Poisoned	14
Overlaid and starved	529	Smothered	26
Palsy	423	Shot	7
Rupture	201	Starved	51
Stone and strangury	863	Vomiting	136
Sciatica	5		
Suddenly	454		

OF PARTICULAR CASUALTIES

My first observation is that few are starved. This appears, for that of the 229,250 which have died we find not above fifty-one to have been starved, excepting helpless infants at nurse, which, being caused rather by carelessness, ignorance, and infirmity of the milch women, is not properly an effect or sign of want of food in the country, or of means to get it.

The observation which I shall add hereunto is that the vast number of beggars swarming up and down this city do all live and seem to be most of them healthy and strong; whereupon I make this question: whether, since they do all live by begging, that is, without any kind of labor, it were not better for the state to keep them, even although they earned nothing, that so they might live regularly, and not in that debauchery, as many beggars do; and that they might be cured of their bodily impotencies, or taught to work, et cetera, each according to his condition and capacity; or, by being employed in some work (not better undone), might be accustomed and fitted for labor? . . .

My next observation is that but few are murdered, viz., not above 86 of the 229,250, which have died of other diseases and casualties; whereas in Paris few nights escape without their tragedy.

The reasons of this we conceive to be two: one is the government and guard of the city by citizens themselves, and that alternately, no man settling into a trade for that employment. And the other is the natural and customary abhorrence of that inhuman crime, and all bloodshed, by most Englishmen: for, of all that are executed, few are for murder.

The lunatics are also but few, viz., 158 in 229,250, though I fear many more than are set down in our Bills, few being entered for such but those who die at Bedlam; and there all seem to die of their lunacy, who died lunatics; for there is much difference in computing the number of lunatics that die (though of fevers and all other diseases, unto which lunacy is no *supersedeas*) and those that die by reason of their madness.

So that, this casualty being so uncertain, I shall not force myself to make any inference from the numbers and proportions we find in our Bills concerning it: only I dare insure any man at this present, well in his wits, for one in a thousand, that he shall not die a lunatic in Bedlam within these seven years, because I find not above one in about 1500 have done so.

OF THE DIFFERENCE BETWEEN THE NUMBERS OF MALES AND FEMALES

The next observation is that there be more males than females.

There have been buried, from the year 1628 to the year 1662, exclusive, 209,436 males, and but 190,474 females: but it will be objected that in London it may be indeed so, though otherwise elsewhere; because London is the great stage and shop of business, wherein the masculine sex bears the greatest part. But we answer that there have been also christened within the same time 139,782 males, and but 130,866 females, and that the country accounts are consonant enough to those of London upon this matter.

What the causes hereof are we shall not trouble ourselves to conjecture, as in other cases: only we shall desire that travelers would inquire whether it be the same in other countries.

We should have given an account how in every age these proportions change here, but that we have Bills of distinction but for thirty-two years, so that we shall pass from hence to some inferences from this conclusion; as, first:

That Christian religion, prohibiting polygamy, is more agreeable to the law of nature, that is, the law of God, than Mahometism, and others, that allow it: for one man's having many women, or wives, by law, signifies nothing, unless there were many women to one man in nature also.

We have hitherto said there are more males than females; we say next that the one exceed the other by about a thirteenth part. So that although more men die violent deaths than women, that is, more are slain in wars, killed by mischance, drowned at sea, and die by the hand of justice; moreover, more men go to colonies, and travel into foreign parts than women; and lastly, more remain unmarried than of women, as fellows of colleges, and apprentices above eighteen, et cetera, yet the said thirteenth part difference bringeth the business but to such a pass that every woman may have a husband without the allowance of polygamy.

Moreover, although a man be prolific forty years, and a woman but five and twenty, which make the males to be as 560 to 325 females, yet the causes above named, and the later marriage of the men, reduce all to an equality.

It is a blessing to mankind that by this overplus of males there is this natural bar to polygamy: for in such a state women could not live in that parity and equality of expense with their husbands as now and here they do.

The reason whereof is not that the husband cannot maintain as splendidly three as one; for he might, having three wives, live himself upon a quarter of his income, that is, in a parity with all three, as well as, having but one, live in the same parity at half with her alone: but rather, because that to keep them all quiet with each other and himself he must keep them all in greater awe and less splendor; which power he having, he will probably use it to keep them all as low as he pleases, and at no more cost than makes for his own pleasure; the poorest subjects (such as this plurality of wives must be) being most easily governed.

Another Natural Law Discovered

ROBERT HOOKE (1635-1703)

IN ITS EARLY DAYS many of the meetings of the Royal Society of London were almost theatrical performances, scientific "freak shows" at which it was proposed to demonstrate some of the latest marvels of "experimental philosophy." There one might have seen, fussing jealously with the apparatus—pumps, balances, springs, microscopes—in whose development he was especially interested, the crabbed "curator of experiments," Robert Hooke. Originally employed by the Hon. Robert Boyle (1627–91), the "father of chemistry and the brother of the Earl of Cork," as a laboratory assistant, Hooke aided Boyle in those air-pump experiments with the vacuum chamber and the "springe" (elasticity) of air which led to the discovery of "Boyle's law": that the volume of a gas is inversely proportional to the pressure exerted on it in a closed chamber (temperature being unchanged). Always disputing priority, as with Newton concerning the laws of gravitation, Hooke felt impelled to discover a law of his own. Now known as Hooke's law is the proposition, given here, that within the elastic limits stress on a body is directly proportional to strain. The curator was one of the good early microscopists. In his "Micrographia" (1665) he gives the name "cell" to the tiny honeycomb cavities that he observed in thinly sliced sections of cork.

English, except for the Latin anagram, was the language in which Hooke communicated his law of elastic force. The present passage appeared in *"De Potentia Restitutiva,"* published in 1678.

THE LAW OF ELASTICITY: STRESS EQUALS STRAIN

THE THEORY of springs, though attempted by divers eminent mathematicians of this age, has hitherto not been published by any. It is now about eighteen years since I first found it out, but, designing to apply it to some particular use, I omitted the publishing thereof.

About three years since, His Majesty was pleased to see the experiment that made out this theory tried at Whitehall, as also my spring watch.

About two years since, I printed this theory in an anagram at the end of my book of the descriptions of helioscopes, viz., *c e i i i n o s s s t t u u, id est, ut tensio sic vis;* that is, the power of any spring is in the same proportion with the tension thereof: that is, if one power stretch or bend it one space, two will bend it two, and three will bend it three, and so forward. Now as the theory is very short, so the way of trying it is very easy.

Take then a quantity of even-drawn wire, either steel, iron, or brass, and coil it on an even cylinder into a helix of what length or number of turns you please, then turn the ends of the wire into loops, by one of which suspend this coil upon a nail, and the other sustain the weight that you would have to extend it, and hanging on several weights, observe exactly to what length each of the weights do extend it beyond the length that its own weight doth stretch it to, and you shall find that if one ounce, or one pound, or one certain weight doth lengthen it one line, or one inch, or one certain length, then two ounces, two pounds, or two weights will extend it two lines, two inches, or two lengths; and three ounces, pounds, or weights, three lines, inches, or lengths; and so forwards. And this is the rule or law of nature, upon which all manner of restituent or springing motion doth proceed, whether it be of rarefaction, or extension, or condensation and compression.

Or take a wire string twenty, or thirty, or forty feet long, and fasten the upper part thereof to a nail, and to the other end fasten a scale to receive the weights: then with a pair of compasses take the distance of the bottom of the scale from the ground or floor underneath, and set down the said distance, then put in weights into the said scale in the same manner as in the former trials, and measure the several stretchings of the said string, and set them down. Then compare the several stretchings of the said string, and you will find that they will always bear the same proportions one to the other that the weights do that made them.

The same will be found, if trial be made, with a piece of dry wood that will bend and return, if one end thereof be fixed in a horizontal posture, and to the other end be hanged weights to make it bend downwards.

The manner of trying the same thing upon a body of air, whether it be for the rarefaction or for the compression thereof, I did about fourteen years since publish in my *"Micrographia,"* and therefore I shall not need to add any further description thereof.

The Laws of Gravitation . . . and Optics

ISAAC NEWTON (1642-1727)

Mortals, congratulate yourselves that so great a man has lived for the honor of the human race.—(Translation of inscription on Newton's tombstone.)

NEWTON, "the greatest name in English science," said of himself: "I do not know what I may appear to the world, but, to myself, I seem to have been only like a boy playing on the seashore, and diverting myself in now and then finding a smoother pebble or a prettier shell than ordinary, whilst the great ocean of truth lay all undiscovered before me." If the word "genius" can be applied to any mortal it fits this tortured, touchy, nerve-racked, introspective bachelor; this secretive, secluded "natural philosopher" and deistic theologian, an English Faust, grimly hand polishing the first reflecting telescope, poring over alchemical books and tending fires and alembics in the dingy "elaboratory" he supported near his unkempt lodging rooms when he was professor of mathematics at Cambridge—and the only man in England, amidst a brilliant company that included Halley, Hooke, and Wren, who could solve astronomical problems on the motion (given the path) of the heavenly bodies. From probing him on these problems enthusiastic Halley eventually extracted from a reluctant Newton the text of the famous *"Principia Mathematica Philosophiae Naturalis"* ("The Mathematical Principles of Natural Philosophy"). The *"Principia,"* as it is commonly known, was finally published in 1687 by Halley at his own expense! That section of the book which made the greatest popular stir in a seafaring nation related to the influence of the moon and the sun on the tides.

Newton was born at Woolsthorpe, in Lincolnshire, in 1642. The fruitful years in his life came early, during the "plague years of 1665–66," when he was forced to return from Cambridge to the country. "In those days I was in the prime of my age for invention," he writes, "and minded mathematics and philosophy more than at any time since." Among the things that he discovered in those productive years were the law of gravity, the falling apple and Kepler's laws assisting; the method of "fluxions," or calculus, over which Newton's friends later disputed bitterly with the German philosopher and mathematician, Leibnitz; the theory of colors, eventually expanded into his second book, "Opticks" (1704); and the binomial theorem of algebra.

In later years *Sir* Isaac Newton, eschewing science, was an Olympian figure; member of Parliament; president of the Royal Society (1703–27); Warden (1696), then Master (1699) of the Mint. He was buried in Westminster Abbey, most highly honored by his countrymen, who were just on the verge of completing an efficient navy and developing a mercantile empire against the Dutch and Portuguese opposition, not because he wrote the *"Principia,"* which few read, but rather because he saved the debased coinage and restored the national credit, without which mercantile conquests would have been impossible.

Latin was the language of the *"Principia,"* a 250,000-word book. The

English translation here given was made by Andrew Motte in 1729, slightly revised by Florian Cajori and published in 1934 (University of California Press). "Opticks" was written in English.

THE MATHEMATICAL PRINCIPLES OF NATURAL PHILOSOPHY—THE *"PRINCIPIA"*

Newton's Preface to the First Edition

SINCE the Ancients (as we are told by Pappus) esteemed the science of mechanics of greatest importance in the investigation of natural things, and the moderns, rejecting substantial forms and occult qualities, have endeavored to subject the phenomena of nature to the laws of mathematics, I have in this treatise cultivated mathematics as far as it relates to philosophy. The ancients considered mechanics in a twofold respect; as rational, which proceeds accurately by demonstration, and practical. To practical mechanics all the manual arts belong, from which mechanics took its name. But as artificers do not work with perfect accuracy, it comes to pass that mechanics is so distinguished from geometry that what is perfectly accurate is called geometrical; what is less so, is called mechanical. However, the errors are not in the art, but in the artificers. He that works with less accuracy is an imperfect mechanic; and if any could work with perfect accuracy, he would be the most perfect mechanic of all, for the description of right lines and circles, upon which geometry is founded, belongs to mechanics. Geometry does not teach us to draw these lines, but requires them to be drawn, for it requires that the learner should first be taught to describe these accurately before he enters upon geometry, then it shows how by these operations problems may be solved. To describe right lines and circles are problems, but not geometrical problems. The solution of these problems is required from mechanics, and by geometry the use of them, when so solved, is shown; and it is the glory of geometry that from those few principles, brought from without it, it is able to produce so many things. Therefore geometry is founded in mechanical practice, and is nothing but that part of universal mechanics which accurately proposes and demonstrates the art of measuring. But since the manual arts are chiefly employed in the moving of bodies, it happens that geometry is commonly referred to their magnitude, and mechanics to their motion. In this sense rational mechanics will be the science of motions resulting from any forces whatsoever, and of the forces required to produce any motions, accurately proposed and demonstrated. This part of mechanics, as far as it extended to the five powers which relate to manual arts, was cultivated by the ancients, who considered gravity (it not being a manual power) no otherwise than in moving weights by those powers. But I consider philosophy rather than arts and write not concerning manual but natural powers, and consider chiefly those things which relate to gravity, levity, elastic force, the resistance of fluids, and the like forces, whether attractive or impulsive; and therefore I offer this work as the mathematical principles of philosophy, for the whole burden of philosophy seems to consist in this—from the phenomena of motions to investigate the forces of nature, and then from these forces to demonstrate the other phenomena; and to this end the general propositions in the first and second Books are directed. In the third Book I give an example of this in the explication of the System of the World; for by the propositions mathematically demonstrated in the former Books, in the third I derive from the celestial phenomena the forces of gravity with which bodies tend to the sun and the several planets. Then from these forces, by other propositions which are also mathematical, I deduce the motions of the planets, the comets, the moon, and the sea. I wish we could derive the rest of the phenomena of Nature by the same kind of reasoning from mechanical principles, for I am induced by many reasons to suspect that they may all depend upon certain forces by which the particles of bodies, by some causes hitherto unknown, are either mutually impelled towards one another, and cohere in regular figures, or are repelled and recede from one another. These forces being unknown, philosophers have hitherto attempted the search of Nature in vain; but I hope the principles here laid down will afford some light either to this or some truer method of philosophy.

In the publication of this work the most acute and universally learned Mr. Edmund Halley not only assisted me in correcting the errors of the press and preparing the geometrical figures, but it was through his solicitations that it came to be published; for when he had obtained of me my demonstrations of the figure of the celestial orbits, he continually pressed me to communicate the same to the Royal Society, who afterwards, by their kind encouragement and entreaties, engaged me to think of publishing them. But after I had begun to consider the inequalities of the lunar motions, and had entered upon some other things relating to the laws and measures of gravity and other forces; and the figures that would be described by bodies attracted according to given laws; and the motion of several bodies moving among themselves; the motion of bodies in resisting mediums; the forces, densities, and motions, of mediums; the orbits of the comets, and such like, I deferred that publication till I had made a search into those matters, and could put forth the whole together. What relates to the lunar motions (being imperfect), I have put all together in the corollaries of Prop. LXVI, to avoid being obliged to propose and distinctly demonstrate the several things there contained in a method more prolix than the subject deserved and interrupt the series of the other propositions. Some things, found out after the rest, I chose to insert in places less suitable, rather than change the number of the propositions and the citations. I heartily beg that what I have here done may be read with forbearance; and that my labors in a subject so difficult may be examined, not so much with the view to censure, as to remedy their defects.

Is. NEWTON

CAMBRIDGE, TRINITY COLLEGE
May 8, 1686

DEFINITIONS

Definition I

The quantity of matter is the measure of the same, arising from its density and bulk conjointly.

Thus air of a double density, in a double space, is quadruple in quantity; in a triple space, sextuple in quantity. The same thing is to be understood of snow, and fine dust or powders, that are condensed by compression or liquefaction; and of all bodies that are by any causes whatever differently condensed. I have no regard in this place to a medium, if any such there is, that freely pervades the interstices between the parts of bodies. It is this quantity that I mean hereafter everywhere under the name of body or mass. And the same is known by the weight of each body, for it is proportional to the weight, as I have found by experiments on pendulums, very accurately made, which shall be shewn hereafter.

Definition II

The quantity of motion is the measure of the same, arising from the velocity and quantity of matter conjointly.

The motion of the whole is the sum of the motions of all the parts; and therefore in a body double in quantity, with equal velocity, the motion is double; with twice the velocity, it is quadruple.

Definition III

The *vis insita,* or innate force of matter, is a power of resisting, by which every body, as much as in it lies, continues in its present state, whether it be of rest, or of moving uniformly forward in a right line.

This force is always proportional to the body whose force it is; and differs nothing from the inactivity of the mass, but in our manner of conceiving it. A body, from the inert nature of matter, is not without difficulty put out of its state of rest or motion. Upon which account, this *vis insita,* may, by a most significant name, be called inertia (*vis inertiae*) or force of inactivity. But a body only exerts this force when another force, impressed upon it, endeavors to change its condition; and the exercise of this force may be considered both as resistance and impulse; it is resistance, in so far as the body, for maintaining its present state, opposes the force impressed; it is impulse, so far as the body, by not easily giving way to the impressed force of another, endeavors to change the state of that other. Resistance is usually ascribed to bodies at rest, and impulse to those in motion; but motion and rest, as commonly conceived, are only relatively distinguished; nor are those bodies always truly at rest, which commonly are taken to be so.

Definition IV

An impressed force is an action exerted upon a body, in order to change its state, either of rest, or of uniform motion in a right line.

This force consists in the action only, and remains no longer in the body when the action is over. For a body maintains every new state it acquires, by its inertia only. But impressed forces are of different origins, as from percussion, from pressure, from centripetal force.

Definition V

A centripetal force is that by which bodies are drawn or impelled, or any way tend, towards a point as to a centre.

Of this sort is gravity, by which bodies tend to the centre of the earth; magnetism, by which iron tends to the loadstone; and that force, whatever it is, by which the planets are continually drawn aside from the rectilinear motions, which otherwise they would pursue, and made to revolve in curvilinear orbits. A stone, whirled about in a sling, endeavors to recede from the hand that turns it; and by that endeavor, distends the sling, and that with so much the greater force, as it is revolved with the greater velocity, and as soon as it is let go, flies away. That force which opposes itself to this endeavor, and by which the sling continually draws back the stone towards the hand, and retains it in its orbit, because it is directed to the hand as the centre of the orbit, I call the centripetal force. And the same thing is to be understood of all bodies, revolved in any orbits. They all endeavor to recede from the centres of their orbits; and were it not for the opposition of a contrary force which restrains them to, and detains them in their orbits, which I therefore call centripetal, would fly off in right lines, with an uniform motion. A projectile, if it was not for the force of gravity, would not deviate towards the earth, but would go off from it in a right line, and that with an uniform motion, if the resistance of the air was taken away. It is by its gravity that it is drawn aside continually from its rectilinear course, and made to deviate towards the earth, more or less, according to the force of its gravity, and the velocity of its motion. The less its gravity is, or the quantity of its matter, or the greater the velocity with which it is projected, the less will it deviate from a rectilinear course, and the farther it will go. If a leaden ball, projected from the top of a mountain by the force of gunpowder, with a given velocity, and in a direction parallel to the horizon, is carried in a curved line to the distance of two miles before it falls to the ground; the same, if the resistance of the air were taken away, with a double or decuple velocity, would fly twice or ten times as far. And by increasing the velocity, we may at pleasure increase the distance to which it might be projected, and diminish the curvature of the line which it might describe, till at last it should fall at the distance of 10, 30, or 90 degrees, or even might go quite round the whole earth before it falls; or lastly, so that it might never fall to the earth, but go forwards into the celestial spaces, and proceed in its motion *in infinitum*. And after the same manner that a projectile, by the force of gravity, may be made to revolve in an orbit, and go round the whole earth, the moon also, either by the force of gravity, if it is endued with gravity, or by any other force, that impels it towards the earth, may be continually drawn aside towards the earth, out of the rectilinear way which by its innate force it would pursue; and would be made to revolve in the orbit which it now describes; nor could the moon without some such force be retained in its orbit. If this force was too small, it would not sufficiently turn the moon out of a rectilinear course; if it was too great, it would turn it too much, and draw down the moon from its orbit towards the earth. It is necessary that the force be of a just quantity, and it belongs to the mathematicians to find the force that may serve exactly to retain a body in a given orbit with a given velocity; and *vice versa,* to determine the curvilinear way into which a body projected from a given place, with a given velocity, may be made to deviate from its natural rectilinear way, by means of a given force.

The quantity of any centripetal force may be considered as of three kinds: absolute, accelerative, and motive.

Definition VI

The absolute quantity of a centripetal force is the measure of the same, proportional to the efficacy of the cause that propagates it from the centre, through the spaces round about.

Thus the magnetic force is greater in one loadstone and less in another, according to their sizes and strength of intensity.

Definition VII

The accelerative quantity of a centripetal force is the measure of the same, proportional to the velocity which it generates in a given time.

Thus the force of the same loadstone is greater at a less distance, and less at a greater: also the force of gravity is greater in valleys, less on tops of exceeding high mountains; and yet less (as shall hereafter be shown), at greater distances from the body of the earth; but at equal distances, it is the same everywhere; because (taking away, or allowing for, the resistance of the air), it equally accelerates all falling bodies, whether heavy or light, great or small.

Definition VIII

The motive quantity of a centripetal force is the measure of the same, proportional to the motion which it generates in a given time.

Thus the weight is greater in a greater body, less in a less body; and, in the same body, it is greater near to the earth, and less at remoter distances. This sort of quantity is the centripetency, or propension of the whole body towards the centre, or, as I may say, its weight; and it is always known by the quantity of an equal and contrary force just sufficient to hinder the descent of the body. . . .

Scholium

Hitherto I have laid down the definitions of such words as are less known, and explained the sense in which I would have them to be understood in the following discourse. I do not define time, space, place and motion, as being well known to all. Only I must observe, that the common people conceive those quantities under no other notions but from the relation they bear to sensible objects. And thence arise certain prejudices, for the removing of which it will be convenient to distinguish them into absolute and relative, true and apparent, mathematical and common.

I. Absolute, true, and mathematical time, of itself, and from its own nature flows equably without relation to anything external, and by another name is called duration: relative, apparent, and common time, is some sensible and external (whether accurate or unequable) measure of duration by the means of motion, which is commonly used instead of true time; such as an hour, a day, a month, a year.

II. Absolute space, in its own nature, without regard to anything external, remains always similar and immovable. Relative space is some movable dimension or measure of the absolute spaces; which our senses determine by its position to bodies; and which is commonly taken for immovable space; such is the dimension of a subterraneous, an aereal, or celestial space, determined by its position in respect of the earth. Absolute and relative space are the same in figure and magnitude; but they do not remain always numerically the same. For if the earth, for instance, moves, a space of our air, which relatively and in respect of the earth remains always the same, will at one time be one part of the absolute space into which the air passes; at another time it will be another part of the same, and so, absolutely understood, it will be continually changed.

III. Place is a part of space which a body takes up, and is according to the space, either absolute or relative. I say, a part of space; not the situation, nor the external surface of the body. For the places of equal solids are always equal; but their surfaces, by reason of their dissimilar figures, are often unequal. Positions properly have no quantity, nor are they so much the places themselves, as the properties of places. The motion of the whole is the same with the sum of the motions of the parts; that is, the translation of the whole, out of its place, is the same thing with the sum of the translations of the parts out of their places; and therefore the place of the whole is the same as the sum of the places of the parts, and for that reason, it is internal, and in the whole body.

IV. Absolute motion is the translation of a body from one absolute place into another; and relative motion, the translation from one relative place into another. Thus in a ship under sail, the relative place of a body is that part of the ship which the body possesses; or that part of its cavity which the body fills, and which therefore moves together with the ship: and relative rest is the continuance of the body in the same part of the ship, or of its cavity. But real, absolute rest, is the continuance of the body in the same part of that immovable space, in which the ship itself, its cavity, and all that it contains, is moved. Wherefore, if the earth is really at rest, the body, which relatively rests in the ship, will really and absolutely move with the same velocity which the ship has on the earth. But if the earth also moves, the true and absolute motion of the body will arise, partly from the true motion of the earth, in immovable space; partly from the relative motion of the ship on the earth; and if the body moves also relatively in the ship, its true motion will arise, partly from the true motion of the earth, in immovable space, and partly from the relative motions as well of the ship on the earth, as of the body in the ship; and from these relative motions will arise the relative motion of the body on the earth. As if that part of the earth, where the ship is, was truly moved toward the east, with a velocity of 10,010 parts; while the ship itself, with a fresh gale, and full sails, is carried towards the west, with a velocity expressed by 10 of those parts; but a sailor walks in the ship towards the east, with 1 part of the said velocity; then the sailor will be moved truly in immovable space towards the east, with a velocity of 10,001 parts, and relatively on the earth towards the west, with a velocity of 9 of those parts. . . .

The effects which distinguish absolute from relative motion are, the forces of receding from the axis of circular motion. For there are no such forces in a circular motion purely relative, but in a true and absolute circular motion, they are greater or less, according to the quantity of the motion. If a vessel, hung by a long cord, is so often turned about that the cord is strongly twisted, then filled with water, and held at rest together with the water; thereupon, by the sudden action of another force, it is whirled about the contrary way, and while the cord is untwisting itself, the vessel continues for some time in this motion; the surface of the water will at first be plain, as before the vessel began to move; but after that, the vessel, by gradually communicating its motion to the water, will make it begin sensibly to revolve, and recede by little and little from the middle, and ascend to the sides of the vessel, forming itself into a concave figure (as I have experienced), and the swifter the motion becomes, the higher will the water rise, till at last, performing its revolutions in the same times with the vessel, it becomes relatively at rest in it. This ascent of the water shows its endeavor to recede from the axis of its motion; and the true and absolute circular motion of the water, which is here directly contrary to the relative, becomes known, and may be measured by this endeavor. At first, when the relative motion of the water in the vessel was greatest, it produced no endeavor to recede from the axis; the water showed no tendency to the circumference, nor any ascent towards the sides of the vessel, but remained of a plain surface, and therefore its true circular motion had not yet begun. But afterwards, when the relative motion of the water had decreased, the ascent thereof towards the sides of the vessel proved its endeavor to recede from the axis; and this endeavor showed the real circular motion of the water continually increasing, till it had acquired its greatest quantity, when the water rested relatively in the vessel. And therefore this endeavor does not depend upon any translation of the water in respect of the ambient bodies, nor can true circular motion be defined by such translation. There is only one real circular motion of any one revolving body, corresponding to only one power of endeavoring to recede from its axis of motion, as its proper and adequate effect; but relative motions, in one and the same body, are innumerable, according to the various relations it bears to external bodies, and like other relations, are altogether destitute of any real effect, any otherwise than they may perhaps partake of that one only true motion. And therefore in their system who suppose that our heavens, revolving below the sphere of the fixed stars, carry the planets along with them; the several parts of those heavens, and the planets, which are indeed relatively at rest in their heavens, do yet really move. For they change their position one to another (which never happens to bodies truly at rest), and being carried together with their heavens, partake of their motions, and as parts of revolving wholes, endeavor to recede from the axis of their motions.

Wherefore relative quantities are not the quantities themselves, whose names they bear, but those sensible measures of them (either accurate or inaccurate), which are commonly used instead of the measured quantities themselves. And if the meaning of words is to be determined by their use, then by the names time, space, place, and motion, their [sensible] measures are properly to be understood; and the expression will be unusual, and purely mathematical, if the measured quantities themselves are meant. On this account, those violate the accuracy of language, which ought to be kept precise, who interpret these words for the measured quantities. Nor do those less defile the purity of mathematical and philosophical truths, who confound real quantities with their relations and sensible measures.

It is indeed a matter of great difficulty to discover, and effectually to distinguish, the true motions of particular bodies from the apparent; because the parts of that immovable space, in which those motions are performed, do by no means come under the observation of our senses.

Yet the thing is not altogether desperate; for we have some arguments to guide us, partly from the apparent motions, which are the differences of the true motions; partly from the forces, which are the causes and effects of the true motions. For instance, if two globes, kept at a given distance one from the other by means of a cord that connects them, were revolved about their common centre of gravity, we might, from the tension of the cord, discover the endeavor of the globes to recede from the axis of their motion, and from thence we might compute the quantity of their circular motions. And then if any equal forces should be impressed at once on the alternate faces of the globes to augment or diminish their circular motions, from the increase or decrease of the tension of the cord, we might infer the increment or decrement of their motions; and thence would be found on what faces those forces ought to be impressed, that the motions of the globes might be most augmented; that is, we might discover their hindmost faces, or those which, in the circular motion, do follow. But the faces which follow being known, and consequently the opposite ones that precede, we should likewise know the determination of their motions. And thus we might find both the quantity and the determination of this circular motion, even in an immense vacuum, where there was nothing external or sensible with which the globes could be compared. But now, if in that space some remote bodies were placed that kept always a given position one to another, as the fixed stars do in our regions, we could not indeed determine from the relative translation of the globes among those bodies, whether the motion did belong to the globes or to the bodies. But if we observed the cord, and found that its tension was that very tension which the motions of the globes required, we might conclude the motion to be in the globes, and the bodies to be at rest; and then, lastly, from the translation of the globes among the bodies, we should find the determination of their motions. But how we are to obtain the true motions from their causes, effects, and apparent differences, and the converse, shall be explained more at large in the following treatise. For to this end it was that I composed it.

Axioms, or Laws of Motion

Law I

Every body continues in its state of rest, or of uniform motion in a right line, unless it is compelled to change that state by forces impressed upon it.

Projectiles continue in their motions, so far as they are not retarded by the resistance of the air, or impelled downwards by the force of gravity. A top, whose parts by their cohesion are continually drawn aside from rectilinear motions, does not cease its rotation, otherwise than as it is retarded by the air. The greater bodies of the planets and comets, meeting with less resistance in freer spaces, preserve their motions both progressive and circular for a much longer time.

Law II

The change of motion is proportional to the motive force impressed; and is made in the direction of the right line in which that force is impressed.

If any force generates a motion, a double force will generate double the motion, a triple force triple the motion, whether that force be impressed altogether and at once, or gradually and successively. And this motion (being always directed the same way with the generating force), if the body moved before, is added to or subtracted from the former motion, according as they directly conspire with or are directly contrary to each other; or obliquely joined, when they are oblique, so as to produce a new motion compounded from the determination of both.

Law III

To every action there is always opposed an equal reaction: or the mutual actions of two bodies upon each other are always equal, and directed to contrary parts.

Whatever draws or presses another is as much drawn or pressed by that other. If you press a stone with your finger, the finger is also pressed by the stone. If a horse draws a stone tied to a rope, the horse (if I may so say) will be equally drawn back towards the stone: for the distended rope, by the same endeavor to relax or unbend itself, will draw the horse as much towards the stone as it does the stone towards the horse, and will obstruct the progress of the one as much as it advances that of the other. If a body impinge upon another, and by its force change the motion of the other, that body also (because of the equality of the mutual pressure) will undergo an equal change, in its own motion, towards the contrary part. The changes made by these actions are equal, not in the velocities but in the motions of bodies; that is to say, if the bodies are not hindered by any other impediments. For, because the motions are equally changed, the changes of the velocities made towards contrary parts are inversely proportional to the bodies. This law takes place also in attractions, as will be proved in the next scholium.

Corollary I

A body by two forces conjoined will describe the diagonal of a parallelogram, in the same time that it would describe the sides, by those forces apart. . . .

Scholium

Hitherto I have laid down such principles as have been received by mathematicians, and are confirmed by abundance of experiments. By the first two Laws and the first two Corollaries, Galileo discovered that the descent of bodies varied as the square of the time, and that the motion of projectiles was in the curve of a parabola; experience agreeing with both, unless so far as these motions are a little retarded by the resistance of the air. When a body is falling, the uniform force of its gravity acting equally, impresses, in equal intervals of time, equal forces upon that body, and therefore generates equal velocities; and in the whole time impresses a whole force, and generates a whole velocity proportional to the time. And the spaces described in proportional times are as the product of the velocities and the times; that is, as the squares of the times. And when a body is thrown upwards, its uniform gravity impresses forces and reduces velocities proportional to the times; and the times of ascending to the greatest heights are as the velocities to be taken away, and those heights are as the product of the velocities and the times, or as the squares of the velocities. And if a body be projected in any direction, the motion arising from its projection is compounded with the motion arising from its gravity. . . .

And as those bodies are equipollent in the impact and reflection, whose velocities are inversely as their innate forces, so in the use of mechanic instruments those agents are equipollent, and mutually sustain each the contrary pressure of the other, whose velocities, estimated according to the determination of the forces, are inversely as the forces.

So those weights are of equal force to move the arms of a balance, which during the play of the balance are inversely as their velocities upwards and downwards; that is, if the ascent or descent is direct, those weights are of equal force, which are reciprocally as the distances of the points at which they are suspended from the axis of the balance; but if they are turned aside by the interposition of oblique planes, or other obstacles, and made to ascend or descend obliquely, those bodies will be equipollent, which are inversely as the heights of their ascent and descent taken according to the perpendicular; and that on account of the determination of gravity downwards.

And in like manner in the pulley, or in a combination of pulleys, the force of a hand drawing the rope directly, which is to the weight, whether ascending directly or obliquely, as the velocity of the perpendicular ascent of the weight to the velocity of the hand that draws the rope, will sustain the weight.

In clocks and such like instruments, made up from a combination of wheels, the contrary forces that promote and impede the motion of the wheels, if they are inversely as the velocities of the parts of the wheel on which they are impressed, will mutually sustain each other.

The force of the screw to press a body is to the force of the hand that turns the handles by which it is moved as the circular velocity of the handle in that part where it is impelled by the hand is to the progressive velocity of the screw towards the pressed body.

The forces by which the wedge presses or drives the two parts of the wood it cleaves are to the force of the mallet upon the wedge as the progress of the wedge in the direction of the force impressed upon it by the mallet is to the velocity with which the parts of the wood yield to the wedge, in the direction of lines perpendicular to the sides of the wedge. And the like account is to be given of all machines.

The power and use of machines consist only in this, that by diminishing the velocity we may augment the force, and the contrary; from whence, in all sorts of proper machines, we have the solution of this problem: *To move a given weight with a given power,* or with a given force to overcome any other given resistance. For if machines are so contrived that the velocities of the agent and resistant are inversely as their forces, the agent will just sustain the resistant, but with a greater disparity of velocity will overcome it. So that if the disparity of velocities is so great as to overcome all that resistance which commonly arises either from the friction of contiguous bodies as they slide by one another, or from the cohesion of continuous bodies that are to be separated, or from the weights of bodies to be raised, the excess of the force remaining, after all those resistances are overcome, will produce an acceleration of motion proportional thereto, as well in the parts of the machine as in the resisting body. But to treat of mechanics is not my present business. I was aiming only to show by those examples the great extent and certainty of the third Law of Motion. For if we estimate the action of the agent from the product of its force and velocity, and likewise the reaction of the impediment from the product of the velocities of its several parts, and the forces of resistance arising from the friction, cohesion, weight, and acceleration of those parts, the action and reaction in the use of all sorts of machines will be found always equal to one another. And so far as the action is propagated by the intervening instruments, and at last impressed upon the resisting body, the ultimate action will be always contrary to the reaction. . . .

PURPOSES OF PHYSICAL AND MATHEMATICAL SCIENCES

These Propositions naturally lead us to the analogy there is between centripetal forces and the central bodies to which those forces are usually directed; for it is reasonable to suppose that forces which are directed to bodies should depend upon the nature and quantity of those bodies, as we see they do in magnetical experiments. And when such cases occur, we are to compute the attractions of the bodies by assigning to each of their particles its proper force, and then finding the sum of them all. I here use the word *attraction* in general for any endeavor whatever, made by bodies to approach to each other, whether that endeavor arise from the action of the bodies themselves, as tending to each other or agitating each other by spirits emitted; or whether it arises from the action of the ether or of the air, or of any medium whatever, whether corporeal or incorporeal, in any manner impelling bodies placed therein towards each other. In the same general sense I use the word *impulse,* not defining in this treatise the species or physical qualities of forces, but investigating the quantities and mathematical proportions of them; as I observed before in the Definitions. In mathematics we are to investigate the quantities of forces with their proportions consequent upon any conditions supposed; then, when we enter upon physics, we compare those proportions with the phenomena of Nature, that we may know what conditions of those forces answer to the several kinds of attractive bodies. And this preparation being made, we argue more safely concerning the physical species, causes, and proportions of the forces. Let us see, then, with what forces spherical bodies consisting of particles endued with attractive powers in the manner above spoken of must act upon one another; and what kind of motions will follow from them. . . .

RULES OF REASONING IN PHILOSOPHY

Rule I. We are to admit no more causes of natural things than such as are both true and sufficient to explain their appearances.

To this purpose the philosophers say that Nature does nothing in vain, and more is in vain when less will serve; for Nature is pleased with simplicity, and affects not the pomp of superfluous causes.

Rule II. Therefore to the same natural effects we must, as far as possible, assign the same causes.

As to respiration in a man and in a beast; the descent of stones in Europe and in America; the light of our culinary fire and of the sun; the reflection of light in the earth, and in the planets.

Rule III. The qualities of bodies, which admit neither intensification nor remission of degrees, and which are found to belong to all bodies within the reach of our experiments, are to be esteemed the universal qualities of all bodies whatsoever.

For since the qualities of bodies are only known to us by experiments, we are to hold for universal all such as universally agree with experiments; and such as are not liable to diminution can never be quite taken away. We are certainly not to relinquish the evidence of experiments for the sake of dreams and vain fictions of our own devising; nor are we to recede from the analogy of Nature, which is wont to be simple, and always consonant to itself. We no other way know the extension of bodies than by our senses, nor do these reach it in all bodies; but because we perceive extension in all that are sensible, therefore we ascribe it universally to all others also. That abundance of bodies are hard, we learn by experience; and because the hardness of the whole arises from the hardness of the parts, we therefore justly infer the hardness of the undivided particles not only of the bodies we feel but of all others. That all bodies are impenetrable, we gather not from reason, but from sensation. The bodies which we handle we find impenetrable, and thence conclude impenetrability to be an universal property of all bodies whatsoever. That all bodies are movable, and endowed with certain powers (which we call the *inertia*) of persevering in their motion, or in their rest, we only infer from the like properties observed in the bodies which we have seen. The extension, hardness, impenetrability, mobility, and inertia of the whole, result from the extension, hardness, impenetrability, mobility, and inertia of the parts; and hence we conclude the least particles of all bodies to be also all extended, and hard and impenetrable, and movable, and endowed with their proper inertia. And this is the foundation of all philosophy. Moreover, that the divided but contiguous particles of bodies may be separated from one another is matter of observation; and, in the particles that remain undivided, our minds are able to distinguish yet lesser parts, as is mathematically demonstrated. But whether the parts so distinguished, and not yet divided, may, by the powers of Nature, be actually divided and separated from one another, we cannot certainly determine. Yet, had we the proof of but one experiment that any undivided particle, in breaking a hard and solid body, suffered a division, we might by virtue of this rule conclude that the undivided as well as the divided particles may be divided and actually separated to infinity.

Lastly, if it universally appears, by experiments and astronomical observations, that all bodies about the earth gravitate towards the earth, and that in proportion to the quantity of matter which they severally contain; that the moon likewise, according to the quantity of its matter, gravitates towards the earth; that, on the other hand, our sea gravitates towards the moon; and all the planets one towards another; and the comets in like manner towards the sun; we must, in consequence of this rule, universally allow that all bodies whatsoever are endowed with a principle of mutual gravitation. For the argument from the appearances concludes with more force for the universal gravitation of all bodies than for their impenetrability; of which, among those in the celestial regions, we have no experiments, nor any manner of observation. Not that I affirm gravity to be essential to bodies: by their *vis insita* I mean nothing but their inertia. This is immutable. Their gravity is diminished as they recede from the earth.

Rule IV. In experimental philosophy we are to look upon propositions inferred by general induction from phenomena as accurately or very nearly true, notwithstanding any contrary hypotheses that may be imagined, till such time as other phenomena occur, by which they may either be made more accurate, or liable to exceptions.

This rule we must follow, that the argument of induction may not be evaded by hypotheses.

Gravitational Forces Are Universal

Corollary I. Hence the weights of bodies do not depend upon their forms and textures; for if the weights could be altered with the forms, they would be greater or less, according to the variety of forms, in equal matter; altogether against experience.

Corollary II. Universally, all bodies about the earth gravitate towards the earth; and the weights of all, at equal distances from the earth's centre, are as the quantities of matter which they severally contain. This is the quality of all bodies within the reach of our experiments; and therefore (by Rule 3) to be affirmed of all bodies whatsoever. If the ether, or any other body, were either altogether void of gravity, or were to gravitate less in proportion to its quantity of matter, then, because (according to Aristotle, Descartes, and others) there is no difference between that and other bodies but in mere form of matter, by a successive change from form to form, it might be changed at last into a body of the same condition with those which gravitate most in proportion to their quantity of matter; and, on the other hand, the heaviest bodies, acquiring the first form of that body, might by degrees quite lose their gravity. And therefore the weights would depend upon the forms of bodies, and with those forms, might be changed: contrary to what was proved in the preceding Corollary.

Corollary III. All spaces are not equally full; for if all spaces were equally full, then the specific gravity of the fluid which fills the region of the air, on account of the extreme density of the matter, would fall nothing short of the specific gravity of quicksilver, or gold, or any other most dense body; and, therefore, neither gold, nor any other body, could descend in air; for bodies do not descend in fluids, unless they are specifically heavier than the fluids. And if the quantity of matter in a given space can, by any rarefaction, be diminished, what should hinder a diminution to infinity?

Corollary IV. If all the solid particles of all bodies are of the same density, and cannot be rarefied without pores, then a void, space, or vacuum must be granted. By bodies of the same density, I mean those whose inertias are in the proportion of their bulks.

Corollary V. The power of gravity is of a different nature from the power of magnetism; for the magnetic attraction is not as the matter attracted. Some bodies are attracted more by the magnet; others less; most bodies not at all. The power of magnetism in one and the same body may be increased and diminished; and is sometimes far stronger, for the quantity of matter, than the power of gravity; and in receding from the magnet decreases not as the square but almost as the cube of the distance, as nearly as I could judge from some rude observations.

That There Is a Power of Gravity Pertaining to All Bodies, Proportional to the Several Quantities of Matter Which They Contain

That all the planets gravitate one towards another, we have proved before; as well as that the force of gravity towards every one of them, considered apart, is inversely as the square of the distance of places from the centre of the planet. And thence (by Prop. LXIX, Book I, and its Corollaries) it follows, that the gravity tending towards all the planets is proportional to the matter which they contain.

Moreover, since all the parts of any planet A gravitate towards any other planet B; and the gravity of every part is to the gravity of the whole as the matter of the part to the matter of the whole; and (by Law III) to every action corresponds an equal reaction; therefore the planet B will, on the other hand, gravitate towards all the parts of the planet A; and its gravity towards any one part will be to the gravity towards the whole as the matter of the part to the matter of the whole. Q.E.D.

Corollary I. Therefore the force of gravity towards any whole planet arises from, and is compounded of, the forces of gravity towards all its parts. Magnetic and electric attractions afford us examples of this; for all attraction towards the whole arises from the attractions towards the several parts. The thing may be easily understood in gravity, if we consider a greater planet, as formed of a number of lesser planets, meeting together in one globe; for hence it would appear that the force of the whole must arise from the forces of the component parts. If it is objected, that, according to this law, all bodies with us must gravitate one towards another, whereas no such gravitation anywhere appears, I answer, that since the gravitation towards these bodies is to the gravitation towards the whole earth as these bodies are to the whole earth, the gravitation towards them must be far less than to fall under the observation of our senses.

Corollary II. The force of gravity towards the several equal particles of any body is inversely as the square of the distance of places from the particles.

THAT THE MOTIONS OF THE PLANETS IN THE HEAVENS MAY SUBSIST AN EXCEEDINGLY LONG TIME

It is shown in the Scholium of Prop. XXII, Book II, that at the height of 200 miles above the earth the air is more rare than it is at the surface of the earth in the ratio of 30 to 0.0000000000003998, or as 75,000,000,000,000 to 1, nearly. And hence the planet Jupiter, revolving in a medium of the same density with that superior air, would not lose by the resistance of the medium the 1,000,000th part of its motion in 1,000,000 years. In the spaces near the earth the resistance is produced only by the air, exhalations, and vapors. When these are carefully exhausted by the air pump from under the receiver, heavy bodies fall within the receiver with perfect freedom, and without the least sensible resistance: gold itself, and the lightest down, let fall together, will descend with equal velocity; and though they fall through a space of four, six, and eight feet, they will come to the bottom at the same time; as appears from experiments. And therefore, the celestial regions being perfectly void of air and exhalations, the planets and comets meeting no sensible resistance in those spaces will continue their motions through them for an immense tract of time.

To Find the Force of the Moon to Move the Sea

Corollary I. Since the waters attracted by the sun's force rise to the height of 1 foot and 11 1/30 inches, the moon's force will raise the same to the height of 8 feet and 7 5/22 inches; and the joint forces of both will raise the same to the height of 10½ feet; and when the moon is in its perigee to the height of 12½ feet, and more, especially when the wind sets the same way as the tide. And a force of that amount is abundantly sufficient to produce all the motions of the sea, and agrees well with the ratio of those motions; for in such seas as lie free and open from east to west, as in the Pacific sea, and in those tracts of the Atlantic and Ethiopic seas which lie without the tropics, the waters commonly rise to 6, 9, 12, or 15 feet; but in the Pacific sea, which is of a greater depth, as well as of a larger extent, the tides are said to be greater than in the Atlantic and Ethiopic seas; for, to have a full tide raised, an extent of sea from east to west is required of no less than 90 degrees. In the Ethiopic sea, the waters rise to a less height within the tropics than in the temperate zones: because of the narrowness of the sea between Africa and the southern parts of America. In the middle of the open sea the waters cannot rise without falling together, and at the same time, upon both the eastern and western shores, when, notwithstanding, in our narrow seas, they ought to fall on those shores by alternate turns; upon this account there is commonly but a small flood and ebb in such islands as lie far distant from the continent. On the contrary, in some ports, where to fill and empty the bays alternately the waters are with great violence forced in and out through shallow channels, the flood and ebb must be greater than ordinary; as at Plymouth and Chepstow Bridge in England, at the mountains of St. Michael, and the town of Avranches, in Normandy, and at Cambaia and Pegu in the East Indies. In these places the sea is hurried in and out with such violence as sometimes to lay the shores under water, sometimes to leave them dry for many miles. Nor is this force of the influx and efflux to be stopped till it has raised and depressed the waters to 30, 40, or 50 feet and above. And a like account is to be given of long and shallow channels or straits, such as the Magellanic straits, and those channels which environ England. The tide in such ports and straits, by the violence of the influx and efflux, is augmented greatly. But on such shores as lie towards the deep and open sea with a steep descent, where the waters may freely rise and fall without that precipitation of influx and efflux, the ratio of the tides agrees with the forces of the sun and moon.

Corollary II. Since the moon's force to move the sea is to the force of gravity as 1 to 2,871,400, it is evident that this force is inappreciable in statical or hydrostatical experiments, or even in those of pendulums. It is in the tides only that this force shows itself by any sensible effect.

GENERAL SCHOLIUM

Bodies projected in our air suffer no resistance but from the air. Withdraw the air, as is done in Mr. Boyle's vacuum, and the resistance ceases; for in this void a bit of fine down and a piece of solid gold descend with equal velocity. And the same argument must apply to the celestial spaces above the earth's atmosphere; in these spaces, where there is no air to resist their motions, all bodies will move with the greatest freedom; and the planets and comets will constantly pursue their revolutions in orbits given in kind and position, according to the laws above explained; but though these bodies may, indeed, continue in their orbits by the mere laws of gravity, yet they could by no means have at first derived the regular position of the orbits themselves from those laws.

The six primary planets are revolved about the sun in circles concentric with the sun, and with motions directed towards the same parts, and almost in the same plane. Ten moons are revolved about the earth, Jupiter, and Saturn, in circles concentric with them, with the same direction of motion, and nearly in the planes of the orbits of those planets; but it is not to be conceived that mere mechanical causes could give birth to so many regular motions, since the comets range over all parts of the heavens in very eccentric orbits; for by that kind of motion they pass easily through the orbs of the planets, and with great rapidity; and in their aphelions, where they move the slowest, and are detained the longest, they recede to the greatest distances from each other, and hence suffer the least disturbance from their mutual attractions.

This most beautiful system of the sun, planets, and comets, could only proceed from the counsel and dominion of an intelligent and powerful Being. And if the fixed stars are the centres of other like systems, these, being formed by the like wise counsel, must be all subject to the dominion of One; especially since the light of the fixed stars is of the same nature with the light of the sun, and from every system light passes into all the other systems: and lest the systems of the fixed stars should, by their gravity, fall on each other, he hath placed those systems at immense distances from one another.

Hitherto we have explained the phenomena of the heavens and of our sea by the power of gravity, but have not yet assigned the cause of this power. This is certain, that it must proceed from a cause that penetrates to the very centres of the sun and planets, without suffering the least diminution of its force; that operates not according to the quantity of the surfaces of the particles upon which it acts (as mechanical causes used to do), but according to the quantity of the solid matter which they contain, and propagates its virtue on all sides to immense distances, decreasing always as the inverse square of the distances. Gravitation towards the sun is made up out of the gravitations towards the several particles of which the body of the sun is composed; and in receding from the sun decreases accurately as the inverse square of the distances as far as the orbit of Saturn, as evidently appears from the quiescence of the aphelion of the planets; nay, and even to the remotest aphelion of the comets, if those aphelions are also quiescent. But hitherto I have not been able to discover the cause of those properties of gravity from phenomena, and I frame no hypotheses; for whatever is not deduced from the phenomena is to be called an hypothesis; and hypotheses, whether metaphysical or physical, whether of occult qualities or mechanical, have no place in experimental philosophy. In this philosophy particular propositions are inferred from the phenomena, and afterwards rendered general by induction. Thus it was that the impenetrability, the mobility, and the impulsive force of bodies, and the laws of motion and of gravitation, were discovered. And to us it is enough that gravity does really exist, and act according to the laws which we have explained, and abundantly serves to account for all the motions of the celestial bodies, and of our sea.

And now we might add something concerning a certain most subtle spirit which pervades and lies hid in all gross bodies; by the force and action of which spirit the particles of bodies attract one another at near distances, and cohere, if contiguous; and electric bodies operate to greater distances, as well repelling as attracting the neighboring corpuscles; and light is emitted, reflected, refracted, inflected, and heats bodies; and all sensation is excited, and the members of animal bodies move at the command of the will, namely, by the vibrations of this spirit, mutually propagated along the solid filaments of the nerves, from the outward organs of sense to the brain, and from the brain into the muscles. But these are things that cannot be explained in few words, nor are we furnished with that sufficiency of experiments which is required to an accurate determination and demonstration of the laws by which this electric and elastic spirit operates.

"OPTICKS": EXPERIMENTS AND QUESTIONS

THE LIGHT OF THE SUN CONSISTS OF RAYS DIFFERENTLY REFRANGIBLE

THE PROOF BY EXPERIMENTS

IN A VERY DARK CHAMBER, at a round hole, about one third part of an inch broad, made in the shut of a window, I placed a glass prism, whereby the beam of the sun's light, which came in at that hole, might be refracted upwards toward the opposite wall of the chamber, and there form a colored image of the sun. The axis of the prism (that is, the line passing through the middle of the prism from one end of it to the other end parallel to the edge of the refracting angle) was in this and the following experiments perpendicular to the incident rays. About this axis I turned the prism slowly, and saw the refracted light on the wall, or colored image of the sun, first to descend, and then to ascend. Between the descent and ascent, when the image seemed stationary, I stopped the prism, and fixed it in that posture, that it should be moved no more. For in that posture the refractions of the light at the two sides of the refracting angle, that is, at the entrance of the rays into the prism, and at their going out of it, were equal to one another. So also in other experiments, as often as I would have the refractions on both sides the prism to be equal to one another, I noted the place where the image of the sun formed by the refracted light stood still between its two contrary motions, in the common period of its progress and regress; and when the image fell upon that place, I made fast the prism. And in this posture, as the most convenient, it is to be understood that all the prisms are placed in the following experiments, unless where some other posture is described. The prism therefore being placed in this posture, I let the refracted light fall perpendicularly upon a sheet of white paper at the opposite wall of the chamber, and observed the figure and dimensions of the solar image formed on the paper by that light. This image was oblong and not oval, but terminated with two rectilinear and parallel sides, and two semicircular ends. On its sides it was bounded pretty distinctly, but on its ends very confusedly and indistinctly, the light there decaying and vanishing by degrees. The breadth of this image answered to the sun's diameter, and was about two inches and the eighth part of an inch, including the penumbra. For the image was eighteen feet and an half distant from the prism, and at this distance that breadth, if diminished by the diameter of the hole in the window-shut, that is by a quarter of an inch, subtended an angle at the prism of about half a degree, which is the sun's apparent diameter. But the length of the image was about ten inches and a quarter, and the length of the rectilinear sides about eight inches; and the refracting angle of the prism, whereby so great a length was made, was 64 degrees. . . .

This image or spectrum PT was colored, being red at its least refracted end T, and violet at its most refracted end P, and yellow, green and blue in the intermediate spaces. Which agrees with the first proposition, that lights which differ in color, do also differ in refrangibility. The length of the image in the foregoing experiments, I measured from the faintest and outmost red at one end, to the faintest and outmost blue at the other end, excepting only a little penumbra, whose breadth scarce exceeded a quarter of an inch, as was said above. . . .

Question. .Are not gross bodies and light convertible into one another, and may not bodies receive much of their activity from the particles of light which enter their composition? For all fixed bodies being heated emit light so long as they continue sufficiently hot, and light mutually stops in bodies as often as its rays strike upon their parts, as we showed above. I know no· body less apt to shine than water; and yet water by frequent distillations changes into fixed earth, as Mr. Boyle has tried; and then this earth being enabled to endure a sufficient heat, shines by heat like other bodies.

The changing of bodies into light, and light into bodies, is very conformable to the course of nature, which seems delighted with transmutations. Water, which is a very fluid tasteless salt, she changes by heat into vapor, which is a sort of air, and by cold into ice, which is a hard, pellucid, brittle, fusible stone; and this stone returns into water by heat, and vapor returns into water by cold. Earth by heat becomes fire, and by cold returns into earth. Dense bodies by fermentation rarefy into several sorts of air, and this air by fermentation, and sometimes without it, returns into dense bodies. . . .

Question. Have not the small particles of bodies certain powers, virtues, or forces, by which they act at a distance, not only upon the rays of light for reflecting, refracting, and inflecting them, but also upon one another for producing a great part of the phenomena of nature? For it's well known, that bodies act one upon another by the attractions of gravity, magnetism, and electricity; and these instances show the tenor and course of nature, and make it not improbable but that there may be more attractive powers than these. For nature is very consonant and conformable to herself. How these attractions may be performed by impulse, I do not here consider. What I call attractions may be performed by impulse or by some other means unknown to me. I use that word here to signify only in general any force by which bodies tend towards one another, whatsoever be the cause. For we must learn from the phenomena of nature what bodies attract one another, and what are the laws and properties of the attraction, before we enquire the cause by which the attraction is performed. The attractions of gravity, magnetism, and electricity reach to very sensible distances, and so have been observed by vulgar eyes, and there may be others which reach to so small distances as hitherto escape observation; and perhaps electrical attraction may reach to such small distances, even without being excited by friction.

The Scientific Foundation of the Life Insurance Business

EDMUND HALLEY (1656-1742)

THE REAPPEARANCE of Halley's comet in 1910, 1835, and 1759, as predicted by the Astronomer Royal, has thrice reconfirmed the brilliance of "the second most illustrious Anglo-Saxon philosopher." Halley was a jovial *bon vivant* as well as an astronomer, mathematician, classical scholar, ship's captain, hydrographer, diplomat, editor, and publisher (of his friend Newton's *"Principia"* and of the "Philosophical Transactions" of the Royal Society, which he served as clerk and secretary). He founded the Society's dining club, at a London coffeehouse (originally Child's); and tradition has it that during the course of an especially convivial evening with Peter the Great, traveling incognito, he even wheeled the Russian monarch through a yew hedge in a barrow.

But Halley was not afraid of work. He often undertook prodigious mathematical calculations, using the logarithms invented by the Scottish laird, Napier of Merchiston (1550–1617), not only in solving astronomical problems but also to "estimate the degrees of mortality of mankind." His "Breslau Tables of Mortality," given here, are the scientific foundation of the life insurance business. A "landlubber captain" in direct but often troubled command of a British naval vessel, the *Paramour Pink,* Halley voyaged twice to South America to make the first magnetic map (1701), showing dip and variation of the compass. Later he meandered in the English Channel to compile still essential hydrographic data on its tides and currents.

English in the original, "An Estimate of the Degrees of the Mortality of Mankind" first appeared in "Philosophical Transactions" in 1693 (Volume XVII, pp. 596–610; 654–56) while "A Synopsis of the Astronomy of Comets" is included in Volume II of Gregory's "The Elements of Astronomy," published in England in 1715.

"ESTIMATE OF THE DEGREES OF MORTALITY OF MANKIND, DRAWN FROM CURIOUS TABLES OF THE BIRTHS AND FUNERALS AT THE CITY OF BRESLAU; WITH AN ATTEMPT TO ASCERTAIN THE PRICE OF ANNUITIES UPON LIVES"

THE CONTEMPLATION of the mortality of mankind has, besides the moral, its physical and political uses, both which have been some years since most judiciously considered by the curious Sir William Petty, in his "Natural and Political Observations on the Bills of Mortality of London," owned by Captain John Graunt; and since in a like treatise on the Bills of Mortality of Dublin. But the deduction from those Bills of Mortality seemed even to their authors to be defective: first, in that the number of the people was wanting; secondly, that the ages of the people dying was not to be had; and lastly, that both London and Dublin, by reason of the great and casual accession of strangers who die therein (as appeareth in both, by the great excess of the funerals above the births), rendered them incapable of being standards for this purpose; which requires, if it were possible, that the people we treat of should not at all be changed, but die where they were born, without any adventitious increase from abroad or decay by migration elsewhere.

This defect seems in a great measure to be satisfied by the late curious tables of the Bills of Mortality at the city of Breslau, lately communicated to this honorable Society by Mr. Justell, wherein both the ages and sexes of all that die are monthly delivered, and compared with the number of the births;—for five years last past, viz., 1687-91, seeming to be done with all the exactness and sincerity possible.

This city of Breslau is the capital city of the province of Silesia; or, as the Germans call it, Schlesia, and is situated on the western bank of the river Oder, anciently called Viadrus, near the confines of Germany and Poland, and very nigh the latitude of London. It is very far from the sea, and as much a mediterranean place as can be desired, whence the confluence of strangers is but small, and the manufacture of linen employs chiefly the poor people of the place, as well as of the country round about; whence comes that sort of linen we usually call your Schlesia linen, which is the chief if not the only merchandise of the place. For these reasons the people of this city seem most proper for a standard; and the rather for that the births do a small matter exceed the funerals. The only thing wanting is the number of the whole people, which in some measure I have endeavored to supply by the comparison of the mortality of the people of all ages, which I shall from the said Bills trace out with all the accuracy possible.

It appears that in the five years mentioned, viz., from '87 to '91 inclusive, there were born 6193 persons and buried 5869; that is, born per annum, 1238, and buried, 1174; whence an increase of the people may be argued of 64 per annum, or of about a twentieth part, which may perhaps be balanced by the levies for the Emperor's service in his wars. But this being contingent, and the births certain, I will suppose the people of Breslau to be increased by 1238 births annually. Of these it appears by the same tables that 348 do die yearly in the first year of their age, and that but 890 do arrive at a full year's age; and likewise that 198 do die in the five years between one and six complete, taken at a medium; so that but 692 of the persons born do survive six whole years. From this age the infants being arrived at some degree of firmness grow less and less mortal; and it appears that of the whole people of Breslau there die yearly, as in the following table:

Age	Number Dying Yearly	Age	Number Dying Yearly
7	11	54	11
8	11	55	9
9	6	56	9
10–13	5½	57–62	10
14	2	63	12
15–17	3½	64–69	9½
18	5	70	14
19–20	6	71	9
21	4½	72	11
22–26	6½	73–76	9½
27	9	77	6
28	8	78–80	7
29–34	7	81	3
35	7	82–83	4
36	8	84	2
37–41	9½	85–89	1
42	8	90	1
43–44	9	91	1
45	7	[92–97	1][1]
46–48	7	98	0
49	10	99	½
[50–53	10½][1]	100	⅗

From this table it is evident that from the age of nine to about twenty-five there does not die above 6 per annum of each age, which is much about 1 per cent of those that are of those ages. And whereas in the fourteen, fifteen, sixteen, seventeen years there appear to die much fewer, as 2 and 3½, yet that seems rather to be attributed to chance, as are the other irregularities in the series of ages, which would rectify themselves were the number of years much more considerable, as twenty instead of five. And by our own experience in Christ Church Hospital I am informed there die of the young lads much about 1 per cent per annum, they being of the aforesaid ages. From twenty-five to fifty there seem to die from 7 to 8 and 9 per annum of each age; and after that to seventy, they growing more crazy, though the number be

[1] Interpolated by the editors.

much diminished, yet the mortality increases, and there are found to die 10 or 11 of each age per annum. From thence the number of the living being grown very small, they gradually decline until there be none left to die, as may be seen at one view in the table.

From these considerations I have formed the adjoined table, whose uses are manifold and give a more just idea of the state and condition of mankind than anything yet extant that I know of. It exhibits the number of people in the city of Breslau of all ages, from the birth to extreme old age, and thereby shows the chances of mortality at all ages; and likewise how to make a certain estimate of the value of annuities for lives, which hitherto has been only done by an imaginary valuation; also the chances that there are that a person of any age proposed does live to any other age given; with many more, as I shall hereafter show. This table does show the number of persons that are living in the age current annexed thereto (see p. 201).

Thus it appears that the whole people of Breslau does consist of 34,000 souls, being the sum total of the persons of all ages in the table.

The first use hereof is to show the proportion of men able to bear arms in any multitude, which are those between eighteen and fifty-six, rather than sixteen and sixty; the one being generally too weak to bear the fatigues of war and the weight of arms; and the other too crazy and infirm from age, notwithstanding particular instances to the contrary. Under eighteen from the table are found in this city 11,997 persons, 3950 above fifty-six, which together make 15,947; so that the residue to 34,000, being 18,053, are persons between those ages. At least one half thereof are males, or 9027; so that the whole force this city can raise of fencible men, as the Scotch call them, is about 9000, or 9/34, or somewhat more than a quarter of the number of souls; which may perhaps pass for a rule for all other places.

The second use of this table is to show the differing degrees of mortality, or rather vitality, in all ages; for if the number of persons of any age remaining after one year be divided by the difference between that and the number of the age proposed, it shows the odds that there are that a person of that age does not die in a year. For instance, a person of twenty-five years of age has the odds of 560 to 7, or 80 to 1, that he does not die in a year (because that of 567 living of twenty-five years of age there do die no more than 7 in a year, leaving 560 of twenty-six years old).

So likewise for the odds that any person does not die before he attain any proposed age, take the number of the remaining persons of the

Age Current	Persons	Age Current	Persons	Age Current	Persons
1	1000	35	490	69	152
2	855	36	481	70	142
3	798	37	472	71	131
4	760	38	463	72	120
5	732	39	454	73	109
6	710	40	445	74	98
7	692	41	436	75	88
8	680	42	427	76	78
9	670	43	417	77	68
10	661	44	407	78	58
11	653	45	397	79	49
12	646	46	387	80	41
13	640	47	377	81	34
14	634	48	367	82	28
15	628	49	357	83	23
16	622	50	340	84	20
17	616	51	335		
18	610	52	324	Age	Persons
19	604	53	313	7	5547
20	598	54	302	14	4584
21	592	55	292	21	4270
22	586	56	282	28	3964
23	579	57	272	35	3604
24	573	58	262	42	3708
25	567	59	252	49	2709
26	560	60	242	56	2194
27	553	61	232	63	1694
28	546	62	222	70	1204
29	539	63	212	77	692
30	531	64	202	84	253
31	523	65	192	100	107
32	515	66	182		
33	507	67	172		34,000
34	499	68	162		Sum Total

age proposed and divide it by the difference between it and the number of those of the age of the party proposed; and that shows the odds there are between the chances of the party's living or dying. As for instance, what are the odds that a man of forty lives 7 years? Take the number of persons of forty-seven years, which in the table is 377, and subtract it from the number of persons of forty years, which is 445, and the difference is 68; which shows that the persons dying in that 7 years are 68, and that it is 377 to 68, or 5½ to 1, that a man of forty does live seven years. And the like for any other number of years.

Use III. But if it be inquired at what number of years, it is an even lay that a person of any age shall die, this table readily performs it. For if the number of persons living of the age proposed be halved, it will be found by the table at what year the said number is reduced to half by mortality; and that is the age to which it is an even wager that a person of the age proposed shall arrive before he die. As, for instance, a person of thirty years of age is proposed; the number of that age is 531, the half thereof is 265, which number I find to be between fifty-seven and fifty-eight years; so that a man of thirty may reasonably expect to live between twenty-seven and twenty-eight years.

Use IV. By what has been said, the price of insurance upon lives ought to be regulated, and the difference is discovered between the price of insuring the life of a man of twenty and fifty. For example it is 100 to 1 that a man of twenty dies not in a year, and but 38 to 1 for a man of fifty years of age.

Use V. On this depends the valuation of annuities upon lives; for 'tis plain that the purchaser ought to pay for only such a part of the value of the annuity as he has chances that he is living. And this ought to be computed yearly, and the sum of all those yearly values, being added together, will amount to the value of the annuity for the life of the person proposed.

Now the present value of money payable after a term of years, at any given rate of interest, either may be had from tables already computed or, almost as compendiously, by the table of logarithms. For the arithmetical complement of the logarithm of unity, and its yearly interest (that is, of 1.06 for 6 per cent being 9.974694) being multiplied by the number of years proposed, gives the present value of one pound [£1] payable after the end of so many years. Then by the foregoing proposition it will be as the number of persons living after that term of years to the number dead; so are the odds that any one person is alive or dead. And by consequence, as the sum of both, or the number of persons living of the age first proposed to the number remaining after so many years (both given by the table), so the present value of the yearly sum payable after the term proposed, to the sum which ought to be paid for the chance the person has to enjoy such an annuity after so many years. And this being repeated for every year of the person's life, the sum of all the present values of those chances is the true value of the annuity.

This will without doubt appear to be a most laborious calculation; but, it being one of the principal uses of this speculation, and having found some compendia for the work, I took the pains to compute the following table, being the short result of a not ordinary number of arithmetical operations. It shows the value of annuities for every fifth year of age, to the seventieth, as follows:

Age	Years Pur-chased	Age	Years Pur-chased	Age	Years Pur-chased
1	10.28	25	12.27	50	9.21
5	13.40	30	11.72	55	8.51
10	13.44	35	11.12	60	7.60
15	13.33	40	10.57	65	6.54
20	12.78	45	9.91	70	5.32

This shows the great advantage of putting money into the present fund lately granted to their majesties, giving 14 per cent per annum, or at the rate of 7 years purchase for a life when young lives, at the usual rate of interest, are worth about 13 years purchase. It shows likewise the advantage of young lives over those in years; a life of ten years being almost worth 13½ years purchase, whereas one of thirty-six is worth but 11.

Use V. Two lives are likewise valuable by the same rule; for the number of chances of each single life, found in the table, being multiplied together, become the chances of the two lives. . . .

Besides the uses mentioned, it may perhaps not be an unacceptable thing to infer from the same tables how unjustly we repine at the shortness of our lives and think ourselves wronged if we attain not old age; whereas it appears hereby that the one half of those that are born are dead in seventeen years' time, 1238 being in that time reduced to 616. So that, instead of murmuring at what we call an untimely death, we ought with patience and unconcern to submit to that dissolution which is the necessary condition of our perishable materials and of our nice and frail structure and composition; and to account it as a blessing that we have survived, perhaps by many years, that period of life whereat the one half of the whole race of mankind does not arrive.

A second observation I make upon the said table is that the growth and increase of mankind is not so much stinted by anything in the nature of the species as it is from the cautious difficulty most people make to adventure on the state of marriage, from the prospect of the trouble and charge of providing for a family. Nor are the poorer sort of people herein to be blamed, since their difficulty of subsisting is occasioned by the unequal distribution of possessions, all being necessarily fed from the earth, of which yet so few are masters. So that, besides themselves and families, they are yet to work for those who own the ground that feeds them; and of such does by very much the greater part of mankind consist. Otherwise it is plain that there might well be four times as many births as we now find.

For by computation from the table I find that there are nearly 15,000 persons above sixteen and under forty-five, of which at least 7000 are women capable to bear children. Of these notwithstanding there are but 1238 born yearly, which is but little more than a sixth part; so that about one in six of these women do breed yearly; whereas, were they all married, it would not appear strange or unlikely that four of six should bring a child every year.

The political consequences hereof I shall not insist on; only the strength and glory of a king being in the multitude of his subjects, I shall only hint that above all things celibacy ought to be discouraged, as by extraordinary taxing and military service. And those who have numerous families of children should be countenanced and encouraged by such laws as the *Jus trium liberorum* [law of three children] among the Romans; but especially by an effectual care to provide for the subsistence of the poor by finding them employments, whereby they may earn their bread without being chargeable to the public.

RETURN OF A COMET PREDICTED

HITHERTO I have considered the orbits of comets as exactly parabolic; upon which supposition it would follow that comets, being impelled toward the sun by a centripetal force, would descend as from spaces infinitely distant, and by their so falling acquire such a velocity as that they may again fly off into the remotest parts of the universe, moving upwards with a perpetual tendency, so as never to return again to the sun.

But since they appear frequently enough, and since some of them can be found to move with a hyperbolic motion, or a motion swifter than what a comet might acquire by its gravity to the sun, 'tis highly probable they rather move in very eccentric elliptic orbits, and make their returns after long periods of time. For so their number will be determinate, and, perhaps, not so very great. Besides, the space between the sun and the fixed stars is so immense that there is room enough for a comet to revolve, though the period of its revolution be vastly long.

Now the *latus rectum* of an ellipsis is to the *latus rectum* of a parabola, which has the same distance in its perihelium as the distance in the aphelium in the ellipsis is to the whole axis of the ellipsis. And the velocities are in a subduplicate ratio of the same. Wherefore in very eccentric orbits the ratio comes very near to a ratio of equality; and the very small difference which happens on account of the greater velocity in the parabola is easily compensated in determining the situation of the orbit.

The principal use, therefore, of this table of the elements of their motions, and that which indeed induced me to construct it, is that whenever a new comet shall appear we may be able to know, by comparing together the elements, whether it be any of those which has appeared before, and consequently to determine its period, and the axis of its orbit, and to foretell its return. And indeed there are many things which make me believe that the comet which Apian observed in the year 1531 was the same with that which Kepler and Longomontanus more accurately described in the year 1607; and which I myself have seen return, and observed in the year 1682.

All the elements agree, and nothing seems to contradict this my opinion besides the inequality of the periodic revolutions; which inequality is not so great neither, as that it may not be owing to physical causes. For the motion of Saturn is so disturbed by the rest of the planets, especially Jupiter, that the periodic time of that planet is uncertain for some whole days together. How much more, therefore, will a comet be subject to suchlike errors, which rises almost four times higher than Saturn, and whose velocity, though increased but a very little, would be sufficient to change its orbit from an elliptical to a parabolical one.

And I am the more confirmed in my opinion of its being the same; for that in the year 1456, in the summertime, a comet was seen passing retrograde between the earth and the sun, much after the same manner; which, though nobody made observations upon it, yet from its period and the manner of its transit I cannot think different from those I have just now mentioned. And since looking over the histories of comets I find, at an equal interval of time, a comet to have been seen about Easter in the year 1305, which is another double period of 151 years before the former.

Hence I think I may venture to foretell that it will return again in the year 1758.

And if it should then so return we shall have no reason to doubt but the rest may return also. Therefore astronomers have a large field wherein to exercise themselves for many ages, before they will be able to know the number of these many and great bodies revolving about the common center of the sun, and to reduce their motions to certain rules.

The First Mercury Thermometer

DANIEL FAHRENHEIT (1686-1736)

THE APPEALINGLY modest personal story of how he came in 1714 to invent the mercury thermometer and the scale of temperature by which his name is daily remembered in English-speaking countries is told here by a German instrument maker, Daniel Fahrenheit, native of Danzig and long resident in Holland. His was one of the early eighteenth-century contributions to the study of the fascinating but complicated physical problem of heat, which will lead us through the work of Joseph Black, Lavoisier, Rumford, Joule, Helmholtz, Kelvin, and Gibbs. Besides Fahrenheit, others who developed scales of temperature were R. A. F. de Réaumur, French naturalist (1683-1757) whose "Réaumur scale" (1730) is still used in many countries; Anders Celsius (1701-44), Swedish astronomer at Upsala, who first calibrated the centigrade thermometer (1742), divided into 100 degrees between the freezing and boiling points of water and universally employed in scientific work; and William Thomson, Lord Kelvin, who premised an "absolute scale" of temperature on which water boils at 373.7 degrees, freezes at 273.7 degrees, and would—theoretically—cease to exist as water if it could ever be gotten down to absolute zero.

Latin was the language in which Fahrenheit contributed to the "Philosophical Transactions" (Vol. XXXIII, p. 1), in 1734, the paper here given.

A PERSONAL STORY OF INVENTION

ABOUT TEN YEARS AGO I read in the "History of the Sciences" issued by the Royal Academy of Paris that the celebrated Amontons, using a thermometer of his own invention, had discovered that water boils at a fixed degree of heat. I was at once inflamed with a great desire to make for myself a thermometer of the same sort, so that I might with my own eyes perceive this beautiful phenomenon of nature and be convinced of the truth of the experiment.

I therefore attempted to construct a thermometer, but because of my lack of experience in its construction my efforts were in vain, though they were often repeated; and since other matters prevented my going on with the development of the thermometer I postponed any further repetition of my attempts to some more fitting time. Though my powers and my time failed me, yet my zeal did not slacken, and I was always desirous of seeing the outcome of the experiment. It then came into my mind what that most careful observer of natural phenomena had written about the correction of the barometer; for he had observed that the height of the column of mercury in the barometer was a little (though sensibly enough) altered by the varying temperature of the mercury. From this I gathered that a thermometer might perhaps be constructed with mercury, which would not be so hard to construct, and by the use of which it might be possible to carry out the experiment which I so greatly desired to try.

When a thermometer of that sort was made (perhaps imperfect in many ways) the result answered to my prayer; and with great pleasure of mind I observed the truth of the thing.

Three years then passed, in which I was occupied with optical and other work, when I became anxious to try by experiment whether other liquids boiled at fixed degrees of heat.

The results of my experiments are contained in the following table, of which the first column contains the liquids used, the second, their specific gravity, the third, the degree of heat which each liquid attains when boiling.

Liquids	Specific Gravity of Liquids at 48° of HEAT	Degree Attained by Boiling
Spirits of Wine or Alcohol	0.8260	176
Rain Water	1.0000	212
Spirits of Niter	1.2935	242
Lye prepared from wine lees	1.5634	240
Oil of Vitriol	1.8775	546

I thought it best to give the specific gravity of each liquid, so that, if the experiments of others already tried, or which may be tried, give different results, it might be determined whether the difference should be looked for as resulting from differences in the specific gravities or from other causes. The experiments were not made at the same time, and hence the liquids were affected by different degrees of temperature or heat, but since their gravity is altered in a different way and unequally, I reduced it by calculation to the degree 48, which in my thermometers holds the middle place between the limit of the most intense cold obtained artificially in a mixture of water, of ice, and of sal ammoniac, or even of sea salt, and the limit of the heat which is found in the blood of a healthy man.

The Beginning of Modern Dentistry

PIERRE FAUCHARD (1678–1761)

VANITY SET THE STAGE for scientific dentistry. The professional life of the "father of modern dentistry," Pierre Fauchard, began in the reign of the Sun King of France, Louis XIV, at whose gilt-edge, resplendent court good looks—which might be marred by bad teeth—often carried off the fairest favors. Fauchard himself, graceful, elegant, courteous, might have passed for an idle nobleman. Actually he worked hard, first at Angers and later (after 1719) in Paris, at pulling, filling, and reconstructing teeth and studying dental disease. Almost singlehanded he established dentistry as a respectable profession; before him, it had been left to itinerant tinkers, vagabonds, and boorish charlatans who made "tooth drawing" a laughable public spectacle. Fauchard had been trained as a naval surgeon; hence he chose the title "The Surgeon-Dentist" ("Le Chirurgien-Dentiste") for his great two-volume textbook, published at Paris in 1728. Among the "aphorisms of dentistry" here selected and arranged from this first dental textbook none bears repetition today more forcibly than that one relating to the cleansing of the teeth.

French was the language of the original. The English translation by Bernard W. Weinberger, D.D.S., is to be found in "Pierre Fauchard, Surgeon-Dentist" (Minneapolis: The Lancet Press, 1941).

"THE SURGEON-DENTIST": SELECTED APHORISMS

¶The little or no care as to the cleansing of the teeth is ordinarily the cause of all the maladies that destroy them.

¶Such as may read this book without the desire of learning how to operate will find in it instruction upon a thousand matters which will be useful and pleasing to them.

¶It requires greater knowledge and skill to extract teeth than is imagined by most men.

¶The relation between the gums and the teeth is such that the diseases of the one may easily extend to the other.

¶The many formations observed in the teeth are so great that it is impossible to describe all kinds and conditions, and wonderful forms which nature occasionally gives to them. If in the formation of every portion of the human body the same variety were shown, we should seldom find anyone who is not malformed.

¶When caries (tooth decay) proceeds so far as to cause pain, it must be removed and in the carious cavity must be placed a little roll of cotton which has been dipped in cinnamon or clove essence. This must be placed in with care so as not to cause too much pressure.

¶It causes me to wonder that those who devote themselves to teeth drawing commonly have their patients sit down upon the floor, as that seems bad and unskillful.

¶I have made and completed many artificial pieces and have discovered methods to replace the loss of a portion of the teeth or all of them, and these substitutes made artificially have become as completely useful as the natural ones.

¶Natural eyes had been artificially imitated and artificial eyes of enamel had been made, but no one had thought to apply this enamel in the construction of artificial teeth, notwithstanding that artificial plates of teeth have a great advantage over artificial eyes. They add as much to the beauty as do these, and aside from this they help to remove a deficiency of a part of the body whose ugliness shocks anyone who looks at it.

¶People who retain their teeth the longest are generally the healthiest, the strongest, the least liable to be sick—and live the longest.

¶There will shortly be more dentists than persons affected with dental disease.

Living Things Get Their Scientific Names

CAROLUS LINNAEUS (1707-78)

What's in a name? . . . A rose by any other name would smell as sweet.

WITH UPWARDS of a million different species of plants and animals to identify, describe, classify, and discuss intelligibly with others, the scientist (taxonomist) has to take a less romantic and more workable viewpoint toward the names he assigns to living things. The great contribution made to the reviving study of natural history by the wandering Swedish botanist and physician, Linnaeus (Karl von Linné), was the demonstration, bringing order out of chaos, that every living thing could be briefly and usably described and its relation to all the rest inferred simply with two Latin words. Thus Linnaeus was the first to identify man as *Homo sapiens* in the binomial nomenclature which stands to this day. He discusses the importance of correct naming and arranging of nature's many species (which he, son of a clergyman, reverently but wrongly regarded as immutably created) in the preface and introduction, given here, to his *"Critica Botanica"* (Leyden, 1737).

This is one of the many botanical works and catalogues which he prepared when he lived in Holland as personal physician and keeper of the magnificent botanical collection and herbarium of his wealthy patron, George Cliffort, a Dutch merchant. Though he had made several scientific exploring trips, to Lapland, for example, for the Swedish Academy of Sciences, Linnaeus left his native land when he found himself on the uncomfortably wrong side in the political squabbles between two court factions, known as "the Hats" and "the Caps." He returned, after travels in France and England, to become, in 1742, professor of botany at the University of Upsala, and was ennobled, in 1761, by Gustav III.

Latin was the original language of the *"Critica Botanica."* The English translation, by Sir Arthur Hort, revised by Miss M. L. Green, was published for the Ray Society in 1938 by Bernard Quaritch, Ltd., London.

CAROLUS LINNAEUS

Doctor of Medicine
Fellow of the Imperial Academy of
Natural Sciences

CRITICA BOTANICA

In which the names of plants,
generic, specific and varietal
are examined, the better
ones retained and the unworthy
ones rejected;

And in which also

THE PRINCIPLES OF NOMENCLATURE

are set forth
or

Fundamenta Botanica, part IV.

To which is added

A DISCOURSE CONCERNING THE NEED FOR
NATURAL HISTORY

by

JOHANNES BROWALLIUS

Leyden, Conrad Wishoff, 1737.

INTRODUCTION

[DEDICATION]

To the foremost botanist of this age

JO. JAC. DILLENIUS

Doctor of Medicine
Sherardian Professor of Botany in the
University of Oxford
Fellow of the Imperial Academy of
Natural Sciences, and of the
Royal Society.

CAROLUS LINNAEUS

gives greeting.

How GREAT a burden has been laid on the shoulders of botanists by disagreement in names, which is the first step toward barbarism, none should know better than you, most illustrious sir, who are today putting the final touches to Sherard's eagerly awaited *"Phytopinax."* Name changes have, however, hitherto been unavoidable among botanists, so long as no laws had been adopted by which names could be judged. Botanists live in a free state, and for them no eternal law can be prescribed unless it be adopted by the citizens both present and future, and indeed unless it be none other than a law that can be shown by argument and example to be so faultless and indispensable that none better can be devised. Before botany can have such laws as I conceive and desire, the various citizens must advance their own arguments, and then let posterity decide on the best.

In publishing my observations concerning names I set your illustrious name at the head of my little book, that I may not be overwhelmed by the criticisms of malicious persons, who are more anxious to find some way of ridiculing the opinions of others than to make any original contribution to science themselves; for the world today recognizes none greater than you. You know how great a price mankind has always set upon the pleasing of great men: for me, not to displease you means no less. At the same time I thank you, as far as may be done here, for the great kindness with which you never failed to surround me while I pursued the arts at Oxford. It was due to you that I wrote much on the theory of botany, when I myself, properly conscious of how lightly I was laden, should long ago have taken in my sails. It was you, lastly, who, accustomed to weighing everything in the scales of sane reason and principle, opened to me the path which, albeit with hesitant steps, I now seek to tread. Graciously receive, therefore, this offering from your devoted disciple. Farewell, noble sir, and as the unshakable pivot of our science may you long be spared.

CLIFFORTIAN MUSEUM
1737, June 22.

PREFACE

What difficulty has been caused to botanists from the revival of the sciences down to the present day by the invention of new names is known to everyone who has handled the subject; accordingly, when at the beginning of the last century the invasion of barbarism threatened by the vast horde of names in use was stemmed by C. Bauhin, by the general consent of botanists anyone who should in future dare to introduce new names was stigmatized with a black mark, and this was well advised, since, in the circumstances, the stage of learning which the science had at that time reached did not make it possible to frame better names.

When at length the commonwealth of botany had been brought by Morison under an ordered constitution, and an eternal law, taken from nature's book, had been promulgated any who should offend against or transgress this law were branded as ignoramuses. No exception was then allowed: all specific names which did not suit the genus in question were to be banned by an inexorable decree of fate. Alas! What widespread wild confusion ensued toward the end of the last century, while the citizens of the commonwealth of botany were distracted by internal strife beneath the triumvirate of Ray, Tournefort, and Rivinus; Tournefort and Rivinus bestowing different names on each genus and the genera being distributed in one way by the one, and in another by the other. At length Tournefort obtained the victory in regard to genera, and, peace being restored, the world of botanists from that time forward fought shy of the making of any more new names.

However, citizens of the commonwealth never ceased to bring in every day new supplies from foreign lands, to distinguish them as they arrived with more suitable names, to restore what was lacking, to repair

previous disasters, to become wiser and devise better counsels, and to
provide for the general well-being of the commonwealth, though not
one of them took upon himself to introduce a complete reformation of
its constitution (for Vaillant died just as he began to do so) or to bestow
new names. Nevertheless by slow and almost imperceptible steps from
Tournefort's time down to the present day more new names have crept
in than were ever bestowed at the bidding of any dictator; this is obvious if one brings into comparison the new names of Feuillée, Com-
melin, Boerhaave, Vaillant, Pontedera, Dillenius, Ruppius, Scheuchzer,
Knaut, Montius, Heucher, Buxbaum, Micheli, Kramer, Burman, et cetera.
An inevitable necessity compels men to run on rocks which they have
not learned to avoid; sound reason enjoins that they should refuse the
road by which it is unsafe to travel; and so also it is fated that botanists should impose wrong names, so long as the science remains an
untilled field, so long as laws and rules have not been framed on which
they [can] erect as on firm foundations the science of botany; and so
the aforesaid botanists have, under pressure of necessity, corrected most
wisely the faulty names given by their predecessors.

As I turn over the laborious works of the authorities I observe them
busied all day long with discovering plants, describing them, drawing
them, bringing them under genera and classes; I find, however, among
them few philosophers, and hardly any who have attempted to develop
nomenclature, one of the two foundations of botany, though that a name
should remain unshaken is quite as essential as attention to genera.
That they can find no rules given by the ancients for the bestowal of
names, no demonstrations or settled principles, is the complaint of
novices, and equally of men practiced in the science. For any rules of
nomenclature which botanists have brought in from time to time are
too specialized for any certain conclusion to be drawn from them.
Again there is so much disagreement between the authorities that the
reader can hardly determine to which in preference to the others he
should give his allegiance, since satisfactory principles are not everywhere to be seen. Wherefore it is not surprising if, when the novice has
developed into a mature botanist, appearing the while to have done
all that was possible, he in his work makes mistakes over nomenclature
and so comes to burden botany with wrong names.

Wherefore we can never hope for a lasting peace and better times
till botanists come to an agreement among themselves about the fixed
laws in accordance with which judgment can be pronounced on names,
that is to say, good names can be absolutely distinguished from bad

ones, the good ones maintained and the bad ones banished without any exception, so that botany firmly built on immovable principles may remain a fortress inviolable and unshaken.

Before botanists can admit such laws it is necessary that someone among them should take upon himself to offer proposals to be examined by other botanists, so that if they are good they may be confirmed, if unsound they may be convicted of unsoundness and abandoned, while something better is put in their place. But, so long as botanists refuse to make this beginning, so long also will they remain in doubt and uncertainty, and false names will accumulate every day to burden botany. Now as hitherto no one has thought fit to undertake this self-denying task, I have determined to make the attempt; for if a citizen in a free commonwealth may speak his mind it will be at least allowable for me to state my principles among botanists! I have not reached such an extreme of hardihood as to believe that all my reasoning is so firmly based but that someone else may propound reasoning much more mature; still, mine will be true until some other principles are shown to be truer. To you, my dearly beloved botanists, I submit my rules, the rules which I have laid down for myself, and in accordance with which I intend to walk. If they seem to you worthy, let them be used by you also; if not, please propound something better!

Half a year ago, when my *"Genera"*[1] came out, I was advised by not a few to publish my observations on nomenclature, since the principles underlying my *"Fundamenta Botanica,"*[2] were regarded as proved by few, indeed by very few. I was prevented from complying with this request by the laborious and exacting charge of the *"Hortus Cliffortianus"* which I had taken on my shoulders; this charge robbed me of not only all my working hours, but also of the rest necessary to health: for the fixing of the day on which I was to strike camp demanded that the web which I had begun to weave should be completely finished. Hence scarcely a moment was left in which to put my notes together or, having done so, to add the finishing touch. Certain friends to whom I was under deep obligations were of opinion that these observations were essential and that, before going on to the species, I should bring them to the light of day. In obedience to the advice of these gentlemen, to whom I felt morally bound to refuse nothing, I corrected my sketchy observations and handed them over to the publisher. And so it was chiefly lack of time which prevented me from giving the work the

[1]*"Genera Plantarum,"* ed. I, Leyden, 1737.
[2]*"Fundamenta Botanica,"* ed. I, Amsterdam, 1736.

final touches of a leisurely pen and thus securing favor for what I had
said. I was unwilling, however, to keep back the work merely to avoid
the shafts of malevolence, which I have never taken pains to conciliate.
For I knew that wiser men, to whose judgment I commit my views,
do not fall under the spell of meretricious language, but have regard
only to principles and examples, and weigh the value of the practice
which follows from these. Further, I knew that, when I was endeavoring
to be of use, they would not call me to account for shortcomings caused
by lack of time.

Another not less formidable cause of delay confronted me, as no
method was open to me save that of examples. For even if I had piled
up several volumes on names, and had reveled in argument to an immoderate extent, without at the same time giving examples, few would
have gathered my meaning; while from the examples alone, without
arguments, all would easily have understood me, the facts before them
speaking for themselves. How could I indicate the plants without giving
names? How give the names without the authority for them? And so,
in giving examples, I was bound also to cite authorities, and in the
course of doing so I foresaw that I should readily lose the favor of those
whom I was most anxious to please. I myself, who have been the life-
long foe of critics, was bound to be reckoned among the critics. By
"critics" I mean those botanists—alas, too many—who, like despots, busy
themselves with gaining honor and authority for themselves from the
disasters of others, who do not trouble to share some little observation of their own with the learned world, unless they can at the same
time point out that another more learned than themselves has failed to
observe these facts; or again who, like pygmies taking their stand on
the shoulders of giants, boast that they can see further—not realizing
that it is not given to all to see everything, that one has excelled in
describing, another in drawing pictures, another in synonyms, another
in minute observations, another in genera, others again in other departments, since the life of an individual man is not long enough to cover
the whole ground, yet in the meantime notable additions have been
made [to the science] while each has attended to or has restored some
one branch of it.

Wherefore, so as not to injure anyone, I determined to cite only the
wiser authorities and those "whose intellects Prometheus formed of
superior clay," feeling assured that from these men of superior learning
I should win indulgence, as I knew that they would never have attained
to such solid learning had they not preferred the advancement of botany

to every other consideration, and that these wiser persons do not defend their own views out of a blind affection for authority, but make the prosperity of botany their only concern. However, if I should wound other botanists of inferior rank, I ask their pardon, having set this down not out of malice but guided by my love of botany.

Accordingly I have written this "Critique" which I offer to the kind reader as a sequel to Chapters VII–X of my *"Fundamenta Botanica,"* by way of explaining §§ 210–324; and I have appended a considerable number of examples, so that anyone may in accordance with them refer names to the laws which apply to them. However, in the section on specific names I have quoted scarcely any examples, since but few worthy ones are in existence, and even at the present time when we are proud of the vigorous growth of botany few, indeed very few botanists, feel certain what plants are species and what varieties. Wherefore in my *"Hortus Cliffortianus,"*[3] which through the bounty of the generous owner of the garden will presently appear, I have endeavored to mark species with specific names.

I would have the reader know that these rules, subject to considerations hereafter to be taken into account, hold good in the mineral and animal kingdoms, fully as much as in botany, and I crave his favor for my venture.

[3]*"Hortus Cliffortianus,"* Amsterdam, 1737.

V SCIENCE COMES OF AGE:
During the French, American, and Industrial Revolutions

Chemistry: Quantitative Analysis Begins

JOSEPH BLACK (1728–99)

ONE OF THE MIDWIVES of the Industrial Revolution, still shaking the world, must be accounted the taciturn Scottish physician, physicist, and chemist, Joseph Black, professor of chemistry at Glasgow and Edinburgh. In the role of physicist, he investigated the problem of what becomes of the hidden, extra, "latent" quantities of heat needed to turn ice to water and water to steam. His assistant in these experiments was James Watt (1736–1817), no mere teakettle observer, who used his results to improve Newcomen's inefficient steam engine, sometime between 1765 and 1769. Heat thus became a usable form of power—and the Industrial Revolution was on. As chemist and physician, Black began the science of *quantitative* chemical analysis, and proved—contrary to eighteenth-century belief—that air is not a simple substance. The object of the early (1755) experiments which led to his discovery of carbon dioxide, called by him "fixed air," was actually to find an alkali milder than the then much advertised "calcined snails" for medical use in treating kidney and bladder stones.

English was Black's written language, though he was born at Bordeaux, in France. The passage on "Latent Heat" is from his "Lectures on the Elements of Chemistry," published posthumously in 1803. The reconstruction of the "fixed air" experiments from Black's own notes by the distinguished British chemist, Sir William Ramsay, appeared in his "Essays Biographical and Chemical" (London: Constable & Co., Ltd., 1908).

LATENT HEAT: CRUX OF THE STEAM ENGINE

IF WE ATTEND to the manner in which ice and snow melt, when exposed to the air of a warm room, or when a thaw succeeds to frost, we can easily perceive that, however cold they might be at the first, they are soon heated up to their melting point, or begin soon at their surface to be changed into water. And if the common opinion had been well founded, if the complete change of them into water required only the further addition of a very small quantity of heat, the mass, though of considerable size, ought all to be melted in a very few minutes or seconds more, the heat continuing incessantly to be communicated from the air around. Were this really the case, the consequences of it would be dreadful in many cases; for, even as things are at present, the melting of great quantities of snow and ice occasions violent torrents, and great inundations in the cold countries, or in the rivers that come from them. But, were the ice and snow to melt as suddenly as they must necessarily do, were the former opinion of the action of heat in melting them well founded, the torrents and inundations would be incomparably more irresistible and dreadful. They would tear up and sweep away everything, and that so suddenly that mankind should have great difficulty to escape from their ravages. This sudden liquefaction does not actually happen; the masses of ice or snow melt with a very slow progress, and require a long time, especially if they be of a large size, such as are the collections of ice, and wreaths of snow, formed in some places during the winter. These, after they begin to melt, often require many weeks of warm weather before they are totally dissolved into water. This remarkable slowness with which ice is melted enables us to preserve it easily during the summer, in the structures called icehouses. It begins to melt in these, as soon as it is put into them; but, as the building exposes only a small surface to the air and has a very thick covering of thatch, and the access of the external air to the inside of it is prevented as much as possible, the heat penetrates the icehouse with a slow progress, and this, added to the slowness with which the ice itself is *disposed* to melt, protracts the total liquefaction of it so long that some of it remains to the end of summer. In the same manner does snow continue on many mountains during the whole summer, in a melting state, but melting so slowly that the whole of that season is not a sufficient time for its complete liquefaction.

This remarkable slowness with which ice and snow melt struck me as quite inconsistent with the common opinion of the modification of heat, in the liquefaction of bodies.

And this very phenomenon is partly the foundation of the opinion I have proposed; for if we examine what happens we may perceive that a great quantity of heat enters the melting ice, to form the water into which it is changed, and that the length of time necessary for the collection of so much heat from the surrounding bodies is the reason of the slowness with which the ice is liquefied. If any person entertain doubts of the entrance and absorption of heat in the melting ice, he needs only to touch it; he will instantly feel that it rapidly draws heat from his warm hand. He may also examine the bodies that surround it or are in contact with it, all of which he will find deprived by it of a great part of their heat; or if he suspend it by a thread, in the air of a warm room, he may perceive with his hand, or by a thermometer, a stream of cold air descending constantly from the ice; for the air in contact is deprived of a part of its heat, and thereby condensed and made heavier than the warmer air of the rest of the room; it therefore falls downwards, and its place round the ice is immediately supplied by some of the warmer air; but this, in turn, is soon deprived of some heat, and prepared to descend in like manner; and thus there is a constant flow of warm air from around, to the sides of the ice, and a descent of the same in a cold state, from the lower part of the mass, during which operation the ice must necessarily receive a great quantity of heat.

It is, therefore, evident that the melting ice receives heat very fast, but the only effect of this heat is to change it into water, which is not in the least sensibly warmer than the ice was before..A thermometer, applied to the drops or small streams of water, immediately as it comes from the melting ice, will point to the same degree as when it is applied to the ice itself, or if there is any difference it is too small to deserve notice. A great quantity, therefore, of the heat, or of the matter of heat, which enters into the melting ice produces no other effect but to give it fluidity, without augmenting its sensible heat; it appears to be absorbed and concealed within the water, so as not to be discoverable by the application of a thermometer. . . .

I therefore set seriously about making experiments, conformable to the suspicion that I entertained concerning the boiling of fluids. My conjecture, when put into form, was to this purpose. I imagined that, during the boiling, heat is absorbed by the water, and enters into the composition of the vapor produced from it, in the same manner as it is absorbed by ice in melting, and enters into the composition of the produced water. And, as the ostensible effect of the heat, in this last case, consists not in warming the surrounding bodies but in rendering the ice fluid, so, in the case of boiling, the heat absorbed does not warm surrounding bodies but converts the water into vapor. In both cases, considered as the cause of warmth, we do not perceive its presence: it is concealed, or latent, and I gave it the name of "latent heat."

"FIXED AIR": CARBON DIOXIDE

(Experimental data reconstructed from his notebooks by
Sir W. Ramsay.)

[*The object of the experiments leading up to the discovery of "fixed air"
was to discover a "milder alkali" for medical use, especially in treating bladder
and kidney stones. He began his experiments with magnesia.*]

As HIS NOTES SHOW, Black began by holding the old view. He attempted
to catch the igneous matter as it escaped from lime, as it becomes "mild"
on exposure to the air: he appears to have made some experiment with
this view; but his comment was, "Nothing escapes—the cup rises considerably by absorbing air." Two pages further on in his notebook he
records an experiment to compare the loss of weight sustained by an
ounce of chalk when it is calcined with its loss when dissolved in "spirit
of salt," or hydrochloric acid; and he then evidently began to suspect the
reason of "mildness" and "causticity."

Another memorandum, a few pages later, shows that he had solved the
mystery. "When I precipitate lime by a common alkali there is no effervescence. The air quits the alkali for the lime, but it is not lime any
longer, but c.c.c. It now effervesces, which good lime will not."

But we must trace the chain of reasoning which led him to come to this
conclusion.

Having prepared "mild" magnesia by mixing Epsom salt or sulphate
of magnesia with carbonate of potash, or "pearl ashes," he found that it
is "quickly dissolved with violent effervescence or explosion of air by
the acids of vitriol, niter, and of common salt, and by distilled vinegar";
that the properties of these salts—the sulphate, nitrate, chloride, and
acetate of magnesium—differ greatly from those of the common alkaline
earths; that when boiled with "sal ammoniac," or chloride of ammonium,
volatile crystals of smelling salts were deposited on the neck of the retort, which, on mixing with the chloride of magnesium remaining in the
retort, reproduced the "mild" magnesia; that a similar effect is produced
by boiling "mild" magnesia with "any calcareous substance"; while the
acid quits the calcareous salt to unite with the magnesia, "mild" magnesia is again precipitated on addition of a dissolved alkali.

On igniting "mild" magnesia, it changed into a white powder, which
dissolved in acids without effervescence. And the process of ignition had
deprived it of seven twelfths of its weight. Black next turned his attention

to the volatile part; he attempted to restore it by dissolving the magnesia in a sufficient quantity of "spirit of vitriol" or dilute sulphuric acid, and separated it again by the addition of alkali. The resulting white powder now effervesced violently with acids, and "recovered all those properties which it had lost by calcination. It had acquired besides an addition of weight nearly equal to what had been lost in the fire; and as it is found to effervesce with acids, part of the addition must certainly be air."

Black here made an enormous stride; he had weighed a gas in combination. He argues further: "It seems therefore evident that the air was forced from the alkali by the acid, and lodged itself in the magnesia." . . .

But it had yet to be demonstrated that fixed air did not share the properties of ordinary atmospheric air. So Black placed four fluid ounces of lime water, as well as four ounces of common water, under the receiver of an air pump, and exhausted the air; air rose from each in about the same quantity; it therefore appeared that the air which quicklime attracts is of a different kind from that which is mixed with water. Quicklime does not attract air when in its most ordinary form, but is capable of being joined to one particular species only, "which is dispersed through the atmosphere, either in the state of a very subtle powder, or, more probably, in that of an elastic fluid. To this I have given the name of *fixed air,* and perhaps very improperly; but I thought it better to use a word already familiar in philosophy than to invent a new name, before we be more fully acquainted with the nature and properties of this substance."

The Discovery of Oxygen

JOSEPH PRIESTLEY (1733–1804)

No ONE COULD have been more surprised, he tells us here himself, than the largehearted, liberal-minded, nonconformist English clergyman, Joseph Priestley, whose curiosity actually brought him credit for the discovery of oxygen on August 1, 1774. Always a stubborn believer in the false "phlogiston" theory (which held that heat was a ponderable substance), Priestley called his new gas "dephlogisticated air"; Lavoisier gave it the name "oxygen" and made it a foundation stone of modern chemistry. These early chemists, understandably enough, found difficulty in distinguishing between surprisingly different kinds of new "airs" and "gases." "Empyreal air" was the name given to oxygen by Carl Wilhelm Scheele (1742–86), a poor Swedish apothecary, discoverer of chlorine, glycerine, barium, ammonia, and numerous organic acids, whose posthumous notes reveal that he had prepared oxygen before Priestley.

Priestley's earliest scientific interest was not in the "pneumatic chemistry" which he founded, but in electricity, on which he published a substantial history in 1767. When he gave up schoolteaching that same year to become pastor at Leeds, he happened to take a house next to a brewery. The quantities of "fixed air" (carbon dioxide) there available provided opportunities for experiment so fascinating that the ever-curious clergyman was betrayed into chemical pursuits.

Priestley died in the United States, to which he had fled with his family in 1794 after a Birmingham mob, incensed with his liberal theology (he was one of the protagonists of Unitarianism in the United States) and his sympathies with the French Revolution, had ransacked and burned his house.

English in the original, the passage quoted here is from Volume II of Priestley's "Experiments and Observations on Different Kinds of Air" (1775).

"A SURPRISING KIND OF AIR"

Presently, after my return from abroad, I went to work upon the *mercurius calcinatus* [red mercuric oxide], which I had procured from Mr. Cadet; and with a very moderate degree of heat I got from about one fourth of an ounce of it an ounce measure of air, which I observed to be not readily imbibed, either by the substance itself from which it had been expelled (for I suffered them to continue a long time together before I transferred the air to any other place) or by water, in which I suffered this air to stand a considerable time before I made any experiment upon it.

In this air, as I had expected, a candle burned with a vivid flame; but what I observed new at this time (November 19), and which surprised me no less than the fact I had discovered before, was that, whereas a few moments' agitation in water will deprive the modified nitrous air of its property of admitting a candle to burn in it, yet, after more than ten times as much agitation as would be sufficient to produce this alteration in the nitrous air, no sensible change was produced in this. A candle still burned in it with a strong flame; and it did not in the least diminish common air, which I have observed that nitrous air, in this state, in some measure does.

But I was much more surprised when, after two days in which this air had continued in contact with water (by which it was diminished about one twentieth of its bulk), I agitated it violently in water about five minutes and found that a candle still burned in it as well as in common air. The same degree of agitation would have made phlogisticated nitrous air fit for respiration indeed, but it would certainly have extinguished a candle.

These facts fully convinced me that there must be a very material difference between the constitution of air from mercurius calcinatus, and that of phlogisticated nitrous air, notwithstanding their resemblance in some particulars. But though I did not doubt that the air from mer- curius calcinatus was fit for respiration, after being agitated in water, as every kind of air without exception, on which I have tried the experi- ment, had been, I still did not suspect that it was respirable in the first instance; so far was I from having any idea of this air being, what it really was, much superior, in this respect, to the air of the atmosphere.

In this ignorance of the real nature of this kind of air I continued from this time (November) to the first of March following; having, in the meantime, been intent upon my experiments on the vitriolic acid air above recited, and the various modifications of air produced by spirit of niter, an account of which will follow. But in the course of this month I not only ascertained the nature of this kind of air, though very gradually, but was led to it by the complete discovery of the constitution of the air we breathe.

Till this first of March 1775 I had so little suspicion of the air from mercurius calcinatus, et cetera, being wholesome, that I had not even thought of applying it to the test of nitrous air; but thinking (as my reader must imagine I frequently must have done) on the candle burning in it after long agitation in water, it occurred to me at last to make the experiment; and putting one measure of nitrous air to two measures of this air, I found, not only that it was diminished, but that it was dimin- ished quite as much as common air, and that the redness of the mixture was likewise equal to that of a similar mixture of nitrous and common air.

After this I had no doubt but that the air from mercurius calcinatus was fit for respiration, and that it had all the other properties of genuine common air. But I did not take notice of what I might have observed, if I had not been so fully possessed by the notion of there being no air better than common air, that the redness was really deeper, and the diminution something greater than common air would have admitted.

Moreover, this advance in the way of truth, in reality, threw me back into error, making me give up the hypothesis I had first formed, viz., that the mercurius calcinatus had extracted spirit of niter from the air; for I now concluded that all the constituent parts of the air were equally, and in their proper proportion, imbibed in the preparation of this substance, and also in the process of making red lead. For at the same time that I made the above-mentioned experiment on the air from mercurius calcinatus I likewise observed that the air which I had extracted from red lead, after the fixed air was washed out of it, was of the same nature, being diminished by nitrous air like common air; but at the same time I was puzzled to find that air from the red precipitate was diminished in the same manner, though the process for making this substance is quite different from that of making the two others. But to this circumstance I happened not to give much attention.

I wish my reader be not quite tired with the frequent repetition of the word "surprise," and others of similar import; but I must go on in that style a little longer. For the next day I was more surprised than ever I had been before with finding that, after the above-mentioned mixture of nitrous air and the air from mercurius calcinatus had stood all night (in which time the whole diminution must have taken place; and, consequently, had it been common air, it must have been made perfectly noxious and entirely unfit for respiration or inflammation), a candle burned in it, and even better than in common air.

I cannot, at this distance of time, recollect what it was that I had in view in making this experiment; but I know I had no expectation of the real issue of it. Having acquired a considerable degree of readiness in making experiments of this kind, a very slight and evanescent motive would be sufficient to induce me to do it. If, however, I had not happened, for some other purpose, to have had a lighted candle before me I should probably never have made the trial; and the whole train of my future experiments relating to this kind of air might have been prevented.

Still, however, having no conception of the real cause of this phenomenon, I considered it as something very extraordinary; but as a property that was peculiar to air that was extracted from these substances, and adventitious; and I always spoke of the air to my acquaintance as being substantially the same thing with common air.

I particularly remember my telling Dr. Price that I was myself perfectly satisfied of its being common air, as it appeared to be so by the test of nitrous air; though, for the satisfaction of others, I wanted a mouse to make the proof quite complete.

On the eighth of this month I procured a mouse and put it into a glass vessel, containing two ounce measures of the air from mercurius calcinatus. Had it been common air, a full-grown mouse, as this was, would have lived in it about a quarter of an hour. In this air, however, my mouse lived a full half hour; and though it was taken out seemingly dead, it appeared to have been only exceedingly chilled; for, upon being held to fire, it presently revived and appeared not to have received any harm from the experiment.

By this I was confirmed in my conclusion that the air extracted from mercurius calcinatus, et cetera, was at least as good as common air; but I did not certainly conclude that it was any better; because, though one mouse would live only a quarter of an hour in a given quantity of air, I knew it was not impossible but that another mouse might have lived in it half an hour; so little accuracy is there in this method of ascertaining the goodness of air; and indeed I have never had recourse to it for my own satisfaction, since the discovery of that most ready, accurate, and elegant test that nitrous air furnishes. But in this case I had a view to publishing the most generally satisfactory account of my experiments that the nature of the thing would admit of.

This experiment with the mouse, when I had reflected upon it some time, gave me so much suspicion that the air into which I had put it was better than common air that I was induced, the day after, to apply the test of nitrous air to a small part of that very quantity of air which the mouse had breathed so long; so that, had it been common air, I was satisfied it must have been very nearly, if not altogether, as noxious as possible, so as not to be affected by nitrous air; when, to my surprise again, I found that though it had been breathed so long it was still better than common air. For after mixing it with nitrous air, in the usual proportion of two to one, it was diminished in the proportion of four and one half to three and one half; that is, the nitrous air had made it two ninths less than before, and this in a very short space of time; whereas I had never found that, in the longest time, any common air was reduced more than one fifth of its bulk by any proportion of nitrous air, nor more than one fourth by any phlogistic process whatever. Thinking of this extraordinary fact upon my pillow, the next morning I put another measure of nitrous air to the same mixture, and to my utter astonishment found that it was farther diminished to almost one half of its original quantity. I then put a third measure to it; but this did not diminish it any farther; but, however, left it one measure less than it was even after the mouse had been taken out of it.

Being now fully satisfied that this air, even after the mouse had breathed it half an hour, was much better than common air; and having a quantity of it still left, sufficient for the experiment, viz., an ounce measure and a half, I put the mouse into it; when I observed that it seemed to feel no shock upon being put into it, evident signs of which would have been visible if the air had not been very wholesome; but that it remained perfectly at its ease another full half hour, when I took it out quite lively and vigorous. Measuring the air the next day, I found it to be reduced from one and one half to two thirds of an ounce measure. And after this, if I remember well (for in my register of the day I only find it noted that it was considerably diminished by nitrous air), it was nearly as good as common air. It was evident, indeed, from the mouse having been taken out quite vigorous, that the air could not have been rendered very noxious.

For my further satisfaction I procured another mouse, and putting it into less than two ounce measures of air extracted from mercurius calcinatus and air from red precipitate (which, having found them to be of the same quality, I had mixed together), it lived three quarters of an hour. But not having had the precaution to set the vessel in a warm place, I suspect that the mouse died of cold. However, as it had lived three times as long as it could probably have lived in the same quantity of common air, and I did not expect much accuracy from this kind of a test, I did not think it necessary to make any more experiments with mice.

Being now fully satisfied of the superior goodness of this kind of air, I proceeded to measure that degree of purity with as much accuracy as I could, by the test of nitrous air; and I began with putting one measure of nitrous air to two measures of this air, as if I had been examining common air; and now I observed that the diminution was evidently greater than common air would have suffered by the same treatment. A second measure of nitrous air reduced it to two thirds of its original quantity, and a third measure to one half. Suspecting that the diminution could not proceed much farther, I then added only half a measure of nitrous air, by which it was diminished still more; but not much, and another half measure made it more than half of its original quantity; so that, in this case, two measures of this air took more than two measures of nitrous air and yet remained less than half of what it was. Five measures brought it pretty exactly to its original dimensions.

At the same time air from the red precipitate was diminished in the same proportion as that from mercurius calcinatus, five measures of nitrous air being received by two measures of this without any increase of dimensions. Now as common air takes about one half of its bulk of nitrous air before it begins to receive any addition to its dimensions from more nitrous air, and this air took more than four half measures before it ceased to be diminished by more nitrous air, and even five half measures made no addition to its original dimensions, I conclude that it was between four and five times as good as common air. It will be seen that I have since procured air better than this, even between five and six times as good as the best common air that I have ever met with.

Father of Modern Chemistry

ANTOINE LAVOISIER (1743-94)

OXYGEN SUPPLY at high altitudes is one of the critical problems of modern aviation. Fliers need it; internal-combustion engines need it. Yet it was scarcely a hundred and fifty years ago that the scrupulous but imaginative French scientist and tax collector, Antoine Lavoisier, the father of modern chemistry, demonstrated beyond cavil that the process of combustion, whether it takes place inside the body, the furnace, or the engine, is nothing more than the uniting of other elements with oxygen. We call the process oxidation; it may take place slowly, as when iron rusts, or rapidly, as when gasoline explodes. It goes on all the time in the human and animal body.

In determining the properties of oxygen and its role in combustion, Lavoisier overthrew for all time the false doctrine of phlogiston, the foolish theory that heat itself (or caloric, as it was called) was an invisible substance or fluid, "the principle of fire," that somehow entered into objects that were set on the fire and vanished from them as they cooled.

Lavoisier lived during, but not through, the French Revolution. He was a victim of the Terror of 1794—guillotined in Paris. "The Republic has no need of scientists (savants)," said the judge who passed sentence. "It took but a moment to cut off his head; it will take a century to produce another like it," mournfully observed his friend Lagrange, the mathematician. Lavoisier's untimely doom undoubtedly arrived not as a result of his manifold scientific activities—for the Republic commissioned many scientists to aid it in producing gunpowder and armament—but rather because he had been active in the management of the Ferme Générale, a private company to which the French Government under the Louis had farmed out the task of collecting taxes.

Lavoisier had a genius for systematic organization. His "Elementary Treatise on Chemistry" (1789) represented the "first great synthesis of chemical principles." He had also a passion for scrupulous exactness in measurements and this was the key to the new chemistry. He was always busy with balances, weighing chemical elements and compounds exactly before and after reactions; he devised ingenious new laboratory equipment that made it practical to weigh gases; he emphasized the importance of the chemical equation as a means of expressing chemical experiments in quantitative terms. It was quite fitting that he should have been a member of the commission appointed in 1790 to establish a uniform system—the decimal system—of weights and measures. It is not improbable that the desperate need for talents of organization and exactitude drew a reluctant Lavoisier into the fatal activity of tax management.

French was the language in which Lavoisier composed the many famous memoirs he presented to the French Royal Academy of Sciences. The passages quoted here are from "Experiments on Respiration of Animals" (*"Expériences sur la respiration des animaux"*), delivered in 1777 and printed in the Academy's chronicles. The English translation, by Thomas Henry, was made the same year.

THE RESPIRATION OF ANIMALS

OF ALL the phenomena of the animal economy, none is more striking, none more worthy the attention of philosophers and physiologists than those which accompany respiration. Little as our acquaintance is with the object of this singular function, we are satisfied that it is essential to life and that it cannot be suspended for any time without exposing the animal to the danger of immediate death. . . .

The experiments of some philosophers, and especially those of Messrs. Hales and Cigna, had begun to afford some light on this important object; and Dr. Priestley has lately published a treatise in which he has greatly extended the bounds of our knowledge; and has endeavored to prove, by a number of very ingenious, delicate, and novel experiments, that the respiration of animals has the property of phlogisticating air, in a similar manner to what is effected by the calcination of metals and many other chemical processes; and that the air ceases not to be respirable till the instant when it becomes surcharged, or at least saturated, with phlogiston.

However probable the theory of this celebrated philosopher may at first sight appear; however numerous and well conducted may be the experiments by which he endeavors to support it, I must confess I have found it so contradictory to a great number of phenomena that I could not but entertain some doubts of it. I have accordingly proceeded on a different plan and have found myself led irresistibly, by the consequences of my experiments, to very different conclusions.

Now air which has served for the calcination of metals is, as we have already seen, nothing but the mephitic residuum of atmospheric air, the highly respirable part of which has combined with the mercury, during the calcination: and the air which has served the purposes of respiration, when deprived of the fixed air, is exactly the same; and, in fact, having combined with the latter residuum about one half of its bulk of dephlogisticated air, extracted from the calx of mercury, I re-established it in its former state and rendered it equally fit for respiration, combustion, et cetera, as common air, by the same method as that I pursued with air vitiated by the calcination of mercury.

The result of these experiments is that, to restore air that has been vitiated by respiration to the state of common respirable air, two effects must be produced: first, to deprive it of the fixed air (carbon dioxide) it contains, by means of quicklime or caustic alkali; secondly, to restore to it a quantity of highly respirable or dephlogisticated air, equal to that which it has lost. Respiration, therefore, acts inversely to these two effects, and I find myself in this respect led to two consequences equally probable, and between which my present experience does not enable me to pronounce. . . .

The first of these opinions is supported by an experiment which I have already communicated to the Academy. For I have shown in a memoir, read at our public Easter meeting, 1775, that dephlogisticated air (oxygen) may be wholly converted into fixed air by an addition of powdered charcoal; and in other memoirs I have proved that this conversion may be effected by several other methods: it is possible, therefore, that respiration may possess the same property, and that dephlogisticated air, when taken into the lungs, is thrown out again as fixed air. . . . Does it not then follow, from all these facts, that this pure species of air has the property of combining with the blood and that this combination constitutes its red color? But whichever of these two opinions we embrace, whether that the respirable portion of the air combines with the blood, or that it is changed into fixed air in passing through the lungs; or lastly, as I am inclined to believe, that both these effects take place in the act of respiration, we may, from facts alone, consider as proved:

I. That respiration acts only on the portion of pure or dephlogisticated air contained in the atmosphere; that the residuum or mephitic part is a merely passive medium which enters into the lungs and departs from them nearly in the same state, without change or alteration.

II. That the calcination of metals, in a given quantity of atmospheric air, is effected, as I have already often declared, only in proportion as the dephlogisticated air, which it contains, has been drained and combined with the metal.

III. That, in like manner, if an animal be confined in a given quantity of air, it will perish as soon as it has absorbed, or converted into fixed air, the major part of the respirable portion of air, and the remainder is reduced to a mephitic state.

IV. That the species of mephitic air, which remains after the calcination of metals, is in no wise different, according to all the experiments I have made, from that remaining after the respiration of animals; provided always that the latter residuum has been freed from its fixed air; that these two residuums may be substituted for each other in every experiment, and that they may each be restored to the state of atmospheric air by a quantity of dephlogisticated air equal to that of which they had been deprived. A new proof of this last fact is that, if the proportion of this highly respirable air, contained in a given quantity of the atmospheric, be increased or diminished, in such proportion will be the quantity of metal which we shall be capable of calcining in it, and, to a certain point, the time which animals will be capable of living in it.

The Atomic Theory

JOHN DALTON (1766–1844)

A COLOR-BLIND schoolteacher, son of a Westmoreland hand-loom weaver, John Dalton followed the quantitative concepts of Lavoisier with an atomic theory that put the newborn *science* of chemistry on a still firmer basis. Taking the lightest of the "indestructible" elements, hydrogen, as a unit (1) of measure, he guessed that the elements would combine in ratios *by weight* of small whole numbers: the "law of multiple proportions." Thus hydrogen and oxygen combine in the ratio of 2 to 1, by weight, to make water, H_2O. The modern system of chemical symbols, in which capital H represents a mass of hydrogen equivalent to its atomic weight, O oxygen, Hg mercury, et cetera, was introduced somewhat later by the Swedish chemist, Jöns Jakob Berzelius (1779–1848).

Dalton's serviceable but not altogether correct ideas were included in his "New System of Chemical Philosophy"; the first of the three volumes, here quoted, was published in 1808. This publication soon (1811, 1814) led to the enunciation of another important physical law, variously called after three men who had a mind in making it: an Italian count, Amadeo Avogadro (1776–1856), and two Frenchmen, Gay-Lussac (1778–1850) and André Ampère (1775–1836), whose better-known work in electricity is memorialized in the unit of electrical current, the ampere. "Avogadro's," "Gay-Lussac's," or "Ampere's law" states that under the same conditions of temperature and pressure equal volumes of *all* gases contain the same number of molecules.

One must distinguish between "atoms" of elementary substances, like H and O, and the molecules of their gaseous compounds, like steam, which is still water, H_2O, changed in its *physical* state but not in its chemical.

Like these other early nineteenth-century scientists, Dalton was not exclusively a chemist. His color blindness spurred him to investigate and write on this interesting physiological phenomenon, which has since been called "Daltonism." (His brother suffered the condition also.) Further, he kept a meteorological diary (as the Rev. Gilbert White had done in the parish of Selborne much earlier) and was familiar enough with the phenomena of electricity to assert, correctly, in 1793 that the aurora borealis, that colorful display of northern lights, was electrical in origin.

English is the original language of "A New System of Chemical Philosophy" (1808).

"A NEW SYSTEM OF CHEMICAL PHILOSOPHY"

ON THE CONSTITUTION OF BODIES

THERE ARE three distinctions in the kinds of bodies, or three states, which have more especially claimed the attention of philosophical chemists;

namely, those which are marked by the terms *elastic fluids, liquids,* and *solids.* A very famous instance is exhibited to us in water, of a body, which, in certain circumstances, is capable of assuming all the three states. In steam we recognize a perfectly elastic fluid, in water a perfect liquid, and in ice a complete solid. These observations have tacitly led to the conclusion, which seems universally adopted, that all bodies of sensible magnitude, whether liquid or solid, are constituted of a vast number of extremely small particles or atoms of matter bound together by a force of attraction, which is more or less powerful according to circumstances. . . .

Whether the ultimate particles of a body, such as water, are all alike, that is, of the same figure, weight, et cetera, is a question of some importance. From what is known, we have no reason to apprehend a diversity in these particulars: if it does exist in water it must equally exist in the elements constituting water, namely, hydrogen and oxygen. Now it is scarcely possible to conceive how the aggregates of dissimilar particles should be so uniformly the same. If some of the particles of water were heavier than others, if a parcel of the liquid on any occasion were constituted principally of these heavier particles, it must be supposed to affect the specific gravity of the mass, a circumstance not known.[1] Similar observations may be made on other substances. Therefore we may conclude that *the ultimate particles of all homogeneous bodies are perfectly alike in weight, figure, et cetera.* In other words, every particle of water is like every other particle of water; every particle of hydrogen is like every other particle of hydrogen, et cetera.

ON CHEMICAL SYNTHESIS

When any body exists in the elastic state its ultimate particles are separated from each other to a much greater distance than in any other state; each particle occupies the center of a comparatively large sphere and supports its dignity by keeping all the rest which, by their gravity or otherwise, are disposed to encroach upon it at a respectful distance. When we attempt to conceive the *number* of particles in an atmosphere it is somewhat like attempting to conceive the number of stars in the universe: we are confounded with the thought. But if we limit the subject by taking a given volume of any gas, we seem persuaded that, let the divisions be ever so minute, the number of particles must be finite;

[1] Known today if deuterium oxide, known as "heavy water," made with "heavy" isotopes of hydrogen, may be so considered.

just as in a given space of the universe the number of stars and planets cannot be infinite.[2]

Chemical analysis and synthesis go no farther than to the separation of particles one from another, and to their reunion. No new creation or destruction of matter is within the reach of chemical agency. We might as well attempt to introduce a new planet into the solar system, or to annihilate one already in existence, as to create or destroy a particle of hydrogen. All the changes we can produce consist in separating particles that are in a state of cohesion or combination, and joining those that were previously at a distance.

In all chemical investigations it has justly been considered an important object to ascertain the relative *weights* of the simples which constitute a compound. But unfortunately the inquiry has terminated here; whereas from the relative weights in the mass the relative weights of the ultimate particles or atoms of the bodies might have been inferred, from which their number and weight in various other compounds would appear, in order to assist and to guide future investigations, and to correct their results.

The First Great Name in American Science

BENJAMIN FRANKLIN (1706–90)

THOUGH HIS CAREER as a printer, publisher, almanac keeper, diplomat, statesman, signer of the Declaration of Independence, and member of the Constitutional Convention—not to mention his exploit with the kite, the key, and the lightning bolt—are well known, too few, perhaps, appreciate that "Poor Richard," Benjamin Franklin, is the first great name in American science. Among his significant scientific contributions, most of which preceded his diplomatic days, can be named invention of the "Franklin stove" and bifocal spectacles; founding of hospitals, libraries, and the first American scientific society, the American Philosophical Society (1743); improvement in public works, such as street lighting and postal systems; description of lead poisoning, an industrial disease of the print shop; and experiments in electricity. Franklin's famous kite experi-

[2]As demonstrated by Archimedes, p. 13.

ment, performed in June 1752 in Philadelphia, was undertaken to prove that lightning, fashioned in the skies by the gods of the weather, was the same stuff that men were making on earth with their newly invented "static electricity machines" and storing in "Mr. Muschenbroek's wonderful bottle," the foil-lined Leyden jar out of Holland. Franklin had completely investigated this "shocking instrument" a year or two after its invention (1745), and had concluded that there were two kinds of electricity, which he named positive and negative.

Franklin was not the only founding father of the Republic who was interested in science. When Thomas Jefferson (1743–1826), author of the Declaration of Independence, rode horseback to his inauguration as third President of the United States in 1801, he carried in his saddlebags specimens of fossil bones on which to lecture before the American Philosophical Society.

English was the language of Franklin's letters, not intended for publication. They were first printed in London (1774), having been gathered together by an anonymous editor who issued them under the title: "Experiments and Observations on Electricity Made at Philadephia in America."

EXPERIMENTS IN ELECTRICITY: THE KITE, THE KEY, AND THE LIGHTNING BOLT; THE ELECTRICAL COOKER

To

PETER COLLINSON

[Philadelphia], 1749

SIR,

. . . Chagrined a little that we have been hitherto able to produce nothing in this way of use to mankind and the hot weather coming on, when electrical experiments are not so agreeable, it is proposed to put an end to them for this season, somewhat humorously, in a party of pleasure on the banks of *Skuylkil.* Spirits, at the same time, are to be fired by a spark sent from side to side through the river, without any other conductor than the water; an experiment which we some time since performed, to the amazement of many.

A turkey is to be killed for our dinner by the *electrical shock,* and roasted by the *electrical jack,* before a fire kindled by the *electrified bottle:* when the healths of all the famous electricians in *England, Holland,*

France, and *Germany* are to be drank in *electrified bumpers,* under the discharge of guns from the *electrical battery*.

April 29, 1749

To

PETER COLLINSON

[Philadelphia] October 19, 1752

SIR,

As frequent mention is made in public papers from *Europe* of the success of the *Philadelphia* experiment for drawing the electric fire from clouds by means of pointed rods of iron erected on high buildings, and, it may be agreeable to the curious to be informed, that the same experiment has succeeded in *Philadelphia,* though made in a different and more easy manner, which is as follows:

Make a small cross of two light strips of cedar, the arms so long as to reach to the four corners of a large thin silk handkerchief when extended; tie the corners of the handkerchief to the extremities of the cross, so you have the body of a kite; which being properly accommodated with a tail, loop, and string, will rise in the air, like those made of paper; but this being of silk, is fitter to bear the wet and wind of a thunder-gust without tearing. To the top of the upright stick of the cross is to be fixed a very sharp-pointed wire, rising a foot or more above the wood. To the end of the twine, next the hand, is to be tied a silk ribbon, and where the silk and twine join, a key may be fastened. This kite is to be raised when a thunder-gust appears to be coming on, and the person who holds the string must stand within a door or window or under some cover, so that the silk ribbon may not be wet; and care must be taken that the twine does not touch the frame of the door or window. As soon as any of the thunder-clouds come over the kite, the pointed wire will draw the electric fire from them, and the kite, with all the twine, will be electrified, and the loose filaments of the twine will stand out every way, and be attracted by an approaching finger. And when the rain has wet the kite and twine, so that it can conduct the electric fire freely, you will find it stream out plentifully from the key on the approach of your knuckle. At this key the phial may be charged; and from electric fire thus obtained, spirits may be kindled, and all the other electric experiments be performed, which are usually done by the help of a rubbed glass globe or tube, and thereby the sameness of the electric matter with that of lightning completely demonstrated.

B. FRANKLIN

LEAD POISONING DESCRIBED

To

BENJAMIN VAUGHAN

Philada, July 31, 1786

DEAR FRIEND,

I recollect, that, when I had the great pleasure of seeing you at South-
ampton, now a 12month since, we had some conversation on the bad
effects of lead taken inwardly; and that at your request I promis'd to
send you in writing a particular account of several facts I then mention'd
to you, of which you thought some good use might be made. I now sit
down to fulfil that promise.

The first thing I remember of this kind was a general discourse in
Boston, when I was a boy, of a complaint from North Carolina against
New England rum, that it poison'd their people, giving them the dry
bellyach, with a loss of the use of their limbs. The distilleries being
examin'd on the occasion, it was found that several of them used leaden
still-heads and worms, and the physicians were of opinion, that the mischief was occasioned by that use of lead. The legislature of Massachusetts
thereupon pass'd an Act, prohibiting under severe penalties the use of
such still-heads and worms thereafter. Inclos'd I send you a copy of the
Act, taken from my printed law-book.

In 1724, being in London, I went to work in the printing-house of Mr.
Palmer, Bartholomew Close, as a compositor. I there found a practice,
I had never seen before, of drying a case of types (which are wet in
distribution) by placing it sloping before the fire. I found this had the
additional advantage, when the types were not only dry'd but heated, of
being comfortable to the hands working over them in cold weather. I
therefore sometimes heated my case when the types did not want drying.
But an old workman, observing it, advis'd me not to do so, telling me I
might lose the use of my hands by it, as two of our companions had
nearly done, one of whom that us'd to earn his guinea a week, could not
then make more than ten shillings, and the other, who had the dangles,
but seven and sixpence. This, with a kind of obscure pain, that I had
sometimes felt, as it were in the bones of my hand when working over
the types made very hot, induced me to omit the practice. But talking
afterwards with Mr. James, a letter-founder in the same Close, and asking

him if his people, who work'd over the little furnaces of melted metal, were not subject to that disorder; he made light of any danger from the effluvia, but ascribed it to particles of the metal swallow'd with their food by slovenly workmen, who went to their meals after handling the metal, without well washing their fingers, so that some of the metalline particles were taken off by their bread and eaten with it. This appeared to have some reason in it. But the pain I had experienc'd made me still afraid of those effluvia.

Being in Derbyshire at some of the furnaces for smelting of lead ore, I was told, that the smoke of those furnaces was pernicious to the neighbouring grass and other vegetables; but I do not recollect to have heard any thing of the effect of such vegetables eaten by animals. It may be well to make the enquiry.

In America I have often observ'd, that on the roofs of our shingled houses, where moss is apt to grow in northern exposures, if there be any thing on the roof painted with white lead, such as balusters, or frames of dormant windows, etc., there is constantly a streak on the shingles from such paint down to the eaves, on which no moss will grow, but the wood remains constantly clean and free from it. We seldom drink rain water that falls on our houses; and if we did, perhaps the small quantity of lead, descending from such paint, might not be sufficient to produce any sensible ill effect on our bodies. But I have been told of a case in Europe, I forgot the place, where a whole family was afflicted with what we call the dry bellyach, or *Colica Pictonum,* by drinking rain-water. It was at a country-seat, which, being situated too high to have the advantage of a well, was supply'd with water from a tank, which received the water from the leaded roofs. This had been drunk several years without mischief; but some young trees planted near the house growing up above the roof, and shedding their leaves upon it, it was suppos'd that an acid in those leaves had corroded the lead they cover'd and furnish'd the water of that year with its baneful particles and qualities.

When I was in Paris with Sir John Pringle in 1767, he visited *La Charité,* a hospital particularly famous for the cure of that malady, and brought from thence a pamphlet containing a list of the names of persons, specifying their professions or trades, who had been cured there. I had the curiosity to examine that list, and found that all the patients were of trades, that, some way or other, use or work in lead; such as plumbers, glaziers, painters, etc., excepting only two kinds, stonecutters and soldiers. These I could not reconcile to my notion, that lead was the cause of that disorder. But on my mentioning this difficulty to a physician of that hospital, he inform'd me that the stonecutters are continually using melted lead to fix the ends of iron balustrades in stone; and that the soldiers had been employ'd by painters, as labourers, in grinding of colours.

This, my dear friend, is all I can at present recollect on the subject. You will see by it, that the opinion of this mischievous effect from lead is at least above sixty years old; and you will observe with concern how long a useful truth may be known and exist, before it is generally receiv'd and practis'd on.

I am, ever, yours most affectionately,
B. FRANKLIN

INVENTION OF BIFOCAL SPECTACLES

To

GEORGE WHATLEY

Passy, May 23, 1785

. . . By Mr. Dollond's saying, that my double spectacles can only serve particular eyes, I doubt he has not been rightly informed of their construction. I imagine it will be found pretty generally true, that the same convexity of glass, through which a man sees clearest and best at the distance proper for reading, is not the best for greater distances. I therefore had formerly two pair of spectacles, which I shifted occasionally, as in travelling I sometimes read, and often wanted to regard the prospects. Finding this change troublesome, and not always sufficiently ready, I had the glasses cut, and half of each kind associated in the same circle, thus,

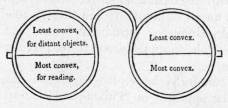

By this means, as I wear my spectacles constantly, I have only to move my eyes up or down, as I want to see distinctly far or near, the proper glasses being always ready. This I find more particularly convenient since my being in France, the glasses that serve me best at table to see what I eat, not being the best to see the faces of those on the other side of the table who speak to me; and when one's ears are not well accustomed to the sounds of a language, a sight of the movements in the features of him that speaks helps to explain; so that I understand French better by the help of my spectacles. . . .

                                                                B. FRANKLIN

Cannon and Casserole: Physics and "Social Sciences"

BENJAMIN THOMPSON (COUNT RUMFORD)
(1753–1814)

PRESIDENT FRANKLIN ROOSEVELT named this Massachusetts-born farm boy, Benjamin Thompson, later Count Rumford of the Holy Roman Empire, as one of the four men who had most influenced his thinking. Rumford was one of the earliest "social scientists," as well as the inquiring physicist, who beautifully demonstrated by experiments (1798) on the boring of brass cannon that heat is not a ponderable substance but a form of *motion*. After fighting first on the Revolutionary and then on the "Loyalist" side in the American Revolution, adventurous young Thompson went to England, where he superintended manufacture of artillery pieces; thence to Bavaria, where the Elector made him Minister of War and Interior and gave him the task, which he successfully met, of dispersing the bread lines of the beggared country. In the course of carrying out what would now be called "social security" policies, the new-made count (1791) discovered technical means of improving housing conditions and economical means of preparing and keeping food. For example, he eliminated smoky chimneys; introduced central heating; invented the chafing dish, casserole, steam table, and coffee percolator. He extolled the virtues of coffee.

English was Rumford's native language. The classic paper on heat, here quoted, first appeared in "Philosophical Transactions" (Vol. 88), 1798.

HEAT IS A FORM OF MOTION: AN EXPERIMENT IN BORING CANNON

IT FREQUENTLY HAPPENS that in the ordinary affairs and occupations of life opportunities present themselves of contemplating some of the most curious operations of nature; and very interesting philosophical experiments might often be made, almost without trouble or expense, by means of machinery contrived for the mere mechanical purposes of the arts and manufactures.

I have frequently had occasion to make this observation, and am persuaded that a habit of keeping the eyes open to everything that is going on in the ordinary course of the business of life has oftener led, as it were by accident, or in the playful excursions of the imagination, put into action by contemplating the most common appearances, to useful doubts, and sensible schemes for investigation and improvement, than all the more intense meditations of philosophers, in the hours expressly set apart for study.

It was by accident that I was led to make the experiments of which I am about to give an account; and, though they are not perhaps of sufficient importance to merit so formal an introduction, I cannot help flattering myself that they will be thought curious in several respects, and worthy of the honor of being made known to the Royal Society.

Being engaged, lately, in superintending the boring of cannon, in the workshops of the military arsenal at Munich, I was struck with the very considerable degree of heat which a brass gun acquires, in a short time, in being bored; and with the still more intense heat (much greater than that of boiling water, as I found by experiment) of the metallic chips separated from it by the borer.

The more I meditated on these phenomena the more they appeared to me to be curious and interesting. A thorough investigation of them seemed even to bid fair to give a farther insight into the hidden nature of heat; and to enable us to form some reasonable conjectures respecting the existence, or non-existence, of an igneous fluid: a subject on which the opinions of philosophers have, in all ages, been much divided.

In order that the Society may have clear and distinct ideas of the speculations and reasonings to which these appearances gave rise in my mind, and also of the specific objects of philosophical investigation they suggested to me, I must beg leave to state them at some length and in such manner as I shall think best suited to answer this purpose.

From whence comes the heat actually produced in the mechanical operation above mentioned?

Is it furnished by the metallic chips which are separated by the borer from the solid mass of metal?

If this were the case, then, according to the modern doctrines of latent heat, and of caloric, the capacity for heat of the parts of the metal, so reduced to chips, ought not only to be changed, but the change undergone by them should be sufficiently great to account for all the heat produced.

But no such change had taken place; for I found, upon taking equal quantities, by weight, of these chips, and of thin slips of the same block of metal separated by means of a fine saw, and putting them, at the same temperature (that of boiling water) into equal quantities of cold water (that is to say, at the temperature of $59\frac{1}{2}°$F.), the portion of water into which the chips were put was not, to all appearance, heated either less or more than the other portion, in which the slips of metal were put.

This experiment being repeated several times, the results were always so nearly the same that I could not determine whether any, or what change, had been produced in the metal, in regard to its capacity for heat, by being reduced to chips by the borer.

From hence it is evident that the heat produced could not possibly have been furnished at the expense of the latent heat of the metallic chips. But, not being willing to rest satisfied with these trials, however conclusive they appeared to me to be, I had recourse to the following still more decisive experiment:

Taking a cannon (a brass six-pounder) cast solid, and rough as it came from the foundry, and fixing it (horizontally) in the machine used for boring, and at the same time finishing the outside of the cannon by turning, I caused its extremity to be cut off; and, by turning down the metal in that part, a solid cylinder was formed, $7\frac{3}{4}$ inches in diameter, and $9\frac{9}{10}$ inches long. . . .

This short cylinder, which was supported in its horizontal position, and turned round its axis, by means of the neck by which it remained united to the cannon, was now bored with the horizontal borer used in boring cannon. . . .

This cylinder being designed for the express purpose of generating heat by friction, by having a blunt borer forced against its solid bottom at the same time that it should be turned round its axis by the force of horses, in order that the heat accumulated in the cylinder might from time to time be measured, a small round hole, 0.37 of an inch only in diameter, and 4.2 inches in depth, for the purpose of introducing a small cylindrical mercurial thermometer, was made in it. . . .

This experiment was made in order to ascertain how much heat was actually generated by friction, when a blunt steel borer being so forcibly shoved (by means of a strong screw) against the bottom of the bore of the cylinder that the pressure against it was equal to the weight of about 10,000 pounds avoirdupois, the cylinder was turned round on its axis (by the force of horses) at the rate of about thirty-two times in a minute. . . .

To prevent, as far as possible, the loss of any part of the heat that was generated in the experiment, the cylinder was well covered up with a fit coating of thick and warm flannel, which was carefully wrapped round it, and defended it on every side from the cold air of the atmosphere. . . .

At the beginning of the experiment the temperature of the air in the shade, as also that of the cylinder, was just 60°F.

At the end of thirty minutes, when the cylinder had made 960 revolutions about its axis, the horses being stopped, a cylindrical mercurial thermometer, whose bulb was $\frac{32}{100}$ of an inch in diameter, and $3\frac{1}{4}$ inches in length, was introduced into the hole made to receive it, in the side of the cylinder, when the mercury rose almost instantly to 130°. . . .

Finding so much reason to conclude that the heat generated in these experiments, or excited, as I would rather choose to express it, was not furnished at the expense of the latent heat or combined caloric of the metal, I pushed my inquiries a step farther and endeavored to find out whether the air did, or did not, contribute anything in the generation of it. . . .

Everything being ready, I proceeded to make the experiment I had projected in the following manner:

The hollow cylinder having been previously cleaned out, and the inside of its bore wiped with a clean towel till it was quite dry, the square iron bar, with the blunt steel borer fixed to the end of it, was put into its place; the mouth of the bore of the cylinder being closed at the same time, by means of the circular piston, through the center of which the iron bar passed.

This being done, the box was put in its place, and the joinings of the iron rod, and of the neck of the cylinder, with the two ends of the box, having been made watertight, by means of collars of oiled leather, the box was filled with cold water (viz., at the temperature of 60°) and the machine was put in motion.

The result of this beautiful experiment was very striking, and the pleasure it afforded me amply repaid me for all the trouble I had had in contriving and arranging the complicated machinery used in making it.

The cylinder, revolving at the rate of about thirty-two times in a minute, had been in motion but a short time when I perceived, by putting my hand into the water and touching the outside of the cylinder, that heat was generated; and it was not long before the water which surrounded the cylinder began to be sensibly warm.

At the end of one hour I found, by plunging a thermometer into the water in the box (the quantity of which fluid amounted to 18.77 pounds avoirdupois, or 2¼ wine gallons) that its temperature had been raised no less than 47 degrees; being now 107° of Fahrenheit's scale.

When thirty minutes more had elapsed, or one hour and thirty minutes after the machinery had been put in motion, the heat of the water in the box was 142°.

At the end of two hours, reckoning from the beginning of the experiment, the temperature of the water was found to be raised to 178°.

At two hours twenty minutes it was 200°; and at two hours thirty minutes it *actually boiled!*

It would be difficult to describe the surprise and astonishment expressed in the countenances of the bystanders, on seeing so large a quantity of cold water heated and actually made to boil without any fire.

Though there was, in fact, nothing that could justly be considered as surprising in this event, yet I acknowledge fairly that it afforded me a degree of childish pleasure, which, were I ambitious of the reputation of a grave philosopher, I ought most certainly rather to hide than to discover.

The quantity of heat excited and accumulated in this experiment was very considerable; for not only the water in the box, but also the box itself (which weighed 15¼ pounds) and the hollow metallic cylinder, and that part of the iron bar which, being situated within the cavity of the box, was immersed in the water, were heated 150 degrees of Fahrenheit's scale; viz., from 60° (which was the temperature of the water, and of the machinery, at the beginning of the experiment) to 210°, the heat of boiling water at Munich.

The total quantity of heat generated may be estimated with some considerable degree of precision. . . .

From the result of these computations it appears that the quantity of heat produced equably, or in a continual stream (if I may use that expression), by the friction of the blunt steel borer against the bottom of the hollow metallic cylinder, in the experiment under consideration, was greater than that produced equably in the combustion of nine wax candles, each three quarters of an inch in diameter, all burning together, or at the same time, with clear bright flames.

As the machinery used in this experiment could easily be carried round by the force of one horse (though, to render the work lighter, two horses were actually employed in doing it), these computations show further how large a quantity of heat might be produced by proper mechanical contrivance, merely by the strength of a horse, without either fire, light, combustion, or chemical decomposition; and, in a case of necessity, the heat thus produced might be used in cooking victuals.

But no circumstances can be imagined in which this method of procuring heat would not be disadvantageous; for more heat might be obtained by using the fodder necessary for the support of a horse, as fuel.

By meditating on the results of all these experiments we are naturally brought to that great question which has so often been the subject of speculation among philosophers; namely:

What is heat? Is there any such thing as an *igneous fluid?* Is there anything that can with propriety be called *caloric?*

We have seen that a very considerable quantity of heat may be excited in the friction of two metallic surfaces and given off in a constant stream or flux, *in all directions,* without interruption or intermission, and without any signs of diminution or exhaustion.

From whence came the heat which was continually given off in this manner, in the foregoing experiments? Was it furnished by the small particles of metal, detached from the larger solid masses, on their being rubbed together? This, as we have already seen, could not possibly have been the case.

Was it furnished by the air? This could not have been the case; for, in three of the experiments, the machinery being kept immersed in water, the access of the air of the atmosphere was completely prevented.

Was it furnished by the water which surrounded the machinery? That this could not have been the case is evident: first, because this water was continually *receiving heat* from the machinery and could not, at the same time, be *giving to,* and *receiving heat from,* the same body; and secondly, because there was no chemical decomposition of any part of this water. Had any such decomposition taken place (which indeed could not reasonably have been expected), one of its component elastic fluids (most probably inflammable air) must, at the same time, have been set at liberty, and in making its escape into the atmosphere would have been detected; but though I frequently examined the water to see if any air bubbles rose up through it, and had even made preparations for catching them, in order to examine them, if any should appear, I could perceive none; nor was there any sign of decomposition of any kind whatever, or other chemical process, going on in the water.

Is it possible that the heat could have been supplied by means of the iron bar to the end of which the blunt steel borer was fixed? Or by the small neck of gun metal by which the hollow cylinder was united to the cannon? These suppositions appear more improbable even than either of those before mentioned; for heat was continually going off, or *out of the machinery,* by both these passages, during the whole time the experiment lasted.

And, in reasoning on this subject, we must not forget to consider that most remarkable circumstance, that the source of the heat generated by friction, in these experiments, appeared evidently to be *inexhaustible.*

It is hardly necessary to add that anything which any *insulated* body, or system of bodies, can continue to furnish *without limitation* cannot possibly be *a material substance:* and it appears to me to be extremely difficult, if not quite impossible, to form any distinct idea of anything, capable of being excited and communicated, in the manner the heat was excited and communicated in these experiments, except it be MOTION.

Foreword to Evolution

JEAN BAPTISTE LAMARCK (1744–1829)

How DOES the giraffe come by his long neck, the snail by his shell, man by his intelligence? Skeptical and revolutionary Frenchmen, sparked by the ideas of such iconoclasts as Descartes, Voltaire, Buffon, and Rousseau, were among the first to question the usual answer: "God made them that way once and for all." It was reserved for poverty-stricken botanist and zoologist Jean Baptiste, Chevalier de Lamarck, custodian of the guillotined King Louis XVI's herbarium, in charge of which "Garden of Plants" the victorious Republic and Empire continued him for a quarter century (1793–1818) with no increase in pay, to lay the firm foundation for the theory of evolution which in the hands of Darwin, Wallace, Huxley, and others finally banished the Bible story of the immutability of species.

Lamarck was schooled in war, trained in medicine, lived in poverty, and died in comparative obscurity. Blind in his later years, though still working long hours at the preparation of new scientific data on invertebrates, in support of his theory, he was sustained principally by the love and care of a single daughter, appropriately named Cornélie. "Posterity will honor you," she told him. Posterity has borne her out. The doctrine of evolution is firmly entrenched, though Lamarck's opinion that the changes in the organs of evolving species came about either by willing or accepting their use or disuse, and his theory that acquired characteristics could be transmitted or inherited, have been rejected.

French was the language in which Lamarck wrote. "What Is a Species?" is compounded from three different essays. Most of it comes from his views on species published in 1803; however, the paragraphs beginning "It appears, as I have already mentioned . . ." and ending ". . . nature has reached the state in which we actually see her" are from the *"Système des animaux sans vertèbres,"* published in 1801; and the final paragraph is from views published in 1806. All the English translations are taken from the book, "Lamarck, the Founder of Evolution," by Alpheus S. Packard, M.D., LL.D., professor of zoology and geology, in Brown University, and published in 1901 by Longmans, Green & Company, London and New York.

WHAT IS A SPECIES?

WHAT is a *species* among living beings?

All those who have much to do with the study of natural history know that naturalists at the present day are extremely embarrassed in defining what they mean by the word "species."

In truth, observation for a long time has shown us, and shows us still in a great number of cases, collections of individuals which resemble each other so much in their organization and by the *ensemble* of their parts that we do not hestitate to regard these collections of similar individuals as constituting so many species.

From this consideration we call *species* every collection of individuals which are alike or almost so, and we remark that the regeneration of these individuals conserves the species and propagates it in continuing successively to reproduce similar individuals.

Formerly it was supposed that each species was immutable, as old as Nature, and that she had caused its special creation by the Supreme Author of all which exists.

But we can impose on Him laws in the execution of His will, and determine the mode which He has been pleased to follow in this respect, so it is only in this way that He permits us to recognize it by the aid of observation. Has not His infinite power created an order of things which successively gives existence to all that we see as well as to all that which exists and which we do not know?

Assuredly, whatever has been His will, the omnipotence of His power is always the same; and in whatever way this supreme will has been manifested, nothing can diminish its greatness. As regards, then, the decrees of this infinite wisdom, I confine myself to the limits of a simple observer of Nature. Then, if I discover anything in the course that Nature follows in her creations, I shall say, without fear of deceiving myself, that it has pleased its author that she possesses this power.

The idea that was held as to species among living bodies was quite simple, easy to grasp, and seemed confirmed by the constancy in the similar form of the individuals which reproduction or generation perpetuated. There still occur among us a very great number of these pretended species which we see every day.

However, the farther we advance in the knowledge of the different organized bodies with which almost every part of the surface of the globe is covered, the more does our embarrassment increase in determining what should be regarded as species, and the greater is the reason for limiting and distinguishing the genera.

As we gradually gather the productions of Nature, as our collections gradually grow richer, we see almost all the gaps filled up, and our lines of demarcation effaced. We find ourselves compelled to make an arbitrary determination, which sometimes leads us to seize upon the slightest differences between varieties to form of them the character of that which we call species, and sometimes one person designates as a variety of such a species individuals a little different, which others regard as constituting a particular species.

I repeat, the richer our collections become, the more numerous are the proofs that all is more or less shaded, that the remarkable differences become obliterated, and that the more often Nature leaves it at our disposal to establish distinctions only minute, and in some degree trivial peculiarities.

But some genera among animals and plants are of such an extent, from the number of species they contain, that the study and the determination of these species are now almost impossible. The species of these genera, arranged in series and placed together according to their natural relations, present, with those allied to them, differences so slight that they shade into each other; and because these species are in some degree confounded with one another they leave almost no means of determining, by expression in words, the small differences which distinguish them.

There are also those who have been for a long time, and strongly, occupied with the determination of the species, and who have consulted rich collections, who can understand up to what point species, among living bodies, merge one into another, and who have been able to convince themselves, in the regions where we see isolated species, that this is only because there are wanting other species which are more nearly related, and which we have not yet collected.

I do not mean to say by this that the existing animals form a very simple series, one everywhere equally graduated; but I say that they form a branching series, irregularly graduated, and which has no discontinuity in its parts, or which at best has not always had, if it is true that it is to be found anywhere. It results from this that the species which terminates each branch of the general series holds a place at least on one side apart from the other allied species which intergrade with them. Behold this state of things, so well known, which I am now compelled to demonstrate.

I have no need of any hypothesis or any supposition for this: I call to witness all observing naturalists. . . .

A great many facts teach us that gradually, as the individuals of one of our species change their situation, climate, mode of life, or habits, they thus receive influences which gradually change the consistence and the proportions of their parts, their form, their faculties, even their organization; so that all of them participate eventually in the changes which they have undergone.

In the same climate very different situations and exposures at first cause simple variations in the individuals which are found exposed there; but as time goes on the continual differences of situation of individuals of which I have spoken, which live and successively reproduce in the same circumstances, give rise among them to differences which are, in some degree, essential to their being, in such a way that at the end of many successive generations these individuals, which originally belonged to another species, are at the end transformed into a new species, distinct from the other.

For example, if the seeds of a grass, or of every other plant natural to a humid field, should be transplanted, by an accident, at first to the slope of a neighboring hill, where the soil, although more elevated, would yet be quite cool, so as to allow the plant to live, and then after having lived there, and passed through many generations there, it should gradually reach the poor and almost arid soil of a mountainside—if the plant should thrive and live there and perpetuate itself during a series of generations, it would then be so changed that the botanists who should find it there would describe it as a separate species.

The same thing happens to animals which circumstances have forced to change their climate, manner of living, and habits; but for these the influences of the causes which I have just cited need still more time than in the case of plants to produce the notable changes in the individuals, though in the long run, however, they always succeed in bringing them about.

The idea of defining under the word "species" a collection of similar individuals which perpetuate the same by generation, and which have existed thus as anciently as Nature, implies the necessity that the individuals of one and the same species cannot mix, in their acts of generation, with the individuals of a different species. Unfortunately observation has proved, and still proves every day, that this consideration has no basis; for the hybrids, very common among plants, and the unions which are often observed between the individuals of very different species among animals, have made us perceive that the limits between these species, supposed to be constant, are not so rigid as is supposed.

In truth, nothing often results from these singular unions, especially when they are very incongruous, as the individuals which result from them are usually sterile; but also, when the disparities are less great, it is known that the drawbacks with which it has to do no longer exist. However, this means alone suffices to gradually create the varieties which have afterwards arisen from races, and which, with time, constitute that which we call *species*. . . .

It appears, as I have already said, that *time* and *favorable conditions* are the two principal means which Nature has employed in giving existence to all her productions. We know that for her time has no limit, and that consequently she has it always at her disposal.

As to the circumstances of which she has had need and of which she makes use every day in order to cause her productions to vary, we can say that they are in a manner inexhaustible.

The essential ones arise from the influence and from all the environing media, from the diversity of local causes, of habits, of movements, of action, finally of means of living, of preserving their lives, of defending themselves, of multiplying themselves, et cetera. Moreover, as the result of these different influences, the faculties, developed and strengthened by use, became diversified by the new habits maintained for long ages, and by slow degrees the structure, the consistence, in a word the nature, the condition of the parts and of the organs consequently participating in all these influences, became preserved and were propagated by generation.

The bird which necessity drives to the water to find there the prey needed for its subsistence separates the toes of its feet when it wishes to strike the water and move on its surface. The skin, which unites these toes at their base, contracts in this way the habit of extending itself. Thus in time the broad membranes which connect the toes of ducks, geese, et cetera, are formed in the way indicated.

But one accustomed to live perched on trees has necessarily the end of the toes lengthened and shaped in another way. Its claws are elongated, sharpened, and are curved and bent so as to seize the branches on which it so often rests.

Likewise we perceive that the shore bird, which does not care to swim, but which, however, is obliged to approach the water to obtain its prey, will be continually in danger of sinking in the mud, but wishing to act so that its body shall not fall into the liquid, it will contract the habit of extending and lengthening its feet. Hence it will result in the generations of these birds which continue to live in this manner that the individuals will find themselves raised as if on stilts, on long naked feet; namely, denuded of feathers up to and often above the thighs.

I could here pass in review all the classes, all the orders, all the genera and species of animals which exist, and make it apparent that the conformation of individuals and of their parts, their organs, their faculties, et cetera, is entirely the result of circumstances to which the race of each species has been subjected by nature.

I could prove that it is not the form either of the body or of its parts which gives rise to habits, to the mode of life of animals, but, on the contrary, it is the habits, the mode of life, and all the influential circumstances which have, with time, made up the form of the body and of the parts of animals. With the new forms new faculties have been acquired, and gradually Nature has reached the state in which we actually see her.

Indeed, we know that all the time that an organ, or a system of organs, is rigorously exercised throughout a long time, not only its power, and the parts which form it, grow and strengthen themselves, but there are proofs that this organ, or system of organs, at that time attracts to itself the principal active forces of the life of the individual, because it becomes the cause which, under these conditions, makes the functions of other organs to be diminished in power.

Thus not only every organ or every part of the body, whether of man or of animals, being for a long period and more vigorously exercised than the others, has acquired a power and facility of action that the same organ could not have had before, and that it has never had in individuals which have exercised less, but also we consequently remark that the excessive employment of this organ diminishes the functions of the others and proportionately enfeebles them.

The man who habitually and vigorously exercises the organ of his intelligence develops and acquires a great facility of attention, of aptitude for thought, et cetera, but he has a feeble stomach and strongly limited muscular powers. He, on the contrary, who thinks little does not easily, and then only momentarily fixes his attention, while habitually giving much exercise to his muscular organs, has much vigor, possesses an excellent digestion, and is not given to the abstemiousness of the savant and man of letters.

Moreover, when one exercises long and vigorously an organ or system of organs, the active forces of life (in my opinion, the nervous fluid) have taken such a habit of acting toward this organ that they have formed in the individual an inclination to continue to exercise which it is difficult for it to overcome.

Hence it happens that the more we exercise an organ, the more we use it with facility, the more does it result that we perceive the need of continuing to use it at the times when it is placed in action. So we remark that the habit of study, of application, of work, or of any other exercise of our organs or of any one of our organs, becomes with time an indispensable need to the individual, and often a passion which it does not know how to overcome. . . .

Thus we are assured that that which is taken for *species* among living bodies, and that all the specific differences which distinguish these natural productions, have no absolute *stability,* but that they enjoy only a relative *stability;* which it is very important to consider in order to fix the limits which we must establish in the determination of that which we must call *species*.

Father of Paleontology and Comparative Anatomy

GEORGES CUVIER (1769–1832)

THE REPUBLIC which guillotined Lavoisier and starved Lamarck soon found that it had need for scientists, savants, and scholars. Of the distinguished naturalists gathered in Paris, including Lamarck, Pierre Latreille (1762–1833), whose work was with insects, and Étienne Geoffrey St. Hilaire (1772–1844), none shone more resplendently than the brilliant "father of comparative anatomy and paleontology," fossil hunter, and systematist, Baron Georges Léopold Chrétien Frédéric Dagobert Cuvier. The baron was almost overweighted with lucrative official positions: Inspector of Education (1802), Councilor of State (1814), chancellor of the University of Paris, and many more. His official weight, in council and spectacular debate, was thrown against the budding theory of evolution; instead, he systematically arranged animals in four branches, vertebrates, molluscs, articulates, and radiates. At the head of "The Animal Kingdom" (*"Le Régne animal"*) he proudly placed the "only two-legged, two-handed" animal, man. Farther down among the mammals came the elephants, whose fossil remains, found near Paris, he had studied so thoroughly that he was able to reconstruct the whole creature from the fossil fragments.

French is the original language of the twenty-volume work, one of the most beautifully illustrated scientific series of all time, "The Animal Kingdom" (Paris, 1816). The English translation of the material here quoted is by the junior editor.

THE ONLY TWO-LEGGED, TWO-HANDED ANIMAL: MAN

FIRST ORDER OF MAMMALS
THE TWO-HANDED OR HUMAN

THERE IS only one genus of man and this genus is unique in its order. Since the [natural] history of man interests us most directly and should stand as the basis of comparison to which we submit the accounts of all other animals, we shall treat it in greater detail.

We shall quickly disclose those particular features of structural organization in which man differs from other mammals; we shall examine the advantages that man's peculiarities give him over other living creatures. . . .

Man's foot is very different from those of monkeys; it is large, the leg drops vertically upon it; the heel bulges out underneath; the toes are short and cannot be bent very far; the great toe, longer and bigger than the others, is placed in the same line and cannot be opposed to the others. The foot is adequate to support the body, but it does not serve to grasp or hold on to [anything]. Since the hands, on their part, are of no use for walking, man is the only animal [that can be considered] truly two-legged and two-handed.

The entire human body is disposed for a vertical posture. Man's feet, as we have seen, furnish him a larger base [of support] than any other mammal has. The strongest muscles support the foot, [leg], and thigh when extended and account for the bulges in the calf and buttocks. The flexors of the leg are attached even higher, permitting the knee to be completely straightened and the calf to show off better. The pelvis, from which the legs and thighs separate, is quite large and gives the trunk a pyramidal shape favorable to equilibrium. The neck of the femur makes a [wide] angle with the shaft of the bone, augmenting still further the separation of the feet and enlarging the base of the body. In the vertical position the head is in equilibrium on the trunk, because its articulation is below its center of gravity.

Even should he want to, a man cannot walk very comfortably on all fours. His short and almost inflexible hind feet throw his knees against the ground; his wide shoulders and arms thrown far from the middle of the body offer poor support. The great striated muscle, which in quadrupeds holds the trunk up between the shoulder blades like a saddle girth, is smaller in man than in any of them. The head is too heavy because of the great size of the brain and the smallness of the sinuses or cavities in the bone. Furthermore, the means of holding [the head] up are too feeble, for man has neither the cervical ligaments nor the disposition of the vertebrae proper to keep them from flexing forward. A man [on all fours] could hold his head more or less in the line of his spine, but then his mouth and eyes would be directed toward the ground; he could not see ahead. On the other hand the position of these organs is perfect when he walks erect.

The blood vessels which feed the brain are not subdivided, as in most quadrupeds, and the blood necessary for so voluminous an organ being rushed there with too great extravagance, apoplexy would be the all too frequent result of the horizontal position.

Man is designed to support himself on his feet only. Thus he keeps his hands entirely free for action, and his sense organs remain in the positions most favorable for observation.

The hands, which derive great advantages from their freedom, are not without it in their structure. The thumb, longer in proportion than in monkeys, permits the greatest ease in picking up small objects. All the fingers, except the ring [third] finger, have separate movements, something which does not occur in other animals, not even monkeys. The nails adorn only one side of the ends of the fingers, permitting firmness in the sense of touch without depriving it of any of its delicacy. The arms which carry the hands have a solid attachment through the large shoulder blades and the strong collarbone.

Though favored by dexterity, man has no advantages on the side of strength. His endurance in the chase is far less than that of the other animals of his stripe; having neither protruding jaws, nor canine fangs, nor sharp claws, he is without offensive arms; and his body lacking a natural protective covering on top and on all sides, he is absolutely without defensive armor. Indeed among all the animals man is the one which has taken the longest time to acquire the powers necessary for his own preservation.

But this physical feebleness has been an advantage for him [nevertheless]. It has forced him to take recourse to his inner self and especially to the intelligence which has been vouchsafed to him in such high degree.

No quadruped approaches man in the size and folds of the hemispheres of the brain, that is, in the part of the brain which serves as the principal instrument of intellectual functions. The posterior part of the same organ extends backward in such a fashion as to cover over the cerebellum. Likewise the shape of man's skull announces the size of his brain, just as the smallness of his face indicates how little predominance is accorded that part of the [central] nervous system connected by the external senses.

However, these external senses, though mediocre in man, are nevertheless rather delicate and well balanced.

The eyes look forward; man cannot see from two sides at the same time, as most quadrupeds [can do], a fact which puts more unity into the results of his sight and fixes more attention upon sensations of this kind. The globe and iris of [the human] eye are both but slightly variable, a fact which restricts vision in focus to one distance at a time and to fixed amounts of light. The external ear, neither very sensitive nor spread out, does not augment the intensity of sounds; yet man is of all animals the one which best distinguishes intonations. Man's nostrils, more complicated than those of monkeys, are of less [importance] than those of all other creatures. Nevertheless, man appears to be the only one whose sense of smell is so delicate as to be offended by bad odors. The delicacy of his sense of smell has an influence on that of taste; and man should have some advantage in this regard, at least over the animals whose tongues are covered with scales. Finally, the fineness of his sense of touch results from [the sensitivity] of his skin and the absence of all insensible parts as well as from the form of his hand, better made than any other to adapt itself to the small irregularities of surfaces.

Man has a particular pre-eminence in his vocal organs. Alone among mammals he can articulate sounds. The form of his mouth and the extreme mobility of his lips are the probable causes. As a result, he has acquired a most precious means of communication, for of all the signs that might be easily used for the transmission of ideas, varied sounds are those which can be perceived at the greatest distance and in more than one direction. . . .

On account of his industry, man enjoys a uniform [year-round] nourishment. Hence he is at all times disposed to the pleasures of love without ever being overwhelmed by [seasons of animal] heat. . . .

SECOND ORDER OF MAMMALS
THE FOUR-HANDED (QUADRUMANES)

Independently of the anatomic details which distinguish man, as we have already pointed out, the quadrumanes differ from our species by very notable characteristics; [namely], that the hind feet have big toes free to oppose the other toes; that the digits of the feet are long and flexible like those of the hand; also that all these species swing from the branches of trees with ease, including those which stand and walk erect only with difficulty, their feet touching [the ground] only on the outer edges, and their narrow pelvis being not at all favorable for equilibrium. They have intestines very like our own; eyes that look forward; breasts on their chests; a pendant verge; a brain with three lobes on each side, whose posterior part covers over the cerebellum; the temporal fossa is separated from the orbital by a bony septum. But for the rest, they depart from our form by degrees, taking on a longer and longer snout, a tail, and a more exclusively four-legged gait. Nevertheless, the freedom of their forearms and the complexity of their hands permit them a great [variety of] actions and gestures similar to those of human beings.

For a long time two divisions of genus were made, monkeys and lemurs. Today in some fashion, through the multiplication of secondary forms, they have become two small families and between them we must place a third genus, marmosets, which belongs neither to the one nor the other.

"The Natural History of Selborne"

GILBERT WHITE (1720–93)

IN THE PARISH of Selborne, a quiet corner of England fifty miles southwest of London, lived a mild-mannered, minutely curious bachelor clergyman, the Rev. Gilbert White. Apparently untouched by the revolutions through which he was living, the recluse clergyman busied himself with observing and recording, in a style that remains a model of quaint English eloquence, weather, birds, trees, and field mice. An amateur "field naturalist," a parochial prototype of Charles Darwin, White was representative of the out-of-the-way, patient men, collectors of plants, birds, and insects, whose "obstinate questionings" about the proper classification of their specimens eventually brought about the great evolution in human thought summed up in Darwin's "Origin of Species."

English is the original language of "The Natural History of Selborne," published in London (1789) by Gilbert's brother, Benjamin White. Of the three letters given here from this book, the first is a composite letter, extracted from various communications to Thomas Pennant, author of "British Zoology"; the second and third are complete letters to Daines Barrington, another naturalist.

MUS MINIMUS—THE TINIEST QUADRUPED IN BRITAIN

To Thomas Pennant, Esq.

Selborne

Dear Sir,

The most unusual birds I ever observed in these parts were a pair of hoopoes (*upupa*) which came several years ago in the summer, and frequented an ornamented piece of ground, which joins to my garden, for some weeks. They used to march about in a stately manner, feeding in the walks, many times in the day; and seemed disposed to breed in my outlet; but were frightened and persecuted by idle boys, who would never let them be at rest.

I have procured some of the mice mentioned in my former letters, a young one and a female with young, both of which I have preserved in brandy. From the color, shape, size, and manner of nesting, I make no doubt but that the species is nondescript. They are much smaller and more slender than the *Mus domesticus medius* of Ray; and have more of the squirrel or dormouse color; their belly is white, a straight line along their sides divides the shades of their back and belly. They never enter into houses; are carried into ricks and barns with the sheaves; abound in harvest, and build their nests amidst the straws of the corn above the ground, and sometimes in thistles. They breed as many as eight at a litter, in a little round nest composed of the blades of grass or wheat.

One of these nests I procured this autumn, most artificially platted, and composed of the blades of wheat; perfectly round, and about the size of a cricket ball; with the aperture so ingeniously closed that there was no discovering to what part it belonged. It was so compact and well filled that it would roll across the table without being discomposed, though it contained eight little mice that were naked and blind. As this nest was perfectly full, how could the dam come at her litter respectively so as to administer a teat to each? Perhaps she opens different places for that purpose, adjusting them again when the business is over: but she could not possibly be contained herself in the ball with her young, which moreover would be daily increasing in bulk. This wonderful procreant cradle, an elegant instance of the efforts of instinct, was found in a wheat field, suspended in the head of a thistle.

As to the small mice, I have farther to remark that though they hang their nests for breeding up amidst the straws of the standing corn, above the ground, yet I find that in the winter they burrow deep in the earth and make warm beds of grass; but their grand rendezvous seems to be in corn ricks, into which they are carried at harvest. A neighbor housed an oat rick lately under the thatch of which were assembled near an hundred, most of which were taken; and some I saw. I measured them and found that, from nose to tail, they were just two inches and a quarter, and their tails just two inches long. Two of them, in a scale, weighed down just one copper halfpenny, which is about the third of an ounce avoirdupois: so that I suppose they are the smallest quadrupeds in this island. A full-grown *Mus medius domesticus* weighs, I find, one ounce, lumping weight, which is more than six times as much as the mouse above; and measures from nose to rump four inches and a quarter, and the same in its tail.

I can show you some good specimens of my new mice. Linnaeus, perhaps, would call the species *Mus minimus*.

It is, I find, in zoology as it is in botany: all nature is so full that that district produces the greatest variety which is the most examined.

Scopoli's new work (which I have just procured) has its merits in ascertaining many of the birds of the Tirol and Carniola. Monographers, come from whence they may, have, I think, fair pretense to challenge some regard and approbation from the lovers of natural history; for, as no man can alone investigate all the works of nature, these partial writers may, each in their department, be more accurate in their discoveries, and freer from errors, than more general writers; and so by degrees may pave the way to an universal correct natural history.

I am, et cetera,
GIL. WHITE

TREES ARE ALEMBICS

To the Hon. Daines Barrington

Selborne, February 7, 1776

DEAR SIR,

In heavy fogs, on elevated situations especially, trees are perfect alembics: and no one that has not attended to such matters can imagine how much water one tree will distill in a night's time by condensing the vapor, which trickles down the twigs and boughs, so as to make the ground below quite in a float. In Newton Lane, in October 1775, on a misty day, a particular oak in leaf dropped so fast that the cartway stood in puddles and the ruts ran with water, though the ground in general was dusty.

In some of our smaller islands in the West Indies, if I mistake not, there are no springs or rivers; but the people are supplied with that necessary element, water, merely by the dripping of some large tall trees which, standing in the bosom of a mountain, keep their heads constantly enveloped with fogs and clouds, from which they dispense their kindly never-ceasing moisture; and so render those districts habitable by condensation alone.

Trees in leaf have such a vast proportion more of surface than those that are naked that, in theory, their condensations should greatly exceed those that are stripped of their leaves; but as the former imbibe also a great quantity of moisture it is difficult to say which drip most: but this I know, that deciduous trees that are entwined with much ivy seem to distill the greatest quantity. Ivy leaves are smooth and thick and cold, and therefore condense very fast; and besides, evergreens imbibe very little. These facts may furnish the intelligent with hints concerning what sorts of trees they should plant round small ponds that they would wish to be perennial; and show them how advantageous some trees are in preference to others.

Trees perspire profusely, condense largely, and check evaporation so much that woods are always moist: no wonder, therefore, that they contribute much to pools and streams.

That trees are great promoters of lakes and rivers appears from a well-known fact in North America; for, since the woods and forests have been grubbed and cleared, all bodies of water are much diminished; so that some streams that were very considerable a century ago will not now drive a common mill. Besides, most woodlands, forests, and chases with us abound with pools and morasses; no doubt for the reason given above.

To a thinking mind few phenomena are more strange than the state of little ponds on the summits of chalk hills, many of which are never dry in the most trying droughts of summer. On chalk hills, I say, because in many rocky and gravelly soils springs usually break out pretty high on the sides of elevated grounds and mountains; but no person acquainted with chalky districts will allow that they ever saw springs in such a soil but in valleys and bottoms, since the waters of so pervious a stratum as chalk all lie on one dead level, as well diggers have assured me again and again.

Now we have many such little round ponds in this district; and one in particular on our sheep down, three hundred feet above my house, which, though never above three feet deep in the middle, and not more than thirty feet in diameter, and containing perhaps not more than two or three hundred hogsheads of water, yet never is known to fail, though it affords drink for three hundred or four hundred sheep, and for at least twenty head of large cattle beside. This pond, it is true, is overhung with two moderate beeches, that, doubtless, at times afford it much supply; but then we have others as small, that, without the aid of trees, and in spite of evaporation from sun and wind, and perpetual consumption by cattle, yet constantly maintain a moderate share of water, without overflowing in the wettest seasons, as they would do if supplied by springs.

By my journal of May 1775, it appears that "the small and even considerable ponds in the vales are now dried up, while the small ponds on the very tops of hills are but little affected." Can this difference be accounted for from evaporation alone, which certainly is more prevalent in bottoms? Or, rather, have not those elevated pools some unnoticed recruits which in the night time counterbalance the waste of the day, without which the cattle alone must soon exhaust them?

And here it will be necessary to enter more minutely into the cause. Dr. Hales, in his "Vegetable Statics," advances, from experiment, that "the moister the earth is the more dew falls on it in a night: and more than a double quantity of dew falls on a surface of water than there does on an equal surface of moist earth." Hence we see that water, by its coolness, is enabled to assimilate to itself a large quantity of moisture nightly by condensation; and that the air, when loaded with fogs and vapors, and even with copious dews, can alone advance a considerable and never-failing resource. Persons that are much abroad, and travel early and late, such as shepherds, fishermen, et cetera, can tell what prodigious fogs prevail in the night on elevated downs, even in the hottest parts of summer; and how much the surfaces of things are drenched by those swimming vapors, though, to the senses, all the while, little moisture seems to fall.

I am, et cetera,
GIL. WHITE

THE MOTION OF BIRDS IN FLIGHT

To the Hon. Daines Barrington

Selborne, August 7, 1778

DEAR SIR,

A good ornithologist should be able to distinguish birds by their air as well as by their colors and shape; on the ground as well as on the wing, and in the bush as well as in the hand. For, though it must not be said that every species of birds has a manner peculiar to itself, yet there is somewhat, in most genera at least, that at first sight discriminates them and enables a judicious observer to pronounce upon them with some certainty. Put a bird in motion . . . *"et vera incessu patuit."* . . .

Thus kites and buzzards sail round in circles with wings expanded and motionless; and it is from their gliding manner that the former are still called in the north of England gleads, from the Saxon verb *glidan,* to glide. The kestrel, or windhover, has a peculiar mode of hanging in the air in one place, his wings all the while being briskly agitated. Hen harriers fly low over heaths or fields of corn, and beat the ground regularly like a pointer or setting dog. Owls move in a buoyant manner, as if lighter than the air; they seem to want ballast. There is a peculiarity belonging to ravens that must draw the attention even of the most incurious—they spend all their leisure time in striking and cuffing each other on the wing in a kind of playful skirmish; and, when they move from one place to another, frequently turn on their backs with a loud croak and seem to be falling to the ground. When this odd gesture betides them, they are scratching themselves with one foot, and thus lose the center of gravity. Rooks sometimes dive and tumble in a frolicsome manner; crows and daws swagger in their walk; woodpeckers fly *volatu undoso,* opening and closing their wings at every stroke, and so are always rising or falling in curves. All of this genus use their tails, which incline downward, as a support while they run up trees. Parrots, like all other hook-clawed birds, walk awkwardly, and make use of their bill as a third foot, climbing and ascending with ridiculous caution. All the *gallinae* parade and walk gracefully, and run nimbly; but fly with difficulty, with an impetuous whirring and in a straight line. Magpies and jays flutter with powerless wings and make no dispatch; herons seem encumbered with too much sail for their light bodies; but these vast hollow wings are necessary in carrying burdens, such as large fishes, and the like; pigeons, and particularly the sort called smiters, have a way of clashing their wings the one against the other over their backs with a loud snap; another variety called tumblers turn themselves over in the air.

Some birds have movements peculiar to the season of love: thus ring-doves, though strong and rapid at other times, yet in the spring hang about on the wing in a toying and playful manner; thus the cock snipe, while breeding, forgetting his former flight, fans the air like the wind-hover; and the greenfinch in particular exhibits such languishing and faltering gestures as to appear like a wounded and dying bird; the king-fisher darts along like an arrow; fern owls or goatsuckers glance in the dusk over the tops of trees like a meteor; starlings, as it were, swim along, while missel thrushes use a wild and desultory flight; swallows sweep over the surface of the ground and water, and distinguish them-selves by rapid turns and quick evolutions; swifts dash round in circles; and the bank martin moves with frequent vacillations like a butterfly.

Most of the small birds fly by jerks, rising and falling as they advance. Most small birds hop; but wagtails and larks walk, moving their legs alternately. Skylarks rise and fall perpendicularly as they sing: wood larks hang poised in the air; and titlarks rise and fall in large curves, singing in their descent. The whitethroat uses odd jerks and gesticula-tions over the tops of hedges and bushes. All the duck kind waddle; divers and auks walk as if fettered, and stand erect on their tails: these are the *compedes* of Linnaeus. Geese and cranes, and most wild fowls, move in figured flights, often changing their position. The secondary remiges of *tringae,* wild ducks, and some others, are very long, and give their wings, when in motion, an hooked appearance. Dabchicks, moor hens, and coots fly erect, with their legs hanging down, and hardly make any dispatch; the reason is plain: their wings are placed too forward out of the true center of gravity; as the legs of auks and divers are situated too backward.

The Malthusian Theory Concerning Misery and Vice

THOMAS MALTHUS (1766–1834)

MISERY AND VICE have not yet vanished from the world. An English clergyman, Thomas Malthus, has given us a very simple explanation as to why these evils must inexorably continue. Starting with two obvious postulates—that food is necessary to man and that "the passion between the sexes is necessary and will remain nearly in its present state," the original Malthusian theory asserts that population, unless checked by wars, famines, diseases, and other instruments breeding misery, would outrun the means of subsistence, no matter what improvements in agricultural science and technology might be achieved. We have yet to disprove the curate of Albury. An able economist, Malthus wrote also on rent.

Charles Darwin and Alfred Russel Wallace were both indebted to Malthus for the central idea of the theory of natural selection. Darwin wrote: "In October 1838 I happened to read for amusement Malthus on population, and being well prepared to appreciate the struggle for existence which everywhere goes on, from long continued observation of the habits of animals and plants, it at once struck me that under these circumstances favorable variations would tend to be preserved and unfavorable ones to be destroyed. The result of this would be the formation of a new species. Here then I had a theory by which to work."

Malthus himself got the idea from Benjamin Franklin! He quotes the American philosopher-scientist's remark, made in 1751, that "there is no bound to the prolific nature of plants or animals but what is made by their crowding and interfering with each other's means of subsistence."

English in the original, the first storm-provoking edition of the later much-revised "Essay on the Principle of Population" appeared in London in 1798.

An

ESSAY

on the

PRINCIPLE OF POPULATION,

As It Affects

THE FUTURE IMPROVEMENT OF SOCIETY,

With Remarks

ON THE SPECULATIONS OF MR. GODWIN,

M. CONDORCET,

And Other Writers.

———

LONDON:

*Printed for J. Johnson, in St. Paul's
Church-Yard.*

———

1798

POPULATION

QUESTION STATED. *Little prospect of a determination of it, from the enmity of the opposing parties. The principal argument against the perfectibility of man and of society has never been fairly answered. Nature of the difficulty arising from population. Outline of the principal argument of the essay.*

The great and unlooked-for discoveries that have taken place of late years in natural philosophy; the increasing diffusion of general knowledge from the extension of the art of printing; the ardent and unshackled spirit of inquiry that prevails throughout the lettered and even unlettered world; the new and extraordinary lights that have been thrown on political subjects, which dazzle and astonish the understanding; and particularly that tremendous phenomenon in the political horizon, the French Revolution, which, like a blazing comet, seems destined either to inspire with fresh life and vigor or to scorch up and destroy the shrinking inhabitants of the earth, have all concurred to lead many able men into the opinion that we were touching on a period big with the most important changes—changes that would in some measure be decisive of the future fate of mankind.

It has been said that the great question is now at issue whether man shall henceforth start forward with accelerated velocity toward illimitable and hitherto unconceived improvement; or be condemned to a perpetual oscillation between happiness and misery, and after every effort remain still at an immeasurable distance from the wished-for goal.

Yet, anxiously as every friend of mankind must look forward to the termination of this painful suspense, and eagerly as the inquiring mind would hail every ray of light that might assist its view into futurity, it is much to be lamented that the writers on each side of this momentous question still keep far aloof from each other. Their mutual arguments do not meet with a candid examination. The question is not brought to rest on fewer points, and even in theory scarcely seems to be approaching to a decision.

The advocate for the present order of things is apt to treat the sect of speculative philosophers either as a set of artful and designing knaves, who preach up ardent benevolence and draw captivating pictures of a happier state of society, only the better to enable them to destroy the present establishments and to forward their own deep-laid schemes of ambition; or as wild and mad-headed enthusiasts whose silly speculations and absurd paradoxes are not worthy the attention of any reasonable man.

The advocate for the perfectibility of man and of society retorts on the defender of establishments a more than equal contempt. He brands him as the slave of the most miserable and narrow prejudices; or as the defender of the abuses of civil society, only because he profits by them. He paints him either as a character who prostitutes his understanding to his interest, or as one whose powers of mind are not of a size to grasp anything great and noble; who cannot see above five yards before him; and who must therefore be utterly unable to take in the views of the enlightened benefactor of mankind.

In this unamicable contest the cause of truth cannot but suffer. The really good arguments on each side of the question are not allowed to have their proper weight. Each pursues his own theory, little solicitous to correct or improve it by an attention to what is advanced by his opponents.

The friend of the present order of things condemns all political speculations in the gross. He will not even condescend to examine the grounds from which the perfectibility of society is inferred. Much less will he give himself the trouble in a fair and candid manner to attempt an exposition of their fallacy.

The speculative philosopher equally offends against the cause of truth. With eyes fixed on a happier state of society, the blessings of which he paints in the most captivating colors, he allows himself to indulge in the most bitter invectives against every present establishment, without applying his talents to consider the best and safest means of removing abuses, and without seeming to be aware of the tremendous obstacles that threaten, even in theory, to oppose the progress of man toward perfection.

It is an acknowledged truth in philosophy that a just theory will always be confirmed by experiment. Yet so much friction and so many minute circumstances occur in practice, which it is next to impossible for the most enlarged and penetrating mind to foresee, that on few subjects can any theory be pronounced just that has not stood the test of experience. But an untried theory cannot fairly be advanced as probable, much less as just, till all the arguments against it have been maturely weighed and clearly and consistently refuted.

I have read some of the speculations on the perfectibility of man and of society with great pleasure. I have been warmed and delighted with the enchanting picture which they hold forth. I ardently wish for such happy improvements. But I see great and, to my understanding, unconquerable difficulties in the way to them. These difficulties it is my present purpose to state; declaring at the same time that, so far from exulting in them as a cause of triumph over the friends of innovation, nothing would give me greater pleasure than to see them completely removed.

The most important argument that I shall adduce is certainly not new. The principles on which it depends have been explained in part by Hume, and more at large by Dr. Adam Smith. It has been advanced and applied to the present subject, though not with its proper weight, or in the most forcible point of view, by Mr. Wallace; and it may probably have been stated by many writers that I have never met with. I should certainly therefore not think of advancing it again, though I mean to place it in a point of view in some degree different from any that I have hitherto seen, if it had ever been fairly and satisfactorily answered.

The cause of this neglect on the part of the advocates for the perfectibility of mankind is not easily accounted for. I cannot doubt the talents of such men as Godwin and Condorcet. I am unwilling to doubt their candor. To my understanding, and probably to that of most others, the difficulty appears insurmountable. Yet these men of acknowledged ability and penetration scarcely deign to notice it, and hold on their course in such speculations with unabated ardor and undiminished confidence. I have certainly no right to say that they purposely shut their eyes to such arguments. I ought rather to doubt the validity of them, when neglected by such men, however forcibly their truth may strike my own mind. Yet in this respect it must be acknowledged that we are all of us too prone to err. If I saw a glass of wine repeatedly presented to a man, and he took no notice of it, I should be apt to think that he was blind or uncivil. A juster philosophy might teach me rather to think that my eyes deceived me and that the offer was not really what I conceived it to be.

In entering upon the argument I must premise that I put out of the question, at present, all mere conjectures; that is, all suppositions, the probable realization of which cannot be inferred upon any just philosophical grounds. A writer may tell me that he thinks man will ultimately become an ostrich. I cannot properly contradict him. But before he can expect to bring any reasonable person over to his opinion he ought to show that the necks of mankind have been gradually elongating; that the lips have grown harder and more prominent; that the legs and feet are daily altering their shape; and that the hair is beginning to change into stubs of feathers. And till the probability of so wonderful a conversion can be shown, it is surely lost time and lost eloquence to expatiate on the happiness of man in such a state; to describe his powers, both of running and flying; to paint him in a condition where all narrow luxuries would be contemned; where he would be employed only in collecting the necessaries of life; and where, consequently, each man's share of labor would be light and his portion of leisure ample.

I think I may fairly make two postulata.

First, that food is necessary to the existence of man.

Secondly, that the passion between the sexes is necessary and will remain nearly in its present state.

These two laws ever since we have had any knowledge of mankind appear to have been fixed laws of our nature; and as we have not hitherto seen any alteration in them, we have no right to conclude that they will ever cease to be what they now are, without an immediate act of power in that Being who first arranged the system of the universe; and for the advantage of His creatures still executes, according to fixed laws, all its various operations.

I do not know that any writer has supposed that on this earth man will ultimately be able to live without food. But Mr. Godwin has conjectured that the passion between the sexes may in time be extinguished. As, however, he calls this part of his work a deviation into the land of conjecture, I will not dwell longer upon it at present than to say that the best arguments for the perfectibility of man are drawn from a contemplation of the great progress that he has already made from the savage state and the difficulty of saying where he is to stop. But toward the extinction of the passion between the sexes no progress whatever has hitherto been made. It appears to exist in as much force at present as it did two thousand or four thousand years ago. There are individual exceptions now as there always have been. But as these exceptions do not appear to increase in number it would surely be a very unphilosophical mode of arguing to infer merely from the existence of an exception that the exception would, in time, become the rule, and the rule the exception.

Assuming then, my postulata as granted, I say that the power of population is indefinitely greater than the power in the earth to produce subsistence for man.

Population, when unchecked, increases in a geometrical ratio. Subsistence increases only in an arithmetical ratio. A slight acquaintance with numbers will show the immensity of the first power in comparison to the second.

By that law of our nature which makes food necessary to the life of man the effects of these two unequal powers must be kept equal.

This implies a strong and constantly operating check on population from the difficulty of subsistence. This difficulty must fall somewhere; and must necessarily be severely felt by a large portion of mankind.

Through the animal and vegetable kingdoms Nature has scattered the seeds of life abroad with the most profuse and liberal hand. She has been comparatively sparing in the room and the nourishment necessary to rear them. The germs of existence contained in this spot of earth, with ample food, and ample room to expand in, would fill millions of worlds in the course of a few thousand years. Necessity, that imperious all-pervading law of nature, restrains them within the prescribed bounds. The race of plants and the race of animals shrink under this great restrictive law. And the race of man cannot, by any efforts of reason, escape from it. Among plants and animals its effects are waste of seed, sickness, and premature death. Among mankind, misery and vice. The former, misery, is an absolutely necessary consequence of it. Vice is a highly probable consequence, and we therefore see it abundantly prevail; but it ought not, perhaps, to be called an absolutely necessary consequence. The ordeal of virtue is to resist all temptation to evil.

This natural inequality of the two powers of population and of production in the earth, and that great law of our nature which must constantly keep their effects equal, form the great difficulty that to me appears insurmountable in the way to the perfectibility of society. All other arguments are of slight and subordinate consideration in comparison of this. I see no way by which man can escape from the weight of this law which pervades all animated nature. No fancied equality, no agrarian regulations in their utmost extent, could remove the pressure of it even for a single century. And it appears, therefore, to be decisive against the possible existence of a society, all the members of which should live in ease, happiness, and comparative leisure, and feel no anxiety about providing the means of subsistence for themselves and families.

Consequently, if the premises are just, the argument is conclusive against the perfectibility of the mass of mankind.

I have thus sketched the general outline of the argument; but I will examine it more particularly; and I think it will be found that experience, the true source and foundation of all knowledge, invariably confirms its truth.

II

The different ratios in which population and food increase. The necessary effects of these different ratios of increase. Oscillation produced by them in the condition of the lower classes of society. Reasons why this oscillation has not been so much observed as might be expected. Three propositions on which the general argument of the essay depends. The different states in which mankind have been known to exist proposed to be examined with reference to these three propositions.

I said that population, when unchecked, increased in a geometrical ratio, and subsistence for men in an arithmetical ratio.

Let us examine whether this position be just.

I think it will be allowed that no state has hitherto existed (at least that we have any account of) where the manners were so pure and simple, and the means of subsistence so abundant, that no check whatever has existed to early marriages; among the lower classes, from a fear of not providing well for their families; or, among the higher classes, from a fear of lowering their condition of life. Consequently in no state that we have yet known has the power of population been left to exert itself with perfect freedom.

Whether the law of marriage be instituted or not, the dictate of nature and virtue seems to be an early attachment to one woman. Supposing a liberty of changing in the case of an unfortunate choice, this liberty would not affect population till it arose to a height greatly vicious; and we are now supposing the existence of a society where vice is scarcely known.

In a state therefore of great equality and virtue, where pure and simple manners prevailed, and where the means of subsistence were so abundant that no part of the society could have any fears about providing amply for a family, the power of population being left to exert itself unchecked, the increase of the human species would evidently be much greater than any increase that has been hitherto known.

In the United States of America, where the means of subsistence have been more ample, the manners of the people more pure, and consequently the checks to early marriages fewer than in any of the modern states of Europe, the population has been found to double itself in twenty-five years.

This ratio of increase, though short of the utmost power of population, yet as the result of actual experience, we will take as our rule; and say that population, when unchecked, goes on doubling itself every twenty-five years, or increases in a geometrical ratio.

Let us now take any spot of earth—this island, for instance—and see in what ratio the subsistence it affords can be supposed to increase. We will begin with it under its present state of cultivation.

If I allow that by the best possible policy, by breaking up more land, and by great encouragements to agriculture, the produce of this island may be doubled in the first twenty-five years, I think it will be allowing as much as any person can well demand.

In the next twenty-five years it is impossible to suppose that the produce could be quadrupled. It would be contrary to all our knowledge of the qualities of land. The very utmost that we can conceive is that the increase in the second twenty-five years might equal the present produce. Let us then take this for our rule, though certainly far beyond the truth, and allow that by great exertion the whole produce of the island might be increased every twenty-five years, by a quantity of subsistence equal to what it at present produces. The most enthusiastic speculator cannot suppose a greater increase than this. In a few centuries it would make every acre of land in the island like a garden.

Yet this ratio of increase is evidently arithmetical.

It may be fairly said, therefore, that the means of subsistence increase in an arithmetical ratio.

Let us now bring the effects of these two ratios together.

The population of the island is computed to be about seven millions; and we will suppose the present produce equal to the support of such a number. In the first twenty-five years the population would be fourteen millions; and, the food being also doubled, the means of subsistence would be equal to this increase. In the next twenty-five years the population would be twenty-eight millions, and the means of subsistence only equal to the support of twenty-one millions. In the next period the population would be fifty-six millions, and the means of subsistence just sufficient for half that number. And at the conclusion of the first century the population would be one hundred and twelve millions, and the means of subsistence only equal to the support of thirty-five millions; which would leave a population of seventy-seven millions totally unprovided for.

A great emigration necessarily implies unhappiness of some kind or other in the country that is deserted. For few persons will leave their families, connections, friends, and native land to seek a settlement in untried foreign climes without some strong subsisting causes of uneasiness where they are, or the hope of some great advantages in the place to which they are going.

But to make the argument more general, and less interrupted by the partial views of emigration, let us take the whole earth, instead of one spot, and suppose that the restraints to population were universally removed. If the subsistence for man that the earth affords was to be increased every twenty-five years by a quantity equal to what the whole world at present produces, this would allow the power of production in the earth to be absolutely unlimited, and its ratio of increase much greater than we can conceive that any possible exertions of mankind could make it.

Taking the population of the world at any number, a thousand millions, for instance, the human species would increase in the ratio of 1, 2, 4, 8, 16, 32, 64, 128, 256, 512, et cetera, and subsistence as 1, 2, 3, 4, 5, 6, 7, 8, 9, 10, et cetera. In two centuries and a quarter the population would be to the means of subsistence as 512 to 10; in three centuries as 4096 to 13; and in two thousand years the difference would be almost incalculable, though the produce in that time would have increased to an immense extent.

No limits whatever are placed to the productions of the earth; they may increase forever and be greater than any assignable quantity; yet still, the power of population being a power of a superior order, the increase of the human species can only be kept commensurate to the increase of the means of subsistence by the constant operation of the strong law of necessity acting as a check upon the greater power.

The effects of this check remain now to be considered.

Among plants and animals the view of the subject is simple. They are all impelled by a powerful instinct to the increase of their species; and this instinct is interrupted by no reasoning or doubts about providing for their offspring. Wherever, therefore, there is liberty, the power of increase is exerted; and the superabundant effects are repressed afterwards by want of room and nourishment, which is common to animals and plants; and, among animals, by becoming the prey of others.

The effects of this check on man are more complicated.

Impelled to the increase of his species by an equally powerful instinct, reason interrupts his career and asks him whether he may not bring beings into the world for whom he cannot provide the means of subsistence. In a state of equality this would be the simple question. In the present state of society other considerations occur. Will he not lower his rank in life? Will he not subject himself to greater difficulties than he at present feels? Will he not be obliged to labor harder? And, if he has a large family, will his utmost exertions enable him to support them? May he not see his offspring in rags and misery, and clamoring for bread that he cannot give them? And may he not be reduced to the grating necessity of forfeiting his independence and of being obliged to the sparing hand of charity for support?

These considerations are calculated to prevent, and certainly do prevent, a very great number in all civilized nations from pursuing the dictate of nature in an early attachment to one woman. And this restraint almost necessarily, though not absolutely so, produces vice. Yet in all societies, even those that are most vicious, the tendency to a virtuous attachment is so strong that there is a constant effort toward an increase of population. This constant effort as constantly tends to subject the lower classes of the society to distress and to prevent any great permanent amelioration of their condition.

The way in which these effects are produced seems to be this.

We will suppose the means of subsistence in any country just equal to the easy support of its inhabitants. The constant effort toward population, which is found to act even in the most vicious societies, increases the number of people before the means of subsistence are increased. The food, therefore, which before supported seven millions, must now be divided among seven millions and a half or eight millions. The poor consequently must live much worse, and many of them be reduced to severe distress. The number of laborers also being above the proportion of the work in the market, the price of labor must tend toward a decrease; while the price of provisions would at the same time tend to rise. The laborer, therefore, must work harder to earn the same as he did before. During this season of distress the discouragements to marriage and the difficulty of rearing a family are so great that population is at a stand. In the meantime the cheapness of labor, the plenty of laborers, and the necessity of an increased industry among them encourage cultivators to employ more labor upon their land; to turn up fresh soil, and to manure and improve more completely what is already in tillage; till ultimately the means of subsistence become in the same proportion to the population as at the period from which we set out. The situation of the laborer being then again tolerably comfortable, the restraints to population are in some degree loosened; and the same retrograde and progressive movements with respect to happiness are repeated.

This sort of oscillation will not be remarked by superficial observers; and it may be difficult even for the most penetrating mind to calculate its periods. Yet that in all old states some such vibration does exist, though from various transverse causes, in a much less marked and in a much more irregular manner than I have described it, no reflecting man who considers the subject deeply can well doubt.

Many reasons occur why this oscillation has been less obvious and less decidedly confirmed by experience than might naturally be expected.

One principal reason is that the histories of mankind that we possess are histories only of the higher classes. We have but few accounts that can be depended upon of the manners and customs of that part of mankind where these retrograde and progressive movements chiefly take place. A satisfactory history of this kind, of one people, and of one period, would require the constant and minute attention of an observing mind during a long life. Some of the objects of inquiry would be: in what proportion to the number of adults was the number of marriages; to what extent vicious customs prevailed in consequence of the restraints upon matrimony; what was the comparative mortality among the children of the most distressed part of the community, and those who lived rather more at their ease; what were the variations in the real price of labor; and what were the observable differences in the state of the lower classes of society, with respect to ease and happiness, at different times during a certain period.

Such a history would tend greatly to elucidate the manner in which the constant check upon population acts, and would probably prove the existence of the retrograde and progressive movements that have been mentioned; though the times of their vibration must necessarily be rendered irregular, from the operation of many interrupting causes, such as the introduction or failure of certain manufactures; a greater or less prevalent spirit of agricultural enterprise; years of plenty, or years of scarcity; wars and pestilence; poor laws; the invention of processes for shortening labor without the proportional extension of the market for the commodity; and, particularly, the difference between the nominal and real price of labor, a circumstance which has perhaps more than any other contributed to conceal this oscillation from common view.

It very rarely happens that the nominal price of labor universally falls; but we well know that it frequently remains the same, while the nominal price of provisions has been gradually increasing. This is, in effect, a real fall in the price of labor; and during this period the condition of the lower orders of the community must gradually grow worse and worse. But the farmers and capitalists are growing rich from the real cheapness of labor. Their increased capitals enable them to employ a greater number of men. Work therefore may be plentiful; and the price of labor would consequently rise. But the want of freedom in the market of labor, which occurs more or less in all communities, either from parish laws or the more general cause of the facility of combination among the rich and its difficulty among the poor, operates to prevent the price of labor from rising at the natural period and keeps it down some time longer; perhaps till a year of scarcity, when the clamor is too loud and the necessity too apparent to be resisted.

The true cause of the advance in the price of labor is thus concealed; and the rich affect to grant it as an act of compassion and favor to the poor, in consideration of a year of scarcity; and, when plenty returns, indulge themselves in the most unreasonable of all complaints, that the price does not again fall; when a little reflection would show them that it must have risen long before, but from an unjust conspiracy of their own.

But though the rich by unfair combinations contribute frequently to prolong a season of distress among the poor, yet no possible form of society could prevent the almost constant action of misery upon a great part of mankind, if in a state of inequality, and upon all, if all were equal.

The theory on which the truth of this position depends appears to me so extremely clear that I feel at a loss to conjecture what part of it can be denied.

That population cannot increase without the means of subsistence is a proposition so evident that it needs no illustration.

That population does invariably increase, where there are the means of subsistence, the history of every people that have ever existed will abundantly prove.

And that the superior power of population cannot be checked without producing misery or vice, the ample portion of these too bitter ingredients in the cup of human life and the continuance of the physical causes that seem to have produced them bear too convincing a testimony.

Letter from a Much-Traveled Lady

LADY MARY WORTLEY MONTAGU (1689–1762)

RARE TODAY is the pock-mocked face tokening escape from death by smallpox. Yet up to the turn of the nineteenth century smallpox was a common and deadly disease. The disappearance of the American Indian owed as much to the ravages of smallpox, not to mention other common diseases like measles and tuberculosis, as to the misuse of "firewater" and to the guns of the early settlers. Preventive medicine took a great turn toward becoming a science, now world-wide in scope, when it was discovered that something could be done to prevent smallpox. Inoculation was the first method tried. It was introduced into England in 1718 through the sponsorship of the witty, clever, much-traveled woman of fashion, Lady Mary Wortley Montagu, wife of the British Ambassador to Turkey, where she first observed the practice of inoculation and described it in one of her sparkling "Letters from the East," published 1716–18. Inoculation is a means of contracting a *mild* case of smallpox deliberately in order to make oneself immune to a serious, pock-marking, and possibly fatal case contracted accidentally. (Vaccination is something different. See p. 279.) Lady Mary was one of the first of the well-educated, widely traveled ladies of fashion who, though influencing their communities, won the title of "bluestockings." A precocious child, she taught herself Latin and early presided at the table of her father, the Duke of Kingston.

English is the language of the original letter.

INOCULATION AGAINST SMALLPOX

I AM GOING to tell you a thing that I am sure will make you wish yourself here. The smallpox, so fatal and so general among us, is here rendered entirely harmless by the invention of ingrafting, which is the term they give it. There is a set of old women who make it their business to perform the operation every autumn, in the month of September, when the great heat is abated. People send to one another to know if any of their family has a mind to have the smallpox; they make parties for this purpose, and when they are met (commonly fifteen or sixteen together), the old woman comes with a nutshell full of the matter of the best sort of smallpox and asks what veins you please to have opened. She immediately rips open that you offer to her with a large needle (which gives you no more pain than a common scratch), and puts into the vein as much venom as can lie upon the head of her needle, and after binds up the little wound with a hollow bit of shell; and in this manner opens four or five veins. The Grecians have commonly the superstition of opening one in the middle of the forehead, in each arm, and on the breast to mark the sign of the cross; but this has a very ill effect, all these wounds leaving little scars, and is not done by those that are not superstitious, who choose to have them in the legs, or that part of the arm that is concealed. The children or young patients play together all the rest of the day and are in perfect health to the eighth. Then the fever begins to seize them, and they keep their beds two days, very seldom three. Every year thousands undergo this operation; and the French ambassador says pleasantly that they take the smallpox here by way of diversion, as they take the waters in other countries. There is no example of anyone that has died in it; and you may believe I am very well satisfied of the safety of this experiment, since I intend to try it on my dear little son.

Vaccination: The Beginning of Preventive Medicine

EDWARD JENNER (1749–1823)

"DON'T THINK, try; be patient, be accurate," was the curt advice given to the young British physician, Edward Jenner, by his distinguished medical teacher, John Hunter. By following this maxim Jenner discovered and proved the value of vaccination against smallpox, a safer procedure than inoculation. He firmly founded the science of preventive medicine, scantily practiced before his time but now affording protection against dozens of diseases. Vaccination differs from inoculation in this respect: the individual is deliberately "infected" with a mild disease, cowpox, which establishes an immunity against accidental contraction of smallpox, while inoculation induces the disease itself, in mild form. Jenner first observed this phenomenon among dairymaids (1796); then tried experiments which permitted him to announce the discovery of vaccination in the beautifully written, epoch-making pamphlet, "Inquiry into the Cause and Effects of the Variolae Vaccinae," published in 1798. The superiority of vaccination over inoculation was quickly demonstrated in England and abroad. In America Benjamin Waterhouse, professor of "physic" at Harvard, undertook to prove its safety and effectiveness by using his own children as subjects; his "History of the Kinepox" is the American classic on this topic. Jenner was one scientist who did not die unrewarded for his contribution to humanity; in 1803 the British Parliament voted him a grant of £10,000 and, in 1806, a second grant of £20,000. *English* is the language of the original essay.

AN INQUIRY INTO THE CAUSES AND EFFECTS OF THE VARIOLAE VACCINAE, A DISEASE DISCOVERED IN SOME OF THE WESTERN COUNTIES OF ENGLAND, PARTICULARLY GLOUCESTERSHIRE, AND KNOWN BY THE NAME OF THE COWPOX

THE DEVIATION of man from the state in which he was originally placed by nature seems to have proved to him a prolific source of diseases. From the love of splendor, from the indulgence of luxury, and from his fondness for amusement he has familiarized himself with a great number of animals, which may not originally have been intended for his associates.

The wolf, disarmed of ferocity, is now pillowed in the lady's lap. The cat, the little tiger of our island, whose natural home is the forest, is equally domesticated and caressed. The cow, the hog, the sheep, and the horse are all, for a variety of purposes, brought under his care and dominion.

There is a disease to which the horse, from his state of domestication, is frequently subject. The farriers call it the grease. It is an inflammation and swelling in the heel, from which issues matter possessing properties of a very peculiar kind, which seems capable of generating a disease in the human body (after it has undergone the modification which I shall presently speak of), which bears so strong a resemblance to the smallpox that I think it highly probable it may be the source of the disease.

In this dairy country a great number of cows are kept, and the office of milking is performed indiscriminately by men- and maidservants. One of the former having been appointed to apply dressings to the heels of a horse affected with the grease, and not paying due attention to cleanliness, incautiously bears his part in milking the cows, with some particles of the infectious matter adhering to his fingers. When this is the case it commonly happens that a disease is communicated to the cows, and from the cows to dairymaids, which spreads through the farm until the most of the cattle and domestics feel its unpleasant consequences. This disease has obtained the name of the cowpox. It appears on the nipples of the cows in the form of irregular pustules. At their first appearance they are commonly of a palish blue, or rather of a color somewhat approaching to livid, and are surrounded by an erysipelatous inflammation. These pustules, unless a timely remedy be applied, frequently degenerate into phagedenic ulcers, which prove extremely troublesome. The animals become indisposed, and the secretion of milk is much lessened. Inflamed spots now begin to appear on different parts of the hands of the domestics employed in milking, and sometimes on the wrists, which quickly run on to suppuration, first assuming the appearance of the small vesications produced by a burn. Most commonly they appear about the joints of the fingers and at their extremities; but whatever parts are affected, if the situation will admit, these superficial suppurations put on a circular form, with their edges more elevated than their center, and of a color distantly approaching to blue. Absorption takes place, and tumors appear in each axilla. The system becomes affected—the pulse is quickened; and shiverings, succeeded by heat, with general lassitude and pains about the loins and limbs, with vomiting, come on. The head is painful, and the patient is now and then even affected with delirium. These symptoms, varying in their degrees of violence, generally continue from one day to three or four, leaving ulcerated sores about the hands, which, from the sensibility of the parts, are very troublesome, and commonly heal slowly, frequently becoming phagedenic, like those from whence they sprung. The lips, nostrils, eyelids, and other parts of the body are sometimes affected with sores; but these evidently arise from their being heedlessly rubbed or scratched with the patient's infected fingers. No eruptions on the skin have followed the decline of the feverish symptoms in any instance that has come to my inspection, one only excepted, and in this case a very few appeared on the arms: they were very minute, of a vivid red color, and soon died away without advancing to maturation; so that I cannot determine whether they had any connection with the preceding symptoms.

Thus the disease makes its progress from the horse to the nipple of the cow, and from the cow to the human subject.

Morbid matter of various kinds, when absorbed into the system, may produce effects in some degree similar; but what renders the cowpox virus so extremely singular is that the person who has been thus affected is forever after secure from the infection of the smallpox; neither exposure to the variolous effluvia, nor the insertion of the matter into the skin, producing this distemper.

In support of so extraordinary a fact I shall lay before my reader a great number of instances.

Case I. Joseph Merret, now as undergardener to the Earl of Berkeley, lived as a servant with a farmer near this place in the year 1770, and occasionally assisted in milking his master's cows. Several horses belonging to the farm began to have sore heels, which Merret frequently attended. The cows soon became affected with the cowpox, and soon after several sores appeared on his hands. Swellings and stiffness in each axilla followed, and he was so much indisposed for several days as to be incapable of pursuing his ordinary employment. Previously to the appearance of the distemper among the cows there was no fresh cow brought into the farm, nor any servant employed who was affected with the cowpox.

In April 1795, a general inoculation taking place here, Merret was inoculated with his family; so that a period of twenty-five years had elapsed from his having the cowpox to this time. However, though the variolous matter was repeatedly inserted into his arm, I found it impracticable to infect him with it; an efflorescence only, taking on an erysipelatous look about the center, appearing on the skin near the punctured parts. During the whole time that his family had the smallpox, one of whom had it very full, he remained in the house with them but received no injury from exposure to the contagion.

It is necessary to observe that the utmost care was taken to ascertain, with the most scrupulous precision, that no one whose case is here adduced had gone through the smallpox previous to these attempts to produce that disease.

Had these experiments been conducted in a large city, or in a populous neighborhood, some doubts might have been entertained; but here, where population is thin, and where such an event as a person's having had the smallpox is always faithfully recorded, no risk of inaccuracy in this particular can arise.

Case II. Sarah Portlock, of this place, was infected with the cowpox when a servant at a farmer's in the neighborhood, twenty-seven years ago.

In the year 1792, conceiving herself, from this circumstance, secure from the infection of the smallpox, she nursed one of her own children who had accidentally caught the disease, but no indisposition ensued. During the time she remained in the infected room variolous matter was inserted into both her arms, but without any further effect than in the preceding case. . . .

Case XVII. The more accurately to observe the progress of the infection I selected a healthy boy, about eight years old, for the purpose of inoculating for the cowpox. The matter was taken from a sore on the hand of a dairymaid, who was infected by her master's cows, and it was inserted, on the fourteenth day of May 1796, into the arm of the boy by means of two superficial incisions, barely penetrating the cutis, each about an inch long.

On the seventh day he complained of uneasiness in the axilla and on the ninth he became a little chilly, lost his appetite, and had a slight headache. During the whole of this day he was perceptibly indisposed and spent the night with some degree of restlessness, but on the day following he was perfectly well.

The appearance of the incisions in their progress to a state of maturation were much the same as when produced in a similar manner by variolous matter. The difference which I perceived was in the state of the limpid fluid arising from the action of the virus, which assumed rather a darker hue, and in that of the efflorescence spreading round the incisions, which had more of an erysipelatous look than we commonly perceive when variolous matter has been made use of in the same manner; but the whole died away (leaving on the inoculated parts scabs and subsequent eschars) without giving me or my patient the least trouble.

In order to ascertain whether the boy, after feeling so slight an affection of the system from the cowpox virus, was secure from the contagion of the smallpox, he was inoculated the first of July following with variolous matter, immediately taken from a pustule. Several slight punctures and incisions were made on both his arms, and the matter was carefully inserted, but no disease followed. The same appearances were observable on the arms as we commonly see when a patient has had variolous matter applied, after having either the cowpox or smallpox. Several months afterwards he was again inoculated with variolous matter, but no sensible effect was produced on the constitution.

After the many fruitless attempts to give the smallpox to those who had had the cowpox, it did not appear necessary, nor was it convenient to me, to inoculate the whole of those who had been the subjects of these late trials; yet I thought it right to see the effects of variolous matter on some of them, particularly William Summers, the first of these patients who had been infected with matter taken from the cow. He was, therefore, inoculated from a fresh pustule; but, as in the preceding cases, the system did not feel the effects of it in the smallest degree. I had an opportunity also of having this boy and William Pead inoculated by my nephew, Mr. Henry Jenner, whose report to me is as follows: "I have inoculated Pead and Barge, two of the boys whom you lately infected with the cowpox. On the second day the incisions were inflamed and there was a pale inflammatory stain around them. On the third day these appearances were still increasing and their arms itched considerably. On the fourth day the inflammation was evidently subsiding, and on the sixth day it was scarcely perceptible. No symptoms of indisposition followed.

"To convince myself that the variolous matter made use of was in a perfect state I at the same time inoculated a patient with some of it who never had gone through the cowpox, and it produced the smallpox in the usual regular manner."

These experiments afforded me much satisfaction; they proved that the matter, in passing from one human subject to another, through five gradations, lost none of its original properties, J. Barge being the fifth who received the infection successively from William Summers, the boy to whom it was communicated from the cow.

I shall now conclude this inquiry with some general observations on the subject, and on some others which are interwoven with it.

Although I presume it may not be necessary to produce further testimony in support of my assertion "that the cowpox protects the human constitution from the infection of the smallpox," yet it affords me considerable satisfaction to say that Lord Somerville, the president of the Board of Agriculture, to whom this paper was shown by Sir Joseph Banks, has found upon inquiry that the statements were confirmed by the concurring testimony of Mr. Dolland, a surgeon, who resides in a dairy country remote from this, in which these observations were made. With respect to the opinion adduced "that the source of the infection is a peculiar morbid matter arising in the horse," although I have not been able to prove it from actual experiments conducted immediately under my own eye, yet the evidence I have adduced appears sufficient to establish it.

They who are not in the habit of conducting experiments may not be aware of the coincidence of circumstances necessary for their being managed so as to prove perfectly decisive; nor how often men engaged in professional pursuits are liable to interruptions which disappoint them almost at the instant of their being accomplished: however, I feel no room for hesitation respecting the common origin of the disease, being well convinced that it never appears among the cows (except it can be traced to a cow introduced among the general herd which has been previously infected, or to an infected servant) unless they have been milked by someone who, at the same time, has the care of a horse affected with diseased heels.

The spring of the year 1797, which I intended particularly to have devoted to the completion of this investigation, proved, from its dryness, remarkably adverse to my wishes; for it frequently happens, while the farmers' horses are exposed to the cold rains which fall at that season, that their heels become diseased, and so cowpox then appeared in the neighborhood.

The active quality of the virus from the horses' heels is greatly increased after it has acted on the nipples of the cow, as it rarely happens that the horse affects his dresser with sores, and as rarely that a milkmaid escapes the infection when she milks infected cows. It is most active at the commencement of the disease, even before it has acquired a puslike appearance; indeed, I am not confident whether this property in the matter does not entirely cease as soon as it is secreted in the form of pus. I am induced to think it does cease, and that it is the thin, darkish-looking fluid only, oozing from the newly formed cracks in the heels, similar to what sometimes appears from erysipelatous blisters, which gives the disease. Nor am I certain that the nipples of the cows are at all times in a state to receive the infection. The appearance of the disease in the spring and the early part of the summer, when they are disposed to be affected with spontaneous eruptions so much more frequently than at other seasons, induces me to think that the virus from the horse must be received upon them when they are in this state, in order to produce effects: experiments, however, must determine these points. But it is clear that, when the cowpox virus is once generated, the cows cannot resist the contagion, in whatever state their nipples may chance to be, if they are milked with an infected hand.

Whether the matter, either from the cow or the horse, will affect the sound skin of the human body I cannot positively determine; probably it will not, unless on those parts where the cuticle is extremely thin, as on the lips, for example. . . .

A medical gentleman (now no more), who for many years inoculated in this neighborhood, frequently preserved the variolous matter intended for his use on a piece of lint or cotton which, in its fluid state, was put into a vial, corked, and conveyed into a warm pocket; a situation certainly favorable for speedily producing putrefaction in it. In this state (not infrequently after it had been taken several days from the pustules) it was inserted into the arms of his patients and brought on inflammation of the incised parts, swellings of the axillary glands, fever, and sometimes eruptions. But what was this disease? Certainly not the smallpox; for the matter, having from putrefaction lost or suffered a derangement in its specific properties, was no longer capable of producing that malady, those who had been inoculated in this manner being as much subject to the contagion of the smallpox as if they had never been under the influence of this artificial disease; and many, unfortunately, fell victims to it who thought themselves in perfect security. . . .

Thus far have I proceeded in an inquiry founded, as it must appear, on the basis of experiment; in which, however, conjecture has been occasionally admitted in order to present to persons well situated for such discussions objects for a more minute investigation. In the meantime I shall myself continue to prosecute this inquiry, encouraged by the hope of its becoming essentially beneficial to mankind.

VI SCIENCE WEDS PROGRESS:
In the Early Nineteenth Century

Nineteenth-Century Chemists

LIEBIG, WÖHLER, DAVY, VAN'T HOFF, ARRHENIUS, KEKULÉ, MENDELYEEV, PERKIN, BAEYER, AND NOBEL

UP TO ASPIRIN AND DYNAMITE

JUSTUS LIEBIG (1803–73) established one of the earliest truly chemical laboratories, at Giessen, Germany, in 1826. Of this important teaching institution, in which agricultural and physiological chemistry were founded, he wrote many years later: .

"At Giessen all were concentrated in the work, and this was a passionate enjoyment. . . . Pupils came to me from all sides. . . . I saw very soon that all progress in organic chemistry depended on its simplification. . . . A kindly fate had brought together in Giessen the most talented youths from all countries of Europe. . . . Everyone was obliged to find his own way for himself. . . . We worked from dawn to the fall of night."

Friedrich Wöhler (1800–82), another German chemist, at Göttingen, published two years later (1828) a brief paper which reported the following epoch-making observation:

"Research gave the unexpected result that, by combination of cyanic acid with ammonia, urea is formed. A noteworthy fact since it furnishes an example of the artificial production of an organic—indeed a so-called *animal*—substance from inorganic materials! . . . I will describe the behavior of artificial urea no further, since it coincides perfectly with that of urea from urine, according to the accounts of Proust, Prout, and others."

Organic chemistry (dealing with carbon compounds) took new impetus from this paper to bring us eventually dyes and drugs (for example, the sulfa drugs, which were originally intended only as dyes), explosives, and plastics. But Wöhler only began practical organic chemurgy.

286

Physical chemistry had its beginnings in the work of Sir Humphry Davy (1778–1829), inventor of the miner's safety lamp, who in addition to making his "greatest discovery"—Michael Faraday—ran electric currents through solutions and thus for the first time isolated such elements as sodium, potassium, and chlorine. This work was carried ahead by Clausius and Faraday, who invented the word "electrolysis" for the process of tearing substances apart by electricity, and the word "ion" for the electrically charged particles in a solution. The great names in the further development of this branch of chemistry are Willard Gibbs, Van't Hoff, and Arrhenius.

Jacobus Hendricus van't Hoff (1852–1911), Dutch physical chemist, laid the foundation for what was called "stereochemistry," or "chemistry in space." After W. Pfeffer, he dealt with the problem of osmosis—the passage and repassage of different kinds of solutions through porous clay or semipermeable membranes (such as body tissues). In a famous paper (1887) "On the Role of Osmotic Pressure in Analogy between Solutions and Gases," he wrote:

"In an investigation whose essential aim was a knowledge of the laws of chemical equilibrium in solutions, it gradually became apparent that there is a deep-seated analogy—indeed almost an identity—between solutions and gases, so far as their physical relations are concerned; provided that with solutions we deal with the so-called osmotic pressure, where with gases we are concerned with the ordinary elastic pressure."

Svante Arrhenius (1859–1927), a Swedish professor, advanced the next important idea about the action of ions in a solution. His theory of electrolytic dissociation asserted that salts in dilute solutions are almost completely ionized. In his famous paper, also published in 1887, he wrote:

"I have designated those molecules whose ions are independent of one another in their movements as active; the remaining molecules, whose ions are firmly combined with one another, as inactive. I have also maintained it as probable that in extreme dilution all the inactive molecules of an electrolyte are transformed into active. . . . The above two assumptions are of the very widest significance. . . . The chemist would have at his disposal an extraordinarily convenient means of determining the molecular weight of every substance soluble in a liquid."

Two more theorists must have our attention:

Friedrich August Kekulé (1829–96), another young German chemist, sat dozing before the fireplace one evening in 1865. Suddenly in the flames he saw the pattern of the benzene ring: the six-sided, double-bonded, closed chain of carbon atoms that became the new guiding star of expanding organic chemistry.

Dmitri Ivanovich Mendelyeev (1834–1907), a Russian chemist, writing down list after list of the then known chemical elements, their atomic weights, their valences, and their physical properties, caught sight of a different kind of pattern—a strange series of "family resemblances" (for example, the halogen family) between the elements. In his important textbook, "The Principles of Chemistry" (1868–70), he succeeded in laying down a Periodic Table of the Elements. There were ninety-two places on his table; not all of them were filled, but he predicted they would be.

What did all this theorizing bring? Let us be satisfied with the briefest retailing of examples whose full list would lead us to the complete catalogue of modern manufactures. The Periodic Table brought about the discovery of all the missing elements and a few more for good measure: we shall cite only radium, helium, and neon.

Organic chemistry? Among its early triumphs were coal-tar dyes, the first of which, mauve purple, was discovered (1856) in a dirty test tube by an eighteen-year-old English boy, William Perkin, whose chemistry teacher had set him at a task so difficult that its solution was delayed to become the chemical triumph of 1944: the manufacture of synthetic quinine. In the meantime Adolf von Baeyer (1835–1917), starting with the same filthy raw material, had produced aspirin.

Solute chemistry? In 1866 a Swedish-born, American-trained art connoisseur and explosives manufacturer, Alfred Nobel (1833–96), found how to dissolve nitroglycerine in gun cotton to make that "safe explosive," dynamite, the open sesame to modern engineering and mining. Nobel left a fortune of $9,200,000, part of the income of which, since 1901, has been used to encourage the development of science by the annual award of prizes in physics and chemistry.

"The Mutual Relation of Electricity, Magnetism, and Motion"

MICHAEL FARADAY (1791–1867)

ORIGINALLY a bookbinder's apprentice, taken into the realm of science as a bottle washer and laboratory assistant to Sir Humphry Davy, Michael

Faraday wore the wrong school tie. Not being a member of the ortho-dox Cambridge school then dominating English science, Faraday's in-tuitively brilliant ideas in chemistry, physics, and the newly discovered field of electromagnetism were but slowly accepted by his countrymen. Yet every dynamo that hums, every electric motor that turns today hymns the genius of this quiet, painstaking Englishman. The red-letter day in the history of electricity may be considered to be March 26, 1832, the date on which Faraday discovered and dutifully recorded in his diary, quoted here, the relations between electric currents and magnetism. Without this magnificent simplification of the diverse phenomena of electricity the "age of electricity" might have been considerably de-layed.

Other important nineteenth-century workers in the field of electro-magnetism preceded Faraday, notably Galvani, Volta, Oersted, and Ampère; others followed him, especially Joseph Henry, Ohm, Wheat-stone, Maxwell, Hertz, J. J. Thomson, and Michael Pupin; but none have surpassed him in importance. Galvani was an Italian physiologist; while dissecting a frog, he accidentally observed twitchings of the mus-cles which he attributed to "animal electricity"; the correct explanation was supplied by Alessandro Volta, who invented the "voltaic pile," the first storage battery, as a means of providing a steady electric current. Electricity and magnetism were joined firmly together as a single field of study—electromagnetism—on the day in 1820 that Hans Christian Oersted, a Dane, observed that the needle of a compass was deflected when brought close to a wire carrying an electric current. Shortly after-ward, Ampère enunciated the celebrated law: "Two parallel and like directed currents attract each other, while two parallel currents of oppo-site direction repel each other."

These were the discoveries which Faraday especially amplified. He was at the time the ill-paid director of the laboratory of the Royal Insti-tution, in London, and had many notable discoveries to his credit. Among his other most important works are included the concept of the mag-netic field and the magnetic "lines of force," production of new kinds of optical glass, discovery of two chlorides of carbon, and—in electricity —researches on electrolysis and the discovery of the plane of rotation of polarized light in a magnetic field.

Like other early nineteenth-century electrophysicists, Faraday became a "man of measure," honored by having a measuring unit of electricity —the farad—named after him. Others whom we remember today as pioneers in this field, memorialized in units of electrical measurement, include Ampère, whose name comes down in the "ammeter" as well as the "ampere" unit of current; Georg Ohm (1787–1854), German physicist after whom we call the unit of electrical resistance the "ohm"; Volta, honored in the "volt"; Galvani, remembered in the words "galvanometer" and "galvanism"; "henry", "coulomb," "watt," "maxwell," and "joule," all of which were originally written with capital letters as proper names.

English, sometimes ungrammatical, for these were personal notes not for publication, was the language in which Faraday kept his diary. The passages given here are from Volume I (September 1820–June 11, 1832) of the illustrated edition of "Faraday's Diary," printed and published by order of the managers of the Royal Institution of Great Britain by G. Bell and Sons, Ltd. (London, 1932), a century after they were written.

NOTES FROM HIS DIARY

Jany. 7th, 1832

Is NOT the evolution of electricity in the wire caused by an electro magnetic pole a presumptive proof that time is required in electric circuit, and perhaps much time; is not effect due to the wire going in the direction of the current in one part and against it in the other?

Experimented in the pond before Kensington Palace. This is a made pond with a Stucco or other artificial bottom, and is supplied with water by one of the Companies, I believe the Chelsea.

It was wonderful to find the electric current from so small a cause as a little saline matter in one cup, or closer contact of the finger on one wire, go through about 500 feet of water and more than 600 feet of wire—still affecting the galvanometer. It shews the extreme care required in delicate and elementary experiments when this instrument is used.

The Duke of Sussex had obtained leave from the King for these expts. to be made in the gardens, and I received all help from Mr. Acton (?) and the men that was required. It was but little, but was very willingly given.

Jany. 12, 1832

Experimented today at Waterloo Bridge by leave of Mr. Bridell the Secy.

Feby. 29, 1832

Have constructed a double galvanometer; i.e., two separate coils and a double needle between; is very delicate and good.

March 26th

Conceived that as electricity in passing made magnetism at right angles, so if electricity still and needle moved in opposite directions, should become a magnet, for then the electricity and metal are relatively moving and that seems the only condition required.

The lines or directions of force between 2 electrical conductors oppositely electrified may be called *electric curves* in analogy to *magnetic curves*. Do they not exist also in the electric current wire?

The mutual relation of electricity, magnetism and motion may be represented by three lines at right angles to each other, any one of which may represent any one of these points and the other two lines the other points. Then if electricity be determined in one line and motion in another, magnetism will be developed in the third; or if electricity be determined in one line and magnetism in another, motion will occur in the third. Or if magnetism be determined first then motion will produce electricity or electricity motion. Or if motion be the first point determined, Magnetism will evolve electricity or electricity magnetism.

More Electricity of the Same Kind

JOSEPH HENRY (1797–1878)

FARADAY'S DISCOVERY that electric currents could be induced was independently and almost simultaneously discovered in America by the gifted professor of natural philosophy at Princeton University, Joseph Henry. The telegraph, finally made practical by Samuel Morse, owed much to the researches of Henry in the principles of the electromagnet upon which electromagnetic telegraphy was based. "Pure science" again set the stage for technology. The eminence of Henry in American science may be judged from the fact that he became in 1846 the first secretary and director of the Smithsonian Institution in Washington, D.C., where, among other activities, he instituted the weather-report system, investigated sunspots and solar radiation.

The Smithsonian Institution was an Englishman's gift to America. It was founded in Washington, D.C., by act of Congress in 1846 upon the bequest of over £100,000 to the United States from James Smithson, British chemist and mineralogist, natural son of the first Duke of Northumberland. Many of Henry's researches were published in the reports of the Smithsonian Institution, publications which have for almost a century remained a mine of information on American scientific development.

English was the language of Henry's paper on induced currents.

INDUCED ELECTRICAL CURRENTS

I HAVE MADE several other experiments in relation to [electricity] but which more important duties will not permit me to verify in time for this paper. I may, however, mention one fact which I have not seen noticed in any work, and which appears to me to belong to the same class of phenomena as those before described. It is this: when a small battery is moderately excited by diluted acid, and its poles, which should be terminated by cups of mercury, are connected by a copper wire not more than a foot in length, no spark is perceived when the connection is either formed or broken; but if a wire thirty or forty feet long be used instead of the short wire, though no spark will be perceptible when the connection is made, yet when it is broken by drawing one end of the wire from its cup of mercury, a vivid spark is produced. If the action of the battery be very intense, a spark will be given by the short wire; in this case it is only necessary to wait a few minutes until the action partially subsides, and until no more sparks are given from the short wire; if the long wire be now substituted a spark will again be obtained. The effect appears somewhat increased by coiling the wire into a helix; it seems also to depend in some measure on the length and thickness of the wire.

I can account for these phenomena only by supposing the long wire to become charged with electricity, which by its reaction on itself projects a spark when the connection is broken.

Conservation of Energy

JAMES PRESCOTT JOULE (1818–89)

A GOD-FEARING Victorian gentleman, bearded and pontifical, the learned and respectable secretary of the Manchester (England) Literary and

Philosophical Society, James Prescott Joule, undertook to lecture at St Ann's Church Reading Room, in Manchester, in May 1847, in order to acquaint his scientifically curious fellow townsmen (some fearful that "modern science" would reveal the world to be running down like an unwound spring) with the great doctrine of the conservation of energy. The idea had been more fully broached in 1842 by a German physician, J. R. von Mayer, and by the then budding genius, Hermann von Helmholtz; but for all their "famous papers," no one gave his contemporaries a plainer and more convincing exposition than Joule of the fact that in countless conversions of energy, from heat to work and vice versa, nothing is ever lost. It was a doctrine toward the establishment of which Joule contributed the crucial experiments, conducted over a period of many years. In a cool, well-insulated cellar, free from adventitious changes in temperature, Joule set up an apparatus, consisting of brass paddlewheels, turned by weights through cans of water, oil, and mercury, to measure just how much work (that is, falling weights) will produce how much heat (increase in the temperature of the liquid). His final answer to this question is given in the "famous memoir" of 1850, quoted in part here.

English was Joule's literary language. The Manchester lecture, entitled "On Matter, Living Force, and Heat" originally appeared in the Manchester "Courier" for May 5 and 12, 1847. The memoir on the mechanical equivalent of heat was delivered before the Royal Society on June 21, 1849, and published next year in Part I of the "Philosophical Transactions" for 1849.

"ON MATTER, LIVING FORCE, AND HEAT"

THE FORCE EXPENDED in setting a body in motion is carried by the body itself, and exists with it and in it, throughout the whole course of its motion. This force possessed by moving bodies is termed by mechanical philosophers *vis viva,* or living force. The term may be deemed by some inappropriate, inasmuch as there is no life, properly speaking, in question; but it is *useful,* in order to distinguish the moving force from that which is stationary in its character as the force of gravity. When, therefore, I employ the term "living force," you will understand that I simply mean the force of bodies in motion. The living force of bodies is regulated by their weight and by the velocity of their motion. You will readily understand that if a body of a certain weight possess a certain quantity of living force, twice as much living force will be possessed by a body of twice the weight, provided both bodies move with equal velocity. But the law by which the velocity of a body regulates its living force is not so obvious. . . .

Thus it will be found that a railway train, going at seventy miles per hour, possesses one hundred times the impetus, or living force, that it does when traveling at seven miles per hour.

A body may be endowed with living force in several ways. It may receive it by the impact of another body. Thus, if a perfectly elastic ball be made to strike another similar ball of equal weight at rest, the striking ball will communicate the whole of its living force to the ball struck and, remaining at rest itself, will cause the other ball to move in the same direction and with the same velocity that it did itself before the collision. Here we see an instance of the facility with which living force may be transferred from one body to another. A body may also be endowed with living force by means of the action of gravitation upon it through a certain distance. If I hold a ball at a certain height and drop it, it will have acquired when it arrives at the ground a degree of living force proportional to its weight and the height from which it has fallen. We see, then, that living force may be produced by the action of gravity through a given distance or space. We may therefore say that the former is of equal value, or *equivalent,* to the latter. Hence, if I raise a weight of one pound to the height of one foot, so that gravity may act on it through that distance, I shall communicate to it that which is of equal value or equivalent to a certain amount of living force; if I raise the weight to twice the height, I shall communicate to it the equivalent of twice the quantity of living force.

You will at once perceive that the living force of which we have been speaking is one of the most important qualities with which matter can be endowed and, as such, that it would be absurd to suppose that it can be destroyed, or even lessened, without producing the equivalent of attraction through a given distance of which we have been speaking. You will therefore be surprised to hear that until very recently the universal opinion has been that living force could be absolutely and irrevocably destroyed at anyone's option. Thus, when a weight falls to the ground, it has been generally supposed that its living force is absolutely annihilated, and that the labor which may have been expended in raising it to the elevation from which it fell has been entirely thrown away and wasted, without the production of any permanent effect whatever. We might reason, *a priori,* that such absolute destruction of living force cannot possibly take place, because it is manifestly absurd to suppose that the powers with which God has endowed matter can be destroyed any more than that they can be created by man's agency; but we are not left with this argument alone, decisive as it must be to every unprejudiced mind. The common experience of everyone teaches him that living force is not *destroyed* by the friction or collision of bodies.

We have reason to believe that the manifestations of living force on our globe are, at the present time, as extensive as those which have existed at any time since its creation, or, at any rate, since the deluge— that the winds blow as strongly, and the torrents flow with equal impetuosity now, as at the remote period of four thousand or even six thousand years ago; and yet we are certain that, through that vast interval of time, the motions of the air and of the water have been incessantly obstructed and hindered by friction.

We may conclude, then, with certainty, that these motions of air and water, constituting living force, are not *annihilated* by friction. We lose sight of them, indeed, for a time; but we find them again reproduced. Were it not so, it is perfectly obvious that long ere this all nature would have come to a dead standstill. What, then, may we inquire, is the cause of this apparent anomaly? How comes it to pass that, though in almost all natural phenomena we witness the arrest of motion and the apparent destruction of living force, we find that no waste or loss of living force has actually occurred?

Experiment has enabled us to answer these questions in a satisfactory manner; for it has shown that, wherever living force is *apparently* destroyed, an equivalent is produced which in process of time may be reconverted into living force. The equivalent is heat.

Experiment has shown that wherever living force is apparently destroyed or absorbed heat is produced. The most frequent way in which living force is thus converted into heat is by means of friction. Wood rubbed against wood or against any hard body, metal rubbed against metal or against any other body—in short, all bodies, solid or even liquid, rubbed against each other, are invariably heated, sometimes even so far as to become red hot. In all these instances the quantity of heat produced is invariably in proportion to the exertion employed in rubbing the bodies together—that is, to the living force absorbed. By fifteen or twenty smart and quick strokes of a hammer on the end of an iron rod of about a quarter of an inch in diameter placed upon an anvil an expert blacksmith will render that end of the iron visibly red hot. Here heat is produced by the absorption of the living force of the descending hammer in the soft iron; which is proved to be the case from the fact that the iron cannot be heated if it be rendered hard and elastic, so as to transfer the living force of the hammer to the anvil.

The general rule, then, is that wherever living force is apparently destroyed, whether by percussion, friction, or any similar means, an exact equivalent of heat is restored. The converse of this proposition is also true, namely, that heat cannot be lessened or absorbed without the production of living force, or its equivalent attraction through space. . . .

In these conversions nothing is ever lost. The same quantity of heat will always be converted into the same quantity of living force. We can therefore express the equivalency in definite language applicable at all times and under all circumstances. Thus the attraction of 817 pounds through the space of one foot is equivalent to, and convertible into, the living force possessed by a body of the same weight of 817 pounds when moving with the velocity of eight feet per second, and this living force is again convertible into the quantity of heat which can increase the temperature of one pound of water by one degree Fahrenheit.

The knowledge of the equivalency of heat to mechanical power is of great value in solving a great number of interesting and important questions. In the case of the steam engine, by ascertaining the quantity of heat produced by the combustion of coal, we can find out how much of it is converted into mechanical power, and thus come to a conclusion how far the steam engine is susceptible of further improvements. Calculations made upon this principle have shown that at least ten times as much power might be produced as is now obtained by the combustion of coal. Another interesting conclusion is that the animal frame, though destined to fulfill so many other ends, is as a machine more perfect than the best-contrived steam engine—that is, is capable of more work with the same expenditure of fuel.

Behold, then, the wonderful arrangements of creation. The earth in its rapid motion round the sun possesses a degree of living force so vast that, if turned into the equivalent of heat, its temperature would be rendered at least one thousand times greater than that of red-hot iron, and the globe on which we tread would in all probability be rendered equal in brightness to the sun itself. And it cannot be doubted that if the course of the earth were changed so that it might fall into the sun that body, so far from being cooled down by the contact of a comparatively cold body, would actually blaze more brightly than before in consequence of the living force with which the earth struck the sun being converted into its equivalent of heat. Here we see that our existence depends upon the *maintenance* of the living force of the earth.

On the other hand, our safety equally depends in some instances upon the *conversion* of living force into heat. You have, no doubt, frequently observed what are called shooting stars, as they appear to emerge from the dark sky of night, pursue a short and rapid course, burst, and are dissipated in shining fragments. From the velocity with which these bodies travel there can be little doubt that they are small planets which, in the course of their revolution round the sun, are attracted and drawn to the earth. Reflect for a moment on the consequences which would ensue if a hard meteoric stone were to strike the room in which we are assembled with a velocity sixty times as great as that of a cannon ball. The dire effects of such a collision are effectually prevented by the atmosphere surrounding our globe, by which the velocity of the meteoric stone is checked and its living force converted into heat, which at last becomes so intense as to melt the body and dissipate it into fragments too small, probably, to be noticed in their fall to the ground. Hence it is that, although multitudes of shooting stars appear every night, few meteoric stones have been found, those few corroborating the truth of our hypothesis by the marks of intense heat which they bear on their surfaces.

Descending from the planetary space and firmament to the surface of our earth, we find a vast variety of phenomena connected with the conversion of living force and heat into one another, which speak in language which cannot be misunderstood of the wisdom and beneficence of the Great Architect of nature. The motion of air which we call *wind* arises chiefly from the intense heat of the Torrid Zone compared with the temperature of the Temperate and Frigid Zones. Here we have an instance of heat being converted into the living force of currents of air. These currents of air, in their progress across the sea, lift up its waves and propel the ships; while in passing across the land they shake the trees and disturb every blade of grass. The waves by their violent motion, the ships by their passage through a resisting medium, and the trees by the rubbing of their branches together and the friction of their leaves against themselves and the air, each and all of them generate heat equivalent to the diminution of the living force of the air which they occasion. The heat thus restored may again contribute to raise fresh currents of air; and thus the phenomena may be repeated in endless succession and variety.

When we consider our own animal frames, "fearfully and wonderfully made," we observe in the motion of our limbs a continual conversion of heat into living force, which may be either converted back again into heat or employed in producing an attraction through space, as when a man ascends a mountain. Indeed the phenomena of nature, whether mechanical, chemical, or vital, consist almost entirely in a continual conversion of attraction through space, living force, and heat into one another. Thus it is that order is maintained in the universe—nothing is deranged, nothing ever lost, but the entire machinery, complicated as it is, works smoothly and harmoniously. And though, as in the awful vision of Ezekiel, "wheel may be in the middle of wheel," and everything may appear complicated and involved in the apparent confusion and intricacy of an almost endless variety of causes, effects, conversions, and arrangements, yet is the most perfect regularity preserved—the whole being governed by the sovereign will of God.

MEMOIR ON THE MECHANICAL EQUIVALENT OF HEAT

IN ACCORDANCE with the pledge I gave the Royal Society some years ago I have now the honor to present it with the results of the experiments I have made in order to determine the mechanical equivalent of heat with exactness.

For a long time it had been a favorite hypothesis that heat consists of "a force or power belonging to bodies," but it was reserved for Count Rumford to make the first experiments decidedly in favor of that view. That justly celebrated natural philosopher demonstrated by his ingenious experiments that the very great quantity of heat excited by the boring of cannon could not be ascribed to a change taking place in the calorific capacity of the metal; and he therefore concluded that the motion of the borer was communicated to the particles of metal, thus producing the phenomena of heat. "It appears to me," he remarks, "extremely difficult, if not quite impossible, to form any distinct idea of anything capable of being excited and communicated in the manner the heat was excited and communicated in these experiments, except it be motion."

One of the most important parts of Count Rumford's paper, though one to which little attention has hitherto been paid, is that in which he makes an estimate of the quantity of mechanical force required to produce a certain amount of heat. . . .

From the explanation given by Count Rumford of the heat arising from the friction of solids, one might have anticipated, as a matter of course, that the evolution of heat would also be detected in the friction of liquid and gaseous bodies. Moreover there were many facts, such as, for instance, the warmth of the sea after a few days of stormy weather, which had long been commonly attributed to fluid friction. Nevertheless the scientific world, preoccupied with the hypothesis that heat is a substance, and following the deductions drawn by Pictet from experiments not sufficiently delicate, have almost unanimously denied the possibility of generating heat in that way.

The first mention, so far as I am aware, of experiments in which the evolution of heat from fluid friction is asserted was in 1842 by Monsieur Mayer, who states that he has raised the temperature of water from 12° C. to 13° C. by agitating it, without, however, indicating the quantity of force employed, or the precautions taken to secure a correct result. In 1843 I announced the fact that "heat is evolved by the passage of water through narrow tubes," and that each degree of heat per pound of water required for its evolution in this way a mechanical force represented by 770 foot pounds.

Subsequently, in 1845 and 1847, I employed a paddle wheel to produce the fluid friction, and obtained the equivalents 781.5, 782.1, and 787.6 respectively from the agitation of water, sperm oil, and mercury. . . .

I will therefore conclude by considering it as demonstrated by the experiments contained in this paper:

1. That the quantity of heat produced by the friction of bodies, whether solid or liquid, is always proportional to the quantity of force expended. And,

2. That the quantity of heat capable of increasing the temperature of a pound of water (weighed *in vacuo,* and taken at between 55° and 60°) by one degree Fahrenheit requires for its evolution the expenditure of a mechanical force represented by the fall of 772 pounds through the space of one foot.

A New Method of Diagnosis

RENÉ LAËNNEC (1781–1826)

THE INNATE DELICACY of a great French physician, René Laënnec, who did not think it fitting to put his ear directly to the bosom of a young

and buxom female patient, led him, as he tells here, to the invention
of the stethoscope and through it to the development of a new and
improved method of diagnosis for chest and heart ailments. The art
of diagnosis, the heart of clinical medicine, was immensely improved
in this period not only through Laënnec's method, called mediate
auscultation—a refined form of listening to the sounds of the heart (e.g.,
murmurs) and the lungs—but also through the efforts of his associates
at the famous Necker and Charité hospitals, in Paris, where Pierre
Louis was laying the foundations of statistical methods in medical
practice and Xavier Bichat, founder of histology (science of minute
anatomy), was formulating a unified physiological theory of the life
process as the sum of those forces which resist death. Half a century
before Laënnec's great invention, made about 1819, an inquiring Austrian
physician, Leopold Auenbrugger (1722–1809), remembering that beer
kegs were tapped by innkeepers to determine how full they were, had
applied this tapping system to the body and invented another method
of diagnosis called "percussion." Both percussion and auscultation are
in use today.

French was the original language of Laënnec's three-part book, "On
Mediate Auscultation". ("De l'auscultation médiate"), first published
in 1819. The English translation by John Forbes was published in London in 1834.

THE INVENTION OF THE STETHOSCOPE

In 1816 I was consulted by a young woman presenting general symptoms of disease of the heart. Owing to her stoutness little information
could be gathered by application of the hand and percussion. The
patient's age and sex did not permit me to resort to the kind of examination I have just described (i.e., direct application of the ear to
the chest). I recalled a well-known acoustic phenomenon, namely, if
you place your ear against one end of a wooden beam the scratch of a
pin at the other extremity is most distinctly audible. It occurred to me
that this physical property might serve a useful purpose in the case
with which I was then dealing. Taking a sheaf of paper, I rolled it
into a very tight roll, one end of which I placed over the praecordial
region, while I put my ear to the other. I was both surprised and gratified at being able to hear the beating of the heart with much greater
clearness and distinctness than I had ever done before by direct application of my ear.

I at once saw that this means might become a useful method for studying not only the beating of the heart but likewise all movements capable of producing sound in the thoracic cavity, and that consequently it might serve for the investigation of respiration, the voice, râles, and even possibly the movements of a liquid effused into the pleural cavity or pericardium.

With this conviction, I at once began and have continued to the present time, a series of observations at the Hospital Necker. As a result I have obtained many new and certain signs, most of which are striking, easy of recognition, and calculated perhaps to render the diagnosis of nearly all complaints of the lungs, pleurae, and heart both more certain and more circumstantial than the surgical diagnosis obtained by use of the sound or by introduction of the finger. . . .

Before proceeding with my subject I consider it my duty to record the various attempts that I have made to improve upon the exploring instrument I at present use; these attempts have proved almost entirely vain, and if I mention them it is in the hope that any other investigator seeking to perfect the instrument will strike out a fresh path.

The first instrument employed by me consisted of a cylinder or roll of paper, sixteen lines in diameter and one foot long, made of three quires of paper rolled very tightly round, and held in position with gummed paper and filed smooth at both ends. However tight the roll may be, there will always remain a tube three or four lines in diameter running up the center, because the sheets of paper composing it can never be rolled completely on themselves. This fortuitous circumstance gave rise, as will be seen, to an important observation upon my part: I found that for listening to the voice the tube is an indispensable factor. An entirely solid body is the best instrument that can be used for listening to the heart; such an instrument would indeed suffice also for hearing respiratory sounds and râles; yet these last two phenomena yield greater intensity of sound if a perforated cylinder is used, hollowed out at one end into a kind of funnel one and one half inches in depth.

The densest bodies are not, as analogy would lead us to suppose, the best materials for constructing these instruments. Glass and metals, apart from their weight and the sensation of cold that they impart in winter, are not such good carriers of the heartbeats and the sounds produced by breathing and râles, as are bodies of lesser density. . . .

Substances of medium density, such as paper, wood, and cane, are those which have always appeared to me preferable to all others. This result may be in contradiction with an axiom of physics; nonetheless I consider it to be quite established.

I consequently employ at the present time a wooden cylinder with a tube three lines in diameter bored right down its axis; it is divisible into two parts by means of a screw and is thus more portable. One of the parts is hollowed out at its end into a wide funnel-shaped depression one and one half inches deep leading into the central tube. A cylinder made like this is the instrument most suitable for exploring breath sounds and râles. It is converted into a tube of uniform diameter with thick walls all the way, for exploring the voice and the heartbeats, by introducing into the funnel or bell a kind of stopper made of the same wood, fitting it quite closely; this is made fast by means of a small brass tube running through it, entering a certain distance into the tubular space running through the length of the cylinder. This instrument is sufficient for all cases, although, as I have already said, a perfectly solid body might perhaps be better for listening to the beating of the heart.

The dimensions indicated above are not altogether unimportant; if the diameter is larger it is not always possible to apply the stethoscope closely against all points of the chest; if the instrument is longer, it becomes difficult to hold it exactly in place; if it were shorter, the physician would often be obliged to adopt an uncomfortable position, which is to be avoided above all things if he desires to carry out accurate observations.

I shall be careful, when discussing each variety of exploration, to mention the positions which experience has taught me to be most favorable for observation and least tiring for both physician and patient.

Suffice it to say for the moment that in all cases the stethoscope should be held like a pen, and that the hand must be placed quite close to the patient's chest in order to make sure that the instrument is properly applied.

A Classic of Epidemiology: "On Cholera"

JOHN SNOW (1813-58)

No "INQUIRING REPORTER," no house-to-house salesman could have been more persistent in ringing the doorbells of strange houses than the Yorkshire-born London physician, John Snow, calling at all the houses and business establishments in the neighborhood of Broad Street, London, to confirm and prove his hunch that the deadly disease, cholera, was a water-borne infection. His description of the Broad Street pump epidemic of 1824 remains a classic of epidemiology, a health detective story; and his suggestions for preventing this disease, even though he did not know the specific bacteriologic agent that contaminated the water, represent the next great advance—after Jenner—in the science of preventive medicine. With safe and adequate water supplies and adequate sewage disposal, cholera has ceased to be a menace in civilized communities; but the painstaking inquiries of this modest British doctor, who carefully plotted all his house-to-house findings on maps of the city of London, were a necessary impetus to the sanitary precautions that now protect us from so many water-borne diseases.

Control of environment has proved far easier than control of individuals. This was notably proved in the building of the Panama Canal, almost a century later, when the knowledge of bacteriology enabled Theobald Smith, a Harvard professor, to prove the insect transmission of disease; and the American Army doctors, Walter Reed, Carroll, Agramonte, and Lazear, to demonstrate (in 1902) that yellow fever was a mosquito-borne disease, just after British Army doctors, Patrick Manson and Sir Ronald Ross, stationed in India, had confirmed the Italian, Grassi's, idea that malaria too was mosquito-borne.

English is the language of Snow's paper on cholera (London, 1824).

THE BROAD STREET PUMP

THE MOST TERRIBLE outbreak of cholera which ever occurred in this kingdom is probably that which took place in Broad Street, Golden Square, and the adjoining streets, a few weeks ago. Within two hundred and fifty yards of the spot where Cambridge Street joins Broad Street there were upwards of five hundred fatal attacks of cholera in ten days. The mortality in this limited area probably equals any that was ever caused in this country, even by the plague; and it was much more sudden, as the greater number of cases terminated in a few hours. The mortality would undoubtedly have been much greater had it not been for the flight of the population. Persons in furnished lodgings left first, then other lodgers went away, leaving their furniture to be sent for when they could meet with a place to put it in. Many houses were closed altogether, owing to the death of the proprietors; and in a great number of instances the tradesmen who remained had sent away their families; so that in less than six days from the commencement of the outbreak the most afflicted streets were deserted by more than three quarters of their inhabitants.

There were a few cases of cholera in the neighborhood of Broad Street, Golden Square, in the latter part of August; and the so-called outbreak, which commenced in the night between the thirty-first of August and the first of September, was, as in all similar instances, only a violent increase of the malady. As soon as I became acquainted with the situation and extent of this irruption of cholera I suspected some contamination of the water of the much-frequented street pump in Broad Street, near the end of Cambridge Street; but on examining the water, on the evening of the third of September, I found so little impurity in it of an organic nature that I hesitated to come to a conclusion. Further inquiry, however, showed me that there was no other circumstance or agent common to the circumscribed locality in which this sudden increase of cholera occurred, and not extending beyond it, except the water of the above-mentioned pump. I found, moreover, that the water varied, during the next two days, in the amount of organic impurity visible to the naked eye, on close inspection, in the form of small white, flocculent particles; and I concluded that, at the commencement of the outbreak, it might possibly have been still more impure.

I requested permission, therefore, to take a list, at the General Register Office, of the deaths from cholera, registered during the week ending the second of September, in the subdistricts of Golden Square, Berwick Street, and St. Ann's, Soho, which was kindly granted. Eighty-nine deaths from cholera were registered during the week in the three subdistricts. Of these, only six occurred in the four first days of the week; four occurred on Thursday, the thirty-first of August; and the remaining seventy-nine on Friday and Saturday. I considered, therefore, that the outbreak commenced on the Thursday; and I made inquiry, in detail, respecting the eighty-three deaths registered as having taken place during the last three days of the week.

On proceeding to the spot, I found that nearly all the deaths had taken place within a short distance of the pump. There were only ten deaths in houses situated decidedly nearer to another street pump. In five of these cases the families of the deceased persons informed me that they always sent to the pump in Broad Street, as they preferred the water to that of the pump which was nearer. In three other cases the

deceased were children who went to school near the pump in Broad
Street. Two of them were known to drink the water; and the parents
of the third think it probable that it did so. The other two deaths, beyond the district which this pump supplies, represent only the amount
of mortality from cholera that was occurring before the irruption took
place.

With regard to the deaths occurring in the locality belonging to the
pump, there were sixty-one instances in which I was informed that the
deceased persons used to drink the pump water from Broad Street,
either constantly or occasionally. In six instances I could get no information, owing to the death or departure of everyone connected with the
deceased individuals; and in six cases I was informed that the deceased
persons did not drink the pump water before their illness.

The result of the inquiry, then, was that there had been no particular
outbreak or increase of cholera, in this part of London, except among
the persons who were in the habit of drinking the water of the above-
mentioned pump well.

I had an interview with the Board of Guardians of St. James's parish,
on the evening of Thursday, September 7, and represented the above
circumstances to them. In consequence of what I said the handle of
the pump was removed on the following day.

The additional facts that I have been able to ascertain are in accordance with those above related; and as regards the small number of
those attacked, who were believed not to have drunk the water from the
Broad Street pump, it must be obvious that there are various ways in
which the deceased persons may have taken it without the knowledge
of their friends. The water was used for mixing with spirits in all the
public houses around. It was used likewise at dining rooms and coffee-
shops. The keeper of a coffeeshop in the neighborhood, which was frequented by mechanics, and where the pump water was supplied at
dinnertime, informed me (on September 6) that she was already aware
of nine of her customers who were dead. The pump water was also
sold in various little shops, with a teaspoonful of effervescing powder
in it, under the name of sherbet; and it may have been distributed in
various other ways with which I am unacquainted. The pump was frequented much more than is usual, even for a London pump in a populous neighborhood.

There are certain circumstances bearing on the subject of this outbreak of cholera which require to be mentioned. The workhouse in
Poland Street is more than three fourths surrounded by houses in which

deaths from cholera occurred, yet out of five hundred and thirty-five inmates only five died of cholera, the other deaths which took place being those of persons admitted after they were attacked. The workhouse has a pump well on the premises, in addition to the supply from the Grand Junction Waterworks, and the inmates never sent to Broad Street for water. If the mortality in the workhouse had been equal to that in the streets immediately surrounding it on three sides, upwards of one hundred persons would have died.

There is a brewery in Broad Street, near to the pump, and on perceiving that no brewer's men were registered as having died of cholera, I called on Mr. Huggins, the proprietor. He informed me that there were about seventy workmen employed in the brewery, and that none of them had suffered from cholera—at least in a severe form—only two having been indisposed, and that not seriously, at the time the disease prevailed. The men are allowed a certain quantity of malt liquor, and Mr. Huggins believes they do not drink water at all; and he is quite certain that the workmen never obtained water from the pump in the street. There is a deep well in the brewery, in addition to the New River water.

At the percussion-cap manufactory, 37 Broad Street, where, I understand, about two hundred workpeople were employed, two tubs were kept on the premises always supplied with water from the pump in the street, for those to drink who wished; and eighteen of these workpeople died of cholera at their own homes, sixteen men and two women.

All the instances of communication of cholera through the medium of water, above related, have resulted from the contamination of a pump well, or some other limited supply of water; and the outbreaks of cholera connected with the contamination, though sudden and intense, have been limited also; but when the water of a river becomes infected with the cholera evacuations emptied from on board ship, or passing down drains and sewers, the communication of the disease, though generally less sudden and violent, is much more widely extended; more especially when the river water is distributed by the steam engine and pipes connected with waterworks. Cholera may linger in the courts and alleys crowded with the poor, for reasons previously pointed out, but I know of no instance in which it has been generally spread through a town or neighborhood, among all classes of the community, in which the drinking water has not been the medium of its diffusion. Each epidemic of cholera in London has borne a strict relation to the nature of the water supply of its different districts, being modified only by poverty and the crowding and want of cleanliness which always attend it.

THE PREVENTION OF CHOLERA

THE MEASURES which are required for the prevention of cholera, and all diseases which are communicated in the same way as cholera, are of a very simple kind. They may be divided into those which may be carried out in the presence of an epidemic, and those which, as they require time, should be taken beforehand.

The measures which should be adopted during the presence of cholera may be enumerated as follows:

1. The strictest cleanliness should be observed by those about the sick. There should be a hand basin, water, and towel in every room where there is a cholera patient, and care should be taken that they are frequently used by the nurse and other attendants, more particularly before touching any food.

2. The soiled bed linen and body linen of the patient should be immersed in water as soon as they are removed, until such time as they can be washed, lest the evacuations should become dry and be wafted about as a fine dust. Articles of bedding and clothing which cannot be washed should be exposed for some time to a temperature of 212° or upwards.

3. Care should be taken that the water employed for drinking and preparing food (whether it come from a pump well or be conveyed in pipes) is not contaminated with the contents of cesspools, house drains, or sewers; or, in the event that water free from suspicion cannot be obtained, it should be well boiled, and, if possible, also filtered.

Works are in progress for supplying a great part of London with water from the Thames, obtained, like that of the Lambeth Company, above Teddington Lock. Although this is not the best possible source for supplying a large town, it is a great improvement on the practice of many of the water companies; and the water, owing to filtration, and especially to its detention in large reservoirs, will probably be quite salubrious: at all events it will be much safer than that of the shallow pump wells of London, which are fed from very polluted sources. It is very desirable that the handles of nearly all the street pumps of London and other large towns should be fastened up, and the water used only for such purposes as watering the streets. A proper supply of water for the shipping in the Thames is much wanted. Water acquires a flat taste by being boiled; but if it is filtered after it becomes cold it gets re-aerated, and the flat or vapid taste is entirely removed.

4. When cholera prevails very much in the neighborhood, all the provisions which are brought into the house should be well washed with clean water and exposed to a temperature of 212° F.; or at least they should undergo one of these processes and be purified either by water or by fire. By being careful to wash the hands, and taking due pre-cautions with regard to food, I consider that a person may spend his time among cholera patients without exposing himself to any danger.

5. When a case of cholera or other communicable disease appears among persons living in a crowded room, the healthy should be removed to another apartment, where it is practicable, leaving only those who are useful to wait on the sick.

6. As it would be impossible to clean out coalpits, and establish privies and lavatories in them, or even to provide the means of eating a meal with anything like common decency, the time of working should be divided into periods of four hours instead of eight, so that the pitmen might go home to their meals and be prevented from taking food into the mines.

7. The communicability of cholera ought not to be disguised from the people, under the idea that the knowledge of it would cause a panic or occasion the sick to be deserted.

British people would not desert their friends or relatives in illness, though they should incur danger by attending to them; but the truth is that to look on cholera as a "catching" disease, which one may avoid by a few simple precautions, is a much less discouraging doctrine than that which supposes it to depend on some mysterious state of the at-mosphere in which we are all of us immersed and obliged to breathe.

The measures which can be taken beforehand to provide against cholera and other epidemic diseases, which are communicated in a similar way, are:

8. To effect good and perfect drainage.

9. To provide an ample supply of water quite free from contamina-tion with the contents of sewers, cesspools, and house drains, or the refuse of people who navigate the rivers.

10. To provide model lodginghouses for the vagrant class, and suffi-cient houseroom for the poor generally.

The great benefit of the model lodginghouses arises from the cir-cumstance that the apartments for cooking, eating, and sleeping are distinct, and that all the proper offices which cleanliness and decency require are provided. The very poor who choose to avail themselves of these institutions suffer a rate of mortality as low as that of the most opulent classes. The public washhouses, which enable poor persons to wash the soiled linen of the sick or the healthy without doing it in the midst of the plates and dishes and provisions of the family, are well calculated to prevent the spread of disease.

11. To inculcate habits of personal and domestic cleanliness among the people everywhere.

12. Some attention should undoubtedly be directed to persons, and especially ships, arriving from infected places, in order to segregate the sick from the healthy. In the instance of cholera the supervision would generally not require to be of long duration.

I feel confident, however, that by attending to the above-mentioned precautions, which I consider to be based on a correct knowledge of the cause of cholera, this disease may be rendered extremely rare, if indeed it may not be altogether banished from civilized countries. And the diminution of mortality ought not to stop with cholera.

How We Digest Our Food: The Scientific Account

WILLIAM BEAUMONT (1785-1853)

GREAT LABORATORIES are now to be found within every metropolis in the civilized world, but it is impossible to foretell where a great scientific mind will arise to discover and develop new truths. "Experiments and Observations on the Gastric Juice and the Physiology of Digestion," 1833, rated as the greatest single contribution to the knowledge of gastric digestion, was produced in the backwoods of America by a much harassed United States Army surgeon with no other laboratory than the gunshot-wounded body of a half-breed Indian. The story of the Connecticut-born surgeon, William Beaumont, and his human laboratory, Alexis St. Martin, is one of the strangest in the history of science. Beaumont's biggest problem, as he was moved from post to post under War Department orders from Washington, was to keep his "laboratory" from deserting him. The Indian, employed by Beaumont at his own expense, was constantly running away!

English was the language in which Beaumont wrote and published his classic pamphlet in 1833.

"EXPERIMENTS AND OBSERVATIONS ON THE GASTRIC JUICE AND THE PHYSIOLOGY OF DIGESTION"

ALEXIS ST. MARTIN, who is the subject of these experiments, was a Canadian, of French descent, at the above-mentioned time about eighteen years of age, of good constitution, robust and healthy. He had been engaged in the service of the American Fur Company, as a voyageur, and was accidentally wounded by the discharge of a musket, on the sixth of June 1822. . . . The whole mass of materials forced from the musket, together with fragments of clothing and pieces of fractured ribs, were driven into the muscles and cavity of the chest.

I saw him in twenty-five or thirty minutes after the accident occurred, and, on examination, found a portion of the lung, as large as a turkey's egg, protruding through the external wound, lacerated and burned; and immediately below this, another protrusion, which, on further examination, proved to be a portion of the stomach, lacerated through all its coats, and pouring out the food he had taken for his breakfast, through an orifice large enough to admit the forefinger. . . .

August 1, 1825. At 12 M., I introduced through the perforation, into the stomach, the following articles of diet, suspended by a silk string, and fastened at proper distances, so as to pass in without pain, viz., a piece of high-seasoned à la mode beef; a piece of raw, salted, fat pork; a piece of raw, salted, lean beef; a piece of boiled, salted beef; a piece of stale bread; and a bunch of raw, sliced cabbage; each piece weighing about two drachms; the lad continuing his usual employment about the house.

At 1:00 P.M., withdrew and examined them. Found the cabbage and bread about half digested; the pieces of meat unchanged. Returned them into the stomach.

At 2:00 P.M., withdrew them again. Found the cabbage, bread, pork, and boiled beef all cleanly digested and gone from the string; the other pieces of meat but very little affected. Returned them into the stomach again.

At 2:00 P.M. [sic], examined again. Found the à la mode beef partly digested; the raw beef was slightly macerated on the surface, but its general texture was firm and entire. The smell and taste of the fluids of the stomach were slightly rancid; and the boy complained of some pain and uneasiness at the breast. Returned them again.

The lad complaining of considerable distress and uneasiness at the stomach, general debility and lassitude, with some pain in his head, I withdrew the string and found the remaining portions of aliment nearly in the same condition as when last examined; the fluid more rancid and sharp. The boy still complaining, I did not return them any more.

August 2. The distress at the stomach and pain in the head continuing, accompanied with costiveness, a depressed pulse, dry skin, coated tongue, and numerous white spots, or pustules, resembling coagulated lymph, spread over the inner surface of the stomach, I thought it advisable to give medicine; and, accordingly, dropped into the stomach, through the aperture, half a dozen calomel pills, four or five grains each; which, in about three hours, had a thorough cathartic effect and removed all the foregoing symptoms, and the diseased appearance of the inner coat of the stomach. The effect of the medicine was the same as when administered in the usual way, by the mouth and esophagus, except the nausea commonly occasioned by swallowing pills.

This experiment cannot be considered a fair test of the powers of the gastric juice. The cabbage, one of the articles which was, in this instance, most speedily dissolved, was cut into small, fibrous pieces, very thin, and necessarily exposed on all its surfaces to the action of the gastric juice. The stale bread was porous, and of course admitted the juice into all its interstices; and probably fell from the string as soon as softened, and before it was completely dissolved. These circumstances will account for the more rapid disappearance of these substances than of the pieces of meat, which were in entire solid pieces when put in. To account for the disappearance of the fat pork, it is only necessary to remark that the fat meat is always resolved into oil by the warmth of the stomach before it is digested. I have generally observed that when he has fed on fat meat or butter the whole superior portion of the contents of the stomach, if examined a short time after eating, will be found covered with an oily pellicle. This fact may account for the disappearance of the pork from the string. I think, upon the whole, and subsequent experiments have confirmed the opinion, that fat meats are less easily digested than lean, when both have received the same advantages of comminution. Generally speaking, the looser the texture and the more tender the fiber, of animal food, the easier it is of digestion.

This experiment is important in a pathological point of view. It con-

firms the opinion that undigested portions of food in the stomach produce all the phenomena of fever; and is calculated to warn us of the
danger of all excesses, where that organ is concerned. It also admonishes
us of the necessity of a perfect comminution of the articles of diet.

The Great Argument Against Needless Deaths in Childbirth

OLIVER WENDELL HOLMES (1809–94)

The text of our life grows far wiser with age,
But how fair was the print on its twentieth page!

THUS WROTE the poet laureate of the class of 1829, Harvard, on the occasion of a typical reunion. Oliver Wendell Holmes, "the autocrat at
the breakfast table," famous father of an equally famous son, the often
dissenting Mr. Justice Holmes of the United States Supreme Court, was
a poet and versifier as well as a physician and anatomist; a man of letters and a teacher of medicine. Professor of anatomy at the Harvard
Medical School in the days when Boston was truly the "hub of the
universe" and New England flowered in the pens of Longfellow, Emer-
son, Whittier, Thoreau, and others, the first Oliver Wendell Holmes
not only held his own in wit and letters, but also employed his superb
literary powers to write the great argument against needless deaths in
childbirth. Holmes's prose commanded conviction, though it also invited opposition. His essay on the contagiousness of puerperal fever, a
disease as old as Hippocrates, undoubtedly saved many a mother from
untimely death. One of the latest chapters in this agelong struggle was
written only during the present decade when the efficacy of the sulfa
drugs against puerperal septicemia was first tried at Queen Charlotte's
Hospital in London.

Others besides Holmes fought the often losing battle for asepsis—
absolute "germ-free" cleanliness—in the practice of obstetrics and
surgery. A young Austrian physician, Ignaz Semmelweiss (1818–65),
sacrificed his career and eventually his reason to preaching the doctrine
(for which he was driven from one hospital to another) that the ob-

stetrician must come to his patients aseptically clean. He advocated disinfecting the hands in chloride of lime before attending childbirth.

Besides his advocacy of asepsis in obstetrics, Holmes the physician made another great literary contribution to medicine: the name "anesthesia" for the state of unconsciousness induced by sulphuric ether and nitrous oxide.

English was the language in which Holmes composed his masterly discussion of puerperal fever. He read the paper at the Boston Society for Medical Improvement in 1843 and published it in the shortly defunct "New England Quarterly Journal for Medicine and Surgery."

"THE CONTAGIOUSNESS OF PUERPERAL FEVER"

IN COLLECTING, enforcing, and adding to the evidence accumulated upon this most serious subject I would not be understood to imply that there exists a doubt in the mind of any well-informed member of the medical profession as to the fact that puerperal fever is sometimes communicated from one person to another, both directly and indirectly. In the present state of our knowledge upon this point I should consider such doubts merely as a proof that the skeptic had either not examined the evidence or, having examined it, refused to accept its plain and unavoidable consequences. I should be sorry to think with Dr. Rigby that it was a case of "oblique vision"; I should be unwilling to force home the *argumentum ad hominem* of Dr. Blundell, but I would not consent to make a question of a momentous fact which is no longer to be considered as a subject for trivial discussions, but to be acted upon with silent promptitude. It signifies nothing that wise and experienced practitioners have sometimes doubted the reality of the danger in question; no man has the right to doubt it any longer. No negative facts, no opposing opinions, be they what they may, or whose they may, can form any answer to the series of cases now within the reach of all who choose to explore the records of medical science.

If there are some who conceive that any important end would be answered by recording such opinions, or by collecting the history of all the cases they could find in which no evidence of the influence of contagion existed, I believe they are in error. Suppose a few writers of authority can be found to profess a disbelief in contagion—and they are very few compared with those who think differently—is it quite clear that they formed their opinions on a view of all the facts, or is it not apparent that they relied mostly on their own solitary experience? Still further, of those whose names are quoted, is it not true that scarcely a single one could, by any possibility, have known the half or the tenth of the facts bearing on the subject which have reached such a frightful amount within the last few years? Again, as to the utility of negative facts, as we may briefly call them—instances, namely, in which exposure has not been followed by disease—although, like other truths, they may be worth knowing, I do not see that they are like to shed any important light upon the subject before us. Every such instance requires a good deal of circumstantial explanation before it can be accepted.

It is not enough that a practitioner should have had a single case of puerperal fever not followed by others. It must be known whether he attended others while this case was in progress, whether he went directly from one chamber to others, whether he took any, and what, precautions. It is important to know that several women were exposed to infection derived from the patient, so that allowance may be made for want of predisposition. Now, if of negative facts so sifted there could be accumulated a hundred for every one plain instance of communication here recorded, I trust it need not be said that we are bound to guard and watch over the hundredth tenant of our fold, though the ninety and nine may be sure of escaping the wolf at its entrance. If anyone is disposed, then, to take a hundred instances of lives, endangered or sacrificed out of those I have mentioned, and make it reasonably clear that within a similar time and compass *ten thousand* escaped the same exposure, I shall thank him for his industry, but I must be permitted to hold to my own practical conclusions, and beg him to adopt or at least to examine them also. Children that walk in calico before open fires are not always burned to death; the instances to the contrary may be worth recording; but by no means if they are to be used as arguments against woolen frocks and high fenders. . . .

The practical point to be illustrated is the following: the disease known as puerperal fever is so far contagious as to be frequently carried from patient to patient by physicians and nurses.

Let me begin by throwing out certain incidental questions which, without being absolutely essential, would render the subject more complicated, and by making such concessions and assumptions as may be fairly supposed to be without the pale of discussion.

1. It is granted that all the forms of what is called puerperal fever may not be, and probably are not, equally contagious or infectious. I

do not enter into the distinctions which have been drawn by authors, because the facts do not appear to me sufficient to establish any absolute line of demarcation between such forms as may be propagated by contagion and those which are never so propagated. This general result I shall only support by the authority of Dr. Ramsbotham, who gives, as the result of his experience, that the same symptoms belong to what he calls the infectious and the sporadic forms of the disease, and the opinion of Armstrong in his original essay. If others can show any such distinction, I leave it to them to do it. But there are cases enough that show the prevalence of the disease among the patients of a single practitioner when it was in no degree epidemic, in the proper sense of the term. I may refer to those of Mr. Roberton and of Dr. Peirson . . . as examples.

2. I shall not enter into any dispute about the particular mode of infection, whether it be by the atmosphere the physician carries about him into the sick chamber, or by the direct application of the virus to the absorbing surfaces with which his hand comes in contact. Many facts and opinions are in favor of each of these modes of transmission. But it is obvious that, in the majority of cases, it must be impossible to decide by which of these channels the disease is conveyed, from the nature of the intercourse between the physician and the patient.

3. It is not pretended that the contagion of puerperal fever must always be followed by the disease. It is true of all contagious diseases that they frequently spare those who appear to be fully submitted to their influence. Even the vaccine virus, fresh from the subject, fails every day to produce its legitimate effect, though every precaution is taken to insure its action. This is still more remarkably the case with scarlet fever and some other diseases.

4. It is granted that the disease may be produced and variously modified by many causes besides contagion, and more especially by epidemic and endemic influences. But this is not peculiar to the disease in question. There is no doubt that smallpox is propagated to a great extent by contagion, yet it goes through the same records of periodical increase and diminution which have been remarked in puerperal fever. If the question is asked how we are to reconcile the great variations in the mortality of puerperal fever in different seasons and places with the supposition of contagion, I will answer it by another question from Mr. Farr's letter to the registrar-general. He makes the statement that "five die weekly of smallpox in the metropolis when the disease is not epidemic," and adds, "the problem for solution is, why do the five deaths

become ten, fifteen, twenty, thirty-one, fifty-eight, eighty-eight, weekly, and then progressively fall through the same measured steps?"

5. I take it for granted that if it can be shown that great numbers of lives have been and are sacrificed to ignorance or blindness on this point no other error of which physicians or nurses may be occasionally suspected will be alleged in palliation of this; but that, whenever and wherever they can be shown to carry disease and death instead of health and safety, the common instincts of humanity will silence every attempt to explain away their responsibility. . . .

The recurrence of long series of cases like those I have cited, reported by those most interested to disbelieve in contagion, scattered along through an interval of half a century, might have been thought sufficient to satisfy the minds of all inquirers that here was something more than a singular coincidence. But if, on a more extended observation, it should be found that the same ominous groups of cases clustering about individual practitioners were observed in a remote country, at different times, and in widely separated regions, it would seem incredible that any should be found too prejudiced or indolent to accept the solemn truth knelled into their ears by the funeral bells from both sides of the ocean—the plain conclusion that the physician and the disease entered, hand in hand, into the chamber of the unsuspecting patient. . . .

I am assured, on unquestionable authority, that "about three years since a gentleman in extensive midwifery business, in a neighboring state, lost in the course of a few weeks eight patients in childbed, seven of them being undoubted cases of puerperal fever. No other physician of the town lost a single patient of this disease during the same period." And from what I have heard in conversation with some of our most experienced practitioners, I am inclined to think many cases of the kind might be brought to light by extensive inquiry.

This long catalogue of melancholy histories assumes a still darker aspect when we remember how kindly nature deals with the parturient female, when she is not immersed in the virulent atmosphere of an impure lying-in hospital, or poisoned in her chamber by the unsuspected breath of contagion. From all causes together not more than four deaths in a thousand births and miscarriages happened in England and Wales during the period embraced by the first report of the registrar-general. In the second report the mortality was shown to be about five in one thousand. In the Dublin Lying-in Hospital, during the seven years of Dr. Collin's mastership, there was one case of puerperal fever to 178 deliveries, or less than six to the thousand, and one death from this disease in 278 cases, or between three and four to the thousand. Yet during this period the disease was endemic in the hospital and might have gone on to rival the horrors of the pestilence of the Maternité, had not the poison been destroyed by a thorough purification. . . .

In the view of these facts it does appear a singular coincidence that one man or woman should have ten, twenty, thirty, or seventy cases of this rare disease following his or her footsteps with the keenness of a beagle, through the streets and lanes of a crowded city, while the scores that cross the same paths on the same errands know it only by name. It is a series of similar coincidences which has led us to consider the dagger, the musket, and certain innocent-looking white powders as having some little claim to be regarded as dangerous. It is the practical inattention to similar coincidences which has given rise to the unpleasant but often necessary documents called indictments, which has sharpened a form of the cephalotome sometimes employed in the case of adults, and adjusted that modification of the fillet which delivers the world of those who happen to be too much in the way while such striking coincidences are taking place. . . .

I need not refer to the case lately read before this society, in which a physician went, soon after performing an autopsy of a case of puerperal fever, to a woman in labor, who was seized with the same disease and perished. The forfeit of that error has been already paid.

At a meeting of the Medical and Chirurgical Society . . . Dr. Merriman related an instance occurring in his own practice, which excites a reasonable suspicion that two lives were sacrificed to a still less dangerous experiment. He was at the examination of a case of puerperal fever at two o'clock in the afternoon. *He took care not to touch the body.* At nine o'clock the same evening he attended a woman in labor; she was so nearly delivered that he had scarcely anything to do. The next morning she had severe rigors, and in forty-eight hours she was a corpse. Her infant had erysipelas and died in two days. . . .

Now add to all this the undisputed fact that within the walls of lying-in hospitals there is often generated a miasm, palpable as the chlorine used to destroy it, tenacious so as in some cases almost to defy extirpation, deadly in some institutions as the plague; which has killed women in a private hospital of London so fast that they were buried two in one coffin to conceal its horrors; which enabled Tonnelle to record 222 autopsies at the Maternité of Paris; which has led Dr. Lee to express his deliberate conviction that the loss of life occasioned by these institutions completely defeats the objects of their founders; and out of this train of cumulative evidence, the multiplied groups of cases clustering about individuals, the deadly results of autopsies, the inoculation by fluids from the living patient, the murderous poison of hospitals—does there not result a conclusion that laughs all sophistry to scorn, and renders all argument an insult?

I have had occasion to mention some instances in which there was an apparent relation between puerperal fever and erysipelas. The length to which this paper has extended does not allow me to enter into the consideration of this most important subject. I will only say that the evidence appears to me altogether satisfactory that some most fatal series of puerperal fever have been produced by an infection originating in the matter or effluvia of erysipelas. . . .

I have no wish to express any harsh feeling with regard to the painful subject which has come before us. If there are any so far excited by the story of these dreadful events that they ask for some word of indignant remonstrance to show that science does not turn the hearts of its followers into ice or stone, let me remind them that such words have been uttered by those who speak with an authority I could not claim. It is as a lesson rather than as a reproach that I call up the memory of these irreparable errors and wrongs. No tongue can tell the heartbreaking calamity they have caused; they have closed the eyes just opened upon a new world of love and happiness; they have bowed the strength of manhood into the dust; they have cast the helplessness of infancy into the stranger's arms, or bequeathed it, with less cruelty, the death of its dying parent. There is no tone deep enough for regret, and no voice loud enough for warning. The woman about to become a mother, or with her newborn infant upon her bosom, should be the object of trembling care and sympathy wherever she bears her tender burden or stretches her aching limbs. The very outcast of the streets has pity upon her sister in degradation when the seal of promised maternity is impressed upon her. The remorseless vengeance of the law, brought down upon its victim by a machinery as sure as destiny, is arrested in its fall at a word which reveals her transient claim for mercy. The solemn prayer of the liturgy singles out her sorrows from the multiplied trials of life, to plead for her in the hour of peril. God forbid that any member of the profession to which she trusts her life, doubly precious at that eventful period, should hazard it negligently, unadvisedly, or selfishly!

There may be some among those whom I address who are disposed to ask the question, What course are we to follow in relation to this matter? The facts are before them, and the answer must be left to their

own judgment and conscience. If any should care to know my own conclusions, they are the following: and in taking the liberty to state them
very freely and broadly, I would ask the inquirer to examine them as
freely in the light of the evidence which has been laid before him.

1. A physician holding himself in readiness to attend cases of midwifery should never take any active part in the post-mortem examination of cases of puerperal fever.

2. If a physician is present at such autopsies, he should use thorough
ablution, change every article of dress, and allow twenty-four hours or
more to elapse before attending to any case of midwifery. It may be well
to extend the same caution to cases of simple peritonitis.

3. Similar precautions should be taken after the autopsy or surgical
treatment of cases of erysipelas, if the physician is obliged to unite such
offices with his obstetrical duties, which is in the highest degree in-
expedient.

4. On the occurrence of a single case of puerperal fever in his practice,
the physician is bound to consider the next female he attends in labor,
unless some weeks at least have elapsed, as in danger of being infected
by him, and it is his duty to take every precaution to diminish her risk
of disease and death.

5. If within a short period two cases of puerperal fever happen close
to each other, in the practice of the same physician, the disease not
existing or prevailing in the neighborhood, he would do wisely to relinquish his obstetrical practice for at least one month, and endeavor
to free himself by every available means from any noxious influence he
may carry about with him.

6. The occurrence of three or more closely connected cases, in the
practice of one individual, no others existing in the neighborhood, and
no other sufficient cause being alleged for the coincidence, is *prima facie*
evidence that he is the vehicle of contagion.

7. It is the duty of the physician to take every precaution that the
disease shall not be introduced by nurses or other assistants, by making
proper inquiries concerning them and giving timely warning of every
suspected source of danger.

8. Whatever indulgence may be granted to those who have heretofore
been the ignorant causes of so much misery, the time has come when
the existence of a private pestilence in the sphere of a single physician
should be looked upon, not as a misfortune, but a crime; and in the
knowledge of such occurrences the duties of the practitioner to his
profession should give way to his paramount obligations to society.

Anesthesia! The Conquest of Pain

CRAWFORD LONG (1815–78)

WILLIAM MORTON (1819–68)

WASHINGTON AYER

"GENTLEMEN, this is no humbug," declared surgeon John Collins Warren on that great day in the history of medicine, October 16, 1846, when painless surgery under ether anesthesia was first publicly demonstrated. Warren had just completed the removal of a tumor from the neck of one Gilbert Abbott, who asserted that he felt no pain during the operation. An eyewitness account of this historic event has come down to us from a young medical student, Washington Ayer, present in the operating theater of the Massachusetts General Hospital, in Boston, on that day.

The anesthetic, sulphuric ether, had been administered by an ambitious young practicing dentist who was also a student at the Harvard Medical School, William T. G. Morton. As great a boon as Morton conferred on mankind by the introduction of anesthesia (he was elected to the American Hall of Fame in 1920), the aftermath of his discovery brought him only grief, bitterness, acrimonious patent litigation, and poverty. For others besides Morton had a hand in developing ether anesthesia, and when he hoped to profit largely by his patent (November 12, 1846) on the use of "letheon," as the first anesthetic was christened, they contested his claims. Among the contestants were Horace Wells, a Hartford, Connecticut, dentist, former partner of Morton, who had used nitrous oxide anesthesia in dental operations but failed in surgical operations; Charles T. Jackson, professor of chemistry in Boston, who had manufactured sulphuric ether to Morton's knowledge and intended to use it as an anesthetic; and Crawford W. Long, a Georgia surgeon.

Credit for the first use of ether as a surgical anesthetic undoubtedly goes to this taciturn back-country Southern surgeon. As attested by his affidavit quoted here, Long actually employed a surgical anesthetic four years before Morton introduced it. However, his discovery was of little use to the world, for he did not publish his experiences until three years after Morton's demonstration, when the patent controversy was raging.

English was the language of the discoverers of anesthesia. Morton's "remarks on the proper mode of administering ether by inhalation" appeared under the imprint of Dutton & Wentworth, Printers, in Boston, in 1847. Long's affidavits were printed in the "Transactions of the Georgia Medical and Surgical Association for 1853." Ayer's eyewitness account is included in "The Semicentennial of Anesthesia," issued in 1897 by the Massachusetts General Hospital.

AN AFFIDAVIT CONCERNING THE FIRST ADMINISTRATION OF A SURGICAL ANESTHETIC

IN THE MONTH of December 1841, or January 1842, the subject of the inhalation of nitrous oxide gas was introduced in a company of young men assembled at night, in the village of Jefferson, Georgia, and the party requested me to prepare them some. I informed them that I had not the requisite apparatus for preparing or using the gas, but that I had an article (sulphuric ether) which would produce equally exhilarating effects and was as safe. The company was anxious to witness its effects; the ether was produced, and all present, in turn, inhaled. They were so much pleased with its effects that they afterward frequently used it and induced others to use it, and the practice became quite fashionable in the country and some of the contiguous counties. On numerous occasions I inhaled the ether for its exhilarating properties and would frequently at some short time subsequently discover bruises or painful spots on my person which I had no recollection of causing, and which I felt satisfied were received while under the influence of ether. I noticed my friends, while etherized, receive falls and blows, which I believed sufficient to cause pain on a person not in a state of anesthesia, and, on questioning them, they uniformly assured me that they did not feel the least pain from these accidents.

Observing these facts, I was led to believe that anesthesia was produced by the inhalation of ether and that its use would be applicable in surgical operations.

The first person to whom I administered ether in a surgical operation was Mr. James M. Venable, who then resided within two miles of Jefferson, and at the present time in Cobb County, Georgia. . . .

Mr. Venable's statement under oath is as follows:

I, James Venable, of the county Cobb and state of Georgia, on oath depose and say that in the year 1842 I resided at my mother's in Jackson County about two miles from the village of Jefferson, and attended the village academy that year. In the early part of the year the young men of Jefferson and the country adjoining were in the habit of inhaling ether for its exhilarating powers, and I inhaled it frequently for that purpose, and was very fond of its use.

While attending the academy I was frequently in the office of Dr. C. W. Long, and having two tumors on the back of my neck, I several times spoke to him about the propriety of cutting them out, but postponed the operation from time to time. On one occasion we had some conversation about the probability that the tumors might be cut while I was under the influence of ether, without my experiencing pain, and he proposed operating on me while under its influence. I agreed to have one tumor cut out, and had the operation performed that evening after school was dismissed. This was in the early part of the spring of 1842.

I commenced inhaling the ether before the operation was commenced and continued it until the operation was over. I did not feel the slightest pain from the operation and could not believe the tumor was removed until it was shown to me.

A month or two after this time Dr. C. W. Long cut out the other tumor situated on the same side of my neck. In this operation I did not feel the least pain until the last cut was made, when I felt a little pain. In this operation I stopped inhaling the ether before the operation was finished.

I inhaled the ether, in both cases, from a towel, which was the common method of taking it.

JAMES VENABLE

GEORGIA } *Sworn to before me*
COBB COUNTY } ALFRED MANES, J.P.
July 23, 1849 }

A PROPER MODE OF ADMINISTERING ETHER BY INHALATION

ALTHOUGH various publications have appeared since the new application of sulphuric ether was discovered which have made it evident that it can be used, both safely and effectually, for the relief of much of the suffering to which the human race is liable, I believe that a manual containing an account of the mode of administering it, the effect which it produces, the symptoms of insensibility, the difficulties and dangers attending its use, and the best means of obviating and removing these, as far as possible, is still a desideratum. This is particularly the case with those who have not had an opportunity to witness its administration but who may wish to make use of it in their own practice. To supply this want, and to avoid the necessity of replying to the letters frequently addressed to me for information upon these subjects, the following pages have been written. To those who have used the ether, many of the directions may appear tediously minute; but to those who have not they will afford desirable information.

In the first place it is of the utmost consequence that the ether which is used should be not only free from all impurities, but as highly concentrated as possible; as some of these impurities would prove injurious if taken into the system, and as, of course, the stronger the ether the sooner the patient comes under its influence. Unrectified sulphuric ether contains, as impurities, alcohol, water, sulphurous acid, and oil of wine; and is unfit for use internally.

In order to make it fit for inhalation unrectified sulphuric ether must be redistilled and washed, and then dried with chloride of calcium. This will free it from the impurities above mentioned, and render it more concentrated than the original article.

The next point I have to treat of is the best mode of administering ether. The earliest experiments were mostly made by pouring ether upon cloths and inhaling it from them. The results obtained in this way were somewhat uncertain and not always satisfactory, and this mode of administering it was, before long, exchanged for that by means of an apparatus which rendered the experiments more uniformly successful. Some alterations and improvements were afterward made in this apparatus, but, substantially, it remained the same as long as it continued in use; and, as many persons may read these pages who have never seen the apparatus, or one like it, a few words by way of description will not, perhaps, be unacceptable.

The apparatus first used consisted of a glass vessel about six inches square, with rounded corners; one opening, two inches in diameter, was left on the top, through which a sponge was inserted and the ether poured, and another, an inch and a half in diameter, on one side for the admission of external air. On the side opposite the last-named opening was a glass tube, two inches in diameter and an inch in length, terminating in a metal mouthpiece three inches long, and of the same caliber as the glass tube. This mouthpiece was provided with two valves, one covering a circular opening, three quarters of an inch in diameter, on the top, and the other extending across it. These valves were so arranged that, when the patient filled his lungs, the upper valve shut down, closing the aperture in the top of the mouthpiece, while the one across the mouthpiece opened and allowed the ethereal vapor, mixed with atmospheric air, to pass into the lungs; and, when he emptied his lungs, the pressure of the expired air closed the valve across the tube, while the same pressure opened the upper valve and allowed the vapor, which had been once breathed, to pass into the room instead of returning into the reservoir. Thus, at each inspiration, the patient had a fresh supply of air thoroughly charged with the vapor of ether, which vapor was continually given off by the sponge which was placed in the reservoir and thoroughly saturated with ether. . . .

When a surgical operation is to be performed, the inhalation should be steadily continued for three minutes without speaking to the patient. If, at the end of this time, the pulse is quickened and the muscles relaxed, so that the head has a tendency to fall on one side, the patient should be told, in a loud, distinct tone, to open his eyes; and, if he does *not* do so, the operation should be immediately commenced. If he does open his eyes, even in a slow and languid manner, he should be directed to close them, and the inhalation should be continued two minutes longer, when the same question may be repeated; and it will usually be found that, by this time, the patient is unconscious. Should this not occur, however, the surgeon should place his hand over about one half of the sponge, so as to prevent loss of ether by evaporation, and continue the inhalation until ten minutes have elapsed from the time when the patient first began to breathe it, calling upon him to open his eyes at intervals of about one minute each. If, at the end of ten minutes, he still continues to open his eyes when directed to do so, the inhalation should be discontinued and not resumed again for at *least* five minutes. At the end of that time two ounces more of ether should be poured upon the sponge, and the inhaling resumed as before; but, if, after inhaling a second time for ten minutes, it does not produce its effect, an interval of *ten* minutes must be allowed to the patient, and then, the ether having been again renewed, the inhaling may be resumed once more. If at the end of the third trial of inhaling ether the patient still remains unaffected by it, the operation had better be deferred until another day; but I can hardly suppose that this will ever happen where the ether is pure and highly concentrated, and has been administered in the manner above described.

AN EYEWITNESS ACCOUNT OF THE DEMONSTRATION OF ETHER ANESTHETIC

The day arrived; the time appointed was noted on the dial when the patient was led into the operating room, and Dr. Warren and a board of the most eminent surgeons in the state were gathered around the sufferer. "All is ready—the stillness oppressive." It had been announced "that a test of some preparation was to be made for which the *astonishing* claim had been made that it would render the person operated upon free from pain." These are the words of Dr. Warren that broke the stillness.

Those present were incredulous, and, as Dr. Morton had not arrived at the time appointed and fifteen minutes had passed, Dr. Warren said with significant meaning, "I presume he is otherwise engaged." This was followed with a "derisive laugh," and Dr. Warren grasped his knife and was about to proceed with the operation. At that moment Dr. Morton entered a side door, when Dr. Warren turned to him and in a strong voice said, "Well, sir, your patient is ready." In a few minutes he was ready for the surgeon's knife, when Dr. Morton said, *"Your* patient is ready, sir."

Here the most sublime scene ever witnessed in the operating room was presented, when the patient placed himself voluntarily upon the table, which was to become the altar of future fame. Not that he did so for the purpose of advancing the science of medicine, nor for the good of his fellow men, for the act itself was purely a personal and selfish one. He was about to assist in solving a new and important problem of therapeutics, whose benefits were to be given to the whole civilized world, yet wholly unconscious of the sublimity of the occasion or the part he was taking.

That was a supreme moment for a most wonderful discovery, and, had the patient died under the operation, science would have waited long to discover the hypnotic effects of some other remedy of equal potency and safety, and it may be properly questioned whether chloroform would have come into use as it has at the present time.

The heroic bravery of the man who voluntarily placed himself upon the table, a subject for the surgeon's knife, should be recorded and his name enrolled upon parchment, which should be hung upon the walls of the surgical amphitheater in which the operation was performed. His name was Gilbert Abbott.

The operation was for a congenital tumor on the left side of the neck, extending along the jaw to the maxillary gland and into the mouth, embracing a margin of the tongue. The operation was successful; and when the patient recovered he declared he had suffered no pain. Dr. Warren turned to those present and said, "Gentlemen, this is no humbug."

Biology Generates a New Science: Cytology

THEODOR SCHWANN (1810–82)

IN THE YEAR that Queen Victoria ascended the British throne (1837) two earnest young German scientists, meticulous and painstaking, came together to compare notes on what they saw in plant and animal tissues with the benefit of the newly available compound microscope. Out of their meeting came the cell theory of biology and a newly fledged science of cytology. The two men were cautious Theodor Schwann, anatomist and naturalist, and aggressive Matthias Schleiden (1804–81), a botanist. In a preliminary announcement (1838) of this unifying theory in the biological sciences Schwann declared: "All the varied forms in the animal tissues are nothing but transformed cells. . . . All my work has authorized me to apply to animals as to plants the doctrine of the individuality of the cells." Next year, in a memorable book from which the quotations here are taken, Schwann carefully delineated those properties of a cell (the name is from Robert Hooke) which distinguish a dead from a living organism. The young founder of the cell theory eventually became professor of anatomy and physiology (1858) at the University of Liége, in Belgium; discovered pepsin, the digestive ferment in the stomach; and undertook much research on conduction of nervous impulses, muscular contraction, and spontaneous generation, the problem out of which Pasteur extracted the germ theory of disease.

German was the language in which Schwann wrote his "Microscopic Studies on the Identity of Structure and Development in Animals and

Plants" ("*Mikroskopische Untersuchungen über die Uebereinstimmung in der Strucktur und dem Wachstum der Thiere und Pflanzen"*), Berlin, 1839. The English translation, by Henry Smith, was published by the Sydenham Society (London, 1847).

THEORY OF THE CELLS IN ANIMALS AND PLANTS

WE SET OUT with the supposition that an organized body is not produced by a fundamental power which is guided in its operation by a definite idea but is developed, according to blind laws of necessity, by powers which, like those of inorganic nature, are established by the very existence of matter. As the elementary materials of organic nature are not different from those of the inorganic kingdom, the source of the organic phenomena can only reside in another combination of these materials, whether it be in a peculiar mode of union of the elementary atoms to form atoms of the second order, or in the arrangement of these conglomerate molecules when forming either the separate morphological elementary parts of organisms or an entire organism. We have here to do with the latter question solely, whether the cause of organic phenomena lies in the whole organism or in its separate elementary parts. If this question can be answered, a further inquiry still remains as to whether the organism or its elementary parts possess this power through the peculiar mode of combination of the conglomerate molecules, or through the mode in which the elementary atoms are united into conglomerate molecules.

We may, then, form the two following ideas of the cause of organic phenomena, such as growth, et cetera. First, that the cause resides in the totality of the organism. By the combination of the molecules into a systematic whole, such as the organism is in every stage of its development, a power is engendered which enables such an organism to take up fresh material from without and appropriate it either to the formation of new elementary parts or to the growth of those already present. Here, therefore, the cause of the growth of the elementary parts resides in the totality of the organism. The other mode of explanation is that growth does not ensue from a power resident in the entire organism, but that each separate elementary part is possessed of an independent power, an independent life, so to speak; in other words, the molecules in each separate elementary part are so combined as to set free a power by which it is capable of attracting new molecules, and so increasing, and the whole organism subsists only by means of the reciprocal action of the single elementary parts. So that here the single elementary parts only exert an active influence on nutrition, and totality of the organism may indeed be a condition, but is not in this view a cause.

In order to determine which of these two views is the correct one we must summon to our aid the results of the previous investigation. We have seen that all organized bodies are composed of essentially similar parts, namely, of cells; that these cells are formed and grow in accordance with essentially similar laws; and, therefore, that these processes must, in every instance, be produced by the same powers. Now, if we find that some of these elementary parts, not differing from the others, are capable of separating themselves from the organism and pursuing an independent growth, we may thence conclude that each of the other elementary parts, each cell, is already possessed of power to take up fresh molecules and grow; and that, therefore, every elementary part possesses a power of its own, an independent life, by means of which it would be enabled to develop itself independently, if the relations which it bore to external parts were but similar to those in which it stands in the organism. The ova of animals afford us examples of such independent cells, growing apart from the organism.

It may, indeed, be said of the ova of higher animals that after impregnation the ovum is essentially different from the other cells of the organism; that by impregnation there is a something conveyed to the ovum which is more to it than an external condition for vitality, more than nutrient matter; and that it might thereby have first received its peculiar vitality, and therefore that nothing can be inferred from it with respect to the other cells. But this fails in application to those classes which consist only of female individuals, as well as with the spores of the lower plants; and, besides, in the inferior plants any given cell may be separated from the plant, and then grow alone. So that here are whole plants consisting of cells which can be positively proved to have independent vitality.

Now, as all cells grow according to the same laws, and consequently the cause of growth cannot in one case lie in the cell, and in another in the whole organism; and since it may be further proved that some cells, which do not differ from the rest in their mode of growth, are developed independently, we must ascribe to all cells an independent vitality; that is, such combinations of molecules as occur in any single cell are capable of setting free the power by which it is enabled to take up fresh molecules. The cause of nutrition and growth resides not in the organism as a whole but in the separate elementary parts—the cells. The failure of growth in the case of any particular cell, when separated from an organized body, is as slight an objection to this theory as it is an objection against the independent vitality of a bee, that it cannot continue long in existence after being separated from its swarm. The manifestation of the power which resides in the cell depends upon conditions to which it is subject only when in connection with the whole [organism].

The question, then, as to the fundamental power of organized bodies resolves itself into that of the fundamental powers of the individual cells. . . .

I think therefore that, in order to explain the distinction between the cell contents and the external cytoblastema, we must ascribe to the cell membrane not only the power in general of chemically altering the substances which it is either in contact with or has imbibed, but also of so separating them that certain substances appear on its inner and others on its outer surface. The secretion of substances already present in the blood, as, for instance, of urea, by the cells with which the urinary tubes are lined, cannot be explained without such a faculty of the cells. There is, however, nothing so very hazardous in it, since it is a fact that different substances are separated in the decompositions produced by the galvanic pile. It might perhaps be conjectured from this peculiarity of the metabolic phenomena in the cells that a particular position of the axes of the atoms composing the cell membrane is essential for the production of these appearances.

Chemical changes occur, however, not only in the cytoblastema and the cell contents, but also in the solid parts of which the cells are composed, particularly the cell membrane. Without wishing to assert that there is any intimate connection between the metabolic power of the cells and galvanism, I may yet, for the sake of making the representation of the process clearer, remark that the chemical changes produced by a galvanic pile are accompanied by corresponding changes in the pile itself.

The more obscure the cause of the metabolic phenomena in the cells is, the more accurately we must mark the circumstances and phenomena under which they occur. One condition to them is a certain temperature, which has a maximum and a minimum. The phenomena are not produced in a temperature below 0° or above 80°R.; boiling heat destroys this faculty of the cells permanently; but the most favorable temperature is one between 10° and 32°R. Heat is evolved by the process itself.

Oxygen, or carbonic acid, in a gaseous form or lightly confined, is essentially necessary to the metabolic phenomena of the cells. The oxygen disappears and carbonic acid is formed, or vice versa, carbonic acid disappears, and oxygen is formed. The universality of respiration is based entirely upon this fundamental condition to the metabolic phenomena of the cells. It is so important that, as we shall see further on, even the principal varieties of form in organized bodies are occasioned by this peculiarity of the metabolic process in the cells.

Each cell is not capable of producing chemical changes in every organic substance contained in solution, but only in particular ones. The fungi of fermentation, for instance, effect no changes in any other solutions than sugar; and the spores of certain plants do not become developed in all substances. In the same manner it is probable that each cell in the animal body converts only particular constituents of the blood.

The metabolic power of the cells is arrested not only by powerful chemical actions, such as destroy organic substances in general, but also by matters which chemically are less uncongenial; for instance, concentrated solutions of neutral salts. Other substances, as arsenic, do so in less quantity. The metabolic phenomena may be altered in quality by other substances, both organic and inorganic, and a change of this kind may result even from mechanical impressions on the cells.

Such are the most essential characteristics of the fundamental powers of the cells, so far as they can as yet be deduced from the phenomena. And now, in order to comprehend distinctly in what the peculiarity of the formative process of a cell, and therefore in what the peculiarity of the essential phenomenon in the formation of organized bodies consists, we will compare this process with a phenomenon of inorganic nature as nearly as possible similar to it. Disregarding all that is specially peculiar to the formation of cells, in order to find a more general definition in which it may be included with a process occurring in inorganic nature, we may view it as a process in which a solid body of definite and regular shape is formed in a fluid at the expense of a substance held in solution by that fluid. The process of crystallization in inorganic nature comes also within this definition, and is, therefore, the nearest analogue to the formation of cells.

Let us now compare the two processes, that the difference of the organic process may be clearly manifest. . . .

In order to render our hypothesis tenable it is merely necessary to show that crystals capable of imbibition can unite with one another according to certain laws. If at their first formation all crystals were isolated, if they held no relation whatever to each other, the view would leave entirely unexplained how the elementary parts of organisms, that is, the crystals in question, become united to form a whole. It is therefore necessary to show that crystals do unite with each other according to certain laws, in order to perceive, at least, the possibility of their uniting also to form an organism, without the need of any further combining power. But there are many crystals in which a union of this kind, according to certain laws, is indisputable; indeed they often form a whole, so like an organism in its entire form that groups of crystals are known in common life by the names of flowers, trees, et cetera. I need only refer to the ice flowers on the windows, or to the lead tree, et cetera. In such instances a number of crystals arrange themselves in groups around others, which form an axis. If we consider the contact of each crystal with the surrounding fluid to be an indispensable condition to the growth of crystals which are not capable of imbibition, but that those which are capable of imbibition, in which the solution can penetrate whole layers of crystals, do not require this condition, we perceive that the similarity between organisms and these aggregations of crystals is as great as could be expected with such difference of substance.

As most cells require for the production of their metabolic phenomena not only their peculiar nutrient fluid but also the access of oxygen and the power of exhaling carbonic acid, or vice versa; so, on the other hand, organisms in which there is no circulation of respiratory fluid, or in which at least it is not sufficient, must be developed in such a way as to present as extensive a surface as possible to the atmospheric air. This is the condition of plants, which require for their growth that the individual cells should come into contact with the surrounding medium in a similar manner, if not in the same degree as occurs in a crystal tree, and in them indeed the cells unite into a whole organism in a form much resembling a crystal tree. But in animals the circulation renders the contact of the individual cells with the surrounding medium superfluous, and they may have more compact forms, even though the laws by which the cells arrange themselves are essentially the same.

The view then that organisms are nothing but the form under which substances capable of imbibition crystallize appears to be compatible with the most important phenomena of organic life, and may be so far admitted that it is a possible hypothesis or attempt toward an explanation of these phenomena. It involves very much that is uncertain and paradoxical, but I have developed it in detail, because it may serve as a guide for new investigations. For even if no relation between crystallization and the growth of organisms be admitted in principle, this view has

the advantage of affording a distinct representation of the organic processes; an indispensable requisite for the institution of new inquiries in a
systematic manner, or for testing by the discovery of new facts a mode
of explanation which harmonizes with phenomena already known.

Scientific Explorer of South America

ALEXANDER VON HUMBOLDT (1769–1859)

No MAN ever had better right to the title "citizen of the world" than
the magnanimous, adventurous, versatile Baron Alexander von Humboldt. Picture him standing in a low hut near the twin fork of South
America's wild Orinoco River and listening gravely as an illiterate Indian poison master, deftly handling crude native pottery and poisonous
liana branches, demonstrates the aboriginal art of preparing curare,
the potently dangerous drug that is still finding new uses in modern
medical practice. See the Baron again, in 1808, unexpectedly and triumphantly returned from his Herculean South American scientific explora-
tions, settling in Paris to a career of writing and lecturing on science,
travel, and discovery that elevated him to a position of popular regard,
second only to Napoleon, as "the foremost man in Europe." Note him
as pensioner—his fortune dissipated in financing scientific exploration
and publications—and companion (from 1827) to King Frederick William of Prussia. Consider him in conversations with Goethe, who said
of him: "I am always struck with fresh amazement in his company. He
may be said to be without a rival in extent of information and acquaintance with existing sciences. He possesses, too, a versatility of genius
which I have never seen equaled."

Only such a man would have been tempted and dared to try what
Von Humboldt set out to do in his final great work, "The Cosmos"—
to provide an accurate and complete description and a unified imaginative conception of the whole physical universe as known to man. Like
any other essay in this direction, "The Cosmos" is a magnificent failure.
No one man can master and expound the knowledge of the whole
world, growing as it must with each stroke of his pen. But Von Humboldt's "Sketch of a Physical Description of the Universe" or "Reflections on the Enjoyment of Nature and the Study of Her Laws"—

subtitles of "The Cosmos"—remains a landmark in the literature of science, eminently worth reading for its literary charm, for its picturesque descriptions of nature, and for its accurate observations in the sciences which Von Humboldt was especially interested in putting on a scale of greater exactness: meteorology, physical geography (his approach is still implicit in every geography text), botany, geology, and natural history. The scope of Von Humboldt's tours and thoughts; his keen sense of the unity and inevitable "internationalism" of Nature and her amanuensis, Science; his own liberal, humane, and intrepid character are well illustrated in the passages from the introduction to "The Cosmos" quoted here.

Alexander von Humboldt was born in Berlin; he was a younger brother to Wilhelm von Humboldt, whose distinguished work on languages and their place in the intellectual development of the human race is one of the cornerstones of the science of comparative philology. Alexander von Humboldt traveled other places than to South and Central America, where he was accompanied by the French botanist, Aimé Bonpland. After completing collegiate studies at Göttingen and a course in mining engineering at Freiberg, young Alexander traveled through Belgium, Holland, England, and France. When he was an old man, in 1829, he conducted a 9000-mile scientific expedition to the Ural Mountains in Asiatic Russia and discovered diamonds and other precious stones which his knowledge of geology enabled him to predict would be there.

His writings undoubtedly gave impetus to other scientific exploring trips, financed by various governments. Notable among these were the expeditions of the British Navy; classic are the voyages of HMS *Beagle* (1831), which carried Charles Darwin; of HMS *Rattlesnake* (1846), aboard which was Thomas Henry Huxley; and of HMS *Challenger* (1872), a culminating expedition which provided a massive series of records in meteorology, natural history, and oceanography.

German was the language in which Von Humboldt wrote his celebrated "Cosmos." Publication was begun in 1847 (two volumes), not completed until 1858. The passages quoted here, in English translation by E. C. Otté, are from Volume I of the London edition of "Cosmos" published in 1849 by Henry G. Bohn and included in Bohn's Scientific Library.

"THE COSMOS"

A SKETCH OF A
PHYSICAL DESCRIPTION OF THE UNIVERSE

*Reflections on the Enjoyment of Nature and the
Study of Her Laws*

I TAKE PLEASURE in persuading myself that scientific subjects may be treated of in language at once dignified, grave, and animated, and that those who are restricted within the circumscribed limits of ordinary life, and have long remained strangers to an intimate communion with nature, may thus have opened to them one of the richest sources of enjoyment by which the mind is invigorated by the acquisition of new ideas. . . .

The earnest and solemn thoughts awakened by a communion with nature intuitively arise from a presentiment of the order and harmony pervading the whole universe, and from the contrast we draw between the narrow limits of our own existence and the image of infinity revealed on every side, whether we look upwards to the starry vault of heaven, scan the far-stretching plain before us, or seek to trace the dim horizon across the vast expanse of ocean. . . .

If I might be allowed to abandon myself to the recollections of my own distant travels, I would instance, among the most striking scenes of nature, the calm sublimity of a tropical night, when the stars, not sparkling, as in our northern skies, shed their soft and planetary light over the gently heaving ocean; or I would recall the deep valleys of the Cordilleras, where the tall and slender palms pierce the leafy veil around them and, waving on high their feathery and arrowlike branches, form, as it were, "a forest above a forest"; or I would describe the summit of the peak of Tenerife, when a horizontal layer of clouds, dazzling in whiteness, has separated the cone of cinders from the plain below, and suddenly the ascending current pierces the cloudy veil, so that the eye of the traveler may range from the brink of the crater, along the vine-clad slopes of Orotava, to the orange gardens and banana groves that skirt the shore. In scenes like these it is not the peaceful charm uniformly spread over the face of nature that moves the heart, but rather the peculiar physiognomy and conformation of the land, the features of the landscape, the ever-varying outline of the clouds, and their blending with the horizon of the sea, whether it lies spread before us like a smooth and shining mirror or is dimly seen through the morning mist. All that the senses can but imperfectly comprehend, all that is most awful in such romantic scenes of nature, may become a source of enjoyment to man, by opening a wide field to the creative powers of his imagination. Impressions change with the varying movements of the mind, and we are led by a happy illusion to believe that we receive from the external world that with which we have ourselves invested it.

When far from our native country, after a long voyage, we tread for the first time the soil of a tropical land, we experience a certain feeling of surprise and gratification in recognizing, in the rocks that surround us, the same inclined schistose strata, and the same columnar basalt covered with cellular amygdaloids, that we had left in Europe, and whose identity of character, in latitudes so widely different, reminds us that the solidification of the earth's crust is altogether independent of climatic influences. But these rocky masses of schist and of basalt are covered with vegetation of a character with which we are unacquainted, and of a physiognomy wholly unknown to us; and it is then, amid the colossal and majestic forms of an exotic flora, that we feel how wonderfully the flexibility of our nature fits us to receive new impressions, linked together by a certain secret analogy. . . .

The powerful effect exercised by nature springs, as it were, from the connection and unity of the impressions and emotions produced; and we can only trace their different sources by analyzing the individuality of objects and the diversity of forces. . . .

Graphic delineations of nature, arranged according to systematic views, are not only suited to please the imagination but may also, when properly considered, indicate the grades of the impressions of which I have spoken, from the uniformity of the seashore, or the barren steppes of Siberia, to the inexhaustible fertility of the torrid zone. If we were even to picture to ourselves Mount Pilatus placed on the Schreckhorn, or the Schneekoppe of Silesia on Mont Blanc, we should not have attained to the height of that great colossus of the Andes, the Chimborazo, whose height is twice that of Mount Etna; and we must pile the Righi, or Mount Athos, on the summit of the Chimborazo in order to form a just estimate of the elevation of the Dhaulagiri, the highest point of the Himalayas. But although the mountains of India greatly surpass the Cordilleras of South America by their astonishing elevations (which after being long contested has at last been confirmed by accurate measurements), they cannot, from their geographical position, present the same inexhaustible variety of phenomena by which the latter are characterized. The impression produced by the grander aspects of nature does not depend exclusively on height. . . .

But the countries bordering on the equator possess another advantage, to which sufficient attention has not hitherto been directed. This portion of the surface of the globe affords in the smallest space the greatest possible variety of impressions from the contemplation of nature. Among the colossal mountains of Cundinamarca, of Quito, and of Peru, furrowed by deep ravines, man is enabled to contemplate alike all the families of plants and all the stars of the firmament. There, at a single glance, the eye surveys majestic palms, humid forests of bambusa, and the varied species of musaceae, while above these forms of tropical vegetation appear oaks, medlars, the sweetbrier, and umbelliferous plants, as in our European homes. There, as the traveler turns his eyes to the vault of heaven, a single glance embraces the constellation of the Southern Cross, the Magellanic clouds, and the guiding stars of the constellation of the Bear, as they circle round the Arctic pole. There the depths of the earth and the vaults of heaven display all the richness of their forms and the variety of their phenomena. There the different climates are ranged the one above the other, stage by stage, like the vegetable zones, whose succession they limit; and there the observer may readily trace the laws that regulate the diminution of heat as they stand indelibly inscribed on the rocky walls and abrupt declivities of the Cordilleras. . . .

In order to trace to its primitive source the enjoyment derived from the exercise of thought it is sufficient to cast a rapid glance on the earliest dawnings of the philosophy of nature, or of the ancient doctrine of the *Cosmos*. We find even among the most savage nations (as my own travels enable me to attest) a certain vague, terror-stricken sense of the all-powerful unity of natural forces, and of the existence of an invisible, spiritual essence manifested in these forces, whether in unfolding the flower and maturing the fruit of the nutrient tree, in upheaving the soil of the forest, or in rending the clouds with the might of the storm. We may here trace the revelation of a bond of union, linking together the visible world and that higher spiritual world which escapes the grasp of the senses. The two become unconsciously blended together, developing in the mind of man, as a simple product of ideal conception, and independently of the aid of observation, the first germ of a *philosophy of nature*. . . .

The history of science teaches us the difficulties that have opposed the progress of this active spirit of inquiry. Inaccurate and imperfect observations have led by false inductions to the great number of physical views that have been perpetuated as popular prejudices among all classes of society. Thus by the side of a solid and scientific knowledge of natural phenomena there has been preserved a system of the pretended results of observation, which is so much the more difficult to shake, as it denies the validity of the facts by which it may be refuted. This empiricism, the melancholy heritage transmitted to us from former times, invariably contends for the truth of its axioms with the arrogance of a narrow-minded spirit. Physical philosophy, on the other hand, when based upon science, doubts because it seeks to investigate, distinguishes between that which is certain and that which is merely probable, and strives incessantly to perfect theory by extending the circle of observation. . . .

We must not confound the disposition of mind in the observer at the time he is pursuing his labors with the ulterior greatness of the views resulting from investigation and the exercise of thought. The physical philosopher measures with admirable sagacity the waves of light of unequal length which by interference mutually strengthen or destroy each other, even with respect to their chemical actions: the astronomer, armed with powerful telescopes, penetrates the regions of space, contemplates, on the extremest confines of our solar system, the satellites of Uranus, or decomposes faintly sparkling points into double stars differing in color. The botanist discovers the constancy of the gyratory motion of the chara in the greater number of vegetable cells, and recognizes in the genera and natural families of plants the intimate relations of organic forms. The vault of heaven, studded with nebulae and stars, and the rich vegetable mantle that covers the soil in the climate of palms, cannot surely fail to produce on the minds of these laborious observers of nature an impression more imposing and more worthy of the majesty of creation than on those who are unaccustomed to investigate the great mutual relations of phenomena. I cannot, therefore, agree with Burke when he says, "it is our ignorance of natural things that causes all our admiration, and chiefly excites our passions.". . .

The mere accumulation of unconnected observations of details, devoid of generalization of ideas, may doubtlessly have tended to create and foster the deeply rooted prejudice that the study of the exact sciences must necessarily chill the feelings and diminish the nobler enjoyments attendant upon a contemplation of nature. Those who still cherish such erroneous views in the present age, and amid the progress of public opinion, and the advancement of all branches of knowledge, fail in duly appreciating the value of every enlargement of the sphere of intellect and the importance of the detail of isolated facts in leading us on to general results. The fear of sacrificing the free enjoyment of nature, under the influence of scientific reasoning, is often associated with an apprehension that every mind may not be capable of grasping the truths of the philosophy of nature.

It is certainly true that in the midst of the universal fluctuation of phenomena and vital forces—in that inextricable network of organisms by turns developed and destroyed—each step that we make in the more intimate knowledge of nature leads us to the entrance of new labyrinths; but the excitement produced by a presentiment of discovery, the vague intuition of the mysteries to be unfolded, and the multiplicity of the paths before us, all tend to stimulate the exercise of thought in every stage of knowledge. The discovery of each separate law of nature leads to the establishment of some other more general law, or at least indicates to the intelligent observer its existence. Nature, as a celebrated physiologist has defined it, and as the word was interpreted by the Greeks and Romans, is "that which is ever growing and ever unfolding itself in new forms." . . .

It is this necessity, this occult but permanent connection, this periodical recurrence in the progressive development of forms, phenomena, and events, which constitute *nature,* obedient to the first impulse imparted to it. Physics, as the term signifies, is limited to the explanation of the phenomena of the material world by the properties of matter. The ultimate object of the experimental sciences is, therefore, to discover laws and to trace their progressive generalization. All that exceeds this goes beyond the province of the physical description of the universe and appertains to a range of higher speculative views. . . .

The knowledge of the laws of nature, whether we can trace them in the alternate ebb and flow of the ocean, in the measured path of comets, or in the mutual attractions of multiple stars, alike increases our sense of the calm of nature, while the chimera so long cherished by the human mind in its early and intuitive contemplations, the belief in a "discord of the elements," seems gradually to vanish in proportion as science extends her empire. . . . Although fixed to one point of space, we eagerly grasp at a knowledge of that which has been observed in different and far distant regions. We delight in tracking the course of the bold mariner through seas of polar ice, or in following him to the summit of that volcano of the Antarctic pole, whose fires may be seen from afar, even at midday. It is by an acquaintance with the results of distant voyages that we may learn to comprehend some of the marvels of terrestrial magnetism and be thus led to appreciate the importance of the establishments of the numerous observatories which, in the present day, cover both hemispheres and are designed to note the simultaneous occurrence of perturbations and the frequency and duration of magnetic storms. . . .

I apply the term "volcanic," in the widest sense of the word, to every action exercised by the interior of a planet on its external crust. The surface of our globe, and that of the moon, manifest traces of this action which, in the former, at least, has varied during the course of ages. Those who are ignorant of the fact that the internal heat of the earth increases so rapidly with the increase of depth, that granite is in a state of fusion about twenty or thirty geographical miles below the surface, cannot have a clear conception of the causes and the simultaneous occurrence of volcanic eruptions at places widely removed from one another, or of the extent and intersection of *circles of commotion* in earthquakes, or of the uniformity of temperature and equality of chemical composition observed in thermal springs during a long course of years. . . .

The superficial half knowledge, so characteristic of the present day, which leads to the introduction of vaguely comprehended scientific views into general conversation also gives rise, under various forms, to the expression of alarm at the supposed danger of a collision between the celestial bodies or of disturbance in the climatic relations of our globe. These phantoms of the imagination are so much the more injurious as they derive their source from dogmatic pretensions to true science. The history of the atmosphere and of the annual variations of its temperature extends already sufficiently far back to show the recurrence of slight disturbances in the mean temperature of any given place, and thus affords sufficient guarantee against the exaggerated apprehension of a general and progressive deterioration of the climates of Europe. . . .

There is, perhaps, some truth in the accusation advanced against many German scientific works that they lessen the value of general views by an accumulation of detail; and do not sufficiently distinguish between those great results which form, as it were, the beacon lights of science and the long series of means by which they have been attained. This method of treating scientific subjects led the most illustrious of our poets to exclaim with impatience: "The Germans have the art of making science inaccessible." An edifice cannot produce a striking effect until the scaffolding is removed, that had of necessity been used during its erection. . . .

It has not unfrequently happened that the researches made at remote distances have often and unexpectedly thrown light upon subjects which had long resisted the attempts made to explain them, within the narrow limits of our own sphere of observation. . . .

On being first examined, all phenomena appear to be isolated, and it is only by the result of a multiplicity of observation, combined by reason, that we are able to trace the mutual relations existing between them. If, however, in the present age, which is so strongly characterized by a brilliant course of scientific discoveries, we perceive a want of connection in the phenomena of certain sciences, we may anticipate the revelation of new facts whose importance will probably be commensurate with the attention directed to these branches of study. Expectations of this nature may be entertained with regard to meteorology, several parts of optics, and to radiating heat, and electromagnetism, since the admirable discoveries of Melloni and Faraday. A fertile field is here opened to discovery, although the voltaic pile has already taught us the intimate connection existing between electric, magnetic, and chemical phenomena. Who will venture to affirm that we have any precise knowledge, in the present day, of that part of the atmosphere which is not oxygen, or that thousands of gaseous substances affecting our organs may not be mixed with the nitrogen, or, finally, that we have even discovered the whole number of the forces which pervade the universe? . . . [1]

In the observation of a phenomena which at first sight appears to be wholly isolated may be concealed the germ of a great discovery. When Aloisio Galvani first stimulated the nervous fiber by the accidental contact of two heterogeneous metals, his contemporaries could never have anticipated that the action of the voltaic pile would discover to us, in the alkalies, metals of a silvery luster, so light as to swim on water, and eminently inflammable; or that it would become a powerful instrument of chemical analysis, and at the same time a thermoscope and a magnet. . . .

An equal appreciation of all branches of the mathematical, physical,

[1] A remarkably prophetic passage! Modern meteorology has given us air-mass analysis; optics foreshadowed the electromagnetic theory of light (Maxwell); studies in heat radiation brought the quantum theory (Planck); rare gases like neon, helium, argon are found in the atmosphere!

and natural sciences is a special requirement of the present age, in which the material wealth and the growing prosperity of nations are principally based upon a more enlightened employment of the products and forces of nature. The most superficial glance at the present condition of Europe shows that a diminution or even a total annihilation of national prosperity must be the award of those states who shrink with slothful indifference from the great struggle of rival nations in the career of the industrial arts. It is with nations as with nature, which, according to a happy expression of Goethe, "knows no pause in progress and development, and attaches her curse on all inaction." The propagation of an earnest and sound knowledge of science can therefore alone avert the dangers of which I have spoken. . . .

By a happy connection of causes and effects we often see the useful linked to the beautiful and the exalted. The improvement of agriculture in the hands of free men, and on properties of a moderate extent—the flourishing state of the mechanical arts freed from the trammels of municipal restrictions—the increased impetus imparted to commerce by the multiplied means of contact of nations with each other—are all brilliant results of the intellectual progress of mankind and of the amelioration of political institutions, in which this progress is reflected. The picture presented by modern history ought to convince those who are tardy in awakening to the truth of the lesson it teaches.

"Principles of Geology"

CHARLES LYELL (1797–1875)

WHILE OTHER SCIENCES were rapidly developing, the biblical story of Creation and the Flood remained the fundamental textbook of geology up to the middle of the eighteenth century—and the science of geology, so named by an Alpine climber and student, H. B. de Saussure, in 1779, became the happy hunting ground for all the speculative, armchair scientists of the day. Fossils, for example, were considered to be the remains of animals lost in the Flood of Noah. The Siberian expeditions of Pallas (1769); the eloquence of the popular French naturalist, Buffon, whose "Theory of the Earth" appeared in 1749; the maps of Guettard, showing superficial mineral and rock distribution (1746); the researches of Desmarest among the old lava columns of the Giant's Causeway on the coast of Ireland—all helped to establish the principle of geological succession, the dimly held theory that the various strata of rock thrust up on the surface of the earth were not of instantaneous creation but rather of slow and orderly growth. But there was no agreement as to how and why formation of strata had occurred. A battle of words raged between the Neptunists, who argued that the earth's crust was formed by layers deposited or precipitated by an ocean that had once covered the entire surface of the globe, and the Vulcanists, who considered that volcanic action accounted for the present contours of the earth.

Two Scotchmen, born in a country where the evidence of the rocks was every day before them, finally laid the foundations of modern geology on the bedrock proposition of uniformitarianism: namely, the theory that the geologic sculpture of past ages can be explained by the natural forces, such as erosion, still operating in the present. The first of the two Scotch founders of modern geology was James Hutton (1726–97), of Edinburgh, whose thirty years' search for an explanation of the topography of the earth was summed up in a poorly written, badly organized memoir, published in 1785. Its merit of original thinking was lost until his friend, John Playfair, summed it up in a classic of scientific literature (1802), entitled, "Illustrations of the Huttonian Theory of the Earth."

The second great Scots-born geologist, Sir Charles Lyell, became the model of a fair-minded, clearheaded British gentleman of science. Gifted with great powers of generalization, master of a clear and logical English style, Lyell produced in three volumes (1830–33) the convincing arguments, drawn largely from the evidence of fossil deposits, in favor of the still acceptable uniformitarian doctrine. Lyell's influence helped pave the way for the later acceptance of the Darwinian theory of evolution. Not only did his researches in geology establish the great antiquity of the earth, providing an enormous range of time in which the evolutionary process might work; but Lyell was also the close personal friend of Charles Darwin and (with Dr. Joseph Hooker) presented Darwin's claims to priority in the theory of evolution at an historic meeting of the Linnaean Society. He further persuaded Darwin to publish the views finally set forth in "The Origin of Species." Lyell did all this in spite of the fact that he personally did not originally believe in Darwin's theory. It was an act of a magnanimous and open-minded giant of science (and a source of great personal satisfaction to Darwin) when Lyell announced himself convinced of Darwin's theory, which he thenceforth vigorously espoused. His learned and responsible discussion of "the antiquity of man" (1863) was an important factor in winning acceptance for Darwinism.

English was the language in which Lyell expressed himself so effectively. The passage quoted here is from Chapter 1 of Volume III of the "Principles of Geology" (London, 1833).

"AN ATTEMPT TO EXPLAIN THE FORMER CHANGES OF THE EARTH'S SURFACE BY REFERENCE TO CAUSES NOW IN OPERATION"

HAVING CONSIDERED, in the preceding volumes, the actual operation of the causes of change which affect the earth's surface and its inhabitants, we are now about to enter upon a new division of our inquiry, and shall therefore offer a few preliminary observations to fix in the reader's mind the connection between two distinct parts of our work and to explain in what manner the plan pursued by us differs from that more usually followed by preceding writers on geology.

All naturalists, who have carefully examined the arrangement of the mineral masses composing the earth's crust, and who have studied their internal structure and fossil contents, have recognized therein the signs of a great succession of former changes; and the causes of these changes have been the object of anxious inquiry. As the first theorists possessed but a scanty acquaintance with the present economy of the animate and inanimate world, and the vicissitudes to which these are subject, we find them in the situation of novices, who attempt to read a history written in a foreign language, doubting the meaning of the most ordinary terms; disputing, for example, whether a shell was really a shell, whether sand and pebbles were the result of aqueous trituration, whether stratification was the effect of successive deposition from water; and a thousand other elementary questions which now appear to us so easy and simple that we can hardly conceive them to have once afforded matter for warm and tedious controversy.

In the first volume we enumerated many prepossessions which biased the minds of the earlier inquirers and checked an impartial desire of arriving at truth. But of all the causes to which we alluded, no one contributed so powerfully to give rise to a false method of philosophizing as the entire unconsciousness of the first geologists of the extent of their own ignorance respecting the operations of the existing agents of change.

They imagined themselves sufficiently acquainted with the mutations now in progress in the animate and inanimate world to entitle them at once to affirm whether the solution of certain problems in geology could ever be derived from the observation of the actual economy of nature, and having decided that they could not, they felt themselves at liberty to indulge their imaginations in guessing what *might be,* rather than inquiring *what is;* in other words, they employed themselves in conjecturing what might have been the course of nature at a remote period, rather than in the investigation of what was the course of nature in their own times.

It appeared to them more philosophical to speculate on the possibilities of the past than patiently to explore the realities of the present, and having invented theories under the influence of such maxims, they were consistently unwilling to test their validity by the criterion of their accordance with the ordinary operations of nature. On the contrary, the claims of each new hypothesis to credibility appeared enhanced by the great contrast of the causes or forces introduced to those now developed in our terrestrial system during a period, as it has been termed, of *repose.*

Never was there a dogma more calculated to foster indolence and to blunt the edge of curiosity than this assumption of the discordance between the former and the existing causes of change. It produced a state of mind unfavorable in the highest conceivable degree to the candid reception of those minute but incessant mutations which every part of the earth's surface is undergoing, and by which the condition of its living inhabitants is continually made to vary. The student, instead of being encouraged with the hope of interpreting the enigmas presented to him in the earth's structure, instead of being prompted to undertake laborious inquiries into the natural history of the organic world and the complicated effects of the igneous and aqueous causes now in operation, was taught to despond from the first. Geology, it was affirmed, could never rise to the rank of an exact science—the greater number of phenomena must forever remain inexplicable or only be partially elucidated by ingenious conjectures. Even the mystery which invested the subject was said to constitute one of its principal charms, affording, as it did, full scope to the fancy to indulge in a boundless field of speculation.

The course directly opposed to these theoretical views consists in an earnest and patient endeavor to reconcile the former indications of change with the evidence of gradual mutations now in progress; restricting us, in the first instance, to known causes, and then speculating on those which may be in activity in regions inaccessible to us. It seeks an interpretation of geological monuments by comparing the changes of which they give evidence with the vicissitudes now in progress, or which may be in progress.

We shall give a few examples in illustration of the practical results already derived from the two distinct methods of theorizing, for we now have the advantage of being enabled to judge by experience of their respective merits and by the respective value of the fruits which they have produced.

In our historical sketch of the progress of geology the reader has seen that a controversy was maintained for more than a century respecting the origin of fossil shells and bones—were they organic or inorganic substances? That the latter opinion should for a long time have prevailed, and that these bodies should have been supposed to be fashioned into their present form by a plastic virtue, or some other mysterious agency, may appear absurd; but it was, perhaps, as reasonable a conjecture as could be expected from those who did not appeal, in the first instance, to the analogy of the living creation, as affording the only source of authentic information. It was only by an accurate examination of living testacea, and by a comparison of the osteology of the existing vertebrated animals with the remains found entombed in ancient strata that this favorite dogma was exploded, and all were, at length, persuaded that these substances were exclusively of organic origin.

In like manner, when a discussion had arisen as to the nature of basalt and other mineral masses, evidently constituting a particular class of rocks, the popular opinion inclined to a belief that they were of aqueous, not of igneous, origin. These rocks, it was said, might have been precipitated from an aqueous solution, from a chaotic fluid, or an ocean which rose over the continents, charged with the requisite mineral ingredients. All are now agreed that it would have been impossible for human ingenuity to invent a theory more distant from the truth; yet we must cease to wonder, on that account, that it gained so many proselytes, when we remember that its claims to probability arose partly from its confirming the assumed want of all analogy between geological causes and those now in action. By what train of investigation were all theorists brought round at length to an opposite opinion and induced to assent to the igneous origin of these formations? By an examination of the structure of active volcanoes, the mineral composition of their lavas and ejections, and by comparing the undoubted products of fire with the ancient rocks in question.

We shall conclude with one more example. When the organic origin of fossil shells had been conceded, their occurrence in strata forming some of the loftiest mountains in the world was admitted as a proof of a great alteration of the relative level of sea and land, and doubts were then entertained whether this change might be accounted for by the partial drying up of the ocean, or by the elevation of the solid land. The former hypothesis, although afterward abandoned by general consent, was at first embraced by a vast majority. A multitude of ingenious speculations were hazarded to show how the level of the ocean might have been depressed, and when these theories had all failed, the inquiry as to what vicissitudes of this nature might now be taking place was, as usual, resorted to in the last instance. The question was agitated whether any changes in the level of sea and land had occurred during the historical period, and by patient research it was soon discovered that considerable tracts of land had been permanently elevated and depressed, while the level of the ocean remained unaltered. It was therefore necessary to reverse the doctrine which had acquired so much popularity, and the unexpected solution of a problem at first regarded as so enigmatical gave, perhaps, the strongest stimulus ever yet afforded to investigate the ordinary operations of nature. For it must have appeared almost as improbable to the earlier geologists that the laws of earthquakes should one day throw light on the origin of mountains, as it must to the first astronomers that the fall of an apple should assist in explaining the motions of the moon.

Of late years the points of discussion in geology have been transferred to new questions, and those, for the most part, of a higher and more general nature; but, notwithstanding the repeated warnings of experience, the ancient method of philosophizing has not been materially modified.

We are now, for the most part, agreed as to what rocks are of igneous and what of aqueous origin; in what manner fossil shells, whether of the sea or of lakes, have been imbedded in strata; how sand may have been converted into sandstone; and are unanimous as to other propositions which are not of a complicated nature; but when we ascend to those of a higher order, we find as little disposition as formerly to make a strenuous effort, in the first instance, to search out an explanation in the ordinary economy of nature. If, for example, we seek for the causes why mineral masses are associated together in certain groups; why they are arranged in a certain order which is never inverted; why there are many breaks in the continuity of the series; why different organic remains are found in distinct sets of strata; why there is often an abrupt passage from an assemblage of species contained in one formation to that in another immediately superimposed—when these and other topics of an equally extensive kind are discussed, we find the habit of indulging conjectures, respecting irregular and extraordinary causes, to be still in full force.

We hear of sudden and violent revolutions of the globe, of the instantaneous elevation of mountain chains, of paroxysms of volcanic energy, declining according to some, and according to others increasing in violence, from the earliest to the latest ages. We are also told of general catastrophes and a succession of deluges, of the alternation of periods of repose and disorder, of the refrigeration of the globe, of the sudden annihilation of whole races of animals and plants, and other hypotheses, in which we see the ancient spirit of speculation revived, and a desire manifested to cut, rather than patiently to untie, the Gordian knot.

In our attempt to unravel these difficult questions we shall adopt a different course, restricting ourselves to the known or possible operations of existing causes; feeling assured that we have not yet exhausted the resources which the study of the present course of nature may provide, and therefore that we are not authorized, in the infancy of our science, to recur to extraordinary agents. We shall adhere to this plan, not only on the grounds explained in the first volume, but because, as we have above stated, history informs us that this method has always put geologists on the road that leads to truth—suggesting views which, although imperfect at first, have been found capable of improvement, until at last adopted by universal consent. On the other hand, the opposite method, that of speculating on a former distinct state of things, has led invariably to a multitude of contradictory systems which have been overthrown one after the other, which have been found quite incapable of modification, and which are often required to be precisely reversed.

In regard to the subjects treated of in our first two volumes, if systematic treatises had been written on these topics, we should willingly have entered at once upon the description of geological monuments properly so called, referring to other authors for the elucidation of elementary and collateral questions, just as we shall appeal to the best authorities in conchology and comparative anatomy in proof of many positions which, but for the labors of naturalists devoted to these departments, would have demanded long digressions. When we find it asserted, for example, that the bones of a fossil animal at Oeningen were those of man, and the fact adduced as a proof of the deluge, we are now able at once to dismiss the argument as nugatory and to affirm the skeleton to be that of a reptile, on the authority of an able anatomist; and when we find among ancient writers the opinion of the gigantic stature of the human race in times of old, grounded on the magnitude of certain fossil teeth and bones, we are able to affirm these remains to belong to the elephant and rhinoceros, on the same authority.

But since, in our attempt to solve geological problems, we shall be called upon to refer to the operation of aqueous and igneous causes, the geographical distribution of animals and plants, the real existence of species, their successive extinction, and so forth, we were under the necessity of collecting together a variety of facts and of entering into long trains of reasoning, which could only be accomplished in preliminary treatises.

These topics we regard as constituting the alphabet and grammar of geology; not that we expect from such studies to obtain a key to the interpretation of all geological phenomena, but because they form the groundwork from which we must rise to the contemplation of more general questions relating to the complicated results to which, in an indefinite lapse of ages, the existing causes of change may give rise.

VII SCIENCE ASSERTS ITSELF:
In the Age of Evolution

"Keystone of the Arch of Evolution"

CHARLES DARWIN (1809–82)

CHARLES DARWIN, the great protagonist of the theory of evolution by means of natural selection, wrote three books still worth reading for their pleasant purveyance of readable information on authentic natural history. Some of the most important passages from all three are quoted here; they give the essence of Darwinism, over which many millions of learned and sometimes angry words have been spilled from pulpits, lecture platforms, and even courtrooms. The needless controversy between "science and religion," set off by the publication of the "Origin of Species" in 1859, has lasted to our own time. The famous Scopes "monkey trial" in Tennessee in 1925, at which lawyer Clarence Darrow—the wits said—made a monkey out of William Jennings Bryan, offers painful proof that prejudice against scientific truth dies but slowly.

Charles Darwin did not discover the theory of evolution; he simply proved it in such masterly argument, so thoroughly documented, that no reasonable man could longer doubt it. Among those who anticipated the theory dethroning man from his ordained place at the pinnacle of creation was Charles Darwin's own grandfather, Erasmus Darwin (1731–1802), botanist, physiologist, and poet, who wrote on "The Loves of Plants" and "Economy of Vegetation." The distinction of the Darwin and Wedgwood families (Charles married Emma Wedgwood) appeared almost the best proof of the theory of eugenics, later propounded on Darwinian principles by his cousin, Francis Galton. Four of Charles Darwin's five sons were themselves distinguished scientists.

If genius is the infinite capacity for taking pains, Charles Darwin stands high in that category. He worked for twenty-five years gathering examples to illustrate the doctrine of natural selection that he had caught from the writing of Thomas Malthus. One reason for the success of the convincing argument propounded in the "Origin of Species," whose instantaneous "success" startled no one more than its author, was the fact that he had made a habit of jotting down in advance every argument that could be brought against his theory and then finding examples or making experiments to disprove the objection. In his mind the monumental "Origin of Species" was simply an abstract of the even greater work that he projected. He wrote with difficulty, called his own style "wretched," and worked through sieges of torturing headaches to complete the "abstract" undertaken at the plea of his friends. The best estimate óf his character has been given by his generous rival in the exposition of the theory of natural selection, Alfred Russel Wallace (q.v.).

Darwin, born at Shrewsbury, England, was originally trained for the ministry; he adopted the career of the naturalist when he signed on the voyage of H.M.S. *Beagle* for an expedition to South America and Australia which lasted five years (1831–36). The most significant place he visited was the Galápagos Archipelago, described here.

English was Darwin's language. "The Journal of Researches into the Geology and Natural History of the Various Countries Visited during the Voyage of H.M.S. *Beagle* Round the World" was first published in 1840. "The Origin of Species by Means of Natural Selection," whose Chapter IV, here quoted, Darwin himself called "the keystone of the arch of evolution," was sold out on the day it was published in December 1859. "The Descent of Man" appeared in 1871.

"THE ORIGIN OF SPECIES BY MEANS OF NATURAL SELECTION"

INTRODUCTION

WHEN on board H.M.S. *Beagle,* as naturalist, I was much struck with certain facts in the distribution of the organic beings inhabiting South America, and in the geological relations of the present to the past inhabitants of that continent. These facts, as will be seen in the latter chapters of this volume, seemed to throw some light on the origin of species—that mystery of mysteries, as it has been called by one of our greatest philosophers. On my return home it occurred to me, in 1837, that something might perhaps be made out on this question by patiently accumulating and reflecting on all sorts of facts which could possibly have any bearing on it. After five years' work I allowed myself to speculate on the subject and drew up some short notes; these I enlarged in 1844 into a sketch of the conclusions, which then seemed to me probable; from that period to the present day I have steadily pursued the same object. I hope that I may be excused for entering on these personal details, as I give them to show that I have not been hasty in coming to a decision.

My work is now (1859) nearly finished; but as it will take me many more years to complete it, and as my health is far from strong, I have been urged to publish this abstract. I have more especially been induced to do this, as Mr. Wallace, who is now studying the natural history of the Malay Archipelago, has arrived at almost exactly the same general conclusions that I have on the origin of species. In 1858 he sent me a memoir on this subject, with a request that I would forward it to Sir Charles Lyell, who sent it to the Linnaean Society, and it is published in the third volume of the journal of that society. Sir C. Lyell and Dr. Hooker, who both knew of my work—the latter having read my sketch of 1844—honored me by thinking it advisable to publish, with Mr. Wallace's excellent memoir, some brief extracts from my manuscripts.

This abstract, which I now publish, must necessarily be imperfect. I cannot here give references and authorities for my several statements; and I must trust to the reader reposing some confidence in my accuracy. No doubt errors will have crept in, though I hope I have always been cautious in trusting to good authorities alone. I can here give only the general conclusions at which I have arrived, with a few facts in illustration, but which, I hope, in most cases will suffice. No one can feel more sensible than I do of the necessity of hereafter publishing in detail all the facts, with references, on which my conclusions have been grounded; and I hope in a future work to do this. For I am well aware that scarcely a single point is discussed in this volume on which facts cannot be adduced, often apparently leading to conclusions directly opposite to those at which I have arrived. A fair result can be obtained only by fully stating and balancing the facts and arguments on both sides of each question; and this is here impossible.

I much regret that want of space prevents my having the satisfaction of acknowledging the generous assistance which I have received from very many naturalists, some of them personally unknown to me. I cannot, however, let this opportunity pass without expressing my deep obligations to Dr. Hooker, who for the last fifteen years has aided me in every possible way by his large stores of knowledge and his excellent judgment.

In considering the origin of species, it is quite conceivable that a naturalist, reflecting on the mutual affinities of organic beings, on their embryological relations, their geographical distribution, geological succession, and other such facts, might come to the conclusion that species had not been independently created but had descended, like varieties, from other species. Nevertheless, such a conclusion, even if well founded, would be unsatisfactory until it could be shown how the innumerable species inhabiting this world have been modified so as to acquire that perfection of structure and coadaptation which justly excites our admiration. Naturalists continually refer to external conditions, such as climate, food, et cetera, as the only possible cause of variation. In one limited sense, as we shall hereafter see, this may be true; but it is preposterous to attribute to mere external conditions the structure, for instance, of the woodpecker, with its feet, tail, beak, and tongue, so admirably adapted to catch insects under the bark of trees. In the case of the mistletoe, which draws its nourishment from certain trees, which has seeds that must be transported by certain birds, and which has flowers with separate sexes absolutely requiring the agency of certain insects to bring pollen from one flower to the other, it is equally preposterous to account for the structure of this parasite, with its relations to several distinct organic beings, by the effects of external conditions, or of habit, or of the volition of the plant itself.

It is, therefore, of the highest importance to gain a clear insight into the means of modification and coadaptation. At the commencement of my observations it seemed to me probable that a careful study of domesticated animals and of cultivated plants would offer the best chance of making out this obscure problem. Nor have I been disappointed; in this and in all other perplexing cases I have invariably found that our knowledge, imperfect though it be, of variation under domestication afforded the best and safest clue. I may venture to express my conviction of the high value of such studies, although they have been very commonly neglected by naturalists.

From these considerations I shall devote the first chapter of this abstract to variation under domestication. We shall thus see that a large amount of hereditary modification is at least possible; and, what is equally or more important, we shall see how great is the power of man in accumulating by his selection successive slight variations. I will then pass on to the variability of species in a state of nature; but I shall, unfortunately, be compelled to treat this subject far too briefly, as it can be treated properly only by giving long catalogues of facts. We shall, however, be enabled to discuss what circumstances are most favorable to variation. In the next chapter the struggle for existence among all organic beings throughout the world, which inevitably follows from the high geometrical ratio of their increase, will be considered. This is the doctrine of Malthus, applied to the whole animal and vegetable kingdoms. As many more indi-

viduals of each species are born than can possibly survive; and as, consequently, there is a frequently recurring struggle for existence, it follows
that any being, if it vary however slightly in any manner profitable to
itself, under the complex and sometimes varying conditions of life, will
have a better chance of surviving, and thus be *naturally selected*. From
the strong principle of inheritance, any selected variety will tend to propagate its new and modified form.

This fundamental subject of natural selection will be treated at some
length in the fourth chapter; and we shall then see how natural selection
almost inevitably causes much extinction of the less improved forms of
life, and leads to what I have called divergence of character. In the next
chapter I shall discuss the complex and little-known laws of variation. In
the five succeeding chapters the most apparent and gravest difficulties in
accepting the theory will be given: namely, first, the difficulties of transitions, or how a simple being or a simple organ can be changed and perfected into a highly developed being or into an elaborately constructed
organ; secondly, the subject of instinct, or the mental powers of animals;
thirdly, hybridism, or the infertility of species and the fertility of varieties when intercrossed and fourthly, the imperfection of the geological
record. In the next chapter I shall consider the geological succession of
organic beings throughout time; in the twelfth and thirteenth, their geographical distribution throughout space; in the fourteenth, their classification or mutual affinities, both when mature and in an embryonic
condition. In the last chapter I shall give a brief recapitulation of the
whole work, and a few concluding remarks.

No one ought to feel surprise at much remaining as yet unexplained in
regard to the origin of species and varieties, if he make due allowance for
our profound ignorance in regard to the mutual relations of the many
beings which live around us. Who can explain why one species ranges
widely and is very numerous, and why another allied species has a narrow
range and is rare? Yet these relations are of the highest importance, for
they determine the present welfare and, as I believe, the future success
and modification of every inhabitant of this world. Still less do we know
of the mutual relations of the innumerable inhabitants of the world
during the many past geological epochs in its history. Although much
remains obscure, and will long remain obscure, I can entertain no doubt,
after the most deliberate study and dispassionate judgment of which I am
capable, that the view which most naturalists until recently entertained,
and which I formerly entertained—namely, that each species has been independently created—is erroneous. I am fully convinced that species are

not immutable; but that those belonging to what are called the same genera are lineal descendants of some other and generally extinct species, in the same manner as the acknowledged varieties of any one species are the descendants of that species. Furthermore, I am convinced that natural selection has been the most important, but not the exclusive, means of modification.

Chapter IV

Natural Selection; or the Survival of the Fittest

How will the struggle for existence . . . act in regard to variation? Can the principle of selection, which we have seen is so potent in the hands of man, apply under nature? I think we shall see that it can act most efficiently. Let the endless number of slight variations and individual differences occurring in our domestic productions and, in a lesser degree, in those under nature be borne in mind; as well as the strength of the hereditary tendency. Under domestication, it may be truly said that the whole organization becomes in some degree plastic. But the variability, which we almost universally meet with in our domestic productions, is not directly produced, as Hooker and Asa Gray have well remarked, by man; he can neither originate varieties nor prevent their occurrence; he can preserve and accumulate such as do occur. Unintentionally he exposes organic beings to new and changing conditions of life, and variability ensues; but similar changes of conditions might and do occur under nature. Let it also be borne in mind how infinitely complex and close-fitting are the mutual relations of all organic beings to each other and to their physical conditions of life; and consequently what infinitely varied diversities of structure might be of use to each being under changing conditions of life. Can it, then, be thought improbable, seeing that variations useful to man have undoubtedly occurred, that other variations useful in some way to each being in the great and complex battle of life should occur in the course of many successive generations? If such do occur, can we doubt (remembering that many more individuals are born than can possibly survive) that individuals having any advantage, however slight, over others, would have the best chance of surviving and of procreating their kind? On the other hand, we may feel sure that any variation in the least degree injurious would be rigidly destroyed. This preservation of favorable individual differences and variations and the destruction of those which are injurious, I have called natural selection, or the survival of the fittest. Variations neither useful nor injurious would not be affected by natural selection, and would be left either a fluctuating element, as perhaps we see in certain polymorphic species, or would ultimately become fixed, owing to the nature of the organism and the nature of the conditions. . . .

We shall best understand the probable course of natural selection by taking the case of a country undergoing some slight physical change, for instance, of climate. The proportional numbers of its inhabitants will almost immediately undergo a change, and some species will probably become extinct. We may conclude, from what we have seen of the intimate and complex manner in which the inhabitants of each country are bound together, that any change in the numerical proportions of the inhabitants, independently of the change of climate itself, would seriously affect the others. If the country were open on its borders, new forms would certainly immigrate, and this would likewise seriously disturb the relations of some of the former inhabitants. Let it be remembered how powerful the influence of a single introduced tree or mammal has been shown to be. But in the case of an island, or of a country partly surrounded by barriers, into which new and better adapted forms could not freely enter, we should then have places in the economy of nature which would assuredly be better filled up, if some of the original inhabitants were in some manner modified; for, had the area been open to immigration, these same places would have been seized on by intruders. In such cases slight modifications, which in any way favored the individuals of any species by better adapting them to their altered conditions, would tend to be preserved; and natural selection would have free scope for the work of improvement. . . .

As man can produce, and certainly has produced, a great result by his methodical and unconscious means of selection, what may not natural selection effect? Man can act only on external and visible characters: Nature, if I may be allowed to personify the natural preservation or survival of the fittest, cares nothing for appearances, except in so far as they are useful to any being. She can act on every internal organ, on every shade of constitutional difference, on the whole machinery of life. Man selects only for his own good: Nature only for that of the being which she tends. Every selected character is fully exercised by her, as is implied by the fact of their selection. Man keeps the natives of many climates in the same country; he seldom exercises each selected character in some peculiar and fitting manner; he feeds a long- and a short-beaked pigeon on the same food; he does not exercise a long-backed or long-legged quadruped in any peculiar manner; he exposes sheep with long and short wool to the same climate. He does not allow the most vigorous males to struggle for the females. He does not rigidly destroy all inferior animals, but protects during each varying season, as far as lies in his power, all his productions. He often begins his selection by some half-monstrous form; or at least by some modification prominent enough to catch the eye or to be plainly useful to him. Under Nature, the slightest differences of structure or constitution may well turn the nicely balanced scale in the struggle for life, and so be preserved. How fleeting are the wishes and efforts of man! How short his time! And consequently how poor will be his results, compared with those accumulated by Nature during whole geological periods! . . .

It may metaphorically be said that natural selection is daily and hourly scrutinizing, throughout the world, the slightest variations; rejecting those that are bad, preserving and adding up all that are good; silently and insensibly working, *whenever and wherever opportunity offers,* at the improvement of each organic being in relation to its organic and inorganic conditions of life. We see nothing of these slow changes in progress until the hand of time has marked the lapse of ages, and then so imperfect is our view into long-past geological ages that we see only that the forms of life are now different from what they formerly were. . . .

It may be well here to remark that with all beings there must be much fortuitous destruction which can have little or no influence on the course of natural selection. For instance a vast number of eggs or seeds are annually devoured, and these could be modified through natural selection only if they varied in some manner which protected them from their enemies. Yet many of these eggs or seeds would perhaps, if not destroyed, have yielded individuals better adapted to their conditions of life than any of those which happened to survive. So again a vast number of mature animals and plants, whether or not they be the best adapted to their conditions, must be annually destroyed by accidental causes, which would not be in the least degree mitigated by certain changes of structure or constitution which would in other ways be beneficial to the species. But let the destruction of the adults be ever so heavy, if the number which can exist in any district be not wholly kept down by such causes—or again let the destruction of eggs or seeds be so great that only a hundredth or a thousandth part are developed—yet, of those which do survive, the best adapted individuals, supposing that there is any variability in a favorable direction, will tend to propagate their kind in larger numbers than the less well adapted. If the numbers be wholly kept down by the causes just indicated, as will often have been the case, natural selection will be powerless in certain beneficial directions; but this is no valid objection to its efficiency at other times and in other ways; for we are far from having any reason to suppose that many species ever undergo modification and improvement at the same time in the same area.

Sexual Selection

Inasmuch as peculiarities often appear under domestication in one sex and become hereditarily attached to that sex, so no doubt it will be under nature. Thus it is rendered possible for the two sexes to be modified through natural selection in relation to different habits of life, as is sometimes the case; or for one sex to be modified in relation to the other sex, as commonly occurs. This leads me to say a few words on what I have called sexual selection. This form of selection depends not on a struggle for existence in relation to other organic beings or to external conditions but on a struggle between the individuals of one sex, generally the males, for the possession of the other sex. The result is not death to the unsuccessful competitor but few or no offspring. Sexual selection is, therefore, less rigorous than natural selection. Generally the most vigorous males, those which are best fitted for their places in nature, will leave most progeny. But in many cases victory depends not so much on general vigor as on having special weapons, confined to the male sex. A hornless stag or spurless cock would have a poor chance of leaving numerous offspring. Sexual selection, by always allowing the victor to breed, might surely give indomitable courage, length to the spur, and strength to the wing to strike in the spurred leg, in nearly the same manner as does the brutal cockfighter by the careful selection of his best cocks. How low in the scale of nature the law of battle descends I know not; male alligators have been described as fighting, bellowing, and whirling round, like Indians in a war dance, for the possession of the females; male salmons have been observed fighting all day long; male stag beetles sometimes bear wounds from the huge mandibles of other males; the males of certain hymenopterous insects have been frequently seen by that inimitable observer, Monsieur Fabre, fighting for a particular female who sits by, an apparently unconcerned beholder of the struggle, and then retires with the conqueror. The war is, perhaps, severest between the males of polygamous animals, and these seem oftenest provided with special weapons. The males of carnivorous animals are already well armed; though to them and to others special means of defense may be given through means of sexual selection, as the mane of the lion, and the hooked jaw to the male salmon; for the shield may be as important for victory as the sword or spear.

Among birds the contest is often of a more peaceful character. All those who have attended to the subject believe that there is the severest rivalry between the males of many species to attract, by singing, the females. The rock thrush of Guiana, birds of paradise, and some others congregate; and successive males display with the most elaborate care, and show off in the best manner, their gorgeous plumage; they likewise perform strange antics before the females, which, standing by as spectators, at last choose the most attractive partner. Those who have closely attended to birds in confinement well know that they often take individual preferences and dislikes: thus Sir R. Heron has described how a pied peacock was eminently attractive to all his hen birds. I cannot here enter on the necessary details; but if man can in a short time give beauty and an elegant carriage to his bantams, according to his standard of beauty, I can see no good reason to doubt that female birds, by selecting, during thousands of generations, the most melodious or beautiful males, according to their standard of beauty, might produce a marked effect. Some well-known laws, with respect to the plumage of male and female birds, in comparison with the plumage of the young, can partly be explained through the action of sexual selection on variations occurring at different ages, and transmitted to the males alone or to both sexes at corresponding ages; but I have not space here to enter on this subject.

Thus it is, as I believe, that when the males and females of any animal have the same general habits of life, but differ in structure, color, or ornament, such differences have been mainly caused by sexual selection: that is, by individual males having had, in successive generations, some slight advantage over other males, in their weapons, means of defense, or charms, which they have transmitted to their male offspring alone. Yet I would not wish to attribute all sexual differences to this agency: for we see in our domestic animals peculiarities arising and becoming attached to the male sex, which apparently have not been augmented through selection by man. The tuft of hair on the breast of the wild turkey cock cannot be of any use, and it is doubtful whether it can be ornamental in the eyes of the female bird; indeed, had the tuft appeared under domestication, it would have been called a monstrosity.

Illustrations of the Action of Natural Selection, or the Survival of the Fittest

In order to make it clear how, as I believe, natural selection acts, I must beg permission to give one or two imaginary illustrations. Let us take the case of a wolf, which preys on various animals, securing some by craft, some by strength, and some by fleetness; and let us suppose that the fleetest prey, a deer for instance, had from any change in the country increased in numbers, or that other prey had decreased in numbers, during that season of the year when the wolf was hardest pressed for food. Under such circumstances the swiftest and slimmest wolves would have the best chance of surviving and so be preserved or selected—provided always that they retained strength to master their prey at this or some other period of the year, when they were compelled to prey on other animals. I can see no more reason to doubt that this would be the result than that man should be able to improve the fleetness of his greyhounds by careful and methodical selection, or by that kind of unconscious selection which follows from each man trying to keep the best dogs without any thought of modifying the breed. I may add that, according to Mr. Pierce, there are two varieties of the wolf inhabiting the Catskill Mountains, in the United States, one with a light greyhoundlike form, which pursues deer, and the other more bulky, with shorter legs, which more frequently attacks the shepherd's flocks.

It should be observed that, in the above illustration, I speak of the slimmest individual wolves, and not of any single strongly marked variation having been preserved. In former editions of this work I sometimes spoke as if this latter alternative had frequently occurred. I saw the great importance of individual differences, and this led me fully to discuss the results of unconscious selection by man, which depends on the preservation of all the more or less valuable individuals, and on the destruction of the worst. I saw, also, that the preservation in a state of nature of any occasional deviation of structure, such as a monstrosity, would be a rare event; and that, if at first preserved, it would generally be lost by subsequent intercrossing with ordinary individuals. Nevertheless, until reading an able and valuable article in the "North British Review" (1867), I did not appreciate how rarely single variations, whether slight or strongly marked, could be perpetuated. The author takes the case of a pair of animals, producing during their lifetime two hundred offspring, of which, from various causes of destruction, only two on an average survive to procreate their kind. This is rather an extreme estimate for most of the higher animals, but by no means so for many of the lower organisms. He then shows that if a single individual were born, which varied in some manner, giving it twice as good a chance of life as that of the other individuals, yet the chances would be strongly against its survival. Supposing it to survive and to breed and that half its young inherited the favorable variation; still, as the reviewer goes on to show, the young would have only a slightly better chance of surviving and breeding; and this chance would go on decreasing in the succeeding generations. The justice of these remarks cannot, I think, be disputed. If, for instance, a bird of some kind could procure its food more easily by having its beak curved, and if one were born with its beak strongly curved, and which consequently flourished, nevertheless there would be a very poor chance of this one individual perpetuating its kind to the exclusion of the common form; but there can hardly be a doubt, judging by what we see taking place under domestication, that this result would follow from the preservation during many generations of a large number of individuals with more or less strongly curved beaks, and from the destruction of a still larger number with the straightest beaks.

It should not, however, be overlooked that certain rather strongly marked variations, which no one would rank as mere individual differences, frequently recur owing to a similar organization being similarly acted on—of which fact numerous instances could be given with our domestic productions. In such cases, if the varying individual did not actually transmit to its offspring its newly acquired character, it would undoubtedly transmit to them, as long as the existing conditions remained the same, a still stronger tendency to vary in the same manner. There can also be little doubt that the tendency to vary in the same manner has often been so strong that all the individuals of the same species have been similarly modified without the aid of any form of selection. Or only a third, fifth, or tenth part of the individuals may have been thus affected, of which fact several instances could be given. Thus Graba estimates that about one fifth of the guillemots in the Faroe Islands consist of a variety so well marked that it was formerly ranked as a distinct species under the name of *Uria lacrymans*. In cases of this kind, if the variation were of a beneficial nature, the original form would soon be supplanted by the modified form, through the survival of the fittest.

To the effects of intercrossing in eliminating variations of all kinds I shall have to recur; but it may be here remarked that most animals and plants keep to their proper homes and do not needlessly wander about; we see this even with migratory birds, which almost always return to the same spot. Consequently each newly formed variety would generally be at first local, as seems to be the common rule with varieties in a state of nature; so that similarly modified individuals would soon exist in a small body together, and would often breed together. If the new variety were successful in its battle for life, it would slowly spread from a central district, competing with and conquering the unchanged individuals on the margins of an ever-increasing circle.

It may be worth while to give another and more complex illustration of the action of natural selection. Certain plants excrete sweet juice, apparently for the sake of eliminating something injurious from the sap: this is effected, for instance, by glands at the base of the stipules in some Leguminosae, and at the backs of the leaves of the common laurel. This juice, though small in quantity, is greedily sought by insects; but their visits do not in any way benefit the plant. Now let us suppose that the juice or nectar was excreted from the inside of the flowers of a certain number of plants of any species. Insects in seeking the nectar would get dusted with pollen and would often transport it from one flower to another. The flowers of two distinct individuals of the same species would thus get crossed; and the act of crossing, as can be fully proved, gives rise to vigorous seedlings which consequently would have the best chance of flourishing and surviving. The plants which produced flowers with the largest glands or nectaries, excreting most nectar, would oftenest be visited by insects and would oftenest be crossed; and so in the long run would gain the upper hand and form a local variety. The flowers, also, which had their stamens and pistils placed, in relation to the size and habits of the particular insects which visited them, so as to favor in any degree the transportal of the pollen, would likewise be favored. We might have taken the case of insects visiting flowers for the sake of collecting pollen instead of nectar; and as pollen is formed for the sole purpose of fertilization, its destruction appears to be a simple loss to the plant; yet if a little pollen were carried, at first occasionally and then habitually, by the pollen-devouring insects from flower to flower, and a cross thus effected, although nine tenths of the pollen were destroyed it might still be a great gain to the plant to be thus robbed; and the individuals which produced more and more pollen, and had larger anthers, would be selected.

When our plant, by the above process long continued, had been rendered highly attractive to insects, they would, unintentionally on their part, regularly carry pollen from flower to flower; and that they do this effectually I could easily show by many striking facts. I will give only one, as likewise illustrating one step in the separation of the sexes of plants. Some holly trees bear only male flowers, which have four stamens producing a rather small quantity of pollen, and a rudimentary pistil; other holly trees bear only female flowers; these have a full-sized pistil, and four stamens with shriveled anthers, in which not a grain of pollen can be detected. Having found a female tree exactly sixty yards from a male tree, I put the stigmas of twenty flowers, taken from different branches, under the microscope, and on all, without exception, there were a few pollen grains, and on some a profusion. As the wind had set for several days from the female to the male tree, the pollen could not thus have been carried. The weather had been cold and boisterous, and therefore not favorable to bees; nevertheless every female flower which I examined had been effectually fertilized by the bees, which had flown from tree to tree in search of nectar. But to return to our imaginary case: as soon as the plant had been rendered so highly attractive to insects that pollen was regularly carried from flower to flower, another process might commence. No naturalist doubts the advantage of what has been called the "physiological division of labor"; hence we may believe that it would be advantageous to a plant to produce stamens alone in one flower or on one whole plant, and pistils alone in another flower or on another plant. . . .

Let us now turn to the nectar-feeding insects; we may suppose the plant, of which we have been slowly increasing the nectar by continued selection, to be a common plant; and that certain insects depended in main part on its nectar for food. I could give many facts showing how anxious bees are to save time: for instance, their habit of cutting holes and sucking the nectar at the bases of certain flowers, which, with a very little more trouble, they can enter by the mouth. Bearing such facts in mind, it may be believed that under certain circumstances individual differences in the curvature or length of the proboscis, et cetera, too slight to be appreciated by us, might profit a bee or other insect, so that certain individuals would be able to obtain their food more quickly than others; and thus the communities to which they belonged would flourish and throw off many swarms inheriting the same peculiarities. The tubes of the corolla of the common red and incarnate clovers (*Trifolium pratense* and *incarnatum*) do not on a hasty glance appear to differ in length; yet the hive bee can easily suck the nectar out of the incarnate clover, but not out of the common red clover, which is visited by humblebees alone; so that whole fields of red clover offer in vain an abundant supply of precious nectar to the hive bee. That this nectar is much liked by the hive bee is certain; for I have repeatedly seen, but only in the autumn, many hive bees sucking the flowers through holes bitten in the base of the tube by humblebees. The difference in the length of the corolla in the two kinds of clover, which determines the visits of the hive bee, must be very trifling; for I have been assured that when red clover has been mown the flowers of the second crop are somewhat smaller, and that these are visited by many hive bees. I do not know whether this statement is accurate; nor whether another published statement can be trusted, namely, that the Ligurian bee which is generally considered a mere variety of the common hive bee, and which freely crosses with it, is able to reach and suck the nectar of the red clover. Thus, in a country where this kind of clover abounded, it might be a great advantage to the hive bee to have a slightly longer or differently constructed proboscis. On the other hand, as the fertility of this clover absolutely depends on bees visiting the flowers, if humblebees were to become rare in any country, it might be a great advantage to the plant to have a shorter or more deeply divided corolla, so that the hive bees should be enabled to suck its flowers. Thus I can understand how a flower and a bee might slowly become, either simultaneously or one after the other, modified and adapted to each other in the most perfect manner, by the continued preservation of all the individuals which presented slight deviations of structure mutually favorable to each other.

I am well aware that this doctrine of natural selection, exemplified in the above imaginary instances, is open to the same objections which were first urged against Sir Charles Lyell's noble views on "the modern changes of the earth, as illustrative of geology"; but we now seldom hear the agencies which we see still at work spoken of as trifling or insignificant, when used in explaining the excavation of the deepest valleys or the formation of long lines of inland cliffs. Natural selection acts only by the preservation and accumulation of small inherited modifications, each profitable to the preserved being; and as modern geology has almost banished such views as the excavation of a great valley by a single diluvial wave, so will natural selection banish the belief of the continued creation of new organic beings, or of any great and sudden modification in their structure. . . .

Divergence of Character

The principle which I have designated by this term is of high importance and explains, as I believe, several important facts. In the first place varieties, even strongly marked ones, though having somewhat of the character of species—as is shown by the hopeless doubts in many cases how to rank them—yet certainly differ far less from each other than do good and distinct species. Nevertheless, according to my view, varieties are species in the process of formation or are, as I have called them, incipient species. How, then, does the lesser difference between varieties become augmented into the greater difference between species? That this does habitually happen we must infer from most of the innumerable species throughout nature presenting well-marked differences; whereas varieties, the supposed prototypes and parents of future well-marked species, present slight and ill-defined differences. Mere chance, as we may call it, might cause one variety to differ in some character from its parents, and the offspring of this variety again to differ from its parent in the very same character and in a greater degree; but this alone would never account for so habitual and large a degree of difference as that between the species of the same genus.

As has always been my practice, I have sought light on this head from our domestic productions. We shall here find something analogous. It will be admitted that the production of races so different as shorthorn and Hereford cattle, race and cart horses, the several breeds of pigeons, et cetera, could never have been effected by the mere chance accumulation of similar variations during many successive generations. In practice a fancier is, for instance, struck by a pigeon having a slightly shorter beak; another fancier is struck by a pigeon having a rather longer beak; and on the acknowledged principle that "fanciers do not and will not admire a medium standard, but like extremes," they both go on (as has actually occurred with the subbreeds of the tumbler pigeon) choosing and breeding from birds with longer and longer beaks, or with shorter and shorter beaks. Again, we may suppose that at an early period of history the men of one nation or district required swifter horses, while those of another required stronger and bulkier horses. The early differences would be very slight; but in the course of time, from the continued selection of swifter horses in the one case, and of stronger ones in the other, the differences would become greater and would be noted as forming two subbreeds. Ultimately, after the lapse of centuries, these subbreeds would become converted into two well-established and distinct breeds. As the differences became greater, the inferior animals with intermediate characters, being neither swift nor very strong, would not have been used for breeding and will thus have tended to disappear. Here, then, we see in man's productions the action of what may be called the principle of divergence, causing differences, at first barely appreciable, steadily to increase, and the breeds to diverge in character, both from each other and from their common parent. . . .

The truth of the principle that the greatest amount of life can be supported by great diversification of structure is seen under many natural circumstances. In an extremely small area, especially if freely open to immigration, and where the contest between individual and individual must be very severe, we always find great diversity in its inhabitants. For instance I found that a piece of turf, three feet by four in size, which had been exposed for many years to exactly the same conditions, supported twenty species of plants, and these belonged to eighteen genera and to eight orders, which shows how much these plants differed from each other. So it is with the plants and insects on small and uniform islets; also in small ponds of fresh water. Farmers find that they can raise most food by a rotation of plants belonging to the most different orders: nature follows what may be called a simultaneous rotation. Most of the animals and plants which live close round any small piece of ground could live on it (supposing its nature not to be in any way peculiar) and may be said to be striving to the utmost to live there; but it is seen that where they come into the closest competition the advantages of diversification of structure, with the accompanying differences of habit and constitution, determine that the inhabitants, which thus jostle each other most closely, shall, as a general rule, belong to what we call different genera and orders.

The same principle is seen in the naturalization of plants through man's agency in foreign lands. . . .

Summary of Chapter

If under changing conditions of life organic beings present individual differences in almost every part of their structure, and this cannot be disputed; if there be, owing to their geometrical rate of increase, a severe struggle for life at some age, season, or year, and this certainly cannot be disputed; then, considering the infinite complexity of the relations of all organic beings to each other and to their conditions of life, causing an infinite diversity in structure, constitution, and habits, to be advantageous to them, it would be a most extraordinary fact if no variations had ever occurred useful to each being's own welfare, in the same manner as so many variations have occurred useful to man. But if variations useful to any organic being ever do occur, assuredly individuals thus characterized will have the best chance of being preserved in the struggle for life; and from the strong principle of inheritance, these will tend to produce offspring similarly characterized. This principle of preservation, or the survival of the fittest, I have called natural selection. It leads to the improvement of each creature in relation to its organic and inorganic conditions of life; and consequently, in most cases, to what must be regarded as an advance in organization. Nevertheless, low and simple forms will long endure if well fitted for their simple conditions of life.

Natural selection, on the principle of qualities being inherited at corresponding ages, can modify the egg, seed, or young, as easily as the adult. Among many animals sexual selection will have given its aid to ordinary selection by assuring to the most vigorous and best adapted males the greatest number of offspring. Sexual selection will also give characters useful to the males alone, in their struggles or rivalry with other males; and these characters will be transmitted to one sex or to both sexes, according to the form of inheritance which prevails.

Whether natural selection has really thus acted in adapting the various forms of life to their several conditions and stations must be judged by the general tenor and balance of evidence given in the following chapters. But we have already seen how it entails extinction; and how largely extinction has acted in the world's history, geology plainly declares. Natural selection also leads to divergence of character; for the more organic beings diverge in structure, habits, and constitution, by so much the more can a large number be supported on the area—of which we see proof by looking to the inhabitants of any small spot, and to the productions naturalized in foreign lands. Therefore during the modification of the descendants of any one species, and during the incessant struggle of all species to increase in numbers, the more diversified the descendants become, the better will be their chance of success in the battle for life. Thus the small differences distinguishing varieties of the same species steadily tend to increase, till they equal the greater differences between species of the same genus, or even of distinct genera.

We have seen that it is the common, the widely diffused and widely ranging species, belonging to the larger genera within each class, which vary most; and these tend to transmit to their modified offspring that superiority which now makes them dominant in their own countries. Natural selection, as has just been remarked, leads to divergence of character and to much extinction of the less improved and intermediate forms of life. On these principles the nature of the affinities, and the generally well-defined distinctions between the innumerable organic beings in each class throughout the world, may be explained. It is a truly wonderful fact—the wonder of which we are apt to overlook from familiarity—that all animals and all plants throughout all time and space should be related to each other in groups, subordinate to groups, in the manner which we everywhere behold—namely, varieties of the same species most closely related, species of the same genus less closely and unequally related, forming sections and subgenera, species of distinct genera much less closely related, and genera related in different degrees, forming subfamilies, families, orders, subclasses, and classes. The several subordinate groups in any class cannot be ranked in a single file, but seem clustered round points, and these round other points, and so on in almost endless cycles. If species had been independently created, no explanation would have been possible of this kind of classification; but it is explained through inheritance and the complex action of natural selection, entailing extinction and divergence of character, as we have seen illustrated. . . .

The affinities of all the beings of the same class have sometimes been represented by a great tree. I believe this simile largely speaks the truth. The green and budding twigs may represent existing species; and those produced during former years may represent the long succession of extinct species. At each period of growth all the growing twigs have tried to branch out on all sides and to overtop and kill the surrounding twigs and branches, in the same manner as species and groups of species have at all times overmastered other species in the great battle for life. The limbs divided into great branches, and these into lesser and lesser branches, were themselves once, when the tree was young, budding twigs, and this connection of the former and present buds by ramifying branches may well represent the classification of all extinct and living species in groups subordinate to groups. Of the many twigs which flourished when the tree was a mere bush, only two or three, now grown into great branches, yet survive and bear the other branches; so with the species which lived during long-past geological periods: very few have left living and modified descendants. From the first growth of the tree, many a limb and branch has decayed and dropped off; and these fallen branches of various sizes may represent those whole orders, families, and genera which have now no living representatives and which are known to us only in a fossil state. As we here and there see a thin straggling branch springing from a fork low down in a tree, and which by some chance has been favored and is still alive on its summit, so we occasionally see an animal like the ornithorhynchus or lepidosiren, which in some small degree connects by its affinities two large branches of life, and which has apparently been saved from fatal competition by having inhabited a protected station. As buds give rise by growth to fresh buds, and these, if vigorous, branch out and overtop on all sides many a feebler branch, so by generation I believe it has been with the great Tree of Life, which fills with its dead and broken branches the crust of the earth and covers the surface with its ever-branching and beautiful ramifications.

"THE DESCENT OF MAN"

CHAPTER I

THE EVIDENCE OF THE DESCENT OF MAN FROM SOME LOWER FORM

HE WHO WISHES to decide whether man is the modified descendant of some pre-existing form would probably first inquire whether man varies, however slightly, in bodily structure and in mental faculties; and if so, whether the variations are transmitted to his offspring in accordance with the laws which prevail with the lower animals. Again, are the variations the result, as far as our ignorance permits us to judge, of the same general causes, and are they governed by the same general laws, as in the case of other organisms; for instance, by correlation, the inherited effects of use and disuse, et cetera? Is man subject to similar malconformations, the result of arrested development, of reduplication of parts, et cetera, and does he display in any of his anomalies reversion to some former and ancient type of structure? It might also naturally be inquired whether man, like so many other animals, has given rise to varieties and sub-races, differing but slightly from each other, or to races differing so much that they must be classed as doubtful species? How are such races distributed over the world; and how, when crossed, do they react on each other in the first and succeeding generations? And so with many other points.

The inquirer would next come to the important point, whether man tends to increase at so rapid a rate as to lead to occasional severe struggles for existence; and consequently to beneficial variations, whether in body or mind, being preserved, and injurious ones eliminated. Do the races or species of men, whichever term may be applied, encroach on and replace one another, so that some finally become extinct? We shall see that all these questions, as indeed is obvious in respect to most of them, must be answered in the affirmative, in the same manner as with the lower animals. But the several considerations just referred to may be conveniently deferred for a time: and we will first see how far the bodily structure of man shows traces, more or less plain, of his descent from some lower form.

The Bodily Structure of Man

It is notorious that man is constructed on the same general type or model as other mammals. All the bones in his skeleton can be compared with corresponding bones in a monkey, bat, or seal. So it is with his muscles, nerves, blood vessels, and internal viscera. The brain, the most important of all the organs, follows the same law, as shown by Huxley and other anatomists. Bischoff, who is a hostile witness, admits that every chief fissure and fold in the brain of man has its analogy in that of the orang; but he adds that at no period of development do their brains perfectly agree; nor could perfect agreement be expected, for otherwise their mental powers would have been the same. . . . But it would be superfluous here to give further details on the correspondence between man and the higher mammals in the structure of the brain and all other parts of the body.

It may, however, be worth while to specify a few points, not directly or obviously connected with structure, by which this correspondence or relationship is well shown.

Man is liable to receive from the lower animals, and to communicate to them, certain diseases, as hydrophobia, variola, the glanders, syphilis, cholera, herpes, et cetera; and this fact proves the close similarity of their tissues and blood, both in minute structure and composition, far more plainly than does their comparison under the best microscope, or by the aid of the best chemical analysis. Monkeys are liable to many of the same non-contagious diseases as we are; thus Rengger, who carefully observed for a long time the *Cebus azaroe* in its native land, found it liable to catarrh, with the usual symptoms, and which, when often recurrent, led to consumption. These monkeys suffered also from apoplexy, inflammation of the bowels, and cataract in the eye. The younger ones when shedding their milk teeth often died from fever. Medicines produced the same effect on them as on us. Many kinds of monkeys have a strong taste for tea, coffee, and spirituous liquors; they will also, as I have myself seen, smoke tobacco with pleasure. Brehm asserts that the natives of northeastern Africa catch the wild baboons by exposing vessels with strong beer, by which they are made drunk. He has seen some of these animals, which he kept in confinement, in this state; and he gives a laughable account of their behavior and strange grimaces. On the following morning they were very cross and dismal; they held their aching heads with both hands and wore a most pitiable expression; when beer or wine was offered them, they turned away with disgust, but relished the juice of lemons. An American monkey, an *Ateles,* after getting drunk on brandy, would never touch it again, and thus was wiser than many men. These trifling facts prove how similar the nerves of taste must be in monkeys and man, and how similarly their whole nervous system is affected.

Man is infested with internal parasites, sometimes causing fatal effects; and is plagued by external parasites, all of which belong to the same genera or families as those infesting other mammals, and in the case of scabies to the same species. Man is subject, like other mammals, birds, and even insects, to that mysterious law which causes certain normal processes, such as gestation, as well as the maturation and duration of various diseases, to follow lunar periods. His wounds are repaired by the same process of healing; and the stumps left after the amputation of his limbs, especially during an early embryonic period, occasionally possess some power of regeneration, as in the lowest animals.

The whole process of that most important function, the reproduction of the species, is strikingly the same in all mammals, from the first act of courtship by the male to the birth and nurturing of the young. Monkeys are born in almost as helpless a condition as our own infants; and in certain genera the young differ fully as much in appearance from the adults as do our children from their full-grown parents. It has been urged by some writers, as an important distinction, that with man the young arrive at maturity at a much later age than with any other animal; but if we look to the races of mankind which inhabit tropical countries the difference is not great, for the orang is believed not to be adult till the age of from ten to fifteen years. Man differs from woman in size, bodily strength, hairiness, et cetera, as well as in mind, in the same manner as do the two sexes of many mammals. So that the correspondence in general structure, in the minute structure of the tissues, in chemical composition and in constitution, between man and the higher animals, especially the anthropomorphous apes, is extremely close.

Embryonic Development

Man is developed from an ovule, about $\frac{1}{125}$ of an inch in diameter, which differs in no respect from the ovules of other animals. The embryo itself at a very early period can hardly be distinguished from that of other members of the vertebrate kingdom. At this period the arteries run in archlike branches, as if to carry the blood to branchiae which are not present in the higher vertebrata, though the slits on the sides of the neck still remain, marking their former position. At a somewhat later period, when the extremities are developed, "the feet of lizards and mammals," as the illustrious Von Baer remarks, "the wings and feet of birds, no less than the hands and feet of man, all arise from the same fundamental form." It is, says Professor Huxley, "quite in the later stages of development that the young human being presents marked differences from the young ape, while the latter departs as much from the dog in its developments as the man does. Startling as this last assertion may appear to be, it is demonstrably true." . . .

But it would be superfluous fully to recapitulate the line of argument given in detail in my "Origin of Species." The homological construction of the whole frame in the members of the same class is intelligible, if we admit their descent from a common progenitor, together with their subsequent adaptation to diversified conditions. On any other view the similarity of pattern between the hand of a man or monkey, the foot of a horse, the flipper of a seal, the wing of a bat, et cetera, is utterly inexplicable. It is no scientific explanation to assert that they have all been formed on the same ideal plan. With respect to development, we can clearly understand, on the principle of variation supervening at a rather late embryonic period, and being inherited at a corresponding period, how it is that the embryos of wonderfully different forms should still retain, more or less perfectly, the structure of their common progenitor. No other explanation has ever been given of the marvelous fact that the embryos of a man, dog, seal, bat, reptile, et cetera, can at first hardly be distinguished from each other. In order to understand the existence of rudimentary organs we have only to suppose that a former progenitor possessed the parts in question in a perfect state, and that under changed habits of life they became greatly reduced, either from simple disuse or through the natural selection of those individuals which were least encumbered with a superfluous part, aided by the other means previously indicated.

Thus we can understand how it has come to pass that man and all other vertebrate animals have been constructed on the same general model, why they pass through the same early stages of development, and why they retain certain rudiments in common. Consequently we ought frankly to admit their community of descent; to take any other view is to admit that our own structure, and that of all the animals around us, is a mere snare laid to entrap our judgment. This conclusion is greatly strengthened if we look to the members of the whole animal series and consider the evidence derived from their affinities or classification, their geographical distribution and geological succession. It is only our natural prejudice, and that arrogance which made our forefathers declare that they were descended from demigods, which leads us to demur to this conclusion. But the time will before long come when it will be thought wonderful that naturalists, who were well acquainted with the comparative structure and development of man, and other mammals, should have believed that each was the work of a separate act of creation. . . .

General Summary

Man scans with scrupulous care the character and pedigree of his horses, cattle, and dogs before he matches them; but when he comes to his own marriage he rarely, or never, takes any such care. He is impelled by nearly the same motives as the lower animals, when they are left to their own free choice, though he is in so far superior to them that he highly values mental charms and virtues. On the other hand he is strongly attracted by mere wealth or rank. Yet he might by selection do something not only for the bodily constitution and frame of his offspring, but for their intellectual and moral qualities. Both sexes ought to refrain from marriage if they are in any marked degree inferior in body or mind; but such hopes are utopian and will never be even partially realized until the laws of inheritance are thoroughly known. Everyone does good service who aids toward this end. When the principles of breeding and inheritance are better understood, we shall not hear ignorant members of our legislature rejecting with scorn a plan for ascertaining whether or not consanguineous marriages are injurious to man.

The advancement of the welfare of mankind is a most intricate problem: all ought to refrain from marriage who cannot avoid abject poverty for their children; for poverty is not only a great evil but tends to its own increase by leading to recklessness in marriage. On the other hand, as Mr. Galton has remarked, if the prudent avoid marriage, while the reckless marry, the inferior members tend to supplant the better members of society. Man, like every other animal, has no doubt advanced to his present high condition through a struggle for existence consequent on his rapid multiplication; and if he is to advance still higher, it is to be feared that he must remain subject to a severe struggle. Otherwise he would sink into indolence, and the more gifted men would not be more successful in the battle of life than the less gifted. Hence our natural rate of increase, though leading to many and obvious evils, must not be greatly diminished by any means. There should be open competition for all men; and the most able should not be prevented by laws or customs from succeeding best and rearing the largest number of offspring. Important as the struggle for existence has been and even still is, yet as far as the highest part of man's nature is concerned there are other agencies more important. For the moral qualities are advanced, either directly or indirectly, much more through the effects of habit, the reasoning powers, instruction, religion, et cetera, than through natural selection; though to this latter agency may be safely attributed the social instincts which afforded the basis for the development of the moral sense.

The main conclusion arrived at in this work, namely, that man is descended from some lowly organized form, will, I regret to think, be highly distasteful to many. But there can hardly be a doubt that we are descended from barbarians. The astonishment which I felt on first seeing a party of Fuegians on a wild and broken shore will never be forgotten by me, for the reflection at once rushed into my mind: Such were our ancestors. These men were absolutely naked and bedaubed with paint, their long hair was tangled, their mouths frothed with excitement, and their expression was wild, startled, and distrustful. They possessed hardly any arts, and like wild animals lived on what they could catch; they had no government, and were merciless to everyone not of their own small tribe. He who has seen a savage in his native land will not feel much shame if forced to acknowledge that the blood of some more humble creature flows in his veins. For my own part I would as soon be descended from that heroic little monkey who braved his dreaded enemy in order to save the life of his keeper, or from that old baboon who, descending from the mountains, carried away in triumph his young comrade from a crowd of astonished dogs, as from a savage who delights to torture his enemies, offers up bloody sacrifices, practices infanticide without remorse, treats his wives like slaves, knows no decency, and is haunted by the grossest superstitions.

Man may be excused for feeling some pride at having risen, though not through his own exertions, to the very summit of the organic scale; and the fact of his having thus risen, instead of having been aboriginally placed there, may give him hope for a still higher destiny in the distant future. But we are not here concerned with hopes or fears, only with the truth as far as our reason permits us to discover it; and I have given the evidence to the best of my ability. We must, however, acknowledge, as it seems to me, that man with all his noble qualities, with sympathy which feels for the most debased, with benevolence which extends not only to other men but to the humblest living creature, with his godlike intellect which has penetrated into the movements and constitution of the solar system—with all these exalted powers—man still bears in his bodily frame the indelible stamp of his lowly origin.

GALÁPAGOS ARCHIPELAGO

(FROM "THE VOYAGE OF THE BEAGLE")

SEPTEMBER 15. This archipelago consists of ten principal islands, of which five exceed the others in size. They are situated under the equator and between five and six hundred miles westward of the coast of America. They are all formed of volcanic rocks; a few fragments of granite curiously glazed and altered by the heat can hardly be considered as an exception. Some of the craters, surmounting the larger islands, are of immense size, and they rise to a height of between three and four thousand feet. Their flanks are studded by innumerable smaller orifices. I scarcely hesitate to affirm that there must be in the whole archipelago at least two thousand craters. These consist either of lava and scoriae, or of finely stratified, sandstonelike tuff. Most of the latter are beautifully symmetrical; they owe their origin to eruptions of volcanic mud without any lava. It is a remarkable circumstance that every one of the twenty-eight tuff craters which were examined had their southern sides either much lower than the other sides or quite broken down and removed. As all these craters have apparently been formed when standing in the sea, and as the waves from the trade wind and the swell from the open Pacific here unite their forces on the southern coasts of all the islands, this singular uniformity in the broken state of the craters, composed of the soft and yielding tuff, is easily explained.

Considering that these islands are placed directly under the equator, the climate is far from being excessively hot; this seems chiefly caused by the singularly low temperature of the surrounding water, brought here by the great southern polar current. Excepting during one short season very little rain falls, and even then it is irregular; but the clouds generally hang low. Hence, while the lower parts of the island are very sterile, the upper parts, at a height of a thousand feet and upward, possess a damp climate and a tolerably luxuriant vegetation. This is especially the case on the windward sides of the islands, which first receive and condense the moisture from the atmosphere. . . .

The natural history of these islands is eminently curious and well deserves attention. Most of the organic productions are aboriginal creations, found nowhere else; there is even a difference between the inhabitants of the different islands; yet all show a marked relationship with those of America, though separated from that continent by an open space of ocean, between five and six hundred miles in width. The archipelago is a little world within itself, or rather a satellite attached to America, whence it has derived a few stray colonists and has received the general character of its indigenous productions. Considering the small size of these islands, we feel the more astonished at the number of their aboriginal beings and at their confined range. Seeing every height crowned with its crater, and the boundaries of most of the lava streams still distinct, we are led to believe that within a period, geologically recent, the unbroken ocean was here spread out. Hence, both in space and time, we seem to be brought somewhat near to that great fact—that mystery of mysteries—the first appearance of new beings on this earth.

Of terrestrial mammals, there is only one which must be considered as indigenous, namely, a mouse (*Mus galápagoensis*), and this is confined, as far as I could ascertain, to Chatham Island, the most easterly island of the group. It belongs, as I am informed by Mr. Waterhouse, to a division of the family of mice characteristic of America. At James Island there is a rat sufficiently distinct from the common kind to have been named and described by Mr. Waterhouse; but as it belongs to the Old World division of the family, and as this island has been frequented by ships for the last hundred and fifty years, I can hardly doubt that this rat is merely a variety produced by the new and peculiar climate, food, and soil to which it has been subjected. Although no one has a right to speculate without distinct facts, yet even with respect to the Chatham Island mouse it should be borne in mind that it may possibly be an American species imported here; for I have seen, in a most unfrequented part of the pampas, a native mouse living in the roof of a newly built hovel, and therefore its transportation in a vessel is not improbable: analogous facts have been observed by Dr. Richardson in North America.

Of land birds I obtained twenty-six kinds, all peculiar to the group and found nowhere else, with the exception of one larklike finch from North America (*Dolichonyx oryzivorus*), which ranges on that continent as far north as 54°, and generally frequents marshes. The other twenty-five birds consist, firstly, of a hawk, curiously intermediate in structure between a buzzard and the American group of carrion-feeding *Polybori;* and with these latter birds it agrees most closely in every habit and even tone of voice. Secondly, there are two owls, representing the short-eared and white barn owls of Europe. Thirdly, a wren, three tyrant flycatchers (two of them species of *Pyrocephalus,* one or both of which would be ranked by some ornithologists as only varieties), and a dove—all analogous to, but distinct from, American species. Fourthly, a swallow, which though differing from the *Progne purpurea* of both Americas only in being rather duller colored, smaller, and slenderer, is considered by Mr. Gould as specifically distinct. Fifthly, there are three species of mocking thrush—a form highly characteristic of America. The remaining land birds form a most singular group of finches, related to each other in the structure of their beaks, short tails, form of body, and plumage; there are thirteen species, which Mr. Gould has divided into four subgroups. All these species are peculiar to this archipelago; and so is the whole group, with the exception of one species of the subgroup *Cactornis,* lately brought from Bow Island, in the Low Archipelago. Of *Cactornis,* the two species may be often seen climbing about the flowers of the great cactus trees; but all the other species of this group of finches, mingled together in flocks, feed on the dry and sterile ground of the lower districts. The males of all, or certainly of the greater number, are jet black; and the females (with perhaps one or two exceptions) are brown. The most curious fact is the perfect gradation in the size of the beaks in the different species of *Geospiza,* from one as large as that of a hawfinch to that of a chaffinch, and (if Mr. Gould is right in including his subgroup, *Certhidea,* in the main group), even to that of a warbler. . . . Seeing this gradation and diversity of structure in one small, intimately related group of birds, one might really fancy that from an original paucity of birds in this archipelago one species had been taken and modified for different ends. In a like manner it might be fancied that a bird, originally a buzzard, had been induced here to undertake the office of the carrion-feeding *Polybori* of the American continent.

Of waders and water birds I was able to get only eleven kinds, and of these only three (including a rail confined to the damp summits of the islands) are new species. Considering the wandering habits of the gulls, I was surprised to find that the species inhabiting these islands is peculiar but allied to one from the southern parts of South America. The far greater peculiarity of the land birds, namely, twenty-five out of twenty-six being new species or at least new races, compared with the waders and web-footed birds, is in accordance with the greater range which these latter orders have in all parts of the world. We shall hereafter see this law of aquatic forms, whether marine or fresh-water, being less peculiar at any given point of the earth's surface than the terrestrial forms of the same classes, strikingly illustrated in the shells, and in a lesser degree in the insects of this archipelago.

Two of the waders are rather smaller than the same species brought from other places; the swallow is also smaller, though it is doubtful whether or not it is distinct from its analogue. The two owls, the two tyrant flycatchers (*Pyrocephalus*), and the dove, are also smaller than the analogous but distinct species, to which they are most nearly related; on the other hand, the gull is rather larger. The two owls, the swallow, all three species of mocking thrush, the dove in its separate colors though not in its whole plumage, the *Totanus,* and the gull are likewise duskier colored than their analogous species; and in the case of the mocking thrush and *Totanus,* than any other species of the two genera. With the exception of a wren with a fine yellow breast, and of a tyrant flycatcher with a scarlet tuft and breast, none of the birds are brilliantly colored, as might have been expected in an equatorial district. Hence it would appear probable that the same causes which here make the immigrants of some species smaller make most of the peculiar Galápageian species also smaller, as well as very generally duskier colored. All the plants have a wretched, weedy appearance, and I did not see one beautiful flower. The insects, again, are small-sized and dull-colored, and, as Mr. Waterhouse informs me, there is nothing in their general appearance which would have led him to imagine that they had come from under the equator. The birds, plants, and insects have a desert character and are not more brilliantly colored than those from southern Patagonia; we may, therefore, conclude that the usual gaudy coloring of the intertropical productions is not related either to the heat or light of those zones, but to some other cause, perhaps to the conditions of existence being generally favorable to life.

We will now turn to the order of reptiles, which gives the most striking character to the zoology of these islands. The species are not numerous, but the numbers of individuals of each species are extraordinarily great. There is one small lizard belonging to a South American genus, and two species (and probably more) of the *Amblyrhynchus*—a genus confined to the Galápagos Islands. . . .

The nature of this lizard's food, as well as the structure of its tail and feet, and the fact of its having been seen voluntarily swimming out at sea, absolutely prove its aquatic habits; yet there is in this respect one strange anomaly, namely, that when frightened it will not enter the water. Hence it is easy to drive these lizards down to any little point overhanging the sea, where they will sooner allow a person to catch hold of their tails than jump into the water. They do not seem to have any notion of biting; but when much frightened they squirt a drop of fluid from each nostril. I threw one several times as far as I could, into a deep pool left by the retiring tide; but it invariably returned in a direct line to the spot where I stood. It swam near the bottom, with a very graceful and rapid movement, and occasionally aided itself over the uneven ground with its feet. As soon as it arrived near the edge, but still being underwater, it tried to conceal itself in the tufts of seaweed, or it entered some crevice. As soon as it thought the danger was past, it crawled out on the dry rocks and shuffled away as quickly as it could. I several times caught this same lizard by driving it down to a point, and though possessed of such perfect powers of diving and swimming, nothing would induce it to enter the water; and as often as I threw it in it returned in the manner above described. Perhaps this singular piece of apparent stupidity may be accounted for by the circumstance that this reptile has no enemy whatever on shore, whereas at sea it must often fall a prey to the numerous sharks. Hence, probably, urged by a fixed and hereditary instinct that the shore is its place of safety, whatever the emergency may be, it there takes refuge. . . .

If we except the eighteen marine, the one fresh-water, and one land shell, which have apparently come here as colonists from the central islands of the Pacific, and likewise the one distinct Pacific species of the Galápageian group of finches, we see that this archipelago, though standing in the Pacific Ocean, is zoologically part of America.

If this character were owing merely to immigrants from America, there would be little remarkable in it; but we see that a vast majority of all the land animals and more than half of the flowering plants are aboriginal productions. It was most striking to be surrounded by new birds, new reptiles, new shells, new insects, new plants, and yet by innumerable trifling details of structure and even by the tones of voice and plumage of the birds to have the temperate plains of Patagonia or the hot dry deserts of northern Chile vividly brought before my eyes. Why, on these small points of land, which within a late geological period must have been covered by the ocean, which are formed of basaltic lava, and therefore differ in geological character from the American continent, and which are placed under a peculiar climate—why were their aboriginal inhabitants, associated, I may add, in different proportions both in kind and number from those on the continent, and therefore acting on each other in a different manner—why were they created on American types of organization? It is probable that the islands of the Cape de Verd group resemble, in all their physical conditions, far more closely the Galápagos Islands than these latter physically resemble the coast of America; yet the aboriginal inhabitants of the two groups are totally unlike; those of the Cape de Verd Islands bearing the impress of Africa, as the inhabitants of the Galápagos Archipelago are stamped with that of America.

I have not as yet noticed by far the most remarkable feature in the natural history of this archipelago; it is that the different islands to a considerable extent are inhabited by a different set of beings. My attention was first called to this fact by the Vice-Governor, Mr. Lawson, declaring that the tortoises differed from the different islands, and that he could with certainty tell from which island any one was brought. I did not for some time pay sufficient attention to this statement, and I had already partially mingled together the collections from two of the islands. I never dreamed that islands, about fifty or sixty miles apart, and most of them in sight of each other, formed of precisely the same rocks, placed under a quite similar climate, rising to a nearly equal height, would have been differently tenanted; but we shall soon see that this is the case. It is the fate of most voyagers no sooner to discover what is most interesting in any locality than they are hurried from it; but I ought, perhaps, to be thankful that I obtained sufficient material to establish this most remarkable fact in the distribution of organic beings. . . .

I will conclude my description of the natural history of these islands by giving an account of the extreme tameness of the birds.

This disposition is common to all the terrestrial species; namely, to the mocking thrushes, the finches, wrens, tyrant flycatchers, the dove, and carrion buzzard. All of them often approached sufficiently near to be killed with a switch, and sometimes, as I myself tried, with a cap or hat. A gun is here almost superfluous; for with the muzzle I pushed a hawk off the branch of a tree. One day, while lying down, a mocking thrush alighted on the edge of a pitcher, made of the shell of a tortoise, which I held in my hand, and began very quietly to sip the water; it allowed me to lift it from the ground while seated on the vessel; I often tried, and very nearly succeeded, in catching these birds by their legs. Formerly the birds appear to have been even tamer than at present. Cowley (in the year 1684) says that the "turtle doves were so tame that they would often alight upon our hats and arms, so as that we could take them alive: they not fearing man, until such time as some of our company did fire at them, whereby they were rendered more shy." Dampier also, in the same year, says that a man in a morning's walk might kill six or seven dozen of these doves. At present, although certainly very tame, they do not alight on people's arms, nor do they suffer themselves to be killed in such large numbers. It is surprising that they have not become wilder; for these islands during the last hundred and fifty years have been frequently visited by buccaneers and whalers; and the sailors, wandering through the woods in search of tortoises, always take cruel delight in knocking down the little birds.

These birds, although now still more persecuted, do not readily become wild: in Charles Island, which had then been colonized about six years, I saw a boy sitting by a well with a switch in his hand, with which he killed the doves and finches as they came to drink. He had already procured a little heap of them for his dinner; and he said that he had constantly been in the habit of waiting by this well for the same purpose. It would appear that the birds of this archipelago, not having as yet learned that man is a more dangerous animal than the tortoise or the *Amblyrhynchus,* disregard him, in the same manner as in England shy birds, such as magpies, disregard the cows and horses grazing in our fields. . . .

In regard to the wildness of birds toward man, there is no way of accounting for it, except as an inherited habit; comparatively few young birds, in any one year, have been injured by man in England, yet almost all, even nestlings, are afraid of him; many individuals, on the other hand, both at the Galápagos and at the Falklands, have been pursued and injured by man, but yet have not learned a salutary dread of him. We may infer from these facts what havoc the introduction of any new beast of prey must cause in a country before the instincts of the indigenous inhabitants have become adapted to the stranger's craft or power.

The Paper Which Spurred Darwin's "Origin of Species"

ALFRED RUSSEL WALLACE (1823-1913)

THIS IS the paper which finally spurred Darwin to write and publish "The Origin of Species." It came to Darwin's hands by post from Ternate, in the Malay Archipelago, where it had been written in February 1858 by a young naturalist, Alfred Russel Wallace, then exploring—as Darwin had done at Galápagos—the distribution of the fauna and flora of the archipelago. Wallace confesses that he drew his inspiration for the central idea, quite independently, from the same source as Darwin: namely, Thomas Malthus. This paper was presented to the Linnaean Society by Darwin's friends, Lyell and Joseph Hooker, as an exhibit appended to a famous letter fairly stating the claims of each man to priority in the discovery.

Though he frequently wrote science like a lawyer briefing an argument—and he was a prolific writer—Wallace was originally trained as a surveyor and architect. His interest in natural history drew him on many collecting trips, first in the Amazon region, later in Malay and Australia, where "Wallace's (imaginary) line" still separates species of animals distinguished by Australian or Asiatic origin. Strangely, for a man of science, he opposed vaccination!

Wallace bore no ill will toward Darwin. In 1870 he wrote: "I have felt all my life, and I still feel, the most sincere satisfaction that Mr. Darwin had been at work long before me, and that it was not left for me to write 'The Origin of Species.' I have long since measured my own strength, and know well that it would be quite unequal to that task. Far abler men than myself may confess that they have not that untiring patience in accumulating and that wonderful skill in using large masses of facts of the most varied kind, that wide and accurate physiological knowledge, that acuteness in devising and skill in carrying out experiments, and that admirable style of composition, at once clear, persuasive, and judicial—qualities which in their harmonious combination mark out Mr. Darwin as the man, perhaps of all men now living, best fitted for the great work he has undertaken and accomplished."

English was the language of Wallace's 7500 word paper entitled, "On the Tendency of Varieties to Depart Indefinitely from the Original Type," and published in the "Journal of the Proceedings of the Linnaean Society" for August 1858.

"ON THE TENDENCY OF VARIETIES TO DEPART INDEFINITELY FROM THE ORIGINAL TYPE"

ONE OF THE STRONGEST arguments which have been adduced to prove the original and permanent distinctness of species is that varieties produced in a state of domesticity are more or less unstable and often have a tendency, if left to themselves, to return to the normal form of the parent species; and this instability is considered to be a distinctive peculiarity of all varieties, even of those occurring among wild animals in a state of nature, and to constitute a provision for preserving unchanged the originally created distinct species. . . .

But it is the object of the present paper to show that this assumption is altogether false, that there is a general principle in nature which will cause many varieties to survive the parent species, and to give rise to successive variations departing further and further from the original type, and which also produces, in domesticated animals, the tendency of varieties to return to the parent form.

THE STRUGGLE FOR EXISTENCE

The life of wild animals is a struggle for existence. The full exertion of all their faculties and all their energies is required to preserve their own existence and provide for that of their infant offspring. The possibility of procuring food during the least favorable seasons and of escaping the attacks of their most dangerous enemies are the primary conditions which determine the existence both of individuals and of entire species. These conditions will also determine the population of a species; and by a careful consideration of all the circumstances we may be enabled to comprehend, and in some degree to explain, what at first sight appears so inexplicable—the excessive abundance of some species, while others closely allied to them are very rare. . . .

Wildcats are prolific and have few enemies; why, then, are they never as abundant as rabbits? The only intelligible answer is that their supply of food is more precarious. It appears evident, therefore, that so long as a country remains physically unchanged the numbers of its animal population cannot materially increase. If one species does so, some others requiring the same kind of food must diminish in proportion. The numbers that die annually must be immense; and as the individual existence of each animal depends upon itself, those that die must be the weakest—the very young, the aged, and the diseased—while those that prolong their existence can only be the most perfect in health and vigor —those who are best able to obtain food regularly and avoid their numerous enemies. It is, as we commenced by remarking, "a struggle for existence," in which the weakest and least perfectly organized must always succumb. . . .

If now we have succeeded in establishing these two points—first, that the animal population of a country is generally stationary, being kept down by a periodical deficiency of food and other checks; and, second, that the comparative abundance or scarcity of the individuals of the several species is entirely due to their organization and resulting habits, which, rendering it more difficult to procure a regular supply of food and to provide for their personal safety in some cases than in others, can only be balanced by a difference in the population which have to exist in a given area—we shall be in a condition to proceed to the consideration of varieties, to which the preceding remarks have a direct and very important application.

USEFUL VARIATIONS WILL TEND TO INCREASE; USELESS OR HURTFUL VARIATIONS TO DIMINISH

Most or perhaps all the variations from the typical form of a species must have some definite effect, however slight, on the habits or capacities of the individuals. Even a change of color might, by rendering them more or less distinguishable, affect their safety; a greater or less development of hair might modify their habits. More important changes, such as an increase in the power or dimensions of the limbs or any of the external organs, would more or less affect their mode of procuring food or the range of country which they could inhabit. It is also evident that most changes would affect, either favorably or adversely, the powers of prolonging existence. An antelope with shorter or weaker legs must necessarily suffer more from the attacks of the feline carnivora; the passenger pigeon with less powerful wings would sooner or later be affected in its powers of procuring a regular supply of food; and in both cases the result must necessarily be a diminution of the population of the modified species.

If, on the other hand, any species should produce a variety having slightly increased powers of preserving existence, that variety must inevitably in time acquire a superiority in numbers. These results must follow as surely as old age, intemperance, or scarcity of food produce an increased mortality. In both cases there may be many individual exceptions; but on the average the rule will invariably be found to hold good. All varieties will therefore fall into two classes—those which under the same conditions would never reach the population of the parent species, and those which would in time obtain and keep a numerical superiority. Now let some alteration of physical conditions occur in the district—a long period of drought, a destruction of vegetation by locusts, the irruption of some new carnivorous animal seeking "pastures new"— any change, in fact, tending to render existence more difficult to the species in question, and tasking its utmost powers to avoid complete extermination; it is evident that, of all the individuals composing the species, those forming the least numerous and most feebly organized variety would suffer first, and, were the pressure severe, must soon become extinct. The same causes continuing in action, the parent species would next suffer, would gradually diminish in numbers, and with a recurrence of similar unfavorable conditions might also become extinct. The superior variety would then alone remain, and on a return to favorable circumstances would rapidly increase in numbers and occupy the place of the extinct species and variety.

Superior Varieties Will Ultimately Extirpate the Original Species

The variety would now have replaced the species, of which it would be a more perfectly developed and more highly organized form. It would be in all respects better adapted to secure its safety and to prolong its individual existence and that of the race. Such a variety could not return to the original form; for that form is an inferior one and could never compete with it for existence. Granted, therefore, a "tendency" to reproduce the original type of the species, still the variety must ever remain preponderant in numbers, and under adverse physical conditions again alone survive. But this new, improved, and populous race might itself in course of time give rise to new varieties, exhibiting several diverging modifications of form, any of which, tending to increase the facilities for preserving existence, must, by the same general law, in their turn become predominant. Here, then, we have progression and continued divergence deduced from the general laws which regulate the existence of animals in a state of nature and from the undisputed fact that varieties do frequently occur. . . .

Lamarck's Hypothesis Very Different from That Now Advanced

The hypothesis of Lamarck—that progressive changes in species have been produced by the attempts of animals to increase the development of their own organs and thus modify their structure and habits—has been repeatedly and easily refuted by all writers on the subject of varieties and species, and it seems to have been considered that when this was done the whole question has been finally settled; but the view here developed renders such hypothesis quite unnecessary, by showing that similar results must be produced by the action of principles constantly at work in nature. The powerful retractile talons of the falcon and the cat tribes have not been produced or increased by the volition of those animals; but among the different varieties which occurred in the earlier and less highly organized forms of these groups, those always survived longest which had the greatest facilities for seizing their prey. Neither did the giraffe acquire its long neck by desiring to reach the foliage of the more lofty shrubs and constantly stretching its neck for the purpose, but because any varieties which occurred among its antetypes with a longer neck than usual at once secured a fresh range of pasture over the same ground as their shorter-necked companions, and on the first scarcity of food were thereby enabled to outlive them. Even the peculiar colors of many animals, more especially of insects, so closely resembling the soil or leaves or bark on which they habitually reside, are explained on the same principle; for though in the course of ages varieties of many tints may have occurred, yet those races having colors best adapted to concealment from their enemies would inevitably survive the longest.

"Darwin's Bulldog"

THOMAS HENRY HUXLEY (1825-95)

THE AVERAGE MAN is quite capable of understanding even the most elaborate concepts of science—and none is more comprehensive than Darwin's theory of organic evolution—if only the scientist who discovers and talks about them will put these ideas in the language of the common man. A persistent practitioner of this policy was one of the clearest and most gifted scientific writers of all time, the English biologist, Thomas Henry Huxley, "Darwin's bulldog;" sideburn-bejowled champion of the theory of evolution. Out of the history of a most common object, a piece of chalk, Huxley was able to expound the highlights of Darwin's theory so that anyone could understand and appreciate it. The essay quoted here endures as one of the great classics of scientific literature.

Trained as a physician, Huxley entered the Royal Navy medical service and served for five years as assistant surgeon on H.M.S. *Rattlesnake*. He returned to London to become the foremost popular scientific lecturer in England; Hunterian professor at the Royal College of Surgeons; Fullerian professor at the Royal Institution; and eventually (1883-85) president of the Royal Society.

English was the language in which Huxley demonstrated beyond cavil that the "literature of power" and the "literature of knowledge"—De Quincey's phrases—could be truly united in the literature of science.

"ON A PIECE OF CHALK"

IF A WELL were sunk at our feet in the midst of the city of Norwich, the diggers would very soon find themselves at work in that white substance almost too soft to be called rock, with which we are all familiar as "chalk."

Not only here, but over the whole county of Norfolk, the well sinker might carry his shaft down many hundred feet without coming to the end of the chalk; and, on the seacoast, where the waves have pared away the face of the land which breasts them, the scarped faces of the high cliffs are often wholly formed of the same material. Northward, the chalk may be followed as far as Yorkshire; on the south coast it appears abruptly in the picturesque western bays of Dorset and breaks into the Needles of the Isle of Wight; while on the shores of Kent it supplies that long line of white cliffs to which England owes her name of Albion.

Were the thin soil which covers it all washed away, a curved band of white chalk, here broader and there narrower, might be followed diagonally across England from Lulworth in Dorset to Flamborough Head in Yorkshire—a distance of over two hundred and eighty miles as the crow flies. From this band to the North Sea, on the east, and the Channel, on the south, the chalk is largely hidden by other deposits; but, except in the Weald of Kent, and Sussex, it enters into the very foundation of all the southeastern counties.

Attaining, as it does in some places, a thickness of more than a thousand feet, the English chalk must be admitted to be a mass of considerable magnitude. Nevertheless, it covers but an insignificant portion of the whole area occupied by the chalk formation of the globe, much of which has the same general characters as ours, and is found in detached patches, some less and others more extensive, than the English. Chalk occurs in northwest Ireland; it stretches over a large part of France— the chalk which underlies Paris being, in fact, a continuation of that of the London basin; it runs through Denmark and Central Europe, and extends southward to North Africa; while eastward it appears in the Crimea and in Syria, and may be traced as far as the shores of the Sea of Aral, in Central Asia. If all the points at which true chalk occurs were circumscribed, they would lie within an irregular oval about three thousand miles in long diameter—the area of which would be as great as that of Europe, and would many times exceed that of the largest existing inland sea—the Mediterranean.

Thus the chalk is no unimportant element in the masonry of the earth's crust, and it impresses a peculiar stamp, varying with the conditions to which it is exposed, on the scenery of the districts in which it occurs. The undulating downs and rounded coombs, covered with sweet-grassed turf, of our inland chalk country, have a peacefully domestic and mutton-suggesting prettiness, but can hardly be called either grand or beautiful. But on our southern coasts the wall-sided cliffs, many hundred feet high, with vast needles and pinnacles standing out in the sea, sharp and solitary enough to serve as perches for the wary cormorant, confer a wonderful beauty and grandeur upon the chalk headlands. And in the East chalk has its share in the formation of some of the most venerable of mountain ranges, such as the Lebanon.

What is this widespread component of the surface of the earth and whence did it come?

You may think this no very hopeful inquiry. You may not unnaturally suppose that the attempt to solve such problems as these can lead to no result, save that of entangling the inquirer in vague speculations, incapable of refutation and of verification. If such were really the case, I should have selected some other subject than a "piece of chalk" for my discourse. But in truth, after much deliberation, I have been unable to think of any topic which would so well enable me to lead you to see how solid is the foundation upon which some of the most startling conclusions of physical science rest.

A great chapter of the history of the world is written in the chalk. Few passages in the history of man can be supported by such an overwhelming mass of direct and indirect evidence as that which testifies to the truth of the fragment of the history of the globe, which I hope to enable you to read with your own eyes tonight. Let me add that few chapters of human history have a more profound significance for ourselves. I weigh my words well when I assert that the man who should know the true history of the bit of chalk which every carpenter carries about in his breeches pocket, though ignorant of all other history, is likely, if he will think his knowledge out to its ultimate results, to have a truer, and therefore a better, conception of this wonderful universe and of man's relation to it than the most learned student who is deep-read in the records of humanity and ignorant of those of nature.

The language of the chalk is not hard to learn, not nearly so hard as

Latin, if you only want to get at the broad features of the story it has to tell; and I propose that we now set to work to spell that story out together.

We all know that if we "burn" chalk the result is quicklime. Chalk, in fact, is a compound of carbonic-acid gas and lime, and when you make it very hot the carbonic acid flies away and the lime is left. By this method of procedure we see the lime, but we do not see the carbonic acid. If, on the other hand, you were to powder a little chalk and drop it into a good deal of strong vinegar, there would be a great bubbling and fizzing, and, finally, a clear liquid, in which no sign of chalk would appear. Here you see the carbonic acid in the bubbles; the lime, dissolved in the vinegar, vanishes from sight. There are a great many other ways of showing that chalk is essentially nothing but carbonic acid and quicklime. Chemists enunciate the result of all the experiments which prove this by stating that chalk is almost wholly composed of "carbonate of lime."

It is desirable for us to start from the knowledge of this fact, though it may not seem to help us very far toward what we seek. For carbonate of lime is a widely spread substance and is met with under very various conditions. All sorts of limestones are composed of more or less pure carbonate of lime. The crust which is often deposited by waters which have drained through limestone rocks, in the form of what are called stalagmites and stalactites, is carbonate of lime. Or, to take a more familiar example, the fur on the inside of a teakettle is carbonate of lime; and, for anything chemistry tells us to the contrary, the chalk might be a kind of gigantic fur upon the bottom of the earth kettle, which is kept pretty hot below.

Let us try another method of making the chalk tell us its own history. To the unassisted eye chalk looks simply like a very loose and open kind of stone. But it is possible to grind a slice of chalk down so thin that you can see through it—until it is thin enough, in fact, to be examined with any magnifying power that may be thought desirable. A thin slice of the fur of a kettle might be made in the same way. If it were examined microscopically, it would show itself to be a more or less distinctly laminated mineral substance, and nothing more.

But the slice of chalk presents a totally different appearance when placed under the microscope. The general mass of it is made up of very minute granules; but imbedded in this matrix are innumerable bodies, some smaller and some larger, but on a rough average not more than a hundredth of an inch in diameter, having a well-defined shape and structure. A cubic inch of some specimens of chalk may contain hundreds of thousands of these bodies, compacted together with incalculable millions of the granules.

The examination of a transparent slice gives a good notion of the manner in which the components of the chalk are arranged and of their relative proportions. But by rubbing up some chalk with a brush in water and then pouring off the milky fluid, so as to obtain sediments of different degrees of fineness, the granules and the minute rounded bodies may be pretty well separated from one another and submitted to microscopic examination, either as opaque or as transparent objects. By combining the views obtained in these various methods each of the rounded bodies may be proved to be a beautifully constructed calcareous fabric, made up of a number of chambers, communicating freely with one another. The chambered bodies are of various forms. One of the commonest is something like a badly grown raspberry, being formed of a number of nearly globular chambers of different sizes congregated together. It is called *globigerina,* and some specimens of chalk consist of little else than globigerinae and granules. Let us fix our attention upon the globigerina. It is the spoor of the game we are tracking. If we can learn what it is and what are the conditions of its existence, we shall see our way to the origin and past history of the chalk. . . .

Happily, however, better evidence in proof of the organic nature of the globigerinae than that of analogy is forthcoming. It so happens that calcareous skeletons, exactly similar to the globigerinae of the chalk, are being formed at the present moment by minute living creatures which flourish in multitudes, literally more numerous than the sands of the seashore, over a large extent of that part of the earth's surface which is covered by the ocean.

The history of the discovery of these living globigerinae and of the part which they play in rock building is singular enough. It is a discovery which, like others of no less scientific importance, has arisen incidentally out of work devoted to very different and exceedingly practical interests. When men first took to the sea they speedily learned to look out for shoals and rocks; and the more the burden of their ships increased the more imperatively necessary it became for sailors to ascertain with precision the depth of the waters they traversed. Out of this necessity grew the use of the lead and sounding line; and, ultimately, marine surveying, which is the recording of the form of coasts and of the depth of the sea, as ascertained by the sounding lead, upon charts.

At the same time it became desirable to ascertain and to indicate the nature of the sea bottom, since this circumstance greatly affects its goodness as holding ground for anchors. Some ingenious tar, whose name deserves a better fate than the oblivion into which it has fallen, attained this object by "arming" the bottom of the lead with a lump of grease, to which more or less of the sand or mud, or broken shells, as the case might be, adhered and was brought to the surface. But, however well adapted such an apparatus might be for rough nautical purposes, scientific accuracy could not be expected from the armed lead, and to remedy its defects (especially when applied to sounding in great depths) Lieutenant Brooke, of the American Navy, some years ago invented a most ingenious machine by which a considerable portion of the superficial layer of the sea bottom can be scooped out and brought up from any depth to which the lead descends. In 1853, Lieutenant Brooke obtained mud from the bottom of the North Atlantic, between Newfoundland and the Azores, at a depth of more than ten thousand feet, or two miles, by the help of this sounding apparatus. The specimens were sent for examination to Ehrenberg, of Berlin, and to Bailey, of West Point, and those able microscopists found that this deep-sea mud was almost entirely composed of the skeletons of living organisms—the greater proportion of these being just like the globigerinae already known to occur in the chalk.

Thus far, the work had been carried on simply in the interests of science, but Lieutenant Brooke's method of sounding acquired a high commercial value when the enterprise of laying down the telegraph cable between this country and the United States was undertaken. For it became a matter of immense importance to know not only the depth of the sea over the whole line along which the cable was to be laid, but the exact nature of the bottom, so as to guard against chances of cutting or fraying the strands of that costly rope. The Admiralty consequently ordered Captain Dayman, an old friend and shipmate of mine, to ascertain the depth over the whole line of the cable and to bring back specimens of the bottom. In former days such a command as this might have sounded very much like one of the impossible things which the young prince in the fairy tales is ordered to do before he can obtain the hand of the princess. However, in the months of June and July 1857 my friend performed the task assigned to him with great expedition and precision, without, so far as I know, having met with any reward of that kind. The specimens of Atlantic mud which he procured were sent to me to be examined and reported upon.

The result of all these operations is that we know the contours and the nature of the surface soil covered by the North Atlantic for a distance of seventeen hundred miles from east to west, as well as we know that of any part of the dry land. It is a prodigious plain—one of the widest and most even plains in the world. If the sea were drained off, you might drive a wagon all the way from Valentia, on the west coast of Ireland, to Trinity Bay, in Newfoundland. And, except upon one sharp incline about two hundred miles from Valentia, I am not quite sure that it would even be necessary to put the skid on, so gentle are the ascents and descents upon that long route. From Valentia the road would lie downhill for about two hundred miles to the point at which the bottom is now covered by seventeen hundred fathoms of sea water. Then would come the central plain, more than a thousand miles wide, the inequalities of the surface of which would be hardly perceptible, though the depth of water upon it now varies from ten thousand to fifteen thousand feet; and there are places in which Mont Blanc might be sunk without showing its peak above water. Beyond this, the ascent on the American side commences, and gradually leads, for about three hundred miles, to the Newfoundland shore.

Almost the whole of the bottom of this central plain (which extends for many hundred miles in a north and south direction) is covered by a fine mud which, when brought to the surface, dries into a grayish-white friable substance. You can write with this on a blackboard if you are so inclined; and, to the eye, it is quite like very soft, grayish chalk. Examined chemically, it proves to be composed almost wholly of carbonate of lime; and if you make a section of it in the same way as that of the piece of chalk was made, and view it with the microscope, it presents innumerable globigerinae embedded in a granular matrix. Thus this deep-sea mud is substantially chalk. I say substantially, because there are a good many minor differences; but as these have no bearing on the question immediately before us—which is the nature of the globigerinae of the chalk—it is unnecessary to speak of them.

Globigerinae of every size, from the smallest to the largest, are associated together in the Atlantic mud, and the chambers of many are filled by a soft animal matter. This soft substance is, in fact, the remains of the creature to which the globigerina shell, or rather skeleton, owes its existence—and which is an animal of the simplest imaginable description. It is, in fact, a mere particle of living jelly, without defined parts of any kind—without a mouth, nerves, muscles, or distinct organs, and only manifesting its vitality to ordinary observation by thrusting out and retracting from all parts of its surface long filamentous processes which serve for arms and legs. Yet this amorphous particle, devoid of everything which, in the higher animals, we call organs, is capable of feeding, growing, and multiplying; of separating from the ocean the small proportion of carbonate of lime which is dissolved in sea water; and of building up that substance into a skeleton for itself, according to a pattern which can be imitated by no other known agency.

The notion that animals can live and flourish in the sea, at the vast depths from which apparently living globigerinae have been brought up, does not agree very well with our usual conceptions respecting the conditions of animal life; and it is not so absolutely impossible as it might at first sight appear to be that the globigerinae of the Atlantic sea bottom do not live and die where they are found.

As I have mentioned, the soundings from the great Atlantic plain are almost entirely made up of globigerinae, with the granules which have been mentioned, and some few other calcareous shells; but a small percentage of the chalky mud—perhaps at most some five per cent of it—is of a different nature and consists of shells and skeletons composed of silex, or pure flint. These silicious bodies belong partly to the lowly vegetable organisms which are called *diatomaceae,* and partly to the minute and extremely simple animals termed *radiolaria*. It is quite certain that these creatures do not live at the bottom of the ocean, but at its surface—where they may be obtained in prodigious numbers by the use of a properly constructed net. Hence it follows that these silicious organisms, though they are not heavier than the lightest dust, must have fallen, in some cases, through fifteen thousand feet of water, before they reached their final resting place on the ocean floor. And considering how large a surface these bodies expose in proportion to their weight, it is probable that they occupy a great length of time in making their burial journey from the surface of the Atlantic to the bottom.

But if the radiolaria and diatoms are thus rained upon the bottom of the sea, from the superficial layer of its waters in which they pass their lives, it is obviously possible that the globigerinae may be similarly derived; and if they were so, it would be much easier to understand how they obtain their supply of food than it is at present. Nevertheless, the positive and negative evidence all points the other way. The skeletons of the full-grown, deep-sea globigerinae are so remarkably solid and heavy in proportion to their surface as to seem little fitted for floating; and, as a matter of fact, they are not to be found along with the diatoms and radiolaria in the uppermost stratum of the open ocean. It has been observed, again, that the abundance of globigerinae, in proportion to other organisms of like kind, increases with the depth of the sea; and that deep-water globigerinae are larger than those which live in shallower parts of the sea; and such facts negative the supposition that these organisms have been swept by currents from the shallows into the deeps of the Atlantic. It therefore seems to be hardly doubtful that these wonderful creatures live and die at the depths in which they are found.

However, the important points for us are that the living globigerinae are exclusively marine animals, the skeletons of which abound at the bottom of deep seas; and that there is not a shadow of reason for believing that the habits of the globigerinae of the chalk differed from those of the existing species. But if this be true, there is no escaping the conclusion that the chalk itself is the dried mud of an ancient deep sea.

In working over the soundings collected by Captain Dayman, I was surprised to find that many of what I have called the "granules" of that mud were not, as one might have been tempted to think at first, the mere powder and waste of globigerinae, but that they had a definite form and size. I termed these bodies "coccoliths," and doubted their organic nature. Dr. Wallich verified my observation and added the interesting discovery that, not unfrequently, bodies similar to these "coccoliths" were aggregated together into spheroids, which he termed "coccospheres." So far as we knew these bodies, the nature of which is extremely puzzling and problematical, were peculiar to the Atlantic soundings. But a few years ago Mr. Sorby, in making a careful examination of the chalk by means of thin sections and otherwise, observed, as Ehrenberg had done before him, that much of its granular basis possesses a definite form. Comparing these formed particles with those in the Atlantic soundings, he found the two to be identical; and thus proved that the chalk, like the surroundings, contains these mysterious coccoliths and coccospheres. Here was a further and most interesting confirmation, from internal evidence, of the essential identity of the chalk with modern deep-sea mud. Globigerinae, coccoliths, and coccospheres are found as the chief constituents of both, and testify to the general similarity of the conditions under which both have been formed.

The evidence furnished by the hewing, facing, and superposition of the stones of the Pyramids that these structures were built by men has no greater weight than the evidence that the chalk was built by globigerinae; and the belief that those ancient pyramid builders were terrestrial and air-breathing creatures like ourselves is not better based than the conviction that the chalk makers lived in the sea. But as our belief in the building of the Pyramids by men is not only grounded on the internal evidence afforded by these structures but gathers strength from multitudinous collateral proofs, and is clinched by the total absence of any reason for a contrary belief; so the evidence drawn from the globigerinae that the chalk is an ancient sea bottom is fortified by innumerable independent lines of evidence; and our belief in the truth of the conclusion to which all positive testimony tends receives the like negative justification from the fact that no other hypothesis has a shadow of foundation. . . .

There is more curious evidence, again, that the process of covering up, or, in other words, the deposit of globigerina skeletons, did not go on very fast. It is demonstrable that an animal of the cretaceous sea might die, that its skeleton might lie uncovered upon the sea bottom long enough to lose all its outward coverings and appendages by putrefaction; and that, after this had happened, another animal might attach itself to the dead and naked skeleton, might grow to maturity, and might itself die before the calcareous mud had buried the whole.

Cases of this kind are admirably described by Sir Charles Lyell. He speaks of the frequency with which geologists find in the chalk a fossilized sea urchin, to which is attached the lower valve of a *crania*. This is a kind of shellfish, with a shell composed of two pieces, of which, as in the oyster, one is fixed and the other free.

"The upper valve is almost invariably wanting, though occasionally found in a perfect state of preservation in the white chalk at some distance. In this case we see clearly that the sea urchin first lived from youth to age, then died and lost its spines, which were carried away. Then the young crania adhered to the bared shell, grew, and perished in its turn; after which, the upper valve was separated from the lower, before the *echinus* became enveloped in chalky mud."

A specimen in the Museum of Practical Geology, in London, still further prolongs the period which must have elapsed between the death of the sea urchin and its burial by the globigerinae. For the outward face of the valve of a crania, which is attached to a sea urchin (*micraster*), is itself overrun by an incrusting coralline which spreads thence over more or less of the surface of the sea urchin. It follows that, after the upper valve of the crania fell off, the surface of the attached valve must have remained exposed long enough to allow of the growth of the whole coralline, since corallines do not live embedded in mud.

The progress of knowledge may one day enable us to deduce from such facts as these the maximum rate at which the chalk can have accumulated, and thus to arrive at the minimum duration of the chalk period. Suppose that the valve of the crania upon which a coralline has fixed itself in the way just described is so attached to the sea urchin that no part of it is more than an inch above the face upon which the sea urchin rests. Then, as the coralline could not have fixed itself, if the crania had been covered up with chalk mud, and could not have lived had itself been so covered, it follows that an inch of chalk mud could not have accumulated within the time between the death and decay of the soft parts of the sea urchin and the growth of the coralline to the full size which it has attained. If the decay of the soft parts of the sea urchin, the attachment, growth to maturity, and decay of the crania, and the subsequent attachment and growth of the coralline took a year (which is a low estimate enough), the accumulation of the inch of chalk must have taken more than a year: and the deposit of a thousand feet of chalk must, consequently, have taken more than twelve thousand years.

The foundation of all this calculation is, of course, a knowledge of the length of time the crania and the coralline needed to attain their full size; and, on this head, precise knowledge is at present wanting. But there are circumstances which tend to show that nothing like an inch of chalk has accumulated during the life of a crania; and, on any probable estimate of the length of that life, the chalk period must have had a much longer duration than that thus roughly assigned to it. . . .

Thus evidence which cannot be rebutted, and which need not be strengthened, though if time permitted I might indefinitely increase its quantity, compels you to believe that the earth, from the time of the chalk to the present day, has been the theater of a series of changes as vast in their amount as they were slow in their progress. The area on which we stand has been first sea and then land, for at least four alternations; and has remained in each of these conditions for a period of great length.

Nor have these wonderful metamorphoses of sea into land, and of land into sea, been confined to one corner of England. During the chalk period, or "cretaceous epoch," not one of the present great physical features of the globe was in existence. Our great mountain ranges, Pyrenees, Alps, Himalayas, Andes, have all been upheaved since the chalk was deposited, and the cretaceous sea flowed over the sites of Sinai and Ararat. All this is certain because rocks of cretaceous or still later date have shared in the elevatory movements which gave rise to these mountain chains; and may be found perched up, in some cases, many thousand feet high upon their flanks. And evidence of equal cogency demonstrates that, though, in Norfolk, the forest bed rests directly upon the chalk, yet it does so not because the period at which the forest grew immediately followed that at which the chalk was formed but because an immense lapse of time, represented elsewhere by thousands of feet of rock, is not indicated at Cromer.

I must ask you to believe that there is no less conclusive proof that a still more prolonged succession of similar changes occurred before the chalk was deposited. Nor have we any reason to think that the first term in the series of these changes is known. The oldest sea beds preserved to us are sands and mud and pebbles, the wear and tear of rocks which were formed in still older oceans.

But, great as is the magnitude of these physical changes of the world, they have been accompanied by a no less striking series of modifications in its living inhabitants. All the great classes of animals, beasts of the field, fowls of the air, creeping things, and things which dwell in the waters flourished upon the globe long ages before the chalk was deposited. Very few, however, if any, of these ancient forms of animal life were identical with those which now live. Certainly not one of the higher animals was of the same species as any of those now in existence. The beasts of the field, in the days before the chalk, were not our beasts of the field, nor the fowls of the air such as those which the eye of man has seen flying, unless his antiquity dates infinitely further back than we at present surmise. If we could be carried back into those times, we should be as one suddenly set down in Australia before it was colonized. We should see mammals, birds, reptiles, fishes, insects, snails, and the like, clearly recognizable as such, and yet not one of them would be just the same as those with which we are familiar, and many would be extremely different.

From that time to the present the population of the world has undergone slow and gradual, but incessant, changes. There has been no grand catastrophe—no destroyer has swept away the forms of life of one period and replaced them by a totally new creation: but one species has vanished and another has taken its place; creatures of one type of structure have diminished, those of another have increased, as time has passed on. And thus, while the differences between the living creatures of the time before the chalk and those of the present day appear startling, if placed side by side, we are led from one to the other by the most gradual progress, if we follow the course of nature through the whole series of those relics of her operations which she has left behind. It is by the population of the chalk sea that the ancient and the modern inhabitants of the world are most completely connected. The groups which are dying out flourish side by side with the groups which are now the dominant forms of life. Thus the chalk contains remains of those strange flying and swimming reptiles, the pterodactyl, the ichthyosaurus, and the plesiosaurus, which are found in no later deposits but abounded in preceding ages. The chambered shells called ammonites and belemnites, which are so characteristic of the period preceding the cretaceous, in like manner die with it.

But among these fading remainders of a previous state of things are some very modern forms of life, looking like Yankee peddlers among a tribe of red Indians. Crocodiles of modern type appear; bony fishes, many of them very similar to existing species, almost supplant the forms of fish which predominate in more ancient seas; and many kinds of living shellfish first become known to us in the chalk. The vegetation acquires a modern aspect. A few living animals are not even distinguishable, as species, from those which existed at that remote epoch. The globigerina of the present day, for example, is not different specifically from that of the chalk; and the same may be said of many other *foraminifera*. I think it probable that critical and unprejudiced examination will show that more than one species of much higher animals have had a similar longevity; but the only example which I can at present give confidently is the snake's-head lamp-shell (*Terebratulina caput serpentis*) which lives in our English seas and abounded (as *Terebratulina striata* of authors) in the chalk.

The longest line of human ancestry must hide its diminished head before the pedigree of this insignificant shellfish. We Englishmen are proud to have an ancestor who was present at the Battle of Hastings. The ancestors of *Terebratulina caput serpentis* may have been present at a battle of ichthyosauria in that part of the sea which, when the chalk was forming, flowed over the site of Hastings. While all around has changed, this *Terebratulina* has peacefully propagated its species from generation to generation, and stands to this day as a living testimony to the continuity of the present with the past history of the globe. . . .

A small beginning has led us to a great ending. If I were to put the bit of chalk with which we started into the hot but obscure flame of burning hydrogen, it would presently shine like the sun. It seems to me that this physical metamorphosis is no false image of what has been the result of our subjecting it to a jet of fervent, though nowise brilliant, thought tonight. It has become luminous, and its clear rays, penetrating the abyss of the remote past, have brought within our ken some stages of the evolution of the earth. And in the shifting "without haste, but without rest" of the land and sea, as in the endless variation of the forms assumed by living beings, we have observed nothing but the natural product of the forces originally possessed by the substance of the universe.

The Father of Eugenics

FRANCIS GALTON (1822–1911)

*". . . and it's greatly to his credit,
That he is an Englishman."*—W. S. GILBERT

IF THE UBIQUITOUS, many-sided English scientist, Francis Galton, could have had his way, everyone in the world would be born an English gentleman or lady, preferably related to the distinguished Darwin and Wedgwood families of which he and his cousin, Charles Darwin, were members. In the course of a lengthy and strenuous life, gentleman Galton managed to do a number of diverse and important things.

As a scientist, he founded the science of eugenics (really the art of being well born), based on his studies of hereditary genius in English families, his anthropometric measurements, his discovery of the ancestral law of heredity, and his adventures in mental testing. As a criminologist, he established the system of fingerprint identification still in use. Linguist, he spoke five languages; explorer, he sought the source of the river Nile; mathematician, he developed the percentile method of dealing with biological statistics and was the predecessor of Karl Pearson in founding the science of biometrics. Meteorologist, he devised the modern weather map; inventor, he invented the ticker tape and the slide whistle named after him; novelist, he wrote a novel at the age of eighty. Author of many scientific papers, he himself has left us with an evaluated summary of his manifold achievements in an autobiography published in 1909, the highlights of which are quoted here.

English—obviously—was the language in which Galton wrote "Memories of My Life." The publisher was E. P. Dutton, New York.

AN ANTHROPOMETRIC LABORATORY

WHEN the International Exhibition of 1884 was under consideration, I offered to equip and maintain a laboratory there, if a suitable place were given, the woodwork set up, and the security of it taken off my hands. . . .

The measurements dealt with keenness of sight and of hearing; color sense, judgment of eye; breathing power; reaction time; strength of pull and of squeeze; force of blow; span of arms; height, both standing and sitting; and weight. The ease of working the instruments that were used was so great that an applicant could be measured in all these respects, a card containing the results furnished him, and a duplicate made and kept for statistical purposes, at the total cost of the threepenny fee for admission. That just defrayed the working expenses.

It is by no means easy to select suitable instruments for such a purpose. They must be strong, easily legible, and very simple, the stupidity and wrongheadedness of many men and women being so great as to be scarcely credible. I used at first the instrument commonly employed for testing the force of a blow. It was a stout deal rod running freely in a tube, with a buffer at one end to be hit with the fist and pressing against a spring at the other. An index was pushed by the rod as far as it entered the tube in opposition to the spring. I found no difficulty whatever in testing myself with it, but before long a man had punched it so much on one side, instead of hitting straight out, that he broke the stout deal rod. It was replaced by an oaken one, but this too was broken, and some wrists were sprained.

I afterward contrived, and used in a subsequent laboratory, a pretty arrangement that gave the swiftness, though not the force of the blow, with absolute safety, and which could be used for other limbs than the arm. The hand held a thread, the other end of which was tied to an elastic band, capable of pulling it back faster than any human hand could follow; so the hand always *retarded* its movement. Its speed was shown by the height to which a bead, actuated by the string (it is needless to explain details), was tossed up in front of a scale. This never failed and was perfectly easy to manipulate.

The observations made in this laboratory were of great use to me later on. Four hundred complete sets are published in the "Anthropometric Institute Journal," (1884) and afford good material for future use in many ways.

Among other instruments that I contrived then or subsequently were small whistles with a screw plug, for determining the highest audible note, the limit of which varies much in different persons and at different ages. A parcel of schoolboys might interchange very shrill and loud whistles quite inaudibly to an elderly master. . . .

I contrived a hollow cane made like a walking stick, having a removable whistle at its lower end, with an exposed India-rubber tube under its curved handle. Whenever I squeezed the tube against the handle, air was pushed through the whistle. I tried it at nearly all the cages in the Zoological Gardens, but with little result of interest, except that it certainly annoyed some of the lions. I have often met with persons who perceived no purely audible sound when very high notes were sounded, but who experienced a peculiar feeling of discomfort which I have occasionally felt myself. This, I think, was the case with some of the lions, who turned away and angrily rubbed their ears with their paws, just as the persons of whom I have spoken often did with their hands. . . .

For testing the muscular sense I used cartridges packed evenly with cotton wool and with shot, so as to be exactly alike on the outsides but of different weights. The weights ran in a regular geometric series and were broken up into sets of three. Each set lay in a grooved square of wood, in any order; the test was to arrange them by the sense of their heaviness, in their proper order, as shown by the inscriptions at one end of each. This method acted quickly, because it was easy to judge by the sometimes hesitating, sometimes decided manner in which a particular set was handled whether or no the differences were clearly perceived, and to substitute others in turn more appropriate to the acuteness of sense of the person tested.

One hears so much about the extraordinary sensitivity of the blind that I was glad of an opportunity of testing a large number of children in an asylum. The nature of the test was fully explained to them, and that the most successful ones were to receive a sweetmeat. It was evident that all did their best, but their performances fell distinctly short of those of ordinary persons. I found afterward a marked correlation between at least this form of sensitiveness and general ability.

After the Health Exhibition was closed in 1885, it seemed a pity that the laboratory should also come to an end, so I asked for and was given a room in the Science Galleries of the South Kensington Museum. I maintained a laboratory there during about six years. . . .

FINGERPRINT IDENTIFICATION: CRIMINOLOGY

THE CHIEF VALUE to me of the laboratory during the latter part of the time of its existence, and the reason why I continued it so long, lay in the convenience it afforded for obtaining and testing the value of finger-prints. My interest in them arose through a request to give a Friday evening lecture at the Royal Institution (which was delivered May 25, 1888) on what is briefly called "Bertillonage"; that is, on the system de-vised by Monsieur Alphonse Bertillon for identifying persons by the measurements of their bodily dimensions. The subject was attracting much interest at the time and had received a great deal of offhand news-paper praise. There was, however, a want of fullness in the published accounts of it, while the principle upon which extraordinarily large statistical claims to its quasi-certainty had been founded was manifestly incorrect, so further information was desirable. The incorrectness lay in treating the measures of different dimensions of the same person as if they were *independent* variables, which they are not. For example, a tall man is much more likely to have a long arm, foot, or finger than a short one. The chances against mistake had been overrated enormously owing to this error; still, the system was most ingenious and very in-teresting.

I made the acquaintance of Monsieur Bertillon during a short visit to Paris and had the opportunity of seeing his system at work. Nothing could exceed the deftness of his assistants in measuring the criminals; their methods were prompt and accurate, and all the accompanying ar-rangements excellently organized. But I had no means of testing its efficiency with closeness, which would have required more time and interference with current work than was permissible. I was nevertheless prepared to give an account at the Royal Institution of what I had seen, but, being desirous of introducing original work of my own, I gave to my lecture the more general title of "Personal Identification and Descrip-tion," on which larger subject there was much new to be said.

When thinking over the matter, the fact occurred to my recollection that thumbmarks had not infrequently been spoken and written about, so I inquired into their alleged use, especially by the Chinese. I also wrote a letter to "Nature" asking for information, which had the im-portant effect of drawing a response from Sir William Herschel, who, as a commissioner in India, had actually used them in his district for many years, as a means of preventing personation. But the system fell into disuse after his departure. Sir William gave me every assistance, by forwarding to me both old and modern fingerprints of himself and others of his family, and in showing his way of making the impressions.

I took up the study very seriously, thinking that fingerprints might prove to be of high anthropological significance, but I may say at once that they are not. I have examined large numbers of persons of different races to our own, as Jews, Basques, red Indians, East Indians of various origins, Negroes, and a fair number of Chinese. Also persons of very different characters and temperaments, as students of science, students of art, Quakers, notabilities of various kinds, and a considerable number of idiots at Earlswood Asylum, without finding any pattern that was characteristic of any of them. But as I continued working at finger-prints, their importance as a means of identification became more and more obvious, and since my theoretical work on heredity, correlation, et cetera, of which I shall speak further, had not yet "taken on," there was spare time for inquiry into fingerprints.

I described the results in the above-mentioned lecture so far as they had then been obtained, and subsequently in a more advanced shape in a memoir read before the Royal Society in 1891. It was argued in it that these patterns had a theoretical significance which has not, I think, even yet been adequately appreciated, which bears on discontinuity in evolu-tion. I showed that the different classes of patterns in fingerprints might be justly compared to different genera. As, however, they had been formed without any aid from natural selection, I concluded that natural selection had no monopoly in molding genera, but that internal condi-tions must be quite as important.

I have always believed that the number of positions of stability in every genus must be limited, from which moderate deviations, but not great ones, are possible without causing destruction. There are limits which, if they can be overpassed without disaster, would require a new position of stability in the organization. Comparatively few intermediate finger patterns are found between a "loop" and a "whorl," these repre-senting two different and well-marked genera or positions of stability.

The modern division of views concerning the immediate causes of evolution, whether it be due to the slow accumulation of small factors or else by the sudden mutations of De Vries, are paralleled by those held by the physicists of the fifties on the method by which a glacier adapts itself to its bed, just as if it were a viscous body, which it certainly is not in the ordinary sense of the word. Professor Tyndall ascribed its adapta-tion of form to a succession of internal crunches and refreezings; in other words, to successive conditions of stability.

It became gradually clear that three facts had to be established before it would be possible to advocate the use of fingerprints for criminal or other investigations. First, it must be proved, not assumed, that the pattern of a fingerprint is constant throughout life. Secondly, that the variety of patterns is really very great. Thirdly, that they admit of being so classified, or "lexiconized," that when a set of them is submitted to an expert it would be possible for him to tell, by reference to a suitable dictionary, or its equivalent, whether a similar set had been already registered. These things I did, but they required much labor.

A committee was appointed by the Home Office to inquire into the different systems of identification that had been adopted or proposed for use with criminals. They visited my laboratory and thoroughly inspected what I had to show. It was a great pleasure to work with and for such sympathetic and keen inquirers, but I regretted all the time that my methods were hardly ripe for inspection; still, they were fairly adequate. The result was a report strongly in favor of their adoption, of which the part that bears on fingerprints is reprinted in my "Fingerprint Directory." . . .

I have said that my method was not so fully elaborated as I should have wished when the committee examined it, so I worked hard at it afterward and published the results in 1895 in the book already mentioned, bearing the title of "Fingerprint Directory," using the term "Directory" in the same sense as in the familiar phrase of "Post Office Directory." It was an unlucky choice of a word, for its equivalent in French means a board of directors, so its title may have misled. This book contained a method of classification far in advance of what I had published before, and is in most essential points the same as that in present use in Scotland Yard.

Sir Edward, then Mr. Henry, when in office in India, came to my laboratory to learn the fingerprint process, and he introduced it first into Bengal, and afterward throughout India. The Bertillon system did not work at all well there, because measurements had to be taken at many different local centers where accuracy could not be guaranteed. Then Mr. Henry was dispatched to the Cape, where great difficulty had arisen about identification, and he introduced fingerprints there also. After this he was called to England, and soon selected to hold his present important post. From what I have seen during the few visits I have paid to Scotland Yard the fingerprint system answers excellently and can deal easily with many thousands of sets—certainly with twenty thousand. . . .

It is necessary for its successful employment that the clerks at the central bureau should be thoroughly acquainted with their work. There is much for them to learn as to the uniform classification of many small groups of often recurring patterns, and in realizing what is and what is not essential to identification. Certain changes in the print may wholly depend on the greater or less pressure of the finger. The impression is usually made by what may be described as the crests of the mountain ridges of the pattern; a strong pressure will show the connecting *cols* as well, so the latter are unimportant. Decipherment is a peculiar art. Gross differences are conspicuous enough to an untrained eye, but even in these a novice may sometimes contrive to make mistakes when an imperfect impression is submitted to him. On the other hand, the art of taking good prints is very easy and may be learned in a single lesson by any intelligent and handy man.

THE ANCESTRAL LAW OF HEREDITY

As THESE LINES are being written, the circumstances under which I first clearly grasped the important generalization that the laws of heredity were solely concerned with deviations expressed in statistical units are vividly recalled to my memory. It was in the grounds of Naworth Castle, where an invitation had been given to ramble freely. A temporary shower drove me to seek refuge in a reddish recess in the rock by the side of the pathway. There the idea flashed across me, and I forgot everything else for a moment in my great delight.

The following question had been much in my mind. How is it possible for a population to remain alike in its features, as a whole, during many successive generations, if the *average* produce of each couple resemble their parents? Their children are not alike, but vary: therefore some would be taller, some shorter than their average height; so among the issue of gigantic couples there would be usually some children more gigantic still. Conversely as to very small couples. But from what I could thus far find, parents had issue less exceptional than themselves. I was very desirous of ascertaining the facts of the case. After much consideration and many inquiries I determined, in 1885, on experimenting with sweet peas, which were suggested to me both by Sir Joseph Hooker and by Mr. Darwin. Their merits are threefold. They have so little tendency to become cross-fertilized that seedsmen do not hesitate to grow differently colored plants in neighboring beds; all the seeds in their pods are of the same size, that is to say, there is no little pea at the end as in the pod of the common pea, and they are very hardy and prolific. I procured a large number of seeds from the same bin and selected seven weights, calling them K (the largest), L, M, N, O, P, and Q (the smallest), forming an arithmetic series. Curiously, their lengths, found by measuring ten of a kind in a row, also formed an arithmetic series, owing, I suppose, to the larger and plumper seeds being more spherical and therefore taking less room for their weight than the others. Ten peas of each of these seven descriptions, seventy in all, formed what I called a "set." . . .

I must stop for a moment to pay tribute to the memory of Mendel, with whom I sentimentally feel myself connected, owing to our having been born in the same year, 1822. His careful and long-continued experiments show how much can be performed by those who, like him and Charles Darwin, never or hardly ever leave their homes, and again how much might be done in a fixed laboratory after a uniform tradition of work had been established. Mendel clearly showed that there were such things as alternative atomic characters of equal potency in descent. How far characters generally may be due to simple, or to molecular characters more or less correlated together, has yet to be discovered.

I had thought of experimenting with mice, as cheap to rear and very prolific, and had taken some steps to that end, when I became aware of the large collections of basset hounds belonging to the late Sir Everard Millais. He offered me every facility. The basset hound records referring to his own and other breeds had been carefully kept, and the studbook he lent me contained accounts of nearly one thousand animals, of which I was able to utilize 817. All were descended from parents of known colors; in 567 of them the colors of all four grandparents were also known. Wherever the printed studbook was deficient, Sir Everard Millais supplied the want in manuscript from the original records. My inquiry was into the heredity of two alternative colors, one containing no black, the other containing it; their technical names were lemon-white and tricolor (black, lemon, white) respectively. I was assured that no difficulty was felt in determining the category to which each individual belonged. These data were fully discussed in a memoir, published (1897) in the "Proceedings of the Royal Society," on what is now termed the "ancestral law," namely, that the *average* contribution of each parent is one fourth, of each grandparent one sixteenth, and so on. Or, in other words, that of the two parents taken together is one half, of the four grandparents together one fourth, and so on. My data were not as numerous as is desirable; still, the results were closely congruous and seem to be a near approximation to the truth. The conclusions have been much discussed and criticized, and they have been modified by Professor Karl Pearson; but they have not been seriously shaken, so far as I know.

The Beginning of Experimental Psychology

HERMANN VON HELMHOLTZ (1821–94)

ON July 23, 1847, a twenty-six-year-old German Army surgeon, son of a poor but well-educated schoolmaster, stood up at the meeting of the Physical Society of Berlin and read a paper which turned out to be a sensational eye opener to the scientific world. The young doctor was Hermann von Helmholtz, a native of Potsdam, and the paper, entitled "The Conservation of Energy," undertook to demonstrate with a mathematical rigor of which none had suspected the young man capable the doctrine that the conservation of energy was applicable everywhere, in living things as well as in inanimate objects. As a result of this startling demonstration Helmholtz quickly rose to positions of eminence in the German university system, then the glory of the educational world. He held professorships of physiology, anatomy, and physics at Königsberg, Bonn, Heidelberg, Berlin, and Charlottenburg. Always he championed the academic freedom of the professors at these institutions.

In 1851 Helmholtz invented the ophthalmoscope with which it was possible to examine the interior of the eye. "Helmholtz has unfolded to us a new world!" exclaimed a grateful colleague. A pillar of German science in its heyday, Helmholtz worked indefatigably at a variety of problems, mostly, as foreshadowed in his sensational paper, aimed at subjects which narrowed the gap between the physical and the biological sciences. Among them were the measurement of the rate of transmission of nerve impulses (previously believed to be instantaneous); physiological optics, or the mechanism of sight and color vision; mechanisms of hearing and qualities of tone, which led him into the field of aesthetics and theories of music, whose scientific foundations he discussed in the mature and penetrating passages quoted here. These efforts have brought him credit for being, along with Wilhelm Wundt (1832–1920), professor at Leipzig, one of the true founders of experimental psychology.

German was the language in which Helmholtz published in 1862 his original 330,000-word tome on "The Sensations of Tone as a physiological basis for the Theory of Music." The English translation given here was made by Alexander J. Ellis, in 1885, from the fourth German edition of 1877. The text is from the fourth English edition, published by Longmans, Green & Company (London and New York, 1912).

"ON THE SENSATION OF SOUND IN GENERAL"

SENSATIONS result from the action of an external stimulus on the sensitive apparatus of our nerves. Sensations differ in kind, partly with the organ of sense excited, and partly with the nature of the stimulus employed. Each organ of sense produces peculiar sensations which cannot be excited by means of any other; the eye gives sensations of light, the ear sensations of sound, the skin sensations of touch. Even when the same sunbeams which excite in the eye sensations of light impinge on the skin and excite its nerves, they are felt only as heat, not as light. In the same way the vibration of elastic bodies heard by the ear can also be felt by the skin, but in that case produce only a whirring, fluttering sensation, not sound. The sensation of sound is therefore a species of reaction against external stimulus, peculiar to the ear and excitable in no other organ of the body, and is completely distinct from the sensation of any other sense.

As our problem is to study the laws of the sensation of hearing, our first business will be to examine how many kinds of sensation the ear can generate and what differences in the external means of excitement or sound correspond to these differences of sensation.

The first and principal difference between various sounds experienced by our ear is that between noises and musical tones. The soughing, howling, and whistling of the wind, the splashing of water, the rolling and rumbling of carriages, are examples of the first kind, and the tones of all musical instruments of the second. Noises and musical tones may certainly intermingle in very various degrees and pass insensibly into one another, but their extremes are widely separated.

The nature of the difference between musical tones and noises can generally be determined by attentive aural observation without artificial assistance. We perceive that generally a noise is accompanied by a rapid alternation of different kinds of sensations of sound. Think, for example, of the rattling of a carriage over granite paving stones, the splashing or seething of a waterfall or of the waves of the sea, the rustling of leaves in a wood. In all these cases we have rapid, irregular, but distinctly perceptible alternations of various kinds of sounds, which crop up fitfully. When the wind howls the alternation is slow, the sound slowly and gradually rises and then falls again. It is also more or less possible to separate restlessly alternating sounds in case of the greater number of other noises. We shall hereafter become acquainted with an instrument, called a resonator, which will materially assist the ear in making this separation. On the other hand, a musical tone strikes the ear as a perfectly undisturbed, uniform sound which remains unaltered as long as it exists, and it presents no alternation of various kinds of constituents. To this, then, corresponds a simple, regular kind of sensation, whereas in a noise many various sensations of musical tone are irregularly mixed up and as it were tumbled about in confusion. We can easily compound noises out of musical tones, as, for example, by simultaneously striking all the keys contained in one or two octaves of a pianoforte. This shows us that musical tones are the simpler and more regular elements of the sensations of hearing, and that we have consequently first to study the laws and peculiarities of this class of sensations.

Then comes the further question: On what difference in the external means of excitement does the difference between noise and musical tone depend? The normal and usual means of excitement for the human ear is atmospheric vibration. The irregularly alternating sensation of the ear in the case of noises leads us to conclude that for these the vibration of the air must also change irregularly. For musical tones, on the other hand, we anticipate a regular motion of the air, continuing uniformly, and in its turn excited by an equally regular motion of the sonorous body, whose impulses were conducted to the ear by the air.

Those regular motions which produce musical tones have been exactly investigated by physicists. They are *oscillations, vibrations,* or *swings,* that is, up-and-down, or to-and-fro motions of sonorous bodies, and it is necessary that these oscillations should be regularly periodic. By a *periodic motion* we mean one which constantly returns to the same condition after exactly equal intervals of time. The length of the equal intervals of time between one state of the motion and its next exact repetition we call the *length of the oscillation,* vibration, or swing, or the *period* of the motion. In what manner the moving body actually moves during one period is perfectly indifferent. As illustrations of periodical motion, take the motion of a clock pendulum, of a stone attached to a string and whirled round in a circle with uniform velocity, of a hammer made to rise and fall uniformly by its connection with a water wheel. All these motions, however different be their form, are periodic in the sense here explained. The length of their periods, which in the cases adduced is generally from one to several seconds, is relatively long in comparison with the much shorter periods of the vibrations producing musical tones, the lowest or deepest of which makes at least thirty in a second, while in other cases their number may increase to several thousand in a second.

Our definition of periodic motion then enables us to answer the question proposed as follows. The sensation of a musical tone is due to a rapid periodic motion of the sonorous body; the sensation of a noise to non-periodic motions.

The musical vibrations of solid bodies are often visible. Although they may be too rapid for the eye to follow them singly, we easily recognize that a sounding string, or tuning fork, or the tongue of a reed pipe, is rapidly vibrating between two fixed limits, and the regular, apparently immovable image that we see, notwithstanding the real motion of the body, leads us to conclude that the backward and forward motions are quite regular. In other cases we can feel the swinging motions of sonorous solids. Thus the player feels the trembling of the reed in the mouthpiece of a clarinet, oboe, or bassoon, or of his own lips in the mouthpieces of trumpets and trombones.

The motions proceeding from the sounding bodies are usually conducted to our ear by means of the atmosphere. The particles of air must also execute periodically recurrent vibrations, in order to excite the sensation of a musical tone in our ear. This is actually the case, although in daily experience sound at first seems to be some agent, which is constantly advancing through the air and propagating itself further and further. We must, however, here distinguish between the motion of the individual particles of air—which takes place periodically backward and forward within very narrow limits—and the propagation of the sonorous tremor. The latter is constantly advancing by the constant attraction of fresh particles into its sphere of tremor.

This is a peculiarity of all so-called *undulatory motions*. Suppose a stone to be thrown into a piece of calm water. Round the spot struck there forms a little ring of wave which, advancing equally in all directions, expands to a constantly increasing circle. Corresponding to this ring of wave, sound also proceeds in the air from the excited point and advances in all directions as far as the limits of the mass of air extend.

The process in the air is essentially identical with that on the surface of the water. The principal difference consists in the spherical propagation of sound in all directions through the atmosphere which fills all surrounding space, whereas the waves of the water can only advance in rings or circles on its surface. The crests of the waves of water correspond in the waves of sound to spherical shells where the air is condensed, and the troughs to shells where it is rarefied. On the free surface of the water the mass when compressed can slip upward and so form ridges, but in the interior of the sea of air the mass must be condensed, as there is no unoccupied spot for its escape.

The waves of water, therefore, continually advance without returning. But we must not suppose that the particles of water of which the waves are composed advance in a similar manner to the waves themselves. The motion of the particles of water on the surface can easily be rendered visible by floating a chip of wood upon it. This will exactly share the motion of the adjacent particles. Now such a chip is not carried on by the rings of wave. It only bobs up and down and finally rests on its original spot. The adjacent particles of water move in the same manner. When the ring of wave reaches them they are set bobbing; when it has passed over them they are still in their old place and remain there at rest while the ring of wave continues to advance toward fresh spots on the surface of the water and sets new particles of water in motion. Hence the waves which pass over the surface of the water are constantly built up of fresh particles of water. What really advances as a wave is only the tremor, the altered form of the surface, while the individual particles of water themselves merely move up and down transiently and never depart far from their original position. . . .

Now let us return to the surface of the water. We have supposed that one of its points has been struck by a stone and set in motion. This motion has spread out in the form of a ring of wave over the surface of the water and, having reached the chip of wood, has set it bobbing up and down. Hence by means of the wave the motion which the stone first excited in one point of the surface of the water has been communicated to the chip which was at another point of the same surface. The process which goes on in the atmospheric ocean about us is of a precisely similar nature. For the stone substitute a sounding body, which shakes the air; for the chip of wood substitute the human ear, on which impinge the waves of air excited by the shock, setting its movable parts in vibration. The waves of air proceeding from a sounding body transport the tremor to the human ear exactly in the same way as the water transports the tremor produced by the stone to the floating chip.

In this way also it is easy to see how a body which itself makes periodical oscillations will necessarily set the particles of air in periodical motion. A falling stone gives the surface of the water a single shock. Now replace the stone by a regular series of drops falling from a vessel with a small orifice. Every separate drop will excite a ring of wave, each ring of wave will advance over the surface of the water precisely like its predecessor, and will be in the same way followed by its successors. In this manner a regular series of concentric rings will be formed and propagated over the surface of the water. The number of drops which fall into the water in a second will be the number of waves which reach our floating chip in a second, and the number of times that this chip will therefore bob up and down in a second, thus executing a periodical motion, the period of which is equal to the interval of time between the falling of consecutive drops. In the same way for the atmosphere, a periodically oscillating sonorous body produces a similar periodical motion, first in the mass of air, and then in the drum skin of our ear, and the period of these vibrations must be the same as that of the vibration in the sonorous body. . . .

THE ENIGMA OF AESTHETICS: A THEORY OF MUSIC

THE CONSTRUCTION of scales and of harmonic tissue is a product of artistic invention and by no means furnished by the natural formation or natural function of our ear, as it has been hitherto most generally asserted. Of course the laws of the natural function of our ear play a great and influential part in this result; these laws are, as it were, the building stones with which the edifice of our musical system has been erected, and the necessity of accurately understanding the nature of these materials in order to understand the construction of the edifice itself has been clearly shown by the course of our investigations upon this very subject. But just as people with differently directed tastes can erect extremely different kinds of buildings with the same stones, so also the history of music shows us that the same properties of the human ear could serve as the foundation of very different musical systems. Consequently it seems to me that we cannot doubt that not merely the composition of perfect musical works of art, but even the construction of our system of scales, keys, chords, in short of all that is usually comprehended in a treatise on thorough bass, is the work of artistic invention and hence must be subject to the laws of artistic beauty. In point of fact, mankind has been at work on the diatonic system for more than twenty-five hundred years since the days of Terpander and Pythagoras, and in many cases we are still able to determine that the progressive changes made in the tonal system have been due to the most distinguished composers themselves, partly through their own independent inventions and partly through the sanction which they gave to the inventions of others by employing them artistically.

The aesthetic analysis of complete musical works of art, and the comprehension of the reasons of their beauty, encounter apparently invincible obstacles at almost every point. But in the field of elementary musical art we have now gained so much insight into its internal connection that we are able to bring the results of our investigations to bear on the views which have been formed and in modern times nearly universally accepted respecting the cause and character of artistic beauty in general. It is, in fact, not difficult to discover a close connection and agreement between them; nay, there are probably fewer examples more suitable than the theory of musical scales and harmony to illustrate the darkest and most difficult points of general aesthetics. Hence I feel that I should not be justified in passing over these considerations, more especially as they are closely connected with the theory of sensual perception, and hence with physiology in general.

No doubt is now entertained that beauty is subject to laws and rules dependent on the nature of human intelligence. The difficulty consists in the fact that these laws and rules, on whose fulfillment beauty depends and by which it must be judged, are not consciously present to the mind, either of the artist who creates the work, or the observer who contemplates it. Art works with design, but the work of art ought to have the appearance of being undesigned, and must be judged on that ground. Art creates as imagination pictures, regularly without conscious law, designedly without conscious aim. A work, known and acknowledged as the product of mere intelligence, will never be accepted as a work of art, however perfect be its adaptation to its end. Whenever we see that conscious reflection has acted in the arrangement of the whole, we find it poor. . . .

And yet we require every work of art to be reasonable, and we show this by subjecting it to a critical examination, and by seeking to enhance our enjoyment and our interest in it by tracing out the suitability, connection, and equilibrium of all its separate parts. The more we succeed in making the harmony and beauty of all its peculiarities clear and distinct, the richer we find it, and we even regard as the principal characteristic of a great work of art that deeper thought, reiterated observation, and continued reflection show us more and more clearly the reasonableness of all its individual parts.

The principal difficulty in pursuing this object is to understand how regularity can be apprehended by intuition without being consciously felt to exist. And this unconsciousness of regularity is not a mere accident in the effect of the beautiful on our mind, which may indifferently exist or not; it is, on the contrary, most clearly, prominently, and essentially important. For through apprehending everywhere traces of regularity, connection, and order, without being able to grasp the law and plan of the whole, there arises in our mind a feeling that the work of art which we are contemplating is the product of a design which far exceeds anything we can conceive at the moment and which hence partakes of the character of the illimitable. . . .

But for all this it is an essential condition that the whole extent of the regularity and design of a work of art should not be apprehended consciously. It is precisely from that part of its regular subjection to reason, which escapes our conscious apprehension, that a work of art exalts and delights us, and that the chief effects of the artistically beautiful proceed, not from the part which we are able fully to analyze.

If we now apply these considerations to the system of musical tones and harmony, we see of course that these are objects belonging to an entirely subordinate and elementary domain, but nevertheless they, too, are slowly matured inventions of the artistic taste of musicians, and consequently they, too, must be governed by the general rules of artistic beauty. Precisely because we are here still treading the lower walks of art and are not dealing with the expression of deep psychological problems, we are able to discover a comparatively simple and transparent solution of that fundamental enigma of aesthetics. . . .

A feeling for the melodic relationship of consecutive tones was first developed, commencing with octave and fifth and advancing to the third. We have taken pains to prove that this feeling of relationship was founded on the perception of identical partial tones in the corresponding compound tones. Now these partial tones are of course present in the sensations excited in our auditory apparatus, and yet they are not generally the subject of conscious perception as independent sensations. The conscious perception of everyday life is limited to the apprehension of the tone compounded of these partials, as a whole, just as we apprehend the taste of a very compound dish as a whole, without clearly feeling how much of it is due to the salt, or the pepper, or other spices and condiments.

After musicians had long been content with the melodic relationship of tones, they began in the Middle Ages to make use of harmonic relationship as shown in consonance. The effects of various combinations of tones also depend partly on the identity or difference of two of their different partial tones, but they likewise partly depend on their combinational tones. Whereas, however, in melodic relationship the equality of the upper partial tones can only be perceived by remembering the preceding compound tone, in harmonic relationship it is determined by immediate sensation, by the presence or absence of beats. Hence in harmonic combinations of tone, tonal relationship is felt with that greater liveliness due to a present sensation as compared with the recollection of a past sensation. The wealth of clearly perceptible relations grows with the number of tones combined. . . .

The development of harmony gave rise to a much richer opening out of musical art than was previously possible, because the far clearer characterization of related combinations of tones by means of chords and chordal sequences allowed of the use of much more distant relationships than were previously available, by modulating into different keys. In this way the means of expression greatly increased as well as the rapidity of the melodic and harmonic transitions which could now be introduced without destroying the musical connection.

As the independent significance of chords came to be appreciated in the fifteenth and sixteenth centuries, a feeling arose for the relationship of chords to one another and to the tonic chord, in accordance with the same law which had long ago unconsciously regulated the relationship of compound tones. The relationship of compound tones depended on the identity of two or more partial tones, that of chords on the identity of two or more notes. For the musician, of course, the law of the relationship of chords and keys is much more intelligible than that of compound tones. He readily hears the identical tones or sees them in the notes before him. But the unprejudiced and uninstructed hearer is as little conscious of the reason of the connection of a clear and agreeable series of fluent chords as he is of the reason of a well-connected melody. He is startled by a false cadence and feels its unexpectedness, but is not at all necessarily conscious of the reason of its unexpectedness. . . .

The recognition of these resemblances between compound tones and between chords reminds us of other exactly analogous circumstances which we must have often experienced. We recognize the resemblance between the faces of two near relations without being at all able to say in what the resemblance consists, especially when age and sex are different, and the coarser outlines of the features consequently present striking differences. And yet notwithstanding these differences—notwithstanding that we are unable to fix upon a single point in the two countenances which is absolutely alike—the resemblance is often so extraordinarily striking and convincing that we have not a moment's doubt about it. Precisely the same thing occurs in recognizing the relationship between two compound tones.

The analogy of these different cases may be carried even farther. When a father and daughter are strikingly alike in some well-marked feature, as the nose or forehead, we observe it at once and think no more about it. But if the resemblance is so enigmatically concealed that we cannot detect it, we are fascinated and cannot help continuing to compare their countenances. And if a painter drew two such heads having, say, a somewhat different expression of character combined with a predominant and striking, though indefinable, resemblance, we should undoubtedly value it as one of the principal beauties of his painting. Our admiration would certainly not be due merely to his technical skill; we should rather look upon his painting as evidencing an unusually delicate feeling for the significance of the human countenance, and find in this the artistic justification of his work.

Now the case is similar for musical intervals. The resemblance of an octave to its root is so great and striking that the dullest ear perceives it; the octave seems to be almost a pure repetition of the root, as it, in fact, merely repeats a part of the compound tone of its root, without adding anything new. Hence the aesthetical effect of an octave is that of a perfectly simple but little attractive interval. The most attractive of the intervals, melodically and harmonically, are clearly the thirds and sixths —the intervals which lie at the very boundary of those that the ear can grasp. The major third and the major sixth cannot be properly appreciated unless the first five partial tones are audible. These are present in good musical qualities of tone. The minor third and the minor sixth are for the most part justifiable only as inversions of the former intervals. The more complicated intervals in the scale cease to have any direct or easily intelligible relationship. They have no longer the charm of the thirds. . . .

Though it is probably correct to say that mankind, in historical development, first learned the means of musical expression from the human voice, it can hardly be denied that these same means of expressing melodic progression act, in artistically developed music, without the slightest reference to the application made of them in the modulations of the human voice and have a more general significance than any that can be attributed to innate instinctive cries. That this is the case appears above all in the modern development of instrumental music, which possesses an effective power and artistic justification that need not be gainsaid, although we may not yet be able to explain it in all its details.

Here I close my work. It appears to me that I have carried it as far as the physiological properties of the sensation of hearing exercise a direct influence on the construction of a musical system, that is, as far as the work especially belongs to natural philosophy. For even if I could not avoid mixing up aesthetic problems with physical, the former were comparatively simple, and the latter much more complicated. This relation would necessarily become inverted if I attempted to proceed further into the aesthetics of music, and to enter on the theory of rhythm, forms of composition, and means of musical expression. In all these fields the properties of sensual perception would of course have an influence at times, but only in a very subordinate degree. The real difficulty would lie in the development of the psychical motives which here assert themselves. Certainly this is the point where the more interesting part of musical aesthetics begins, the aim being to explain the wonders of great works of art, and to learn the utterances and actions of the various affections of the mind. But, however alluring such an aim may be, I prefer leaving others to carry out such investigations, in which I should feel myself too much of an amateur, while I myself remain on the safe ground of natural philosophy, in which I am at home.

From Physiology to Psychology

WILLIAM JAMES (1842–1910)

WILLIAM JAMES, born in New York City, was a physician, philosopher, and psychologist. His brother, Henry James, was a novelist. But so subtle was Henry in his delineations of character, and so concrete and precise in choice of words to pin down evanescent ideas was William, that it has since been said, "Henry James wrote novels like a psychologist; William James wrote psychology like a novelist." William James began his career by teaching anatomy and physiology at Harvard in 1872. By the time he published his "Principles of Psychology," in 1890, he had lifted the young science of psychology, child of physiology and philosophy, to a rank of academic dignity. The question which he was studying in the eighties— "What is an emotion?"—cannot be said to be finally answered even today. But no one has surpassed James in the clear statement of the problem, as quoted here. With Carl Lange (1834–1900), a Danish physician and psychologist, he set forth the James-Lange theory of the emotions. As a psychologist, he was a great believer in the power of habit; as a religionist (and he wrote most brilliantly on "The Varieties of Religious Experience"), he held hopefully for a religion of healthy-mindedness. As a philosopher, he is noted as one of the founders of the characteristically American philosophy of pragmatism: the test of value is usefulness.

English was the language of the James brothers. William's essay here quoted in part originally appeared in the publication "Mind" (Volume 9, pp. 188–205, 1884).

WHAT IS AN EMOTION?

I SHOULD SAY first of all that the only emotions I propose expressly to consider here are those that have a distinct bodily expression. That there are feelings of pleasure and displeasure, of interest and excitement, bound up with mental operations but having no obvious bodily expression for their consequence, would, I suppose, be held true by most readers. Certain arrangements of sounds, of lines, of colors, are agreeable, and others the reverse, without the degree of the feeling being sufficient to quicken the pulse or breathing, or to prompt to movements of either the body or the face. Certain sequences of ideas charm us as much as others tire us. It is a real intellectual delight to get a problem solved, and a real intellectual torment to have to leave it unfinished. The first set of examples, the sounds, lines, and colors, are either bodily sensations or the images of such. The second set seem to depend on processes in the ideational centers exclusively. Taken together, they appear to prove that there are pleasures and pains inherent in certain forms of nerve action as such, wherever that action occur. The case of these feelings we will at present leave entirely aside and confine our attention to the more complicated cases in which a wave of bodily disturbance of some kind accompanies the perception of the interesting sights or sounds, or the passage of the exciting train of ideas. Surprise, curiosity, rapture, fear, anger, lust, greed, and the like become then the names of the mental states with which the person is possessed. The bodily disturbances are said to be the "manifestation" of these several emotions, their "expression" or "natural language"; and these emotions themselves, being so strongly characterized both from within and without, may be called the *standard* emotions.

Our natural way of thinking about these standard emotions is that the mental perception of some fact excites the mental affection called the emotion, and that this latter state of mind gives rise to the bodily expression. My thesis on the contrary is that *the bodily changes follow directly the* PERCEPTION *of the exciting fact, and that our feeling of the same changes as they occur* IS *the emotion.* Common sense says we lose our fortune, are sorry and weep; we meet a bear, are frightened and run; we are insulted by a rival, are angry and strike. The hypothesis here to be defended says that this order of sequence is incorrect, that the one mental state is not immediately induced by the other, that the bodily manifestations must first be interposed between, and that the more rational statement is that we feel sorry because we cry, angry because we strike, afraid because we tremble, and not that we cry, strike, or tremble because we are sorry, angry, or fearful, as the case may be. Without the bodily states following on the perception, the latter would be purely cognitive in form, pale, colorless, destitute of emotional warmth. We might then see the bear and judge it best to run, receive the insult and deem it right to strike, but we could not actually *feel* afraid or angry.

Stated in this crude way, the hypothesis is pretty sure to meet with immediate disbelief. And yet neither many nor farfetched considerations are required to mitigate its paradoxical character and possibly to produce conviction of its truth.

To begin with, readers of this journal do not need to be reminded that the nervous system of every living thing is but a bundle of predispositions to react in particular ways upon the contact of particular features of the environment. As surely as the hermit crab's abdomen presupposes the existence of empty whelk shells somewhere to be found, so surely do the hound's olfactories imply the existence, on the one hand, of deers' or foxes' feet, and on the other, the tendency to follow up their tracks. The neural machinery is but a hyphen between determinate arrangements of matter outside the body and determinate impulses to inhibition or discharge within its organs. When the hen sees a white oval object on the ground, she cannot leave it; she must keep upon it and return to it, until at last its transformation into a little mass of moving, chirping down elicits from her machinery an entirely new set of performances. The love of man for woman, or of the human mother for her babe, our wrath at snakes and our fear of precipices, may all be described similarly, as instances of the way in which peculiarly conformed pieces of the world's furniture will fatally call forth most particular mental and bodily reactions, in advance of, and often in direct opposition to, the verdict of our deliberate reason concerning them. The labors of Darwin and his successors are only just beginning to reveal the universal parasitism of each special creature upon other special things, and the way in which each creature brings the signature of its special relations stamped on its nervous system with it upon the scene.

Every living creature is in fact a sort of lock, whose wards and springs presuppose special forms of key—which keys, however, are not born attached to the locks, but are sure to be found in the world near by as life goes on. And the locks are indifferent to any but their own keys. The egg fails to fascinate the hound, the bird does not fear the precipice, the snake waxes not wroth at his kind, the deer cares nothing for the woman or the human babe. Those who wish for a full development of this point of view should read Schneider's *"Der thierische Wille"*—no other book shows how accurately anticipatory are the actions of animals, of the specific features of the environment in which they are to live.

Now among these nervous anticipations are of course to be reckoned the emotions, so far as these may be called forth directly by the perception of certain facts. In advance of all experience of elephants no child can but be frightened if he suddenly find one trumpeting and charging upon him. No woman can see a handsome little naked baby without delight, no man in the wilderness see a human form in the distance without excitement and curiosity. I said I should consider these emotions only so far as they have bodily movements of some sort for their accompaniments. But my first point is to show that their bodily accompaniments are much more far-reaching and complicated than we ordinarily suppose.

In the earlier books on expression, written mostly from the artistic point of view, the signs of emotion visible from without were the only ones taken account of. Sir Charles Bell's celebrated "Anatomy of Expression" noticed the respiratory changes; and Bain's and Darwin's treatises went more thoroughly still into the study of the visceral factors involved —changes in the functioning of glands and muscles, and in that of the circulatory apparatus. But not even a Darwin has exhaustively enumerated *all* the bodily affections characteristic of any one of the standard emotions. More and more, as physiology advances, we begin to discern how almost infinitely numerous and subtle they must be. The researches of Mosso with the plethysmograph have shown that not only the heart, but the entire circulatory system, forms a sort of sounding board, which every change of our consciousness, however slight, may make reverberate. Hardly a sensation comes to us without sending waves of alternate constriction and dilatation down the arteries of our arms. The blood vessels of the abdomen act reciprocally with those of the more outward parts. The bladder and bowels, the glands of the mouth, throat, and skin, and the liver are known to be affected gravely in certain severe emotions and are unquestionably affected transiently when the emotions are of a lighter sort. That the heartbeats and the rhythm of breathing play a leading part in all emotions whatsoever is a matter too notorious for proof. And what is really equally prominent, but less likely to be admitted until special attention is drawn to the fact, is the continuous co-operation of the voluntary muscles in our emotional states. Even when no change of outward attitude is produced, their inward tension alters to suit each varying mood and is felt as a difference of tone or of strain. In depression the flexors tend to prevail; in elation or belligerent excitement the extensors take the lead. And the various permutations and combinations of which these organic activities are susceptible make it abstractly possible that no shade of emotion, however slight, should be without a bodily reverberation as unique, when taken in its totality, as is the mental mood itself.

The immense number of parts modified in each emotion is what makes it so difficult for us to reproduce in cold blood the total and integral expression of any one of them. We may catch the trick with the voluntary muscles, but fail with the skin, glands, heart, and other viscera. Just as an artificially imitated sneeze lacks something of the reality, so the attempt to imitate an emotion in the absence of its normal instigating cause is apt to be rather "hollow."

The next thing to be noticed is this, that every one of the bodily changes, whatsoever it be, is *felt,* acutely or obscurely, the moment it occurs. If the reader has never paid attention to this matter, he will be both interested and astonished to learn how many different local bodily feelings he can detect in himself as characteristic of his various emotional moods. It would be perhaps too much to expect him to arrest the tide of any strong gust of passion for the sake of any such curious analysis as this; but he can observe more tranquil states, and that may be assumed here to be true of the greater which is shown to be true of the less. Our whole cubic capacity is sensibly alive; and each morsel of it contributes its pulsations of feeling, dim or sharp, pleasant, painful, or dubious, to that sense of personality that every one of us unfailingly carries with him. It is surprising what little items give accent to these complexes of sensibility. When worried by any slight trouble, one may find that the focus of one's bodily consciousness is the contraction, often quite inconsiderable, of the eyes and brows. When momentarily embarrassed, it is something in the pharynx that compels either a swallow, a clearing of the throat, or a slight cough; and so on for as many more instances as might be named. Our concern here being with the general view rather than with the details, I will not linger to discuss these but, assuming the point admitted that every change that occurs must be felt, I will pass on

I now proceed to urge the vital point of my whole theory, which is this. If we fancy some strong emotion, and then try to abstract from our consciousness of it all the feelings of its characteristic bodily symptoms, we find we have nothing left behind, no "mind stuff" out of which the emotion can be constituted, and that a cold and neutral state of intellectual perception is all that remains. It is true that, although most people, when asked, say that their introspection verifies this statement, some persist in saying theirs does not. Many cannot be made to understand the question. When you beg them to imagine away every feeling of laughter and of tendency to laugh from their consciousness of the ludicrousness of an object, and then to tell you what the feeling of its ludicrousness would be like, whether it be anything more than the perception that the object belongs to the class "funny," they persist in replying that the thing proposed is a physical impossibility and that they always *must* laugh if they see a funny object. Of course the task proposed is not the practical one of seeing a ludicrous object and annihilating one's tendency to laugh. It is the purely speculative one of subtracting certain elements of feeling from an emotional state supposed to exist in its fullness, and saying what the residual elements are.

I cannot help thinking that all who rightly apprehend this problem will agree with the proposition above laid down. What kind of an emotion of fear would be left if the feelings neither of quickened heartbeats nor of shallow breathing, neither of trembling lips nor of weakened limbs, neither of goose flesh nor of visceral stirrings, were present, it is quite impossible to think. Can one fancy the state of rage and picture no ebullition of it in the chest, no flushing of the face, no dilatation of the nostrils, no clenching of the teeth, no impulse to vigorous action, but in their stead limp muscles, calm breathing, and a placid face? The present writer, for one, certainly cannot. The rage is as completely evaporated as the sensation of its so-called manifestations, and the only thing that can possibly be supposed to take its place is some cold-blooded and dispassionate judicial sentence, confined entirely to the intellectual realm, to the effect that a certain person or persons merit chastisement for their sins. In like manner of grief: what would it be without its tears, its sobs, its suffocation of the heart, its pang in the breastbone? A feelingless cognition that certain circumstances are deplorable, and nothing more.

Every passion in turn tells the same story. A purely disembodied human emotion is a nonentity. I do not say that it is a contradiction in the nature of things; or that pure spirits are necessarily condemned to cold intellectual lives; but I say that for *us* emotion dissociated from all bodily feeling is inconceivable. The more closely I scrutinize my states the more persuaded I become that whatever moods, affections, and passions I have are in very truth constituted by, and made up of, those bodily changes we ordinarily call their expression or consequence; and the more it seems to me that if I were to become corporeally anesthetic I should be excluded from the life of the affections, harsh and tender alike, and drag out an existence of merely cognitive or intellectual form. Such an existence, although it seems to have been the ideal of ancient sages, is too apathetic to be keenly sought after by those born after the revival of the worship of sensibility, a few generations ago.

But if the emotion is nothing but the feeling of the reflex bodily effects of what we call its "object," effects due to the connate adaptation of the nervous system to that object, we seem immediately faced by this objection: most of the objects of civilized men's emotions are things to which it would be preposterous to suppose their nervous systems connately adapted. Most occasions of shame and many insults are purely conventional, and vary with the social environment. The same is true of many matters of dread and of desire, and of many occasions of melancholy and regret. In these cases, at least, it would seem that the ideas of shame, desire, regret, et cetera, must first have been attached by education and association to these conventional objects before the bodily changes could possibly be awakened. And if in *these* cases the bodily changes follow the ideas, instead of giving rise to them, why not then in all cases?

To discuss thoroughly this objection would carry us deep into the study of purely intellectual aesthetics. A few words must here suffice. We will say nothing of the argument's failure to distinguish between the idea of an emotion and the emotion itself. We will only recall the well-known evolutionary principle that when a certain power has once been fixed in an animal by virtue of its utility in presence of certain features of the environment it may turn out to be useful in presence of other features of the environment that had originally nothing to do with either producing or preserving it. A nervous tendency to discharge being once there, all sorts of unforeseen things may pull the trigger and let loose the effects. That among these things should be conventionalities of man's contriving is a matter of no psychological consequence whatever. The most important part of my environment is my fellow man. The consciousness of his attitude toward me is the perception that normally unlocks most of my shames and indignations and fears. The extraordinary sensitiveness of this consciousness is shown by the bodily modifications wrought in us by the awareness that our fellow man is noticing us *at all*. No one can walk across the platform at a public meeting with just the same muscular innervation he uses to walk across his room at home. No one can give a message to such a meeting without organic excitement. "Stage fright" is only the extreme degree of that wholly irrational personal self-consciousness which everyone gets in some measure as soon as he feels the eyes of a number of strangers fixed upon him, even though he be inwardly convinced that their feeling toward him is of no practical account. This being so, it is not surprising that the additional persuasion that my fellow man's attitude means either well or ill for me should awaken stronger emotions still. In primitive societies "well" may mean handing me a piece of beef, and "ill" may mean aiming a blow at my skull. In our "cultural age," "ill" may mean cutting me in the street, and "well" giving me an honorary degree. What the action itself may be is quite insignificant so long as I can perceive in it intent or *animus*. That is the emotion-arousing perception; and may give rise to as strong bodily convulsions in me, a civilized man experiencing the treatment of an artificial society, as in any savage prisoner of war, learning whether his captors are about to eat him or to make him a member of their tribe.

But now, this objection disposed of, there arises a more general doubt. Is there any evidence, it may be asked, for the assumption that particular perceptions *do* produce widespread bodily effects by a sort of immediate physical influence, antecedent to the arousal of an emotion or emotional idea?

The only possible reply is that there is most assuredly such evidence. In listening to poetry, drama, or heroic narrative we are often surprised at the cutaneous shiver which like a sudden wave flows over us, and at the heart-swelling and the lachrymal effusion that unexpectedly catch us at intervals. In listening to music the same is even more strikingly true. If we abruptly see a dark moving form in the woods, our heart stops beating, and we catch our breath instantly and before any articulate idea of danger can arise. If our friend goes near to the edge of a precipice, we get the well-known feeling of "all-overishness," and we shrink back, although we positively *know* him to be safe and have no distinct imagination of his fall. The writer well remembers his astonishment, when a boy of seven or eight, at fainting when he saw a horse bled. The blood was in a bucket, with a stick in it, and, if memory does not deceive him, he stirred it round and saw it drip from the stick with no feeling save that of childish curiosity. Suddenly the world grew black before his eyes, his ears began to buzz, and he knew no more. He had never heard of the sight of blood producing faintness or sickness, and he had so little repugnance to it, and so little apprehension of any other sort of danger from it, that even at that tender age, as he well remembers, he could not help wondering how the mere physical presence of a pailful of crimson fluid could occasion in him such formidable bodily effects.

Imagine two steel knife blades with their keen edges crossing each other at right angles, and moving to and fro. Our whole nervous organization is "on edge" at the thought; and yet what emotion can be there except the unpleasant nervous feeling itself, or the dread that more of it may come? The entire fund and capital of the emotion here is the senseless bodily effect the blades immediately arouse. This case is typical of a class: where an ideal emotion seems to precede the bodily symptoms, it is often nothing but a representation of the symptoms themselves. One who has already fainted at the sight of blood may witness the preparations for a surgical operation with uncontrollable heart sinking and anxiety. He anticipates certain feelings, and the anticipation precipitates their arrival. I am told of a case of morbid terror, of which the subject confessed that what possessed her seemed, more than anything, to be the fear of fear itself. In the various forms of what Professor Bain calls "tender emotion," although the appropriate object must usually be directly contemplated before the emotion can be aroused, yet sometimes thinking of the symptoms of the emotion itself may have the same effect. In sentimental natures the thought of "yearning" will produce real "yearning." And, not to speak of coarser examples, a mother's imagination of the caresses she bestows on her child may arouse a spasm of parental longing.

In such cases as these we see plainly how the emotion both begins and ends with what we call its effects or manifestations. It has no mental *status* except as either the presented feeling, or the idea, of the manifestations; which latter thus constitute its entire material, its sum and substance, and its stock in trade. And these cases ought to make us see how in all cases the feeling of the manifestations may play a much deeper part in the constitution of the emotion than we are wont to suppose.

If our theory be true, a necessary corollary of it ought to be that any voluntary arousal of the so-called manifestations of a special emotion ought to give us the emotion itself. Of course in the majority of emotions this test is inapplicable; for many of the manifestations are in organs over which we have no volitional control. Still, within the limits in which it can be verified, experience fully corroborates this test. Everyone knows how panic is increased by flight and how the giving way to the symptoms of grief or anger increases those passions themselves. Each fit of sobbing makes the sorrow more acute and calls forth another fit stronger still, until at last repose only ensues with lassitude and with the apparent exhaustion of the machinery. In rage it is notorious how we "work ourselves up" to a climax by repeated outbreaks of expression. Refuse to express a passion, and it dies. Count ten before venting your anger, and its occasion seems ridiculous. Whistling to keep up courage is no mere figure of speech. On the other hand, sit all day in a moping posture, sigh, and reply to everything with a dismal voice, and your melancholy lingers. There is no more valuable precept in moral education than this, as all who have experience know: if we wish to conquer undesirable emotional tendencies in ourselves, we must assiduously, and in the first instance cold-bloodedly, go through the *outward motions* of those contrary dispositions we prefer to cultivate. The reward of persistency will infallibly come, in the fading out of the sullenness or depression, and the advent of real cheerfulness and kindliness in their stead. Smooth the brow, brighten the eye, contract the dorsal rather than the ventral aspect of the frame, and speak in a major key, pass the genial compliment, and your heart must be frigid indeed if it do not gradually thaw!

The only exceptions to this are apparent, not real. The great emotional expressiveness and mobility of certain persons often lead us to say, "They would feel more if they talked less." And in another class of persons the explosive energy with which passion manifests itself on critical occasions seems correlated with the way in which they bottle it up during the intervals. But these are only eccentric types of character, and within each type the law of the last paragraph prevails. The sentimentalist is so constructed that "gushing" is his or her normal mode of expression. Putting a stopper on the "gush" will only to a limited extent cause more "real" activities to take its place; in the main it will simply produce listlessness. On the other hand, the ponderous and bilious "slumbering volcano," let him repress the expression of his passions as he will, will find them expire if they get no vent at all; while if the rare occasions multiply which he deems worthy of their outbreak, he will find them grow in intensity as life proceeds.

I feel persuaded there is no real exception to the law. The formidable effects of suppressed tears might be mentioned, and the calming results of speaking out your mind when angry and having done with it. But these are also but specious wanderings from the rule. Every perception must lead to *some* nervous result. If this be the normal emotional expression, it soon expends itself, and in the natural course of things a calm succeeds. But if the normal issue be blocked from any cause, the currents may under certain circumstances invade other tracts, and there work different and worse effects. Thus vengeful brooding may replace a burst of indignation; a dry heat may consume the frame of one who fain would weep, or he may, as Dante says, turn to stone within; and then tears or a storming fit may bring a grateful relief. When we teach children to repress their emotions, it is not that they may *feel* more; quite the reverse. It is that they may *think* more! For to a certain extent whatever nerve currents are diverted from the regions below must swell the activity of the thought tracts of the brain.

The last great argument in favor of the priority of the bodily symptoms to the felt emotion is the ease with which we formulate by its means pathological cases and normal cases under a common scheme. In every asylum we find examples of absolutely unmotived fear, anger, melancholy, or conceit; and others of an equally unmotived apathy which persists in spite of the best of outward reasons why it should give way. In the former cases we must suppose the nervous machinery to be so "labile" in some one emotional direction that almost every stimulus, however inappropriate, will cause it to upset in that way, and as a consequence to engender the particular complex of feelings of which the psychic body of the emotion consists. Thus, to take one special instance, if inability to draw deep breath, fluttering of the heart, and that peculiar epigastric change felt as "precordial anxiety," with an irresistible tendency to take a somewhat crouching attitude and to sit still, and with perhaps other visceral processes not now known, all spontaneously occur together in a certain person, his feeling of their combination *is* the emotion of dread, and he is the victim of what is known as morbid fear. A friend who has had occasional attacks of this most distressing of all maladies tells me that in his case the whole drama seems to center about the region of the heart and respiratory apparatus, that his main effort during the attacks is to get control of his inspirations and to slow his heart, and that the moment he attains to breathing deeply and to holding himself erect the dread, ipso facto, seems to depart.

The account given to Brachet by one of his own patients of her opposite condition, that of emotional insensibility, has been often quoted, and deserves to be quoted again:

"I still continue [she says] to suffer constantly; I have not a moment of comfort, and no human sensations. Surrounded by all that can render life happy and agreeable, still to me the faculty of enjoyment and of feeling is wanting—both have become physical impossibilities. In everything, even in the most tender caresses of my children, I find only bitterness. I cover them with kisses, but there is something between their lips and mine; and this horrid something is between me and all the enjoyments of life. My existence is incomplete. The functions and acts of ordinary life, it is true, still remain to me; but in every one of them there is something wanting—to wit, the feeling which is proper to them, and the pleasure which follows them. . . .

"*Each of my senses, each part of my proper self, is as it were separated from me and can no longer afford me any feeling; this impossibility seems to depend upon a void which I feel in the front of my head, and to be due to the diminution of the sensibility over the whole surface of my body, for it seems to me that I never actually reach the objects which I touch. . . . I feel well enough the changes of temperature on my skin, but I no longer experience the internal feeling of the air when I breathe. . . .*

"All this would be a small matter enough, but for its frightful result, which is that of the impossibility of any other kind of feeling and of any sort of enjoyment, although I experience a need and desire of them that render my life an incomprehensible torture. Every function, every action of my life remains, but deprived of the feeling that belongs to it, of the enjoyment that should follow it. My feet are cold, I warm them, but gain no pleasure from the warmth. I recognize the taste of all I eat, without getting any pleasure from it. . . . My children are growing handsome and healthy, everyone tells me so, I see it myself, but the delight, the inward comfort I ought to feel, I fail to get. Music has lost all charm for me; I used to love it dearly. My daughter plays very well, but for me it is mere noise. That lively interest which a year ago made me hear a delicious concert in the smallest air their fingers played—that thrill, that general vibration which made me shed such tender tears—all that exists no more."

Other victims describe themselves as closed in walls of ice or covered with an India-rubber integument, through which no impression penetrates to the sealed-up sensibility.

If our hypothesis be true, it makes us realize more deeply than ever how much our mental life is knit up with our corporeal frame, in the strictest sense of the term. Rapture, love, ambition, indignation, and pride, considered as feelings, are fruits of the same soil with the grossest bodily sensations of pleasure and of pain.

The Germ Theory of Disease

LOUIS PASTEUR (1822–95)

SOMETIMES pure science leads to unexpectedly important industrial applications; conversely, the attempt of a gifted scientist to solve immediate and practical problems of industry may lead to the origination and development of theories of far greater practical value than the solution of the problem at hand. Nowhere has this truism been exemplified better than in the life of Louis Pasteur, trained as a chemist, employed by the French Government as an industrial trouble shooter, and elevated by his own incisive intuition and unruffled patience to become the founder of modern bacteriology, the father of the germ theory of disease, benefactor of mankind and perhaps the greatest name in French science.

The wine in Orleans is turning to vinegar. Pasteur showed the vintners how to keep it from spoiling by heating it to 55°C. But the process of "pasteurization," applied to milk, has been of even greater importance in reducing infant death rates. . . . *The silkworms in Alais are dying of pébrine and the silk industry in southern France is in danger of extinction.* Pasteur studied the problem for five years (1865–70). By the time the victorious Prussians had entered Paris, a devastating personal tragedy to this loyal French scientist, Pasteur had discovered that the silkworms suffered not from one but from two diseases. Thus he caught the vital idea that just as there were specific *ferments,* that is, each kind of microorganism produced its own kind of fermentation, so also specific bacteria caused particular diseases. The application of this germ theory of disease to clinical medicine and surgery has saved more lives than even wars have destroyed. . . . *The sheep are dying of anthrax, the chickens of cholera.* Pasteur went to work on these problems. Now his work was made easier by the correlative researches of other men who flocked to the newly founded science of bacteriology; most notably, an upcountry German physician, Robert Koch (1843–1910), who developed the technique of staining bacteria, established postulates for proving the specific infectiousness of various bacteria, and isolated the anthrax and tubercle bacilli. Pasteur developed the culture medium—neutralized urine—for the anthrax bacilli. On a flock of 100 sheep, half vaccinated, half not, he conclusively demonstrated that the animals could be saved by immunizing them with old cultures. The theory of immunity, however, brought even greater triumphs. Pasteur himself, as he describes here, achieved the conquest of rabies by the process of immunization (1885). The work of Roux, at the Pasteur Institute in Paris, led to the development of diphtheria antitoxin, perfected by Von Behring. And successful immunization against tetanus, yellow fever, and other diseases continues to add luster to the name of Pasteur.

Pasteur worked better than he wrote. He has a diffuse style and nowhere does he summarize his most significant findings. As characteristic as anything of his literary productions is the brief passage quoted here from his "Memoir on Organic Corpuscles Which Exist in the Atmosphere" (Paris, 1862), in which he rehearsed the history of the theories of spontaneous generation, whose falsity was permanently established by his own crucial experiments with the dust-free gooseneck flask.

French was Pasteur's tongue. The English translations are by Dorothy H. Clendening, from "A Source Book of Medical History" (New York: Paul B. Hoeber-Harper & Brothers, 1942). "Prevention of Rabies" is adapted from the translation of D. Berger, in "The Founders of Modern Medicine" (New York: Walden Publications, 1940).

THEORY OF SPONTANEOUS GENERATION UPSET

[*The theory of spontaneous generation of living creatures goes back to Aristotle. As late as the seventeenth century it was stated that frogs were produced by marsh mud, eels in river water. Opposed to this doctrine of spontaneous generation, held by Buffon and Needham, is the hypothesis that "life comes from life." The question was hotly debated in France during the nineteenth century. Pasteur, devising a "gooseneck flask," settled it for all time in his experiments undertaken as a result of the following prize question proposed by the French Academy of Science.*]

TRY, *by careful experiment, to throw a new light on the question of spontaneous generation.*

The question seemed so obscure that Biot was distressed to see me engaged in these researches and implored my obedience to his advice, to accept a time limit, at the end of which I would abandon the subject if I had not conquered the difficulties which beset me. Dumas said to me at the same time, "I would never advise anyone to spend too much time on that subject."

What need was there for me to stick to it?

Twenty years ago the chemists discovered a really extraordinary group of phenomena, classified under the generic name of *fermentations.* All demanded the concurrence of two substances: one *fermentable*—like sugar, the other *nitrogenizable*—always an albuminoid substance. Here is the theory which was universally accepted: the albuminoid substances showed a change when they were exposed to contact with air, a particular oxidation of an unknown nature which gives them the character of a *ferment.* That is to say, the property of acting on fermentable substances by contact.

There was a ferment, the oldest, the most remarkable of all, that was known to be an organic being—beer yeast. But because, in all the fermentations discovered more recently than the discovery of the fact of the composition of beer yeast (1836), the physiologists were unable to recognize the existence of organic beings, even by careful research, they had gradually abandoned (some with much regret) Cagniard de Latour's hypothesis of a probable relation of the composition of this ferment to its property of being a ferment, and applied to beer yeast a general theory by saying: "It is not because it is organic that beer yeast is active, it is because it has been in contact with air. It is the dead part of the yeast, that which was alive and which is in the course of alteration, which acts on the sugar."

My studies led me to entirely different conclusions. I found that all properly called fermentations—viscous, lactic, butyric, fermentation of tartaric acid, malic acid, urine—were always correlative to the presence and multiplication of organic beings. And so far as the composition of beer yeast being a hindrance to the theory of fermentation, it was, on the contrary, from that that it became the common rule and was the type of all properly called ferments. In my opinion albuminoid substances were never ferments but the food of the ferments. The true ferments were organic beings.

PREVENTION OF RABIES

AFTER MAKING almost innumerable experiments, I have discovered a prophylactic method which is practical and prompt, and which has already in dogs afforded me results sufficiently numerous, certain, and successful, to warrant my having confidence in its general applicability to all animals, and even to man himself.

This method depends essentially on the following facts:

The inoculation of the infective spinal cord of a dog suffering from ordinary rabies under the dura mater of a rabbit always produces rabies after a period of incubation having a mean duration of about fifteen days.

If, by the above method of inoculation, the virus of the first rabbit is passed into a second, and that of the second into a third, and so on, in series, a more and more striking tendency is soon manifested toward a diminution of the duration of the incubation period of rabies in the rabbits successively inoculated.

The virus of rabies at a constant degree of virulence is contained in the spinal cords of these rabbits throughout their whole extent.

If portions, a few centimeters long, are removed from these spinal cords with every possible precaution to preserve their purity, and are then suspended in dry air, the virulence slowly disappears, until at last it entirely vanishes. The time within which this extinction of virulence is brought about varies a little with the thickness of the morsels of spinal cord, but chiefly with the external temperature. The lower the temperature the longer is the virulence preserved. These results form the central scientific point in the method.

These facts being established, a dog may be rendered refractory to rabies in a relatively short time in the following way:

Every day morsels of fresh infective spinal cord from a rabbit which has died of rabies, developed after an incubation period of seven days, are suspended in a series of flasks, the air in which is kept dry by placing fragments of potash at the bottom of the flask. Every day also a dog is inoculated under the skin with a Pravaz' syringeful of sterilized broth, in which a small fragment of one of the spinal cords has been broken up, commencing with a spinal cord far enough removed in order of time from the day of the operation to render it certain that the cord was not at all virulent. (This date had been ascertained by previous experiments.) On the following days the same operation is performed with more recent cords, separated from each other by an interval of two days, until at last a very virulent cord, which has only been in the flask for two days, is used.

The dog has now been rendered refractory to rabies. It may be inoculated with the virus of rabies under the skin, or even after trephining, on the surface of the brain, without any subsequent development of rabies.

Never having once failed when using this method, I had in my possession fifty dogs, of all ages and of every race, refractory to rabies, when three individuals from Alsace unexpectedly presented themselves at my laboratory, on Monday, the sixth of last July.

Théodore Vone, grocer, of Meissengott, near Schlestadt, bitten in the arm, July 4, by his own dog, which had gone mad.

Joseph Meister, aged nine years, also bitten on July 4, at eight o'clock in the morning, by the same dog. This child had been knocked over by the dog and presented numerous bites, on the hands, legs, and thighs, some of them so deep as to render walking difficult. The principal bites had been cauterized at eight o'clock in the evening of July 4, only twelve hours after the accident, with phenic acid, by Dr. Weber, of Villé.

The third person, who had not been bitten, was the mother of little Joseph Meister.

At the examination of the dog, after its death by the hand of its master, the stomach was found full of hay, straw, and scraps of wood. The dog was certainly rabid. Joseph Meister had been pulled out from under him covered with foam and blood.

Monsieur Vone had some severe contusions on the arm, but he assured me that his shirt had not been pierced by the dog's fangs. As he had nothing to fear, I told him that he could return to Alsace the same day, which he did. But I kept young Meister and his mother with me.

The weekly meeting of the Académie des Sciences took place on July 6. At it I met our colleague, Dr. Vulpian, to whom I related what had just happened. Monsieur Vulpian, and Dr. Grancher, professor in the Faculté de Médecine, had the goodness to come and see little Joseph Meister at once, and to take note of the condition and the number of his wounds. There were no less than fourteen.

The opinion of our learned colleague, and of Dr. Grancher, was that, owing to the severity and the number of the bites, Joseph Meister was almost certain to take rabies. I then communicated to Monsieur Vulpian and to Monsieur Grancher the new results which I had obtained from the study of rabies since the address which I had given at Copenhagen a year earlier.

The death of this child appearing to be inevitable, I decided, not without lively and sore anxiety, as may well be believed, to try upon Joseph Meister the method which I had found constantly successful with dogs. . . .

Consequently, on July 6, at eight o'clock in the evening, sixty hours after the bites on July 4, and in the presence of Drs. Vulpian and Grancher, young Meister was inoculated under a fold of skin raised in the right hypochondrium, with half a Pravaz' syringeful of the spinal cord of a rabbit, which had died of rabies on June 21. It had been preserved since then, that is to say, fifteen days, in a flask of dry air.

In the following days fresh inoculations were made. I thus made thirteen inoculations, and prolonged the treatment to ten days. I shall say later on that a smaller number of inoculations would have been sufficient. But it will be understood how, in the first attempt, I would act with a very special circumspection. . . .

On the last days, therefore, I had inoculated Joseph Meister with the most virulent virus of rabies, that, namely, of the dog, reinforced by passing a great number of times from rabbit to rabbit, a virus which produces rabies after seven days' incubation in these animals, after eight or ten days in dogs. . . .

Joseph Meister, therefore, has escaped not only the rabies, which would have been caused by the bites he received, but also the rabies with which I have inoculated him in order to test the immunity produced by the treatment, a rabies more virulent than ordinary canine rabies.

The final inoculation with very virulent virus has this further advantage, that it puts a period to the apprehensions which arise as to the consequences of the bites. If rabies could occur it would declare itself more quickly after a more virulent virus than after the virus of the bites. Since the middle of August I have looked forward with confidence to the future good health of Joseph Meister. At the present time, three months and three weeks have elapsed since the accident; his state of health leaves nothing to be desired. . . .

The Founder of Antiseptic Surgery

JOSEPH LISTER (1827–1912)

MODERN MILITARY SURGERY has in some instances achieved a mortality rate of less than 1 per cent for wounds received in battle. Yet Napoleon's surgeon-in-chief, Larrey, reported but two survivals in several thousand cases of amputation at the hip. Suppuration of the wound was the usual cause of death. The situation was but little improved half a century later when a grave, patient, Quaker-born surgeon, Joseph Lister, son of the founder of modern microscopy, graduate at London, having served for six years as house surgeon under Syme at Edinburgh, proceeded to become professor of surgery at Glasgow. The tragic odor of suppurating wounds following fractures and amputations—the charnel-house odor of the pre-asepsis hospital—continued to smite his nostrils and stir a hope almost smothered in despair. In 1860 Lister became acquainted with Pasteur's work on spontaneous generation, caught the importance of the germ theory of disease, realized that pus, however "laudable," from suppurating wounds might be suppressed by killing the germs that were causing it. Shortly thereafter he heard about carbolic acid, used to disinfect sewage. Putting two and two together, he decided to kill the germs that contaminated wounds and fractures by dressing them with dilute carbolic-acid bandages and spraying the site of the wound and the operating rooms with the same antiseptic. The results were far better than anything that had previously been attained; and even though antiseptic surgery, in which germs were killed, was soon superseded by aseptic surgery, in which germs were excluded through absolute cleanliness of person and environment, Lister deserves the lion's credit for introducing the modern era of surgery.

English was the language in which Lister addressed the surgical section at the annual meeting of the British Medical Association in Dublin, August 9, 1867, "On the Antiseptic Principle in the Practice of Surgery." The address was first published as an article in the September 21, 1867, issue of the "British Medical Journal."

"ON THE ANTISEPTIC PRINCIPLE OF THE PRACTICE OF SURGERY"

IN THE COURSE of an extended investigation into the nature of inflammation, and the healthy and morbid conditions of the blood in relation to it, I arrived several years ago at the conclusion that the essential cause of suppuration in wounds is decomposition, brought about by the influence of the atmosphere upon blood or serum retained within them, and, in the case of contused wounds, upon portions of tissue destroyed by the violence of the injury.

To prevent the occurrence of suppuration with all its attendant risks was an object manifestly desirable, but till lately apparently unattainable, since it seemed hopeless to attempt to exclude the oxygen which was universally regarded as the agent by which putrefaction was effected. But when it had been shown by the researches of Pasteur that the septic properties of the atmosphere depended not on the oxygen, or any gaseous constituent, but on minute organisms suspended in it, which owed their energy to their vitality, it occurred to me that decomposition in the injured part might be avoided without excluding the air by applying as a dressing some material capable of destroying the life of the floating particles. Upon this principle I have based a practice of which I will now attempt to give a short account.

The material which I have employed is carbolic or phenic acid, a volatile organic compound, which appears to exercise a peculiarly destructive influence upon low forms of life, and hence is the most powerful antiseptic with which we are at present acquainted.

The first class of cases to which I applied it was that of compound fractures, in which the effects of decomposition in the injured part were especially striking and pernicious. The results have been such as to establish conclusively the great principle that all local inflammatory mischief and general febrile disturbances which follow severe injuries are due to the irritating and poisonous influence of decomposing blood or sloughs. For these evils are entirely avoided by the antiseptic treatment, so that limbs which would otherwise be unhesitatingly condemned to amputation may be retained, with confidence of the best results.

In conducting the treatment, the first object must be the destruction of any septic germs which may have been introduced into the wounds, either at the moment of the accident or during the time which has since elapsed. This is done by introducing the acid of full strength into all accessible recesses of the wound by means of a piece of rag held in dressing forceps and dipped into the liquid.[1] This I did not venture to do in the earlier cases; but experience has shown that the compound which carbolic acid forms with the blood, and also any portions of tissue killed by its caustic action, including even parts of the bone, are disposed of by absorption and organization, provided they are afterward kept from decomposing. We are thus enabled to employ the antiseptic treatment efficiently at a period after the occurrence of the injury at which it would otherwise probably fail. Thus I have now under my care, in Glasgow Infirmary, a boy who was admitted with compound fracture of the leg as late as eight and one half hours after the accident, in whom, nevertheless, all local and constitutional disturbance was avoided by means of carbolic acid, and the bones were soundly united five weeks after his admission.

The next object to be kept in view is to guard effectually against the spreading of decomposition into the wound along the stream of blood and serum which oozes out during the first few days after the accident, when the acid applied has been washed out or dissipated by absorption and evaporation. This part of the treatment has been greatly improved during the past few weeks. The method which I have hitherto published (see "Lancet" for March 16, 23, 30, and April 27 of the present year) consisted in the application of a piece of lint dipped in the acid, overlapping the sound skin to some extent and covered with a tin cap, which was daily raised in order to touch the surface of the lint with the antiseptic. This method certainly succeeded well with wounds of moderate size; and indeed I may say that in all the many cases of this kind which have been so treated by myself or my house surgeons not a single failure has occurred. When, however, the wound is very large, the flow of blood and serum is so profuse, especially during the first twenty-four hours, that the antiseptic application cannot prevent the spread of decomposition into the interior unless it overlaps the sound skin for a very considerable distance, and this was inadmissible by the method described above, on account of the extensive sloughing of the surface of the cutis which it would involve. This difficulty has, however, been overcome by employing a paste composed of common whiting (carbonate of lime) mixed with a solution of one part of

---

[1] The addition of a few drops of water to a considerable quantity of the acid induces it to assume permanently the liquid form.

carbolic acid in four parts of boiled linseed oil so as to form a firm putty. This application contains the acid in too dilute a form to excoriate the skin, which it may be made to cover to any extent that may be thought desirable, while its substance serves as a reservoir of the antiseptic material. So long as any discharge continues the paste should be changed daily, and in order to prevent the chance of mischief occurring during the process a piece of rag dipped in the solution of carbolic acid in oil is put on next the skin and maintained there permanently, care being taken to avoid raising it along with the putty. This rag is always kept in an antiseptic condition from contact with the paste above it and destroys any germs which may fall upon it during the short time that should alone be allowed to pass in the changing of the dressing. The putty should be in a layer about a quarter of an inch thick and may be advantageously applied rolled out between two pieces of thin calico, which maintain it in the form of a continuous sheet, which may be wrapped in a moment round the whole circumference of a limb if this be thought desirable, while the putty is prevented by the calico from sticking to the rag which is next the skin. When all discharge has ceased, the use of the paste is discontinued, but the original rag is left adhering to the skin till healing by scabbing is supposed to be complete. I have at present in the hospital a man with severe compound fracture of both bones of the left leg, caused by direct violence, who, after the cessation of the sanious discharge under the use of the paste, without a drop of pus appearing, has been treated for the last two weeks exactly as if the fracture was a simple one. During this time the rag, adhering by means of a crust of inspissated blood collected beneath it, has continued perfectly dry, and it will be left untouched till the usual period for removing the splints in a simple fracture, when we may fairly expect to find a sound cicatrix beneath it.

We cannot, however, always calculate on so perfect a result as this. More or less pus may appear after the lapse of the first week, and the larger the wound the more likely this is to happen. And here I would desire earnestly to enforce the necessity of persevering with the antiseptic application in spite of the appearance of suppuration, so long as other symptoms are favorable. The surgeon is extremely apt to suppose that any suppuration is an indication that the antiseptic treatment has failed, and that poulticing or water dressing should be resorted to. But such a course would in many cases sacrifice a limb or a life. I cannot, however, expect my professional brethren to follow my advice blindly in such a matter, and therefore I feel it necessary to place before them, as shortly as I can, some pathological principles intimately connected not only with the point we are immediately considering but with the whole subject of this paper.

If a perfectly healthy granulating sore be well washed and covered with a plate of clean metal, such as block tin, fitting its surface pretty accurately, and overlapping the surrounding skin an inch or so in every direction and retained in position by adhesive plaster and a bandage, it will be found, on removing it after twenty-four or forty-eight hours, that little or nothing that can be called pus is present, merely a little transparent fluid, while at the same time there is an entire absence of the unpleasant odor invariably perceived when water dressing is changed. Here the clean metallic surface presents no recesses like those of porous lint for the septic germs to develop in, the fluid exuding from the surface of the granulations has flowed away undecomposed, and the result is the absence of suppuration. This simple experiment illustrates the important fact that granulations have no inherent tendency to form pus, but do so only when subjected to preternatural stimulus. Further, it shows that the mere contact of a foreign body does not of itself stimulate granulations to suppurate; whereas the presence of decomposing organic matter does. These truths are even more strikingly exemplified by the fact that I have elsewhere recorded ("Lancet," March 23, 1867), that a piece of dead bone free from decomposition may not only fail to induce the granulations around it to suppurate, but may actually be absorbed by them; whereas a bit of dead bone soaked with putrid pus infallibly induces suppuration in its vicinity. . . .

I left behind me in Glasgow a boy, thirteen years of age, who, between three and four weeks previously, met with a most severe injury to the left arm, which he got entangled in a machine at a fair. There was a wound six inches long and three inches broad, and the skin was very extensively undermined beyond its limits, while the soft parts were generally so much lacerated that a pair of dressing forceps introduced at the wound and pushed directly inward appeared beneath the skin at the opposite aspect of the limb. From this wound several tags of muscle were hanging, and among them was one consisting of about three inches of the triceps in almost its entire thickness; while the lower fragment of the bone, which was broken high up, was protruding four inches and a half, stripped of muscle, the skin being tucked in under it. Without the assistance of the antiseptic treatment I should certainly have thought of nothing else but amputation at the shoulder joint; but as the radial pulse could be felt and the fingers had sensation I did not hesitate to try to save the limb and adopted the plan of treatment above described, wrapping the arm from the shoulder to below the elbow in the antiseptic application, the whole interior of the wound, together with the protruding bone, having previously been freely treated with strong carbolic acid. About the tenth day the discharge, which up to that time had been only sanious and serous, showed a slight admixture of slimy pus; and this increased till (a few days before I left) it amounted to about three drams in twenty-four hours. But the boy continued as he had been after the second day, free from unfavorable symptoms, with pulse, tongue, appetite, and sleep natural and strength increasing, while the limb remained as it had been from the first, free from swelling, redness, or pain. I therefore persevered with the antiseptic dressing; and before I left the discharge was already somewhat less, while the bone was becoming firm. I think it likely that, in that boy's case, I should have found merely a superficial sore had I taken off all the dressings at the end of the three weeks; though, considering the extent of the injury, I thought it prudent to let the month expire before disturbing the rag next the skin. But I feel sure that if I had resorted to ordinary dressing when the pus first appeared the progress of the case would have been exceedingly different.

The next class of cases to which I have applied the antiseptic treatment is that of abscesses. Here also the results have been extremely satisfactory and in beautiful harmony with the pathological principles indicated above. The pyogenic membrane, like the granulations of a sore, which it resembles in nature, forms pus not from any inherent disposition to do so but only because it is subjected to some preternatural stimulation. In an ordinary abscess, whether acute or chronic, before it is opened the stimulus which maintains the suppuration is derived from the presence of pus pent up within the cavity. When a free opening is made in the ordinary way this stimulus is got rid of, but, the atmosphere gaining access to the contents, the potent stimulus of decomposition comes into operation, and pus is generated in greater abundance than before. But when the evacuation is effected on the antiseptic principle, the pyogenic membrane, freed from the influence of the former stimulus without the substitution of a new one, ceases to suppurate (like the granulations of a sore under metallic dressing), furnishing merely a trifling amount of clear serum, and, whether the opening be dependent or not, rapidly contracts and coalesces. At the same time any constitutional symptoms previously occasioned by the accumulation of the matter are got rid of without the slightest risk of the irritative or hectic fever hitherto so justly dreaded in dealing with large abscesses.

In order that the treatment may be satisfactory the abscess must be seen before it is opened. Then, except in very rare and peculiar cases,[2] there are no septic organisms in the contents, so that it is needless to introduce carbolic acid into the interior. Indeed, such a procedure would be objectionable, as it would stimulate the pyogenic membrane to unnecessary suppuration. All that is requisite is to guard against the introduction of living atmospheric germs from without, at the same time that free opportunity is afforded for the escape of the discharge from within. . . .

Ordinary contused wounds are, of course, amenable to the same treatment as compound fractures, which are a complicated variety of them. I will content myself with mentioning a single instance of this class of cases. In April last a volunteer was discharging a rifle when it burst and blew back the thumb with its metacarpal bone, so that it could be bent back as on a hinge at the trapezial joint, which had evidently been opened, while all the soft parts between the metacarpal bones of the thumb and forefinger were torn through. I need not insist before my present audience on the ugly character of such an injury. My house surgeon, Mr. Hector Cameron, applied carbolic acid to the whole raw surface and completed the dressing as if for compound fracture. The hand remained free from pain, redness, or swelling, and with the exception of a shallow groove, all the wound consolidated without a drop of matter, so that if it had been a clean cut it would have been regarded as a good example of primary union. The small granulating surface soon healed, and at present a linear cicatrix alone tells of the injury he has sustained, while his thumb has all its movements and his hand a fine grasp.

If the severest forms of contused and lacerated wounds heal thus kindly under the antiseptic treatment, it is obvious that its application to simple incised wounds must be merely a matter of detail. . . .

It would carry me far beyond the limited time which, by the rules of the Association, is alone at my disposal were I to enter into the various

---

[2]As an instance of one of these exceptional cases I may mention that of an abscess in the vicinity of the colon, and afterwards proved by post-mortem examination to have once communicated with it. Here the pus was extremely offensive when evacuated, and exhibited vibrios under the microscope.

applications of the antiseptic principle in the several special departments of surgery.

There is, however, one point more that I cannot but advert to, viz., the influence of this mode of treatment upon the general healthiness of a hospital. Previously to its introduction the two large wards in which most of my cases of accident and of operation are treated, were among the unhealthiest in the whole surgical division of the Glasgow Royal Infirmary, in consequence apparently of those wards being unfavorably placed with reference to the supply of fresh air; and I have felt ashamed when recording the results of my practice to have so often to allude to hospital gangrene or pyemia. It was interesting, though melancholy, to observe that whenever all or nearly all the beds contained cases with open sores, these grievous complications were pretty sure to show themselves; so that I came to welcome simple fractures, though in themselves of little interest either for myself or the students, because their presence diminished the proportion of open sores among the patients. But since the antiseptic treatment has been brought into full operation, and wounds and abscesses no longer poison the atmosphere with putrid exhalations, my wards, though in other respects under precisely the same circumstances as before, have completely changed their character; so that during the last nine months not a single instance of pyemia, hospital gangrene, or erysipelas has occurred in them.

As there appears to be no doubt regarding the cause of this change, the importance of the fact can hardly be exaggerated.

"The Lady with the Lamp" Makes Nursing Respectable

FLORENCE NIGHTINGALE (1820-1910)

FLORENCE NIGHTINGALE, "the lady with the lamp," "the heroine of the Crimea," an "eminent Victorian," first woman to receive the Order of Merit, made nursing a respected and respectable profession. The "most memorable date in the history of nursing," according to Nutting and Dock, was June 15, 1860, the day when the Nightingale School for Nurses opened its doors at St. Thomas's Hospital in London. The establishment was made possible by the Nightingale Fund, to which grateful soldiers and an enthusiastic public had subscribed £50,000 in testimony toward the reforms in nursing and sanitation that this persistent, executive-minded gentlewoman had accomplished in the teeth of official army opposition at Scutari during the Crimean War.

To the question, "What was a pre-Nightingale nurse?" the London "Times," in 1857, offered this description: "Lectured by committees, preached at by chaplains, scowled on by treasurers and stewards, scolded by matrons, bullied by dressers, grumbled at and abused by patients, insulted if old and ill-favored, talked flippantly to if middle-aged and good-humored, seduced if young—they are what any woman would be under the same circumstances." Florence Nightingale's ideas and ideals soon changed all that.

Florence Nightingale was a gentlewoman, the exceptionally well-educated daughter of wealthy English parents. Zealous in reform, she had systematically studied hospital practice and—shocking to her friends —had actually taken nurse's training at Pastor Fliedner's Kaiserwerth nursing school in Germany before her great opportunity in the Crimea came through her friendship with sympathetic Sidney Herbert, the Secretary of War.

English was the language in which the heroine of the Crimea expressed herself, often with great fervency. "Report on the Crimea" includes excerpts from a lengthy report entitled, "Notes on Matters Affecting the Health, Efficiency, and Hospital Administration of the British Army," submitted to the Secretary of War, upon request, and published in 1858. The first paragraph is taken from another paper, entitled "Army Sanitary Administration and Its Reform under the Late Lord Herbert," read at the London meeting of the *Congrès de Bienfaisance,* June 1862.

"Notes on Nursing" are extracted from "Notes on Nursing: What It Is and What It Is Not" (New York: D. Appleton & Company, 1860). "What a Nurse Is to Be" was published in Quain's "Dictionary of Medicine" (London: Longmans, Green & Company, 1894).

REPORT ON THE CRIMEA

IN TIMES PAST war has been conducted in more or less forgetfulness, sometimes in total oblivion, of the fact that the soldier is a mortal man, subject to all the ills following on wet and cold, want of shelter, bad food, excessive fatigue, bad water, intemperate habits, and foul air. . . . And who can tell how much systematic attempts made by all nations to diminish the horrors of that great curse, war, may not lead the way to its total disappearance from the earth? The faithful records of all wars are records of preventable suffering, disease, and death. It is needless to illustrate this truth, for we all know it. But it is only from our latest sorrow, the Crimean catastrophe, that dates the rise of army sanitary administration in this country. . . . No provision was made for the systematic care of the soldier's health, but only for his sickness. . . . In all our wars our general hospitals have been signal failures, fatal examples of how to kill, not to cure.

It is not denied that a large part of the British force perished from causes not the unavoidable or necessary results of war . . . (10,053 men, or sixty per cent per annum, perished in seven months, from disease alone, upon an average strength of 28,939. This mortality exceeds that of the Great Plague). . . . The question arises, must what has here occurred occur again?

No tribunal has ever yet tried this question. It hardly seems to have occurred to the national mind. . . .

Immediately after the troops went to the East the practical inefficiency of the Army Medical Department began to show itself.

It would, indeed, be difficult to frame a system of administration more likely to lose an army at any time than this. Here is the first downward step of our noble Army to destruction.

The great calamity is now drawing to its height. . . . Had half the ingenuity exercised in sending out lime juice been expended in making that article unnecessary, the Army might have returned to England alive and well. From this point the correspondence seems to read as if the medical office was to register post-mortem appearances, instead of keeping the patient in health—as if the business of the police was to record murders instead of preventing them.

In order to make this intelligible it is necessary to give a short summary of what the Army did receive in vegetables and blankets. . . . For three months this Army had not had the means of cleanliness (no soap) either as to their persons or clothing: and what the state of the men was, on arriving at Scutari, let those who saw it testify.

One would think that the fact, well known by this time, of an army having all but perished would have been of itself a sufficient reason for the severest animadversion from the head of the Army Medical Department. But no. The Sebastopol Committee is to have the doings of that department before it, and Dr. Smith writes to his principal medical officer:

"I beg you to supply me, and that immediately"—with what?—"with every kind of information which you may deem likely to enable me to establish a character for it [the department] which the public appears desirous to prove that it does not possess." What hope for the Army after this? He might as well have said, "Never mind anything if you only enable me to free the department from blame. . . ."

Let it not be said, "It is all past, let bygones be bygones." A future war is not past. We are speaking for the future. Otherwise it may be prophesied . . . that, exactly in the proportion in which similar circumstances recur, will similar destruction recur. We shall do as before and lose again half an army from disease.

NOTES ON NURSING

IN WATCHING DISEASE, both in private houses and in public hospitals, the thing which strikes the experienced observer most forcibly is this, that the symptoms or the sufferings generally considered to be inevitable, and incident to the disease, are very often not symptoms of the disease at all, but of something quite different—of the want of fresh air, or of light, or of warmth, or of quiet, or of cleanliness, or of punctuality and care in the administration of diet, of each or of all of these. And this quite as much in private as in hospital nursing.

The reparative process which nature has instituted and which we call disease has been hindered by some want of knowledge or attention, in one or in all of these things, and pain, suffering, or interruption of the whole process sets in.

If a patient is cold, if a patient is feverish, if a patient is faint, if he is sick after taking food, if he has a bedsore, it is generally the fault not of the disease but of the nursing.

I use the word "nursing" for want of a better. It has been limited to signify little more than the administration of medicines and the application of poultices. It ought to signify the proper use of fresh air, light, warmth, cleanliness, quiet, and the proper selection and administration of diet—all at the least expense of vital power to the patient.

It has been said and written scores of times that every woman makes a good nurse. I believe, on the contrary, that the very elements of nursing are all but unknown. . . .

The art of nursing, as now practiced, seems to be expressly constituted to unmake what God had made disease to be, viz., a reparative
process. . . .

If a nurse declines to do these [menial] things for her patient, "because it is not her business," I should say that nursing was not her calling. I have seen surgical "sisters," women whose hands were worth to
them two or three guineas a week, down upon their knees scouring a
room or hut because they thought it otherwise not fit for their patients
to go into. I am far from wishing nurses to scour. It is a waste of power.
But I do say that these women had the true nursing calling—the good
of their sick first, and second only the consideration what it was their
"place" to do; and that women who wait for the housemaid to do this,
or for the charwoman to do that, when their patients are suffering, have
not yet the making of a nurse in them.

The most important practical lesson that can be given to nurses is to
teach them what to observe, how to observe, what symptoms indicate
improvement, what the reverse, which are of importance, which are the
evidence of neglect, and of what kind of neglect.

FRESH AIR

The extraordinary confusion between cold air and ventilation even
in the minds of well-educated people illustrates this. To make a room
cold is by no means necessary to ventilate it. Nor is it at all necessary,
to ventilate a room, to chill it. . . . Another extraordinary fallacy is the
dread of the night air. What air can we breathe at night but night air?
The choice is between pure night air from without and foul night air
from within. Most people prefer the latter. An unaccountable choice.
What will they say if it is proved to be true that fully one half of all
the disease we suffer from is occasioned by people sleeping with their
windows shut?

WHAT A NURSE IS TO BE

A REALLY GOOD nurse must needs be of the highest class of character. It
needs hardly be said that she must be (1) chaste, in the sense of the
Sermon on the Mount—a good nurse should be the Sermon on the
Mount herself. It should naturally seem impossible to the most unchaste
to utter even an immodest jest in her presence. Remember this great

and dangerous peculiarity of nursing, and especially of hospital nursing, namely, that it is the only case, queens not excepted, where a woman is really in charge of men. And a really good, trained ward "sister" can keep order in a men's ward better than a military wardmaster or sergeant. (2) Sober, in spirit as well as in drink, and temperate in all things. (3) Honest, not accepting the trifling fee or bribe from the patients or friends. (4) Truthful, and to be able to tell the truth includes attention and observation, to observe truly; memory, to remember truly; power of expression, to tell truly what one has observed truly; as well as intention to speak the truth, the whole truth, and nothing but the truth. (5) Trustworthy, to carry out directions intelligently and perfectly, unseen as well as seen, "to the Lord" as well as unto men—no mere eye service. (6) Punctual to a second, and orderly to a hair—having everything ready in order before she begins her dressings or her work about the patients: nothing forgotten. (7) Quiet, yet quick: quick without hurry, gentle without slowness; discreet without self-importance, no gossip. (8) Cheerful, hopeful, not allowing herself to be discouraged by unfavorable symptoms; not given to distress the patient by anticipations of an unfavorable result. (9) Cleanly to the point of exquisiteness, both for the patient's sake and for her own; neat and ready. (10) Thinking of her patient and not of herself, "tender over his occasions" or wants, cheerful and kindly, patient, ingenious and feat.[1] The best definition can be found, as always, in Shakespeare, where he says that to be "nurse-like" is to be—

> So kind, so duteous, diligent,
> So tender over his occasions, true,
> So feat.

The Principles of Sanitation

WILLIAM THOMPSON SEDGWICK (1855-1921)

WILLIAM THOMPSON SEDGWICK ranks as one of the outstanding American sanitarians and biologists. He was professor of biology at the Massa-

[1] Apt in doing the right thing at the right time.

chusetts Institute of Technology for thirty years (1891–1921). He was one of the great apostles of the "sanitary awakening" which swept America in the 1890s. His inspired teaching and lucidity of expression in his written works, of which "The Principles of Sanitary Science and Public Health" is the classic example, went far toward promoting the gospel of cleanliness in these well-plumbed United States. To him we owe the dicta that "the common drinking cup is anathema"; that "dirt is dangerous." The relation of the new knowledge of biology to the public health was foremost in his thoughts. The headings of the early chapters in his great work emphasize this thought, for they read: "The Etiology or the Causes of Disease—Ancient and Modern," "The Rise and Influence of Bacteriology," "Sanitary Aspects of the Struggle for Existence—Factors Effecting Survival," "Infection and Contagion—the Paths and Portals by Which They Enter the Body," and "Dirt, Dust, Air and Disease— the Living Earth," the chapter which in part is quoted here.

English was the language in which Sedgwick wrote and first published in 1901 his classic work on sanitary science under the title: "The Principles of Sanitary Science and Public Health"; including the quotations from the chapter on "Dirt, Dust, Air and Disease." The text is taken from the edition revised by Samuel C. Prescott, Sc.D., and Murray P. Horwood, Ph.D., of the Massachusetts Institute of Technology, in 1935, and published by The Macmillan Company, New York.

DIRT AND DISEASE

THE EXPERIENCE of the race has shown that one of the most effective vehicles of disease is dirt. The word "dirt" appears to be derived from an old Saxon word *drit,* meaning excrement; but the modern form of the word "dirt" has taken on a more extended and less definite meaning. As ordinarily used, it may be the synonym of dust, soil, filth, or almost any form of uncleanliness, whether such uncleanliness imply the presence of infection or only that of pollution. Still it can hardly be denied that even at present the word "dirt" signifies something distinctly more filthy than do the words "earth," "soil," or "dust." It is easy to see in the origin of the word the reason for this, and after what has been said concerning the primary sources of infection and the efficiency of secretions and excrement as vehicles of disease, no surprise need be felt that dirt is regarded with suspicion by all intelligent and well-informed persons.

Unquestionably the general fear of dirt among the intelligent is not in all cases discriminating. There are forms of dirt which carry with them very little of danger, and a certain recognition of this fact is shown in such expressions as "good clean earth." . . .

Filth is looked upon by the sanitarian of today, therefore, as dangerous chiefly because it may contain the more or less attenuated germs of disease, and not so much as formerly because it may be a "breeding place" for such germs. It is a vehicle rather than a source.

THE PHILOSOPHY OF CLEANLINESS

From what has now been said, it is easy to perceive the reasons for the modern philosophy of cleanliness. Dirt is dangerous, not because it is "of the earth, earthy," but because it is too often *drit* or excrement; and the love of cleanliness or the abhorrence of dirt, which is becoming established in all highly civilized peoples, is doubtless a resultant of the dearly bought experience of the race, which has shown that dirt is dangerous and therefore to be dreaded. Cleanliness, or the absence of dirt, is not merely an aesthetic adornment—though doubtless an acquired taste; it is above all a sanitary safeguard, the importance of which has been learned by hard experience. In other words, to be clean is in a measure to be safe from disease; and cleanliness applies not only to the person but extends also to the personal environment and especially to the food supply, the water supply, the milk supply, et cetera.

Probably the greatest sanitary step ever taken by the race was the application of high temperatures to the preparation of food, i.e., cookery. There is very little doubt that far more important than any increase in the digestibility of food effected by cookery is the destruction of parasites, visible and invisible, within it thus brought about. Charles Lamb was probably right in attributing the love of cookery to the improvement in the flavors of food which it occasions, as is described in his well-known version of the discovery in the case of roast pig; and yet there is every reason to believe that the sanitary improvement wrought by the discovery of cookery was even more important than either the gustatory or the nutritive improvement. It is difficult to see how infection could have been otherwise than very common and very disastrous before the invention of cookery, for even to this day uncooked food forms one of the principal vehicles for the conveyance of parasites and disease germs.

PERSONAL VERSUS PUBLIC CLEANLINESS

It follows as a matter of course that personal cleanliness is more important than public cleanliness. In other words, that the avoidance of personal filth is far more necessary than, for example, is cleanliness of streets, dooryards, alleys, and the like. And yet public supplies are public dangers. If the public water supply, for example, be infected, no matter how scrupulously clean the residents of a city may be in respect to their persons, they will run very serious risks of disease if they drink from it. The same thing may be said of the public milk supply; and nothing is more impressive to the practical sanitarian than to witness an epidemic of typhoid fever in a wealthy and well-cared-for quarter of a city, where the inhabitants are personally clean, the houses are unexceptionable, the plumbing perfect, the drains in good condition, the tableware and linen spotless, and yet typhoid fever is present perhaps in nearly every family because of a polluted and infected milk supply or water supply. It must never be forgotten that the sanitary chain is no stronger than its weakest part, and that no matter how clean and wholesome all other conditions may be, if there is one point from which the germs of infectious disease may find admission into the body, danger may be imminent. Nothing is more instructive than to discover cities or towns in which great complaint is made of filth in the streets—from which, after all, comparatively little danger is likely to come—while an impure water supply or milk supply is being used with absolute confidence, or blindness, or ignorance.

PUBLIC DRINKING CUPS AND THEIR DANGERS

The march of sanitary progress has brought home clearly the grave dangers that lurk in the use of the common drinking cup. The various pathogenic microbes that are found in the saliva and sputum, especially those responsible for the so-called respiratory diseases, may be transmitted from person to person in this way. What has been said about drinking cups as a potential vehicle of disease germs applies in a measure to communion cups, "roller" towels, razors and shaving brushes in barbershops, and unclean dishes, spoons, et cetera. Sanitary fountains have been devised and are in use in many places, thus doing away with the public drinking cup, and insofar as they are successful in preventing contact between the lips of the user and the orifice of the bubbler, thus protecting the bubbler from pollution with the washings from the mouth, they deserve the warm commendation of sanitarians. The arrangement by which this is accomplished is very simple, and for use in public places, schools, institutions, and the like it is a great sanitary safeguard. The common drinking cup, wherever found, must be regarded as a sanitary abomination and should not be tolerated any longer.

Waves in the Ether Again: Forerunner of Radio

JAMES CLERK MAXWELL (1831–79)

ONLY YESTERDAY, radio; today, radar, the warning device; tomorrow, television; all operating on the same principle of electromagnetic waves traveling through Huygens' mysterious "ether" at the speed of light. The demonstration that electromagnetic waves are indeed propagated through the medium of the ether at the velocity of light, the mathematical key to practical radio, radar, and television transmission, was first made by a subtle Scotch physicist, astronomer, and mathematician, James Clerk Maxwell, a "physicist's physicist." Born and educated in Edinburgh, Maxwell was successively professor of physics at Marischal College, Aberdeen; professor of physics and astronomy at King's College, London; and, from 1871, professor of experimental physics at Cambridge, where he supervised the building of the famous Cavendish laboratory. His scientific bent was apparent early; at fifteen he had written a paper on a mechanical method of tracing Cartesian ovals; at eighteen, one on the equilibrium of elastic solids. He worked in many fields: in astronomy, writing a prize essay on "the stability of Saturn's rings," in 1859; in the kinetic theory of gases, here assuming the impossible existence of "sorting demons," tiny beings who would open and shut a door between two vessels of gas so intelligently that all the fastest-moving molecules might be collected in one chamber; in thermodynamics, where he was among the first to recognize the genius of the American, Willard Gibbs; in electromagnetism, where, having caught the torch from Faraday, he passed it on to Hertz, Marconi, and De Forest.

Maxwell's great "Treatise on Electricity and Magnetism" was published in 1873. However, he had previously expounded his central thesis that light and electricity are essentially the same thing in the essay quoted here. It is not easy reading and will be better understood if one first reads Hertz's essay, which follows, on the relation between light and electricity. The phenomena were better understood in Hertz's day. When Maxwell wrote and composed his complex mathematical equations, the problem of the velocity of light on the earth had only recently been solved—by Fizeau, who passed a ray of light between the teeth of a revolving wheel to a mirror and back again.

English was Maxwell's language when he did not speak the language of pure mathematics. "A Dynamical Theory of the Electromagnetic Field" first appeared in "Philosophical Transactions" (Vol. 155, p. 459, 1865).

"A DYNAMICAL THEORY OF THE ELECTROMAGNETIC FIELD"

THE MOST OBVIOUS mechanical phenomenon in electrical and magnetical experiments is the mutual action by which bodies in certain states set each other in motion at a sensible distance. The first step, therefore, is to ascertain the magnitude and direction of the force acting between the bodies. This force depends on the relative position of the bodies and on their electric or magnetic condition. Hence it seems at first sight natural to explain the facts by assuming the existence of something either at rest or in motion in each body. This "something," which constitutes the electric or magnetic state of the body, is capable of acting at a distance according to mathematical laws.

Mathematical theories of statical electricity, magnetism, mechanical action between conductors, and induction of currents have thus been formed. These theories do not expressly consider the surrounding medium. They assume particles which have the property of acting on one another at a distance by attraction and repulsion. Monsieur W. Weber has found it necessary to assume further that the force between two electric particles depends on their relative velocity as well. The mechanical difficulties involved prevent me from considering this theory as an ultimate one, though it may yet be useful.

I have therefore preferred to seek an explanation of the facts in another direction, by supposing them to be produced by actions which go on in the surrounding medium as well as in the excited bodies.

The theory I propose may therefore be called a theory of the *electromagnetic field,* because it has to do with the space in the neighborhood of electric or magnetic bodies. It may also be called a *dynamical* theory, because it assumes matter in motion—producing observed electromagnetic phenomena—in that space.

The electromagnetic field is that part of space which contains and surrounds bodies in electric or magnetic conditions. It may be filled with any kind of matter or empty of gross matter, as in the case of vacuums. There is always enough matter left to receive and transmit the undulations of light and heat. The undulations are those of an ethereal substance, not of gross matter whose presence merely modifies in some way the motion of the ether.

From the phenomena of heat and light we receive data giving us some reason to believe in the existence of a pervading medium, of small but real density, capable of being set in motion and of transmitting motion from one part to another with great, but not infinite, velocity.

The parts of this pervading medium must be so connected that the motion of one part depends on the motion of the rest. At the same time these connections must be capable of a certain kind of elastic yielding, since the communication of motion is not instantaneous but occupies time.

The medium is therefore capable of receiving and storing up two kinds of energy: namely, "actual" energy, depending on the motion of its parts, and "potential" energy, consisting of work done in recovering from displacement by virtue of its elasticity.

The propagation of undulations consists in the continual transformation of one of these forms of energy into the other, alternately. At any instant the amount of energy in the whole medium is equally divided, so that half is energy of motion and half is elastic resilience.

According to the theory which I propose to explain, electromotive force—which will produce a current, heat, or decompose a body—is the force called into play during the communication of motion from one part of the medium to another.

But when electromotive force acts on a dielectric substance, such as glass, sulphur, or air, it produces a state of polarization, described as a state in which every particle has its opposite poles in opposite conditions. In a dielectric under electromotive force we may conceive that the electricity in each molecule is displaced. One side is rendered positively and the other negatively electrical. But the electricity remains entirely connected with the molecule and does not pass from one molecule to another.

The effect of this action on the whole dielectric mass is to produce a general displacement of electricity in a certain direction. This displacement does not amount to a current, because when it has reached a certain value it becomes constant. But it is the commencement of a current.

Electric displacement according to our theory is a kind of elastic yielding to the action of electromotive force. It is similar to that which takes place in structures and machines owing to the want of perfect rigidity in the connections. Electric displacement explains why a dielectric does not instantly return to its primitive state when the electromotive force is removed. This phenomenon, exhibited by almost all solid dielectric substances, gives rise to the residual charge in the Leyden jar and to several phenomena of electric cables.

It appears, therefore, that certain phenomena in electricity and magnetism lead to the same conclusion as those of optics, namely:

There is an ethereal medium pervading all bodies and modified only in degree by their presence.

The parts of this medium are capable of being set in motion by electric currents and magnets.

This motion is communicated from one part of the medium to another by forces arising from the connections of those parts.

Under the action of these forces there is a certain yielding, depending on the elasticity of these connections.

Therefore energy in two different forms may exist in the medium. One form is the actual energy of the motion of its parts; the other is the potential energy stored up in the connections by virtue of their elasticity.

Thus, then, we are led to the conception of a complicated mechanism capable of a vast variety of motion but at the same time subject to the general laws of dynamics. We ought to be able to work out all the consequences of its motion, provided we know the form of the relation between the motions of the parts. The induction of one current by another and the mechanical action between conductors carrying currents give the clue. The phenomenon of the induction of currents has been deduced from their mechanical action by Helmholtz and Thomson [Lord Kelvin]. I have followed the reverse order and deduced the mechanical action from the laws of induction. I have then described experimental methods of determining the quantities, L, M, N, on which these phenomena depend.

I then apply the phenomena of induction and attraction of currents to the exploration of the electromagnetic field with a magnet. I show the distribution of its equipotential magnetic surfaces, cutting the lines of force at right angles.

In order to bring these results within the power of symbolical calculation I then express them in the form of the general equations of the electromagnetic field. There are twenty of these equations in all, involving twenty variable quantities, such as electric displacement, electromotive force, strength of a current and its electromagnetic effect, and free electricity.

I then express in terms of these quantities the intrinsic energy of the electromagnetic field. This depends partly on its magnetic and partly on its electric polarization at every point.

From this I determine the mechanical force acting, first, on a movable conductor carrying an electric current; secondly, on a magnetic pole; thirdly, on an electrified body.

The last result—namely, the mechanical force acting on an electrified body—gives rise to an independent method of electrical measurement. It is founded on electrostatic effects. The relation between the units of measurement depends on what I have called the "electric elasticity" of the medium. It is a velocity, which has been experimentally determined by Messieurs Weber and Kohlrausch.

I then show how to calculate the electrostatic capacity of a condenser and the specific inductive capacity of a dielectric.

The general equations are next applied to the case of a magnetic disturbance propagated through a non-conducting field. It is shown that the only disturbances which can be so propagated are those transverse to the direction of propagation. The velocity of propagation is the velocity v, found from experiments such as those of Weber. It expresses the number of electrostatic units of electricity which are contained in one electromagnetic unit.

The velocity is so nearly that of light that it seems we have strong reason to conclude that light itself (including radiant heat and other radiations if any) is an electromagnetic disturbance in the form of waves propagated through the electromagnetic field according to electromagnetic laws.

The conception of the propagation of transverse magnetic disturbances to the exclusion of normal ones is distinctly set forth by Professor Faraday in his "Thoughts on Ray Vibrations." The electromagnetic theory of light, as proposed by him, is the same in substance as that which I have begun to develop, except that in 1846 there were no data to calculate the velocity of propagation.

The First Radio Reception

HEINRICH HERTZ (1857–94)

THE FIRST RADIO SET, transmitter and receiver, ever built was constructed in the laboratories of a young German physicist, Heinrich Hertz, professor at the University of Bonn. Hardly recognizable as such, the first radio set was an electrical "tuning fork" with which Hertz was attempting to prove the actual physical existence of the electromagnetic waves whose hypothetical existence might be inferred from the equations of Maxwell. With his crude apparatus Hertz not only discovered radio waves (once called hertzian waves) in 1888 but also measured their wave length and velocity and showed that they could be reflected, refracted, and polarized (that is, rotated in a plane). Hertz modestly discusses in the simple and charming paper quoted here his own contributions to the problems of electromagnetism and optics, at last combined into one field. The "undulatory series" now includes not only light and radio (electromagnetic) waves, but also heat waves, infrared, ultraviolet and cosmic rays, and X rays. [For a simple description of the theory of wave motions, read the papers by Huygens and Helmholtz included in this volume.]

German was the language in which Hertz addressed the sixty-second meeting of the German Association for the Advancement of Natural Science and Medicine in Heidelberg (September 1889), bringing them up to date on the relations between light and electricity. The English translation of this characteristic lecture was published in "The Miscellaneous Papers of Heinrich Hertz" (London and New York: The Macmillan Co.).

"ON THE RELATIONS BETWEEN LIGHT AND ELECTRICITY"

WHEN ONE SPEAKS of the relations between light and electricity, the lay mind at once thinks of the electric light. With this the present lecture is not concerned. To the mind of the physicist there occur a series of delicate mutual reactions between the two agents, such as the rotation of the plane of polarization by the current or the alteration of the resistance of a conductor by the action of light. In these, however, light and electricity do not directly meet; between the two there comes an intermediate agent—ponderable matter. With this group of phenomena again we shall not concern ourselves. Between the two agents there are yet other relations—relations in a closer and stricter sense than those already mentioned. I am here to support the assertion that light of every kind is itself an electrical phenomenon—the light of the sun, the light of a candle, the light of a glowworm.

Take away from the world electricity, and light disappears; remove from the world the luminiferous ether, and electric and magnetic actions can no longer traverse space. This is our assertion. It does not date from today or yesterday; already it has behind it a long history. In this history its foundations lie. Such researches as I have made upon this subject form but a link in a long chain. And it is of the chain, and not only of the single link, that I would speak to you. I must confess that it is not easy to speak of these matters in a way at once intelligible and accurate. It is in empty space, in the free ether, that the processes which we have to describe take place. They cannot be felt with the hand, heard by the ear, or seen by the eye. They appeal to our intuition and conception, scarcely to our senses. Hence we shall try to make use, as far as possible, of the intuitions and conceptions which we already possess. Let us, therefore, stop to inquire what we do with certainty know about light and electricity before we proceed to connect the one with the other.

What, then, is light? Since the time of Young and Fresnel we know that it is a wave motion. We know the velocity of the waves, we know their length, we know that they are transversal waves; in short, we know completely the geometrical relations of the motion. To the physicist it is inconceivable that this view should be refuted; we can no longer entertain any doubt about the matter. It is morally certain that the wave theory of light is true, and the conclusions that necessarily follow from it are equally certain. It is therefore certain that all space known to us is not empty but is filled with a substance, the ether, which can be thrown into vibration. But whereas our knowledge of the geometrical relations of the processes in this substance is clear and definite, our conceptions of the physical nature of these processes is vague, and the assumptions made as to the properties of the substance itself are not altogether consistent.

At first, following the analogy of sound, waves of light were freely regarded as elastic waves and treated as such. But elastic waves in fluids are only known in the form of longitudinal waves. Transversal elastic waves in fluids are unknown. They are not even possible; they contradict the nature of the fluid state. Hence men were forced to assert that the ether which fills space behaves like a solid body. But when they considered and tried to explain the unhindered course of the stars in the heavens, they found themselves forced to admit that the ether behaves like a perfect fluid. These two statements together land us in a painful and unintelligible contradiction which disfigures the otherwise beautiful development of optics. Instead of trying to conceal this defect let us turn to electricity; in investigating it we may perhaps make some progress toward removing the difficulty.

What, then, is electricity? This is at once an important and a difficult question. It interests the lay as well as the scientific mind. Most people who ask it never doubt the existence of electricity. They expect a description of it—an enumeration of the peculiarities and powers of this wonderful thing. To the scientific mind the question rather presents itself in the form: Is there such a thing as electricity? Cannot electrical phenomena be traced back, like all others, to the properties of the ether and of ponderable matter? We are far from being able to answer this question definitely in the affirmative. In our conceptions the thing conceived of as electricity plays a large part. The traditional conceptions of electricities which attract and repel each other, and which are endowed with actions at a distance as with spiritual properties—we are all familiar with these, and in a way fond of them; they hold undisputed sway as common modes of expression at the present time. The period at which these conceptions were formed was the period in which Newton's law of gravitation won its most glorious successes, and in which the idea of direct action at a distance was familiar. Electric and magnetic attractions followed the same law as gravitational attraction; no wonder men thought the simple assumption of action at a distance sufficient to explain these phenomena, and to trace them back to their ultimate intelligible cause.

The aspect of matters changed in the present century, when the reactions between electric currents and magnets became known; for these have an infinite manifoldness, and in them motion and time play an important part. It became necessary to increase the number of actions at a distance and to improve their form. Thus the conception gradually lost its simplicity and physical probability. Men tried to regain this by seeking for more comprehensive and simple laws—so-called elementary laws. Of these the celebrated Weber's law is the most important example. Whatever we may think of its correctness, it is an attempt which altogether formed a comprehensive system full of scientific charm; those who were once attracted into its magic circle remained prisoners there. And if the path indicated was a false one, warning could only come from an intellect of great freshness—from a man who looked at phenomena with an open mind and without preconceived opinions, who started from what he saw, not from what he had heard, learned, or read. Such a man was Faraday.

Faraday, doubtless, heard it said that when a body was electrified something was introduced into it; but he saw that the changes which took place only made themselves felt outside and not inside. Faraday was taught that forces simply acted across space; but he saw that an important part was played by the particular kind of matter filling the space across which the forces were supposed to act. Faraday read that electricities certainly existed, whereas there was much contention as to the forces exercised by them; but he saw that the effects of these forces were clearly displayed, whereas he could perceive nothing of the electricities themselves. And so he formed a quite different, an opposite conception of the matter. To him the electric and magnetic forces became the actually present, tangible realities; to him electricity and magnetism were the things whose existence might be disputable.

The lines of force, as he called the forces independently considered, stood before his intellectual eye in space as conditions of space, as tensions, whirls, currents, whatever they might be—that he was himself unable to state—but there they were, acting upon each other, pushing and pulling bodies about, spreading themselves about and carrying the action from point to point. To the objection that complete rest is the only condition possible in empty space he could answer, Is space really empty? Do not the phenomena of light compel us to regard it as being filled with something? Might not the ether which transmits the waves of light also be capable of transmitting the changes which we call electric and magnetic force? Might there not conceivably be some connection between these changes and the light waves? Might not the latter be due to something like a quivering of the lines of force?

Faraday had advanced as far as this in his ideas and conjectures. He could not prove them, although he eagerly sought for proof. He delighted in investigating the connection between light, electricity, and magnetism. The beautiful connection which he did discover was not the one which he sought. So he tried again and again, and his search only ended with his life. Among the questions which he raised there was one which continually presented itself to him: Do electric and magnetic forces require time for their propagation? When we suddenly excite an electromagnet by a current, is the effect perceived simultaneously at all distances? Or does it first affect magnets close at hand, then more distant ones, and lastly, those which are quite far away? When we electrify and discharge a body in rapid succession, does the force vary at all distances simultaneously? Or do the oscillations arrive later, the further we go from the body? In the latter case the oscillation would propagate itself as a wave through space. Are there such waves? To these questions Faraday could get no answer.

And yet the answer is most closely connected with his own fundamental conceptions. If such waves of electric force exist, traveling freely from their origin through space, they exhibit plainly to us the independent existence of the forces which produce them. There can be no better way of proving that these forces do not act across space, but are propagated from point to point, than by actually following their progress from instant to instant. The questions asked are not unanswerable; indeed they can be attacked by very simple methods. If Faraday had had the good fortune to hit upon these methods, his views would forthwith have secured recognition. The connection between light and electricity would at once have become so clear that it could not have escaped notice even by eyes less sharpsighted than his own.

But a path so short and straight as this was not vouchsafed to science. For a while experiments did not point to any solution, nor did the current theory tend in the direction of Faraday's conceptions. The assertion that electric forces could exist independently of their electricities was in direct opposition to the accepted electrical theories. Similarly the prevailing theory of optics refused to accept the idea that waves of light could be other than elastic waves. Any attempt at a thorough discussion of the one or the other of these assertions seemed almost to be idle speculation. All the more must we admire the happy genius of the man who could connect together these apparently remote conjectures in such a way that they mutually supported each other and formed a theory of which everyone was at once bound to admit that it was at least plausible. This was an Englishman—Maxwell.

You know the paper which he published in 1865 upon the electromagnetic theory of light. It is impossible to study this wonderful theory without feeling as if the mathematical equations had an independent life and an intelligence of their own, as if they were wiser than ourselves, indeed wiser than their discoverer, as if they gave forth more than he had put into them. And this is not altogether impossible: it may happen when the equations prove to be more correct than their discoverer could with certainty have known. It is true that such comprehensive and accurate equations only reveal themselves to those who with keen insight pick out every indication of the truth which is faintly visible in nature. The clue which Maxwell followed is well known to the initiated. It had attracted the attention of other investigators: it had suggested to Reimann and Lorentz speculations of a similar nature, although not so fruitful in results. Electricity in motion produces magnetic force, and magnetism in motion produces electric force; but both of these effects are only perceptible at high velocities. Thus velocities appear in the mutual relations between electricity and magnetism, and the constant which governs these relations and continually recurs in them is itself a velocity of exceeding magnitude. This constant was determined in various ways, first by Kohlrausch and Weber, by purely electrical experiments, and proved to be identical, allowing for the experimental errors incident to such a difficult measurement, with another important velocity—the velocity of light.

This might be an accident, but a pupil of Faraday's could scarcely regard it as such. To him it appeared as an indication that the same ether must be the medium for the transmission of both electric force and light. The two velocities which were found to be nearly equal must really be identical. But in that case the most important optical constants must occur in the electrical equations. This was the bond which Maxwell set himself to strengthen. He developed the electrical equations to such an extent that they embraced all the known phenomena, and in addition to these a class of phenomena hitherto unknown—electric waves. These waves would be transversal waves, which might have any wave length but would always be propagated in the ether with the same velocity—that of light. And now Maxwell was able to point out that waves having just these geometrical properties do actually occur in nature, although we are accustomed to denote them not as electrical phenomena but by the special name of light. If Maxwell's electrical theory was regarded as false, there was no reason for accepting his views as to the nature of light. And if light waves were held to be purely elastic waves, his electrical theory lost its whole significance. But if one approached the structure without any prejudices arising from the views commonly held, one saw that its parts supported each other like the stones of an arch stretching across an abyss of the unknown and connecting two tracts of the known.

On account of the difficulty of the theory the number of its disciples at first was necessarily small. But everyone who studied it thoroughly became an adherent and forthwith sought diligently to test its original assumptions and its ultimate conclusions. Naturally the test of experiment could for a long time be applied only to separate statements, to the outworks of the theory.

I have just compared Maxwell's theory to an arch stretching across an abyss of unknown things. If I may carry on the analogy further, I would say that for a long time the only additional support that was given to this arch was by way of strengthening its two abutments. The arch was thus enabled to carry its own weight safely; but still its span was so great that we could not venture to build up further upon it as upon a secure foundation. For this purpose it was necessary to have special pillars built up from the solid ground, and serving to support the center of the arch. One such pillar would consist in proving that electrical or magnetic effects can be directly produced by light. This pillar would support the optical side of the structure directly and the electrical side indirectly. Another pillar would consist in proving the existence of waves of electric or magnetic force capable of being propagated after the manner of light waves. This pillar again would directly support the electrical side, and indirectly the optical side.

In order to complete the structure symmetrically, both pillars would have to be built; but it would suffice to begin with one of them. With the former we have not as yet been able to make a start; but fortunately, after a protracted search, a safe point of support for the latter has been found. A sufficiently extensive foundation has been laid down; a part of the pillar has already been built up; with the help of many willing hands it will soon reach the height of the arch and so enable this to bear the weight of the further structure which is to be erected upon it. At this stage I was so fortunate as to be able to take part in the work. To this I owe the honor of speaking to you today; and you will therefore pardon me if I now try to direct your attention solely to this part of the structure. Lack of time compels me, against my will, to pass by the researches made by many other investigators; so that I am not able to show you in how many ways the path was prepared for my experiments, and how near several investigators came to performing these experiments themselves.

Was it then so difficult to prove that electric and magnetic forces need time for their propagation? Would it not have been easy to charge a Leyden jar and to observe directly whether the corresponding disturbance in a distant electroscope took place somewhat later? Would it not have sufficed to watch the behavior of a magnetic needle while someone at a distance suddenly excited an electromagnet?

As a matter of fact these and similar experiments had already been performed without indicating that any interval of time elapsed between the cause and the effect. To an adherent of Maxwell's theory this is simply a necessary result of the enormous velocity of propagation. We can only perceive the effect of charging a Leyden jar or exciting a magnet at moderate distances, say up to ten meters. To traverse such a distance, light, and therefore according to the theory electric force likewise, takes only the thirty millionth part of a second. Such a small fraction of time we cannot directly measure or even perceive. It is still more unfortunate that there are no adequate means at our disposal for indicating with sufficient sharpness the beginning and end of such a short interval. If we wish to measure a length correctly to the tenth part of a millimeter it would be absurd to indicate the beginning of it with a broad chalk line. If we wish to measure a time correctly to the thousandth part of a second it would be absurd to denote its beginning by the stroke of a big clock.

Now the time of discharge of a Leyden jar is, according to our ordinary ideas, inconceivably short. It would certainly be that if it took about the thirty thousandth part of a second. And yet for our present purpose even that would be a thousand times too long. Fortunately nature here provides us with a more delicate method. It has long been known that the discharge of a Leyden jar is not a continuous process, but that, like the striking of a clock, it consists of a large number of oscillations, of discharges in opposite senses which follow each other at exactly equal intervals. Electricity is able to simulate the phenomena of elasticity. The period of a single oscillation is much shorter than the total duration of the discharge, and this suggests that we might use a single oscillation as an indicator. But, unfortunately, the shortest oscillation yet observed takes fully a millionth of a second. While such an oscillation is actually in progress its effects spread out over a distance of three hundred meters; within the modest dimensions of a room they would be perceived almost at the instant the oscillation commenced. Thus no progress could be made with the known methods; some fresh knowledge was required.

This came in the form of the discovery that not only the discharge of Leyden jars but, under suitable conditions, the discharge of every kind of conductor gives rise to oscillations. These oscillations may be much shorter than those of the jars. When you discharge the conductor of an electrical machine you excite oscillations whose period lies between a hundred millionth and a thousand millionth of a second. It is true that these oscillations do not follow each other in a long continuous series; they are few in number and rapidly die out. It would suit our experiments much better if this were not the case. But there is still the possibility of success if we can only get two or three such sharply defined indications. So in the realm of acoustics, if we were denied the continuous tones of pipes and strings, we could get a poor kind of music by striking strips of wood.

We now have indicators for which the thirty thousandth part of a second is not too short. But these would be of little use to us if we were not in a position to actually perceive their action up to the distance under consideration, viz., about ten meters. This can be done by very simple means. Just at the spot where we wish to detect the force we place a conductor, say a straight wire, which is interrupted in the middle by a small spark gap. The rapidly alternating force sets the electricity of the conductor in motion and gives rise to a spark at the gap. The method had to be found by experience, for no amount of thought could well have enabled one to predict that it would work satisfactorily. For the sparks are microscopically short, scarcely a hundredth of a millimeter long; they only last about a millionth of a second. It almost seems absurd and impossible that they should be visible; but in a perfectly dark room they *are* visible to an eye which has been well rested in the dark. Upon this thin thread hangs the success of our undertaking.

In beginning it we are met by a number of questions. Under what conditions can we get the most powerful oscillations? These conditions we must carefully investigate and make the best use of. What is the best form we can give to the receiver? We may choose straight wires or circular wires, or conductors of other forms; in each case the choice will have some effect upon the phenomena. When we have settled the form, what size shall we select? We soon find that this is a matter of some importance, that a given conductor is not suitable for the investigation of all kinds of oscillations, that there are relations between the two which remind us of the phenomena of resonance in acoustics. And lastly, are there not an endless number of positions in which we can expose a given conductor to the oscillations? In some of these the sparks are strong, in others weaker, and in others they entirely disappear.

I might perhaps interest you in the peculiar phenomena which here arise, but I dare not take up your time with these, for they are details— details when we are surveying the general results of an investigation, but by no means unimportant details to the investigator when he is engaged upon work of this kind. They are the peculiarities of the instruments with which he has to work; and the success of a workman depends upon whether he properly understands his tools. The thorough study of the implements, of the questions above referred to, formed a very important part of the task to be accomplished. After this was done, the method of attacking the main problem became obvious.

If you give a physicist a number of tuning forks and resonators and ask him to demonstrate to you the propagation in time of sound waves, he will find no difficulty in doing so even within the narrow limits of a room. He places a tuning fork anywhere in the room, listens with the resonator at various points around and observes the intensity of the sound. He shows how at certain points this is very small, and how this arises from the fact that at these points every oscillation is annulled by another one which started subsequently but traveled to the point along a shorter path. When a shorter path requires less time than a longer one, the propagation is a propagation in time. Thus the problem is solved. But the physicist now further shows us that the positions of silence follow each other at regular and equal distances: from this he determines the wave length, and, if he knows the time of vibration of the fork, he can deduce the velocity of the wave.

In exactly the same way we proceed with our electric waves. In place of the tuning fork we use an oscillating conductor. In place of the resonator we use our interrupted wire, which may also be called an electric resonator. We observe that in certain places there are sparks at the gap, in others none; we see that the dead points follow each other periodically in ordered succession. Thus the propagation in time is proved and the wave length can be measured. Next comes the question whether the waves thus demonstrated are longitudinal or transverse. At a given place we hold our wire in two different positions with reference to the wave: in one position it answers, in the other not. This is enough—the question is settled: our waves are transversal. Their velocity has now to be found. We multiply the measured wave length by the calculated period of oscillation and find a velocity which is about that of light. If doubts are raised as to whether the calculation is trustworthy, there is still another method open to us. In wires, as well as in air, the velocity of electric waves is enormously great, so that we can make a direct comparison between the two.

Now the velocity of electric waves in wires has long since been directly measured. This was an easier problem to solve, because such waves can be followed for several kilometers. Thus we obtain another measurement, purely experimental, of our velocity, and if the result is only an approximate one it at any rate does not contradict the first.

All these experiments in themselves are very simple, but they lead to conclusions of the highest importance. They are fatal to any and every theory which assumes that electric force acts across space independently of time. They mark a brilliant victory for Maxwell's theory.

Thermodynamics: The Flow of Heat

J. WILLARD GIBBS (1839–1903)

GERMAN SCIENTISTS spoke with reverence of *"Jibbs aus Yali"*—"Gibbs of Yale"—long before the residents of his native city of New Haven, in Connecticut, appreciated the subtly enormous mathematical genius of the quiet, unassuming bachelor professor of mathematical physics who dwelt meekly all his adult life with his fond and perhaps dominating married sister not a block away from the house where he was born. Gibbs was a Yale man through and through; his father, a noted Hebrew scholar, was professor of sacred literature in the Yale Divinity School; Josiah Willard Gibbs II studied, tutored, and taught at Yale throughout his entire deep-thinking professional career. Scientific honors came to him, including the Rumford and Copley medals, presidency of the American Mathematical Association, and the enthusiastic esteem of foreign scientists, notably Maxwell and Ostwald (who took the trouble of translating his works into German), best able to appreciate the significance of his incisive thinking in the difficult field of thermodynamics. Gibbs's mathematical thinking laid the basis for the whole development of physical chemistry.

To the mathematically initiated, his great paper "On the Equilibrium of Heterogeneous Substances," the opening paragraphs of which are quoted here, remains a mine of fruitful though rigorous information. Of this work a recent commentator, P. S. Epstein, in "A Commentary on the Scientific Writings of J. Willard Gibbs" (Yale University Press, 1936) says: "We see here a phenomenon almost unparalleled in the history of science. A young investigator, having discovered an entirely new branch of science, gave in a single contribution an exhaustive treatment of it which foreshadowed the development of theoretical chemistry for a quarter of a century." It is not surprising that the people of New Haven, and even Gibbs's non-mathematical colleagues on the Yale faculty, failed to understand during his lifetime the importance of his work. First, he was personally modest, though kindly and approachable; second, his subject was intricate; third, his style of writing, as the brief sample given here must illustrate, was bald, abstract, and uninspiring, almost a translation from mathematics directly into a Latinized English.

Besides Gibbs, the important workers in the field of thermodynamics were Rumford, Joule, Sadi Carnot (1796–1832), a French military engineer who pioneered the field with his investigations on the "motive power of fire" and the cycle of the heat engine, part of the heat (never 100 per cent) going into work, the rest being dissipated; Rudolph Clausius (1822–88), German mathematical physicist who invented the term "entropy"; Ludwig Boltzmann (1844–1906), Austrian physicist whose studies in radiation led up to the modern quantum theory; Maxwell; and Lord Kelvin, who voiced the important principle of the dissipation of energy. All their work established the famous "second law of thermodynamics," which states—popularly—that heat must always pass from hot to cold. "Heat cannot of itself, without the performance of work by some external agency, pass from a cold to a warmer body." This, incidentally, is the scientific reason why it is impossible to invent a "perpetual motion" machine.

English was the language in which Gibbs wrote so mathematically. His original 160,000-word paper, "On the Equilibrium of Heterogeneous Substances," was published in installments in the October 1875, May 1876, and May 1877 issues of the "Transactions of the Connecticut Academy." His own abstract, here quoted, was first published in the "American Journal of Science" (Third series, 14: 441, December 1878).

"ON THE EQUILIBRIUM OF HETEROGENEOUS SUBSTANCES"

It is an inference naturally suggested by the general increase of entropy which accompanies the changes occurring in any isolated material system that when the entropy of the system has reached a maximum the system will be in a state of equilibrium. Although this principle has by no means escaped the attention of physicists, its importance does not appear to have been duly appreciated. Little has been done to develop the principle as a foundation for the general theory of thermodynamic equilibrium.

The principle may be formulated as follows, constituting a criterion of equilibrium:

1. For the equilibrium of any isolated system it is necessary and suffi-

cient that in all possible variations of the state of the system which do not alter its energy, the variation of its entropy shall either vanish or be negative.

The following form, which is easily shown to be equivalent to the preceding, is often more convenient in application:

2. For the equilibrium of any isolated system it is necessary and sufficient that in all possible variations of the state of the system which do not alter its entropy, the variation of its energy shall either vanish or be positive.

More Thermodynamics

WILLIAM THOMSON (LORD KELVIN) (1824-1907)

BUSY, aggressive, and articulate, where Gibbs was reticent and secluded, the other great nineteenth-century master in the field of thermodynamics, Belfast-born William Thomson, later Lord Kelvin, made a reputation on his theories and a fortune out of his inventions. Employed as a scientific expert in the laying of the Atlantic cables in 1857-58 and 1865-66, Thomson invented many instruments essential to successful underwater telegraphic service, including the mirror galvanometer, the siphon recorder, and (with Fleeming Jenkin) the curb transmitter. Other inventions, among hundreds, were a tide predictor, an improved mariner's compass, and a harmonic analyzer. Nor was the canny professor at the University of Glasgow averse to battling for his patent rights and the monetary returns thereunto.

As a mathematician and physicist, Kelvin laid the foundation of the theory of electric oscillations, advocated the absolute scale of temperature (see Fahrenheit), and propounded the doctrine of the dissipation of energy. This theory held that while the total energy in a system might remain constant the *useful* energy was constantly diminishing. With a keen insight into Joule's demonstration of the convertibility of heat and work, he quickly recognized that it was against all reason and common sense to believe that every process in the world could be translated into the properties of a perfect machine which would run backward as well as forward. He combats this idea of the perfect mechanism of the universe in the brief passage quoted here. The language is that of the accomplished platform lecturer, which Kelvin was. Modern scientific epistemologists, like Sir Arthur Eddington, agree with the fundamental concept here voiced that, even if time can be considered to run backward into the past and forward into the future, entropy can only run in one direction; namely, down—to a state of complete thermodynamic equilibrium.

English was Kelvin's language. The passage here quoted originally appeared in the "Proceedings of the Royal Society of Edinburgh" (8: 325-31, 1874).

IF NATURE COULD RUN BACKWARD

IF, THEN, the motion of every particle of matter in the universe were precisely reversed at any instant, the course of nature would be simply reversed forever after. The bursting bubble of foam at the foot of a waterfall would reunite and descend into the water; the thermal motions would reconcentrate their energy and throw the mass up the fall in drops re-forming into a close column of ascending water. Heat which had been generated by the friction of solids and dissipated by conduction, and radiation with absorption, would come again to the place of contact and throw the moving body back against the force to which it had previously yielded. Boulders would recover from the mud the materials required to rebuild them into their previous jagged forms, and would become reunited to the mountain peak from which they had formerly broken away. And if, also, the materialistic hypothesis of life were true, living creatures would grow backward, with conscious knowledge of the future but with no memory of the past, and would become again unborn.

But the real phenomena of life infinitely transcend human science, and speculation regarding consequences of their imagined reversal is utterly unprofitable. Far otherwise, however, is it in respect to the reversal of the motions of matter uninfluenced by life, a very elementary consideration of which leads to the full explanation of the theory of dissipation of energy.

VIII SCIENCE SIRES THE TWENTIETH CENTURY

Aerodynamics: The Scientific Key to Aviation

SAMUEL P. LANGLEY (1834–1906)

THE TWENTIETH CENTURY—the air age! Credit the Wright brothers and their historic flight at Kitty Hawk on December 17, 1903. But pay equal respect to the father of aerodynamics, the self-made scientist, Samuel Pierpont Langley who, after countless discouragements, here detailed in the fascinating narrative published after his death—with the word "folly" erroneously appended to his name—was the first man to achieve the flight—half a mile—of a mechanically propelled heavier-than-air machine. Langley's nine-pound, steam-driven model aerodrome No. 5 took the air over the Potomac River on May 6, 1896. Among those who witnessed (and photographed) the famous first flight was Langley's close personal friend, Alexander Graham Bell, inventor of the telephone.

Langley was born in Roxbury, Massachusetts. Though he never had more than a high school education, he became professor of physics and astronomy at the Western University of Pennsylvania (now the University of Pittsburgh) and later (1881) secretary of the Smithsonian Institution in Washington. In Pittsburgh he invented the "whirling table," with which it was possible to measure the amount of power theoretically necessary to permit horizontal flight of a heavier-than-air flying machine. The unexpected and crucial finding was that the faster—within limits—an airfoil (for example, the wing of an airplane) travels through the air the less power it takes. As he continued his researches in the untrodden science of aerodynamics he constructed countless rubber-band-driven toy models of airplanes, which might have been seen launched from the windows of the Allegheny Observatory. There Langley, the astronomer, invented the bolometer, an instrument for measuring the distribution of heat, and used it to study solar radiation, a subject on which he soon became a world-wide authority. It is important to realize that Langley was risking a high scientific reputation when he "dabbled" in aerodynamics, for man's dream of flying like the birds, old as the mythical

Greek characters of Icarus and Daedalus, was considered only the refuge of scientific crackpots and fanatic inventors.

English was the language in which Langley's copiously illustrated "Memoir on Mechanical Flight," running to 150,000 words, was written. It was published by the Smithsonian Institution in 1911, five years after Langley's death. The early sections of Part I, here quoted, were written by Langley as early as 1897. Later sections were completed and edited from his official records by his assistant, Charles M. Manly, the man who was at the controls the day that the highly publicized first flight of "Langley's $50,000 folly" ended disastrously in the Potomac, just nine days (December 8, 1903) before the Wright brothers' flight at Kitty Hawk.

"MEMOIR ON MECHANICAL FLIGHT"

I ANNOUNCED in 1891, as the result of experiments carried on by me through previous years, that it was possible to construct machines which would give such a velocity to inclined surfaces that bodies indefinitely heavier than the air could be sustained upon it and moved through it with great velocity. In particular, it was stated that a plane surface in the form of a parallelogram of 76.2 cm. $\times$ 12.2 cm. (30 $\times$ 4.8 inches), weighing 500 grams (1.1 pounds), could be driven through the air with a velocity of 20 meters (65.6 feet) per second in absolutely horizontal flight, with an expenditure of 1/200 horsepower, or, in other terms, that 1 horsepower would propel and sustain in horizontal flight, at such a velocity (that is, about 40 miles an hour), a little over 200 pounds' weight of such surface, where the specific gravity of the plane was a matter of secondary importance, the support being derived from the elasticity and inertia of the air upon which the body is made to run rapidly.

It was further specifically remarked that it was not asserted that planes of any kind were the best forms to be used in mechanical flight, nor was it asserted, without restrictions, that mechanical flight was absolutely possible, since this depended upon our ability to get horizontal flight during transport, and to leave the earth and to return to it in safety. Our ability actually to do this, it was added, would result from the practice of some unexplored art or science which might be termed Aerodromics, but on which I was not then prepared to enter. . . .

It is to be remembered that the mechanical difficulties of artificial flight have been so great that, so far as is known, never at any time in the history of the world previous to my experiment of May 1896 had any such mechanism, however actuated, sustained itself in the air for more than a few seconds—never, for instance, a single half minute—and those models which had sustained themselves for these few seconds had been in almost every case actuated by rubber springs, and had been of such size that they should hardly be described as more than toys. This refers to actual flights in free air, unguided by any track or arm, for, since the most economical flight must always be a horizontal one in a straight line, the fact that a machine has lifted itself while pressed upward against an overhead track which compels the aerodrome to move horizontally and at the proper angle for equilibrium, is no proof at all of real "flight."

I desire to ask the reader's consideration of the fact that even ten years ago [i.e., 1887] the whole subject of mechanical flight was so far from having attracted the general attention of physicists or engineers, that it was generally considered to be a field fitted rather for the pursuits of the charlatan than for those of the man of science. Consequently, he who was bold enough to enter it found almost none of those experimental data which are ready to hand in every recognized and reputable field of scientific labor. Let me reiterate the statement, which even now seems strange, that such disrepute attached so lately to the attempt to make a "flying machine," that hardly any scientific men of position had made even preliminary investigations, and that almost every experiment to be made was made for the first time. To cover so vast a field as that which aerodromics is now seen to open, no lifetime would have sufficed. The preliminary experiments on the primary question of equilibrium and the intimately associated problems of the resistance of the sustaining surfaces, the power of the engines, the method of their application, the framing of the hull structure which held these, the construction of the propeller, the putting of the whole in initial motion, were all to be made, and could not be conducted with the exactness which would render them final models of accuracy.

I beg the reader, therefore, to recall as he reads that everything here has been done with a view to putting a trial aerodrome successfully in flight within a few years, and thus giving an early demonstration of the only kind which is conclusive in the eyes of the scientific man, as well as of the general public—a demonstration that mechanical flight is possible —by actually flying.

All that has been done, has been with an eye principally to this imme- diate result, and all the experiments given in this book are to be con- sidered only as approximations to exact truth. All were made with a view, not to some remote future, but to an arrival within the compass of a few years at some result in actual flight that could not be gainsaid or mistaken.

Although many experimenters have addressed themselves to the problem within the last few years—and these have included men of education and skill—the general failure to arrive at any actual flight has seemed to throw a doubt over the conclusions which I had announced as theoretically possible.

When, therefore, I was able to state that on May 6, 1896, such a degree of success had been attained that an aerodrome, built chiefly of steel, and driven by a steam engine, had indeed flown for over half a mile—that this machine had alighted with safety, and had performed a second flight on the same day, it was felt that an advance had been made, so great as to constitute the long-desired experimental demonstration of the possibility of mechanical flight. . . .

In all discussions of flight, especially of soaring flight, the first source to which one naturally looks for information is birds. But here correct deductions from even the most accurate of observations are very difficult, because the observation cannot include all of the conditions under which the bird is doing its work. If we could but see the wind, the problem would be greatly simplified, but as the matter stands, it may be said that much less assistance has been derived from studious observations on bird flight than might have been anticipated, perhaps because it has been found thus far impossible to reproduce in the flying machine or aerostatic model the shape and condition of wing with its flexible and controllable connection with the body, and especially the instinctive control of the wing to meet the requirements of flight that are varying from second to second, and which no automatic adjustment can adequately meet.

At the time I commenced these experiments, almost the only flying machine which had really flown was a toylike model, suggested by A. Penaud, a young Frenchman of singular mechanical genius, who contributed to the world many most original and valuable papers on Aeronautics, which may be found in the journal "L'Aeronaute." His aeroplane is a toy in size, with a small propeller whose blades are usually made of two feathers, or of stiff paper, and whose motive power is a twisted strand of rubber. This power maintains it in the air for a few seconds and with an ordinary capacity for flight of fifty feet or so, but it embodies a device for automatically securing horizontal flight, which its inventor was the first to enunciate.

Although Penaud recognized that, theoretically, two screws are necessary in an aerial propeller, as the use of a single one tends to make the apparatus revolve on itself, he adopted the single screw on account of the greater simplicity of construction that it permitted. . . .

My own earliest models employed a light wooden frame with two propellers, which were each driven by a strand of twisted rubber. In later forms, the rubber was enclosed and the end strains taken up by the thinnest tin-plate tubes, or, better still, paper tubes strengthened by shellac.

Little was known to me at that time as to the proper proportions between wing surface, weight, and power; and while I at first sought to infer the relation between wing surface and weight from that of soaring birds, where it varies from one half to one square foot of wing surface to the pound, yet the ratio was successively increased in the earlier models, until it became four square feet to one pound. It may be well to add, however, that the still later experiments with the steam-driven models, in which the supporting surface was approximately two square feet to the pound, proved that the lack of ability of these early rubber-driven models to properly sustain themselves even with four square feet of wing surface to the pound was largely due to the fact that the wings themselves had not been stiff enough to prevent their being warped by the air pressure generated by their forward motion.

During the years I presently describe, these tentative constructions were renewed at intervals without any satisfactory result, though it became clear from repeated failures that the motive power at command would not suffice, even for a few seconds' flight, for models of sufficient size to enable a real study to be made of the conditions necessary for successful flight.

In these earliest experiments everything had to be learned about the relative position of the center of gravity and what I have called the center of pressure. In regard to the latter term, it might at first seem that since the upward pressure of the air is treated as concentrated at one point of the supporting surface, as the weight is at the center of gravity, this point should be always in the same position for the same supporting surface. This relation, however, is never constant. How paradoxical seems the statement that, if ab be such a supporting surface in the form of a plane of uniform thickness and weight, suspended at c (ac being somewhat greater than cb) and subjected to the pressure of a wind in the direction of the arrow, the pressure on the lesser arm cb will overpower that on the greater arm $ac!$ We now know, however, that this must be so, and why, but as it was not known to the writer till determined by experiments published later in "Experiments in Aerodynamics," all this was worked out by trial in the models.

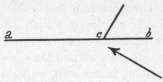

It was also early seen that the surface of support could be advantageously divided into two, with one behind the other, or one over the other, and this was often, though not always, done in the models.

At the very beginning another difficulty was met which has proved a constant and ever-increasing one with larger models—the difficulty of launching them in the air. It is frequently proposed by those unfamiliar with this difficulty, to launch the aerodrome by placing it upon a platform car or upon the deck of a steamer, and running the car or boat at an increasing speed until the aerodrome, which is free to rise, is lifted by the wind of advance. But this is quite impracticable without means to prevent premature displacement, for the large surface and slight weight render any model of considerable size unmanageable in the least wind, such as is always present in the open air. It is, therefore, necessary in any launching apparatus that the aerodrome be held rigidly until the very moment of release, and that instant and simultaneous release from the apparatus be made at all the sustaining points at the proper moment.

There is but a very partial analogy in this case to the launching of a ship, which is held to her ways by her great weight. Here, the "ship" is liable to rise from its ways or be turned over laterally at any instant, unless it is securely fastened to them in a manner to prevent its rising, but not to prevent its advancing.

The experiments with rubber-driven models commenced in April 1887 at the Allegheny Observatory were continued at intervals (partly there, but chiefly in Washington) for three or four years, during which time between thirty and forty independent models were constructed, which were so greatly altered in the course of experiment that more nearly one hundred models were in reality tried. The result of all this extended labor was wholly inconclusive, but as subsequent trials of other motors (such as compressed air, carbonic-acid gas, electric batteries, and the like) proved futile, and (before the steam engine) only the rubber gave results, however unsatisfactory, in actual flight, from which anything could be learned, I shall give some brief account of these experiments which preceded and proved the necessity of using the steam engine, or other like energetic motor, even in experimental models.

An early attempt was made in April 1887 with a model consisting of a frame formed of two wooden pieces, each about 1 meter long and 4 cm. wide, made for lightness, of star-shaped section, braced with cross-pieces and carrying two long strips of rubber, each about 1 mm. thick, 30 mm. wide, 2 meters long, doubled, weighing 300 grams. Each of these strips could be wound to about 300 turns, one end being made fast to the front of the frame, the other to the shaft of a four-bladed propeller 30 cm. in diameter. The wings were made of lightest pine frames, over which paper was stretched, and were double, one being superposed upon the other. Each was 15 cm. wide and 120 cm. long. The distance between them was 12 cm. and the total surface a little more than 3,600 sq. cm. (four square feet). In flying, the rubber was so twisted that the propellers were run in opposite directions. The weight of the whole apparatus was not quite one kilogram, or about one pound to two feet of sustaining surface, which proved to be entirely too great a weight for the power of support. When placed upon the whirling table, it showed a tendency to soar at a speed of about ten miles an hour, but its own propellers were utterly insufficient to sustain it.

In this attempt, which was useful only in showing how much was to be learned of practical conditions, the primary difficulty lay in making the model light enough and sufficiently strong to support its power. This difficulty continued to be fundamental through every later form; but besides this, the adjustment of the center of gravity to the center of pressure of the wings, the disposition of the wings themselves, the size of the propellers, the inclination and number of their blades, and a great number of other details, presented themselves for examination. Even in the first model, the difficulty of launching the machine or giving it the necessary preliminary impulse was disclosed—a difficulty which may perhaps not appear serious to the reader, but which in fact required years of experiment to remove. . . .

In June 1889, however, new rubber-driven models were made in which the wooden frames were replaced by tubes of light metal, which, however, were still too heavy, and these subsequently by tubes of paper covered with shellac, which proved to be the lightest and best material in proportion to its strength that had been found. The twisted rubber was carried within these tubes, which were made just strong enough to withstand the end strain it produced. The front end of the rubber being made fast to an extremity of the tube, the other end was attached directly to the shaft of the propeller, which in the early models was still supplied with four blades. . . .

The aerodromes made at this time were too heavy, as well as too large, to be easily launched by hand, and it was not until 1891 that the first one was constructed light enough to actually fly. This first flight was obtained from the north window of the dome of the Allegheny Observatory, on March 28, 1891, and imperfect as it was, served to show that the proper balancing of the aerodrome which would bring the center of gravity under the center of pressure, so as to give a horizontal flight, had yet to be obtained.

From this time on until 1893 experiments continued to be made with rubber-driven models, of which, as has been stated, nearly forty were constructed, some with two propellers, some with one; some with one propeller in front and one behind; some with plane, some with curved, wings; some with single, some with superposed, wings; some with two pairs of wings, one preceding and one following; some with the Penaud tail; and some with other forms. . . .

The wings in general were flat, but in some cases curved. The rubber was usually wound to about one hundred turns, and trouble continually arose from its "kinking" and unequal unwinding, which often caused most erratic flights.

It is sufficient to say of these that, rude as they were, much was learned from them about the condition of the machines in free air, which could never be learned from the whirling table or other constrained flight.

The advantages and also the dangers of curved wings as compared with plane ones were shown, and the general disposition which would secure an even balance was ascertained; but all this was done with extreme difficulty, since the brief flights were full of anomalies, arising from the imperfect conditions of observation. For instance, the motor power was apparently exhausted more rapidly when the propellers were allowed to turn with the model at rest than when it was in motion, though in theory, in the latter case, more power would seem to be expended and a greater speed of revolution obtained in a given time. The longest flights obtainable did not exceed six or eight seconds in time, nor eighty to one hundred feet in distance, and were not only so brief, but, owing to the spasmodic action of the rubber and other causes, so irregular, that it was extremely difficult to obtain even the imperfect results which were actually deduced from them. . . .

The difficulties of these long-continued early experiments were enhanced by the ever-present difficulty which continued through later ones, that it was almost impossible to build the model light enough to enable it to fly, and at the same time strong enough to withstand the strains which flight imposed upon it. The models were broken up by their falls after a few flights, and had to be continually renewed, while owing to the slightness of their construction the conditions of observation could not be exactly repeated; and these flights themselves, as has already been stated, were so brief in time (usually less than six seconds), so limited in extent (usually less than twenty meters), and so wholly capricious and erratic, owing to the nature of the rubber motor and other causes, that very many experiments were insufficient to eliminate these causes of mal-observation.

AVAILABLE MOTORS

In the introductory chapter to "Experiments in Aerodynamics," it was asserted that:

"These researches have led to the result that mechanical sustentation of heavy bodies in the air, combined with very great speeds, is not only possible, but within the reach of mechanical means we actually possess."

It was, however, necessary to make a proper selection in order to secure that source of power which is best adapted to the requirements of mechanical flight. Penaud had used India rubber as the cheapest and at the same time the most available motor for the toys with which he was experimenting, but when models were constructed that were heavier than anything made prior to 1887, it appeared, after the exhaustive trials with rubber referred to in the preceding chapter, that something which could give longer and steadier flights must be used as a motor, even for the preliminary trials, and the construction of the large steam-driven model known as No. 0, and elsewhere described, was begun. Even before the completion of this, the probability of its failure grew so strong that experiments were commenced with other motors, which it was hoped might be consistent with a lighter construction.

These experiments which commenced in the spring of 1892, and continued for nearly a twelvemonth, were made upon the use of compressed air, carbonic-acid gas, electricity in primary and storage batteries, and numerous other contrivances, with the result that the steam engine was finally returned to, as being the only one that gave any promise of immediate success in supporting a machine which would teach the conditions of flight by actual trial, though it may be added that the gas engine, which was not tried at this time on account of engineering difficulties, was regarded from the first as being the best in theory and likely to be ultimately resorted to. All others were fundamentally too heavy, and weight was always the greatest enemy. . . .

The gas engine possesses great theoretical advantages. At the time of these experiments, the gas engine most available for the special purposes of the models was one driven by air drawn through gasoline. As the builders could not agree to reduce the weight of a one horsepower engine more than one half of the then usual model, and as the weight of the standard engine was 470 pounds, it was obvious that to reduce this weight to the limit of less than three pounds was impracticable under the existing conditions, and all consideration of the use of gas was abandoned provisionally, although a gasoline engine of elementary simplicity was designed but never built. I purposed, however, to return to this attractive form of power if I were ever able to realize its theoretical advantages on the larger scale which would be desirable. . . .

In November 1891, after the long and unsatisfactory experiments with rubber-driven models already referred to, and before most of the experiments with other available motors than steam had been made, I commenced the construction of the engines and the design of the hull of a steam-driven aerodrome, which was intended to supplement the experiments given in "Aerodynamics" by others made under the conditions of actual flight.

In designing this first aerodrome, here called No. o, there was no precedent or example, and except for the purely theoretical conditions ascertained by the experiments described in "Aerodynamics," everything was unknown. Next to nothing was known as to the size or form, as to the requisite strength, or as to the way of attaching the sustaining surfaces; almost nothing was known as to the weight permissible, and nothing as to the proper scale on which to build the aerodrome, even if the design had been obtained, while everything which related to the actual construction of boiler and engines working under such unprecedented conditions was yet to be determined by experiment.

The scale of the actual construction was adopted under the belief that it must be large enough to carry certain automatic steering apparatus which I had designed, and which possessed considerable weight. I decided that a flying machine if not large enough to carry a manager should in the absence of a human directing intelligence have some sort of automatic substitute for it, and be large enough to have the means of maintaining a long and steady flight, during which the problems (which the rubber-driven models so imperfectly answered) could be effectually solved.

When, in 1891, it was decided to attempt to build this steam aerodrome, the only engine that had been made up to that time with any claim to the lightness and power I was seeking was the Stringfellow engine, exhibited at the Crystal Palace in London in 1868, which it was then announced developed one horsepower for a total weight (boiler and engines) of thirteen pounds. The original engine came into the possession of the Institution in 1889 as a historical curiosity, but on examination it was at once evident that it never had developed, and never could develop, the power that had been attributed to it, and probably not one tenth so much. . . .

After studying various forms for the hull or body of the prospective aerodrome, I was led to adopt the lines which Nature has used in the mackerel as most advantageous so far as the resistance of the air was concerned, but it proved to be difficult in construction to make the lines of the bow materially different from those of the stern, and in this first model the figure was symmetrical throughout.

As I wish that my experience may be of benefit to the reader, even in its failures, I will add that I made the not-unnatural mistake of building on the plan on which the hull of an ordinary ship is constructed; that is, making the hull support the projecting bowsprit and other parts. In the aerodrome, what corresponds to the bowsprit must project far in advance of the hull to sustain the front wings, and a like piece must project behind it to sustain the rear wings and the tail, or the supporting surfaces of whatever kind. The mistake of the construction lay in disjoining these two and connecting them indirectly by the insufficiently strong hull which supported them. This hull was formed of longitudinal U-shaped ribs of thin steel, which rested on rings made of an alloy of aluminum, which possessed the lightness of the latter metal with very considerable toughness, but which was finally unsatisfactory. I may say parenthetically that in none of the subsequent constructions has the lightness of aluminum[1] been found to compensate for its very many disadvantages. The two rods, which were each one meter in length, were with difficulty kept rigorously in line, owing to the yielding of the constructionally weak hull. It would have been better, in fact, to have carried the rod straight through at any inconvenience to the disposition of the boilers and the engine. . . .

On the whole, the result of the first actual trial of an aerodrome in the field was disconcerting, for unless the result was due to the wings

[1]The situation is radically altered today. Aluminum is commonly used in airplane construction.

being placed in a position wholly unfavorable to support, there seemed to be no doubt that either the engine power or the supporting surface was insufficient. . . .

As the end of the year 1892 approached and with it the completion of an aerodrome of large size which had to be started upon its flight in some way, the method and place of launching it pressed for decision. One thing at least seemed clear. In the present stage of experiment, it was desirable that the aerodrome should—if it must fall—fall into water where it would suffer little injury and be readily recovered, rather than anywhere on land, where it would almost certainly be badly damaged. . . .

Finally, the idea, which seems obvious enough when stated, presented itself of building a kind of houseboat, not to get up initial motion by the boat's own velocity, but to furnish an elevated platform, which could be placed in the midst of a considerable expanse of water, if desired, under conditions which admitted of turning in the direction of the wind, as it need hardly be repeated that it was indispensable to the machine, as it is to the bird, to rise in the face of a wind, if there be any wind at all.

The houseboat in question was nothing more than a scow about thirty feet long by twelve feet wide, upon which a small house was erected, to be used for the occasional storing of the aerodromes. On account of the accidents which were certain to occur in the first attempts, it was fitted up with the means of making small repairs. On the roof of the house there was a platform upon which the operator stood when making a launch, and upon which were mounted the launching devices hereafter described.

This boat was completed in November 1892.

1893

By the kindness of the Superintendent of the Coast Survey, the houseboat was towed in May 1893 down to Chopawamsic Island, a small island near the western bank of the Potomac River, not far from the Quantico station of the Washington and Richmond Railroad Company.

The houseboat was at all times moored somewhere on the west side of the island, in the stretch of quiet water between that and the west shore of the river. The waters here are, with the exception of a narrow channel, very shallow, and, indeed, partly dry at low tide, so that there was no danger of an aerodrome being lost, unless its flight carried it a long distance away and over the land.

Field Trials

Aerodrome No. 4 had a single midrod, a flying weight of 9 pounds, and supporting surface, consisting of wings and tail, of 18 square feet. Its engines, with about 100 pounds' pressure, developed an aggregate of 0.4 horsepower, and lifted 50 per cent of the flying weight. The propellers were 60 cm. (2 feet) in diameter and $1\frac{1}{4}$ pitch ratio.

The aerodrome was intended to be launched by a contrivance called the "starter," which was an inclined rod, hinged at the bottom, on the top of which the aerodrome was supported on a rod which was thrown down at the instant of flight, giving the aerodrome a slight forward impulse, with the expectation that it would get up sufficient initial speed to soar from the action of its propellers.

On November 18 the writer (L), with Dr. Barus (B) and the two mechanics (R and M), went to Quantico by an early train, and superintended with interested expectation the arrangements for this first trial in the open air of the mechanism which had now been over two years in preparation.

We met with an unexpected difficulty—that of launching the aerodrome at all, for though the wind was only a very gentle breeze, it was only by holding it down with the hands that it was possible to keep the aerodrome in position for the launch, during the few minutes which passed from the time it was placed upon the apparatus to the time of releasing it. Whether the launching device itself might be effective or not could not be ascertained, since it was found that nothing which could even be called an attempt to launch could be made except in an absolute calm; a condition of things very difficult for anyone to understand who has not passed through the experience. The writer returned to Washington at the close of the day without having done anything, but having learned a great deal.

November 20. L, with B and M, came down again, and waited until four twenty, when, the breeze having fallen to almost a calm, the aerodrome was maintained in place on the launching apparatus with great difficulty, while it was repeatedly set on fire by the scattering liquid fuel. Finally it was let go, and fell close to the houseboat, the tail striking the edge of the platform. The immediate cause of failure was the defective launching apparatus, for the design of which the writer felt himself responsible. . . .

Eight trips were made to Quantico and, far from any flight having been made, not once even was the aerodrome launched at all. The principal cause for this lay in the unrecognized amount of difficulty introduced by the very smallest wind, irrespective of the unfitness of the launching apparatus to give the desired initial speed and direction. . . .

1896[2]

The important changes in the steam-driven models which had been begun in the previous fall, and which in the case of No. 4 had been so extensive as to convert it into a new aerodrome, No. 6, were continued during the early spring, and it was not until the last of April that the models Nos. 5 and 6 were ready for actual test in free flight.

The condition of No. 5, which made the first successful flight, is given in a data sheet for May 6, 1896. Although the changes, as well as the modifications in the boilers and burners of both aerodromes had undoubtedly effected a great improvement in every detail of the machines, the disappointments experienced in the preceding years prevented any great feeling of confidence that the trials which were now to be made would be entirely successful. On May 4, however, the two mechanics, Mr. Reed and Mr. Maltby, were sent down to Quantico with Aerodromes Nos. 5 and 6, and Mr. Langley, accompanied by Dr. Graham Bell, who had been invited to witness the tests, followed on the afternoon of the fifth. On May 6 the wind was so very high all the morning that a test was found impracticable. During the forenoon, however, the wind gradually died down, and by 1 P.M. was blowing from six to ten miles an hour from the northeast. At 1.10 P.M. Aerodrome No. 6 was launched, but the guy wire uniting the wings having apparently caught on one of the fixed wooden strips which held the wings down, the left wing was broken before the aerodrome was really launched, and the result was that the machine slowly settled down in the water by the boat, breaking the propellers and slightly injuring the Penaud tail.

After removing No. 6 from the water, No. 5 was placed on the launching car and immediately prepared for a test. At 3.05 P.M. it was launched at a steam pressure of 150 pounds and started directly ahead into the gentle breeze which was then blowing. The height of the launching track above the water was about twenty feet.

Immediately after leaving the launching track, the aerodrome slowly descended three or four feet, but immediately began to rise, its midrod pointing upward at an increasing angle until it made about ten degrees

[2]The narrative is continued by Mr. Manly, Langley's chief assistant.

with the horizon and then remained remarkably constant at this angle through the flight. Shortly after leaving the launching track the aerodrome began to circle to the right and moved around with great steadiness, traversing a spiral path. . . .

The aerodrome made two complete turns and started on the third one. During the first two turns the machine was constantly and steadily ascending, and at the end of the second turn it had reached a height variously estimated by the different observers at from 70 to 100 feet. When at this height, and after the lapse of one minute and twenty seconds, the propellers were seen to be moving perceptibly slower and the machine began to descend slowly, at the same time moving forward and changing the angle of inclination of the midrod until the bow pointed slightly downward. It finally touched the water to the south of the houseboat, the time the machine was in the air having been one minute and thirty seconds from the moment of launching. The distance actually traversed, as estimated by plotting its curved path on the coast-survey chart and then measuring this path, was approximately 3,300 feet, which is the mean of three independent estimates. This estimate of the distance was checked by noting the number of revolutions of the propellers as recorded by the revolution counter, which was set in motion at the moment the machine was launched. On the assumption that the slip of the propellers was not greater than 50 per cent, the 1,166 revolutions as shown by the counter would indicate a distance traveled of 2,430 feet. As it was felt very certain that the slip of the propellers could not have amounted to as much as 50 per cent, it seemed a conservative estimate to place the length of flight at 3,300 feet, which would mean a rate of travel of between twenty and twenty-five miles an hour. The circular path traversed by the aerodrome was accounted for by the fact that the guy wires on one of the wings had not been tightened up properly, thus causing a difference in the lifting effect of the two sides.

The aerodrome was immediately recovered from the water and preparations made for a second test, the machine being launched again at 5.10 P.M. at a steam pressure of 160 pounds. The conditions were the same as at the first trial, except that the wind had changed from north to south and was perhaps of less velocity than before. The path traversed by the aerodrome in this second trial was almost a duplicate of the previous one, except that on account of the change in the direction of the wind the machine was launched in the opposite direction. In tightening up the guy wires, which had not been properly adjusted in the previous test, they were probably tightened somewhat too much, since in this second test the aerodrome circled toward the left, whereas in the first flight it had circled toward the right. The aerodrome made three complete turns, rising to a height of approximately sixty feet with its midrod inclined to the horizon at a slightly greater angle than before. The propellers again ceased turning while the machine was high in the air, and it glided forward and downward and finally settled on the water after having been in the air one minute and thirty-one seconds. The distance traveled was estimated as before, by plotting the path on the coast-survey chart, and was found to be 2,300 feet.

During these flights several photographs were secured of the machine while it was actually in the air, some of the pictures being taken by Dr. [Alexander Graham] Bell and others by Mr. F. E. Fowle.

Just what these flights meant to Mr. Langley can be readily understood. They meant success! For the first time in the history of the world a device produced by man had actually flown through the air, and had preserved its equilibrium without the aid of a guiding human intelligence. Not only had this device flown, but it had been given a second trial and had again flown and had demonstrated that the result obtained in the first test was no mere accident.

X Rays Discovered: Radiology Begins and Crystallography Is Invigorated

LENNEP, PREUSSEN

WILLIAM CONRAD ROENTGEN (1845-1923)

"THE FUTURE of physics is in the fifth decimal place." Such was the opinion seriously, and a little sadly, held by many distinguished classical physicists just before the turn of the twentieth century. The nineteenth century—the century of progress—they mourned because it had progressed so triumphantly that it had left them with nothing more exciting to do than calculate physical constants to the fifth decimal place.

Then, abruptly, everything changed. Within ten years the discoveries of Roentgen, Becquerel, Pierre and Marie Curie, Rutherford, Soddy, Max Planck, J. J. Thomson, Albert Einstein, and others had completely revolutionized the older classical physics and opened entirely new worlds to conquer inside the atom and outside the solar system.

The paper which heralded the advent of the new (and higher) physics was read on December 28, 1895, at the meeting of the Würzburg (Germany) Physical and Medical Society. The author was the Prussian-born professor of physics at Würzburg, William Conrad Roentgen. He called the attention of the meeting to a new kind of rays that could be produced in a vacuum tube. He called them X rays; they had the astounding property of passing through solid matter, the denser parts of which cast shadows on a photographic plate or fluorescent screen behind. With these rays, Roentgen placidly announced, it was possible to see the bones of the hand. He was prepared to demonstrate. The chairman of the meeting offered himself as a subject. The X-ray machine was turned on; the bones stood out clearly; an X-ray picture of them, still preserved, was taken. The meeting was electrified. The society immediately voted to call the "new kind of rays" Roentgen rays in honor of their discoverer. Roentgen went on to a higher post, professor at Munich (1900–20); was awarded the 1901 Nobel prize in physics; but his reputation will eternally rest on the paper, quoted here, which inaugurated a new era in physics.

The value of X rays in medical and surgical diagnosis and treatment (in, for example, such diverse conditions as fractures, cancer, and tuberculosis—where paper "scout" films are often used in mass case-finding) cannot be overestimated. The whole science of radiology is founded on Roentgen's discovery. There were many martyrs to this particular science, for X rays were employed in medical practice for some time before it was found that cumulative small doses may be dangerous, requiring amputation of overexposed parts, and may even be fatal.

X rays also contributed greatly to the physical sciences, especially crystallography and metallurgy. The true nature of crystalline structure was finally delineated with the aid of X-ray beams. British physicists, the Braggs, father (Sir William Henry) and son (William Lawrence), were jointly awarded the 1915 Nobel prize in physics for this achievement. Today giant X-ray machines are used to examine heavy steel gun barrels, die castings, and other critical metallic parts that must not fail in action.

German was the language of Roentgen's original 4000-word paper "On a New Kind of Rays." The English translation appears in the book, "William Conrad Roentgen and the Early History of the Roentgen Rays," by Otto Glaser (London: John Bale, Sons and Danielsson, 1933).

"ON A NEW KIND OF RAYS"

IF THE DISCHARGE of a fairly large induction coil be made to pass through a Hittorf vacuum tube, or through a Lenard tube, a Crookes' tube, or other similar apparatus, which has been sufficiently exhausted, the tube being covered with thin, black cardboard which fits it with tolerable closeness, and if the whole apparatus be placed in a completely darkened room, there is observed at each discharge a bright illumination of a paper screen covered with barium platinocyanide, placed in the vicinity of the induction coil, the fluorescence thus produced being entirely independent of the fact whether the coated or the plain surface is turned toward the discharge tube. This fluorescence is visible even when the paper screen is at a distance of two meters from the apparatus.

It is easy to prove that the cause of the fluorescence proceeds from the discharge apparatus, and not from any other point in the conducting circuit.

The most striking feature of this phenomenon is the fact that an active agent here passes through a black cardboard envelope, which is opaque to the visible and the ultraviolet rays of the sun or of the electric arc; an agent, too, which has the power of producing active fluorescence. Hence we may first investigate the question whether other bodies also possess this property.

We soon discover that all bodies are transparent to this agent, though in very different degrees. I proceed to give a few examples: Paper is very transparent;[1] behind a bound book of about one thousand pages I saw the fluorescent screen light up brightly, the printer's ink offering scarcely a noticeable hindrance. In the same way the fluorescence appeared behind a double pack of cards; a single card held between the apparatus and the screen being almost unnoticeable to the eye. A single sheet of tinfoil is also scarcely perceptible; it is only after several layers have been placed over one another that their shadow is distinctly seen on the screen. Thick blocks of wood are also transparent, pine boards 2 or 3 cm. thick absorbing only slightly. A plate of aluminum about 15 mm. thick, though it enfeebled the action seriously, did not cause the fluorescence to disappear entirely. Sheets of hard rubber several centi-

---

[1] By "transparency" of a body I denote the relative brightness of a fluorescent screen placed close behind the body, referred to the brightness which the screen shows under the same circumstances though without the interposition of the body.

meters thick still permit the rays to pass through them.[2] Glass plates of equal thickness behave quite differently, according as they contain lead (flint glass) or not; the former are much less transparent than the latter. If the hand be held between the discharge tube and the screen, the darker shadow of the bones is seen within the slightly dark shadow image of the hand itself. Water, carbon disulphide, and various other liquids, when they are examined in mica vessels, seem also to be transparent. That hydrogen is to any considerable degree more transparent than air I have not been able to discover. Behind plates of copper, silver, lead, gold, and platinum, the fluorescence may still be recognized, though only if the thickness of the plates is not too great. Platinum of a thickness of 0.2 mm. is still transparent; the silver and copper plates may even be thicker. Lead of a thickness of 1.5 mm. is practically opaque, and on account of this property this metal is frequently most useful. A rod of wood with a square cross-section (20 by 20 mm.), one of whose sides is painted white with lead paint, behaves differently according as to how it is held between the apparatus and the screen. It is almost entirely without action when the X rays pass through it parallel to the painted side; whereas the stick throws a dark shadow when the rays are made to traverse it perpendicular to the painted side. In a series similar to that of the metals themselves their salts can be arranged with reference to their transparency, either in the solid form or in solution. . . .

Of special significance in many respects is the fact that photographic dry plates are sensitive to the X rays. We are, therefore, in a condition to determine more definitely many phenomena, and so the more easily to avoid deception; wherever it has been possible, therefore, I have controlled, by means of photography, every important observation which I have made with the eye by means of the fluorescent screen.

In these experiments the property of the rays to pass almost unhindered through thin sheets of wood, paper, and tinfoil is most important. The photographic impressions can be obtained in a nondarkened room with the photographic plates either in the holders or wrapped up in paper. On the other hand, from this property it results as a consequence that undeveloped plates cannot be left for a long time in the neighborhood of the discharge tube, if they are protected merely by the usual covering of pasteboard and paper.

It appears questionable, however, whether the chemical action on the

[2]For brevity's sake I shall use the expression "rays," and to distinguish them from others of this name, I shall call them "X rays."

silver salts of the photographic plates is directly caused by the X rays. It is possible that this action proceeds from the fluorescent light which, as noted above, is produced in the glass plate itself or perhaps in the layer of gelatin. "Films" can be used just as well as glass plates.

I have not yet been able to prove experimentally that the X rays are able also to produce a heating action; yet we may well assume that this effect is present, since the capability of the X rays to be transformed is proved by means of the observed fluorescence phenomena. It is certain, therefore, that all the X rays which fall upon a substance do not leave it again as such.

The retina of the eye is not sensitive to these rays. Even if the eye is brought close to the discharge tube, it observes nothing, although, as experiment has proved, the media contained in the eye must be sufficiently transparent to transmit the rays. . . .

One observation in this connection should, however, be mentioned, as at first sight it seems to prove the opposite. I exposed to the X rays a photographic plate which was protected from the light by black paper, and the glass side of which was turned toward the discharge tube giving the X rays. The sensitive film was covered, for the most part, with polished plates of platinum, lead, zinc, and aluminum, arranged in the form of a star. On the developed negative it was seen plainly that the darkening under the platinum, the lead, and particularly the zinc, was stronger than under the other plates, the aluminum having exerted no action at all. It appears, therefore, that these three metals reflect the rays. Since, however, other explanations of the stronger darkening are conceivable, in a second experiment, in order to be sure, I placed between the sensitive film and the metal plates a piece of thin aluminum foil, which is opaque to ultraviolet rays but is very transparent to the X rays. Since the same result substantially was again obtained, the reflection of X rays from the metals above named is proved. . . .

It might be possible that the arrangement of particles in the substance exercised an influence on its transparency; that, for instance, a piece of calcite might be transparent in different degrees for the same thickness, according as it is traversed in the direction of the axis, or at right angles to it. Experiments, however, on calcite and quartz gave a negative result.

It is well known that Lenard came to the conclusion, from the results of his beautiful experiments on the transmission of the cathode rays of Hittorf through a thin sheet of aluminum, that these rays are phenomena of the ether, and that they diffuse themselves through all bodies. We can say the same of our rays. . . .

Other substances behave in general like air; they are more transparent to X rays than to cathode rays.

A further difference, and a most important one, between the behavior of cathode rays and of X rays lies in the fact that I have not succeeded, in spite of many attempts, in obtaining a deflection of the X rays by a magnet, even in very intense fields.

The possibility of deflection by a magnet has, up to the present time, served as a characteristic property of the cathode rays. . . .

I therefore reach the conclusion that the X rays are not identical with the cathode rays, but that they are produced by the cathode rays at the glass wall of the discharge apparatus.

This production does not take place in glass alone, but, as I have been able to observe in an apparatus closed by a plate of aluminum 2 mm. thick, in this metal also. Other substances are to be examined later.

The justification for calling by the name "rays" the agent which proceeds from the wall of the discharge apparatus, I derive in part from the entirely regular formation of shadows, which are seen when more or less transparent bodies are brought between the apparatus and the fluorescent screen (or the photographic plate).

I have observed, and in part photographed, many shadow pictures of this kind, the production of which has a particular charm. I possess, for instance, photographs of the shadow of the profile of a door which separates the rooms in which, on one side, the discharge apparatus was placed, on the other the photographic plate; the shadow of the bones of the hand; the shadow of a covered wire wrapped on a wooden spool; of a set of weights enclosed in a box; of a compass in which the magnetic needle is entirely enclosed by metal; of a piece of metal whose lack of homogeneity becomes noticeable by means of the X rays, et cetera.

Another conclusive proof of the rectilinear propagation of the X rays is a pinhole photograph which I was able to make of the discharge apparatus while it was enveloped in black paper; the picture is weak but unmistakably correct. . . .

There seems to exist some kind of relationship between the new rays and light rays; at least this is indicated by the formation of shadows, the fluorescence and the chemical action produced by them both. Now, we have known for a long time that there can be in the ether longitudinal vibrations besides the transverse light vibrations, and, according to the views of different physicists, these vibrations must exist. Their existence, it is true, has not been proved up to the present, and consequently their properties have not been investigated by experiment.

Ought not, therefore, the new rays to be ascribed to longitudinal vibrations in the ether?

I must confess that in the course of the investigation I have become more and more confident of the correctness of this idea, and so, therefore, permit myself to announce this conjecture, although I am perfectly aware that the explanation given still needs further confirmation.

Photography Contributes to Science

HENRI BECQUEREL (1852–1908)

THE FIRST HINT of the spontaneous disintegration of apparently solid substances, the phenomenon called radioactivity, was observed in 1896 by a French physicist, scion of a distinguished French family of scientists, Antoine Henri Becquerel, under circumstances described in the brief passage here quoted. Becquerel was the friend and tutor of the Curies, especially Marie, and was awarded with them the 1903 Nobel prize in physics for investigations of uranium and radioactive substances. Radioactive rays are known as "Becquerel rays."

At the time that the covered photographic plate supplied Becquerel with the first glimpse of radioactivity, the art and science of photography was less than a century old. The first photograph was made only in 1802, by Josiah Wedgwood, the potter, who threw shadows upon white paper moistened with silver nitrate. He could not, however, fix his prints. Louis Daguerre, a Paris opera painter, inventor of daguerreotype (copper coated with a thin film of silver iodide), discovered in 1839 how to fix prints with sodium hyposulphite, the "photographer's hypo." Collodion film was introduced in 1850. Archer invented the wet plate in 1851, Maddox the dry plate twenty years later. Better dry plates were perfected by George Eastman, who invented the "Kodak" and the roll of film which made possible Thomas Edison's "Kinetoscope" in 1893 and the entire motion picture industry today.

French was the language in which Becquerel wrote upon the radiation from uranium under the title *"Sur les radiations émises par phosphorescence"* in *"Comptes Rendus"* (Volume 22, p. 420, 1896). The English translation is from "A Source Book in Physics," edited by William Francis Magie (New York and London: McGraw-Hill Book Company, 1935).

THE PECULIAR BEHAVIOR OF URANIUM

WITH THE DOUBLE sulphate of uranium and potassium, of which I possess crystals in the form of a thin transparent crust, I have made the following experiment:

I wrapped a Lumière photographic plate with bromized emulsion with two sheets of thick black paper, so thick that the plate did not become clouded by exposure to the sun for a whole day. I placed on the paper a plate of the phosphorescent substance, and exposed the whole thing to the sun for several hours. When I developed the photographic plate I saw the silhouette of the phosphorescent substance in black on the negative. If I placed between the phosphorescent substance and the paper a coin or a metallic screen pierced with an openwork design, the image of these objects appeared on the negative.

The same experiments can be tried with a thin sheet of glass placed between the phosphorescent substance and the paper, which excludes the possibility of a chemical action resulting from vapors which might emanate from the substance when heated by the sun's rays.

We may therefore conclude from these experiments that the phosphorescent substance in question emits radiations which penetrate paper that is opaque to light, and reduce silver salts. . . .

I particularly insist on the following fact, which appears to me exceedingly important and not in accord with the phenomena which one might expect to observe: the same encrusted crystals placed with respect to the photographic plates in the same conditions and acting through the same screens, but protected from the excitation of incident rays and kept in the dark, still produce the same photographic effects. I may relate how I was led to make this observation: among the preceding experiments some had been made ready on Wednesday the twenty-sixth and Thursday the twenty-seventh of February and as on those days the sun only showed itself intermittently I kept my arrangements all prepared and put back the holders in the dark in the drawer of the case, and left in place the crusts of uranium salt. Since the sun did not show itself again for several days I developed the photographic plates on the first of March, expecting to find the images very feeble. The silhouettes appeared on the contrary with great intensity. I at once thought that the action might be able to go on in the dark, and I arranged the following experiment.

At the bottom of a box made of opaque cardboard I placed a photographic plate, and then on the sensitive face I laid a crust of uranium salt which was convex, so that it only touched the emulsion at a few points; then alongside of it I placed on the same plate another crust of the same salt, separated from the emulsion by a thin plate of glass; this operation was carried out in the darkroom, the box was shut, was then enclosed in another cardboard box, and put away in a drawer.

I did the same thing with a holder closed by an aluminum plate, in which I put a photographic plate and then laid on it a crust of uranium salt. The whole was enclosed in an opaque box and put in a drawer. After five hours I developed the plates, and the silhouettes of the encrusted crystals showed black, as in the former experiment, and as if they had been rendered phosphorescent by light. . . .

It is important to notice that this phenomenon seems not to be attributable to luminous radiation emitted by phosphorescence, since at the end of one hundredth of a second these radiations become so feeble that they are scarcely perceptible.

Radioactivity: Inside the Atom

MARIE SKLODOWSKA CURIE (1867–1934)

THE GREATEST love story in the history of science revolves about the life of the greatest woman scientist, Marie Sklodowska Curie. The story of her life has been touchingly told by her daughter, Eve Curie. Born in Warsaw, Poland, serious-minded Marie Sklodowska came to Paris to study science; met and married (1895) Pierre Curie, a professor at the Paris School of Physics and Chemistry; worked indefatigably with him in complicated and often disheartening research problems that turned out triumphantly in the discovery of the radioactive elements, polonium and radium; shared with him (and Becquerel) the 1903 Nobel prize in physics; bore him two accomplished daughters, Eve and Irène; succeeded him as professor of general physics at the Sorbonne when he was tragically and untimely killed in a traffic accident. Later Madame Curie was again awarded a Nobel prize—in chemistry (1911)—for her further work on radium and its compounds; became director of the research department of the Radium Institute of the University of Paris;

organized radiological service in hospitals during World War I; came to America in 1922 to accept a gift of a gram of radium—the most expensive substance in the world—from the grateful women of America.

Important as the employment of radium in medical practice has become (especially in the treatment of cancer), it should be realized that Madame Curie's claim to scientific fame rests not only on her backbreaking isolation of this new element from tons of Joachimstal pitchblende ore, but also upon her early recognition and insistence on the fact that radioactivity was a phenomenon, new to science, that took place inside the atom itself. Previously it had been held that the atom, "smallest particle of matter," was by definition indivisible and indestructible. With the concept of intra-atomic radioactivity was born the new science of atomic physics. Many important developments (the whole science of electronics, for example) have been made in this field, but none more spectacular than that made by Madame Curie's daughter, Irène, who with her husband, Frédéric Joliot, succeeded in synthesizing new radioactive elements and thus in terms of the most modern physical chemistry brought true the alchemist's ancient dream of transmutation of the elements.

English was the language in which Madame Curie so charmingly summarized the outstanding facts of her scientific career for an enthusiastic audience gathered impromptu in the chapel of Vassar College to hear the single public address of her 1922 American tour. Polish, of course, was her native tongue, French, her usual language. This touching essay, "The Discovery of Radium," reprinted in full, was originally circulated as the Ellen S. Richards Monograph ✗2, issued by the Bureau of Publication of Vassar College.

THE DISCOVERY OF RADIUM

I COULD TELL you many things about radium and radioactivity and it would take a long time. But as we cannot do that, I shall give you only a short account of my early work about radium. Radium is no more a baby; it is more than twenty years old, but the conditions of the discovery were somewhat peculiar, and so it is always of interest to remember them and to explain them.

We must go back to the year 1897. Professor Curie and I worked at that time in the laboratory of the School of Physics and Chemistry where Professor Curie held his lectures. I was engaged in some work on uranium rays which had been discovered two years before by Professor Becquerel. I shall tell you how these uranium rays may be detected. If you take a photographic plate and wrap it in black paper and then on this plate, protected from ordinary light, put some uranium salt and leave it a day, and the next day the plate is developed, you notice on the plate a black spot at the place where the uranium salt was. This spot has been made by special rays which are given out by the uranium and are able to make an impression on the plate in the same way as ordinary light. You can also test those rays in another way, by placing them on an electroscope. You know what an electroscope is. If you charge it, you can keep it charged several hours and more, unless uranium salts are placed near to it. But if this is the case the electroscope loses its charge and the gold or aluminum leaf falls gradually in a progressive way. The speed with which the leaf moves may be used as a measure of the intensity of the rays; the greater the speed, the greater the intensity.

I spent some time in studying the way of making good measurements of the uranium rays, and then I wanted to know if there were other elements, giving out rays of the same kind. So I took up a work about all known elements and their compounds and found that uranium compounds are active and also all thorium compounds, but other elements were not found active, nor were their compounds. As for the uranium and thorium compounds, I found that they were active in proportion to their uranium or thorium content. The more uranium or thorium, the greater the activity, the activity being an atomic property of the elements, uranium and thorium.

Then I took up measurements of minerals and I found that several of those which contain uranium or thorium or both were active. But then the activity was not what I could expect; it was greater than for uranium or thorium compounds, like the oxides which are almost entirely composed of these elements. Then I thought that there should be in the minerals some unknown element having a much greater radioactivity than uranium or thorium. And I wanted to find and to separate that element, and I settled to that work with Professor Curie. We thought it would be done in several weeks or months, but it was not so. It took many years of hard work to finish that task. There was not *one* new element; there were several of them. But the most important is radium, which could be separated in a pure state.

All the tests for the separation were done by the method of electrical measurements with some kind of electroscope. We just had to make chemical separations and to examine all products obtained, with respect to their activity. The product which retained the radioactivity was considered as that one which had kept the new element; and, as the radioactivity was more strong in some products, we knew that we had succeeded in concentrating the new element. The radioactivity was used in the same way as a spectroscopical test.

The difficulty was that there is not much radium in a mineral; this we did not know at the beginning. But we now know that there is not even one part of radium in a million parts of good ore. And, too, to get a small quantity of pure radium salt, one is obliged to work up a huge quantity of ore. And that was very hard in a laboratory.

We had not even a good laboratory at that time. We worked in a hangar where there were no improvements, no good chemical arrangements. We had no help, no money. And because of that, the work could not go on as it would have done under better conditions. I did myself the numerous crystallizations which were wanted to get the radium salt separated from the barium salt, with which it is obtained, out of the ore. And in 1902 I finally succeeded in getting pure radium chloride and determining the atomic weight of the new element, radium, which is 226, while that of barium is only 137.

Later I could also separate the metal radium, but that was a very difficult work; and, as it is not necessary for the use of radium to have it in this state, it is not generally prepared that way.

Now, the special interest of radium is in the intensity of its rays, which is several million times greater than the uranium rays. And the effects of the rays make the radium so important. If we take a practical point of view, then the most important property of the rays is the production of physiological effects on the cells of the human organism. These effects may be used for the cure of several diseases. Good results have been obtained in many cases. What is considered particularly important is the treatment of cancer. The medical utilization of radium makes it necessary to get that element in sufficient quantities. And so a factory of radium was started, to begin with, in France, and later in America, where a big quantity of ore named carnotite is available. America does produce many grams of radium every year but the price is still very high because the quantity of radium contained in the ore is so small. The radium is more than a hundred thousand times dearer than gold.

But we must not forget that when radium was discovered no one knew that it would prove useful in hospitals. The work was one of pure science. And this is a proof that scientific work must not be considered from the point of view of the direct usefulness of it. It must be done for itself, for the beauty of science, and then there is always the chance that a scientific discovery may become, like the radium, a benefit for humanity.

But science is not rich; it does not dispose of important means; it does not generally meet recognition before the material usefulness of it has been proved. The factories produce many grams of radium every year, but the laboratories have very small quantities. It is the same for my laboratory, and I am very grateful to the American women who wish me to have more of radium, and give me the opportunity of doing more work with it.

The scientific history of radium is beautiful. The properties of the rays have been studied very closely. We know that particles are expelled from radium with a very great velocity, near to that of light. We know that the atoms of radium are destroyed by expulsion of these particles, some of which are atoms of helium. And in that way it has been proved that the radioactive elements are constantly disintegrating, and that they produce, at the end, ordinary elements, principally helium and lead. That is, as you see, a theory of transformation of atoms, which are not stable, as was believed before, but may undergo spontaneous changes.

Radium is not alone in having these properties. Many having other radioelements are known already: the polonium, the mesothorium, the radiothorium, the actinium. We know also radioactive gases, named emanations. There is a great variety of substances and effects in radioactivity. There is always a vast field left to experimentation and I hope that we may have some beautiful progress in the following years. It is my earnest desire that some of you should carry on this scientific work, and keep for your ambition the determination to make a permanent contribution to science.

Atomic Physics: The Interpretation of the Atom

FREDERICK SODDY (1877-   )

THE DISCOVERY of radioactive elements by the Curies in France reverberated throughout the entire scientific world. At McGill University in

Montreal, Canada, in 1900, two keen-witted young scientists, Ernest Rutherford, professor of physics, and Frederick Soddy, demonstrator in chemistry, tore vigorously into the new problem of radioactivity. Together they developed the theory of atomic disintegration of radioactive elements (including radium, uranium, thorium, mesothorium, et cetera). Eventually there was established a "timetable" for the rate of change of each of the radioactive elements: after changing through "half lives," ranging from seconds to thousands of years, all radioactive elements end up as lead. Soddy's unique contribution to the theories of radioactivity was the concept of "isotopes," a discovery described clearly in the passages here quoted from his often-revised book, "The Interpretation of the Atom" (London, John Murray, 1932)..Further study of isotopes on the part of an American investigator, Indiana-born (1893) Harold Clayton Urey, professor at Columbia University, enabled him to discover and produce "heavy hydrogen" and eventually "heavy water," compounded with the heavier isotopes of hydrogen. Urey was awarded the 1934 Nobel prize in chemistry.

"I am not among those who can bow down and worship the square root of minus one," declared Soddy, characteristically, in the preface to "The Interpretation of the Atom." He was at the time (1919–36) Dr. Lee's professor of chemistry at Oxford and not altogether in sympathy with the relativity-minded scientific epistemologists at Cambridge. Soddy also was awarded a Nobel prize in chemistry, 1921. Before going to Oxford he taught successively at the universities of London, Glasgow, and Aberdeen.

English is the language of the original.

ISOTOPES: BUILDING BLOCKS OF "HEAVY WATER"

IMPLICATIONS OF ATOMIC CHANGE. Until the interpretation of radioactivity, the atoms had been, as Clerk-Maxwell put it in 1873, the permanent foundation stones of the universe. A new world was opened up when it was discovered that the two heaviest and most complex of the atoms were spontaneously breaking up and passing through a long succession of unstable and more or less ephemeral forms. Discoveries, such as the discovery of the production of helium from radium and the production of radium from uranium, any one of which would have startled the chemists of any earlier century, now followed from the theory of atomic disintegration as a matter of course, being predicted beforehand, much as a skilled billiard player will declare his stroke before he plays it. For the sake of trying to get a general view of the subject, let us postpone their more detailed consideration and pass on at once to what was the strangest result of all. For even the chemist, of all people the one most familiar with the meaning and implications of that little word change, not only did not foresee this one, but took some considerable time and the accumulation of a wealth of examples before understanding it. In 1911 to 1913 three or four converging lines of evidence, drawn from both the physical and chemical developments of the subject, revealed a new type of complexity in the chemical elements which had never before been even suspected.

If at the end of the summer, after the garden bulbs had been dug up to be stored indoors against the winter frost, they had the misfortune to become all mixed up, a skilled gardener, no doubt, might easily sort the crocuses from the tulips and the tulips from the hyacinths, but he would be a very remarkable one if he could sort each of the various bulbs into their several varieties, the white, the yellow, the blue, and so on. Yet next year, after they had flowered again, anyone not color-blind could do it. So it has proved for—of all unlikely things—the chemical elements. "By their fruits ye shall know them."

The chemist dealing with unchanging elements sorts them easily enough into their several varieties. But let them change into one another and what subtle internal distinctions between the different atoms of the same element are at once disclosed! So it was left for the radio-chemists to discover, first, that many of the new radioelements, which are produced by different parents and which in due course change quite differently into different products, are chemically indistinguishable and identical. Once mixed together they cannot be separated again from one another by any process of chemical analysis whatever.

The Displacement Law. So soon as the very complicated sequences of changes [in the disintegration of radioactive substances such as thorium, ionium, and radium] were sufficiently unraveled, and the chemistry of the successive products sufficiently studied, a very simple and comprehensive generalization was found to connect the type of change the radioelement undergoes—whether an α-ray change or a β-ray change—with the chemical character of the product. It is now known as the Displacement Law. As regards the α-ray change it dates from 1911, when it was pointed out by the author that the product in this case has the chemical nature of the element *two places preceding* the parent in the Periodic Table. The complete generalization dates from February 1913, when K. Fajans in Germany, and A. S. Russell and the author in this country from the results of Fleck's researches, all independently extended the generalization to the case of β-ray changes. So extended, it fitted the whole of the known disintegration series into the Periodic Table without any definite exception. In the β-ray change the product has the chemical nature of the element *one place after* the parent in the Periodic Table. . . .

Thus from the type of ray expelled we may at once predict the chemical nature of the product, and vice versa. Many such predictions were at once made from the generalization and confirmed by experiment, so that all the lacunae in this part of the subject were in 1913 cleared up in a flash. Thus it predicted that some of the members of the active deposits must be chemically identical with thallium, and so it proved. The advances so made were of paramount interest and importance to the subject of radioactivity proper, as will be dealt with in the sequel. But the real advance was on a far wider front. For the Displacement Law explained in the simplest and most direct manner that veritable cryptogram, the Periodic Table itself.

The α-particle carries two elementary atomic charges or units of positive electricity, and its expulsion from the atom reduces the positive charge of the atom by two units so that it occupies a place in the Table two places preceding that occupied previously. The β-particle is the electron or atom of negative electricity, and its expulsion from the atom reduces the negative charge by one unit—which is the same, electrically, as increasing the positive charge by one unit—and the atom then occupies a place in the Table one place after that occupied previously. So that the successive elements in the Table differ from one another by the single atomic or unit charge of electricity. Going in the direction of increasing atomic weight, each place corresponds with one unit of positive electricity more than the last place.

We arrive at the fundamental conclusion that the successive places in the Periodic Table correspond with a succession of integers which represent, in a manner still to be elaborated, the numbers of unit positive charges of electricity in the atom of matter. The Periodic Law is itself nothing else but the most general consequence of the modern view that electricity is atomic. All of this in a general way was the obvious conclusion from the Displacement Law. . . .

Isotopes. According to the Displacement Law, after one α- and two β-ray changes, in any order it is "as you were" with regard to the chemical character. We get back again, after an αββ triple change in any order, into *the same place* in the Periodic Table as we started from, and, whenever this occurs, the product is chemically inseparable from and identical with its great-grandfather. The product of the $\alpha\beta\beta$ triple change is the isotope of the original parent, the word *isotope* being coined for this purpose as meaning simply "the same place." As such triple changes are frequent in the disintegration series we have at once the explanation of the curious atavism displayed by so many of the products, and their tendency to revert in chemical character to that of a previous member of the series, which at first seemed so puzzling and difficult to explain. Or we may put it another way. The passage of the series through the Periodic Table is not straightforward but alternating, so that in the same series the same place may be passed through more than once.

Remembering that the most skilled chemists have absolutely failed by any method of chemical analysis, not only to separate any mixture of radioactive isotopes, but even to effect the slightest change in the proportion in which they are mixed, under conditions when even a slight alteration could readily be detected by radioactive measurement, these results clearly established a most important result. The chemical character of an element is entirely determined by a particular integral value representing in some way the net positive charge of its atom, irrespective of its mass. After the triple $\alpha\beta\beta$ change, the mass of the atom is reduced by four units, but its net charge is unaffected. Again, mesothorium I is isotopic with radium, though the former, being produced from thorium of atomic weight 232 by loss of a helium atom, has an atomic weight 228, whereas the latter is produced from uranium and has the atomic weight 226, two units less. Nevertheless, two such totally different elements are to the chemist identical and would be considered, but for their radioactivity, to be the same element.

The identity of the properties of isotopes is not confined to their chemistry. It extends also to all the usual physical criteria used for their characterization, such as the melting point and boiling point of the element and its compounds, and to the ordinary arc, spark, and X-ray spectra. But it does not extend to any physical property or constant— such as the density, the rate of diffusion, and so on—which depends directly upon the mass of the atom or the molecule, unless, of course, it happens that the atomic weights of the isotopes are identical, that is to say that they are "isobaric" as well as isotopic. . . .

Integral Atomic Weights and Prout's Hypothesis. Once the existence of isotopes had been revealed through the course of radioactive changes, it was natural to ask whether they did not exist among the common elements. At first, all that could certainly be said was that if any of the common elements were really mixtures of isotopes of different atomic mass, the chemist, at least, would not have recognized it by his methods of analysis. At the same time, there were good reasons to believe that the discovery of isotopes might clear up naturally an exceedingly curious unexplained peculiarity about the atomic weights.

Prout's hypothesis, which was put forward at the beginning of last century, that all the elements are built up out of the condensation of hydrogen, would make the atomic weights integers in terms of that of hydrogen as the unit. Indeed, it was the desire to put this to a conclusive experimental test that underlay the long series of more and more accurate determinations of the atomic weights, which began with the classical determinations of Stas (1840), and for which last century was specially distinguished. The results were exceedingly curious. In the first place the fundamental ratio of the atomic weights of hydrogen and oxygen was against the view, for oxygen was found to be 15.88 if hydrogen is unity, or hydrogen is 1.00775 if oxygen is 16.

But, as accurate values were obtained for more and more of the elements, it was found that a large proportion of those known to the highest degree of accuracy were practically integral values in terms of oxygen as 16, though not in terms of hydrogen as unity. This is naturally the more likely to be true for the lighter elements. In the heavier, a whole integer may be only a fraction of 1 per cent of the value, and, to test this point for these, much greater accuracy must be attained than is required for the lighter elements. Eight out of the first sixteen elements besides oxygen have practically exact integral values on the O=16 standard. They are helium, 4; carbon, 12; nitrogen, 14; oxygen, 16; fluorine, 19; sodium, 23; aluminum, 27; phosphorus, 31; and sulphur, 32. While some of the others, notably magnesium, 24.3, and chlorine, 35.45, depart from the integral value beyond all possibility of the deviation being due to error of experiment, Mallet in 1880 had calculated that the probability of this approximation to integral values being due to chance was over 1,000 to 1 against.

So that, in a modified form, with oxygen, 16, or helium, 4, as the standard, Prout's hypothesis fitted about half of the best-known atomic weights. The probable explanation was made obvious by the discovery of isotopes. For the integral values would correspond to those elements which were homogeneous, and the fractional values to those that were mixtures, being then merely a mean value of the various individuals in arbitrary proportions. So it has proved, except for hydrogen itself and for bromine, an element with an atomic weight on the oxygen standard of almost exactly 80, but really a mixture in practically equal proportion of atoms of weights 79 and 81. . . .

However, to the newer and later determinations, a small but systematic departure has been established. Beginning with hydrogen, where the departure is greatest, being 7.75 parts per thousand in excess, it becomes steadily less and, in the middle of the series, reaches a minimum, about one part per thousand in deficit. Then the opposite occurs, so that for atomic weights in the neighborhood of 200 the values become exact integers again. This may well prove to be one of the most important discoveries of the present century. For it is connected up with the Einstein principle of the equivalence of mass and energy, and these minute variations may in reality prove the measure of the internal energy of different elements, and of their relative stability to transmutational changes.

Electronics Is Born

J. J. THOMSON (1856–1940)

ELECTRONICS is strictly a twentieth-century science. Prior to that astounding decade, 1895–1905, at the turn of the century, the decade from Roentgen to Einstein which created the revolutionary scientific outlook of the twentieth century, no one had dreamed of doors opened, colors matched, gadgets counted by an "electric eye"; "brain waves" made visible and audible, voices carried round the world, attacking airplanes spotted with the aid of electron tubes; moving pictures "televised through the ether," motors stopped and started, metals welded by means of electronic valves. Indeed, on the evening of April 29, 1897, when the professor of physics at Cambridge University, English-born Joseph John Thomson, announced the discovery of the electron under the name of "corpuscles of electricity," his scientific colleagues thought that he was fooling them.

Thomson came to his conclusions concerning the existence of the electron, a particle smaller than the atom, not through the study of radioactivity but through experiments, following Hertz, on the behavior of electrical "beams," cathode rays, streaming from a negative to a positive pole through a glass tube (forerunner of the radio tube) from which practically all air or other gas was evacuated by a fast-working, high-power vacuum pump. Until his death J. J. Thomson was one of the "grand old men" of modern English science. Though he taught (1905–18) also at the Royal Institution, London, he is especially gratefully remembered for his masterly development of the Cavendish Research Laboratory at Cambridge. The Nobel prize in physics came to him in 1906, a distinction which his son, George Paget Thomson, working in electronics, also achieved in 1937.

An electron is too small to be seen under a microscope, even an electron microscope. The first man to visualize the electron, however, in the sense that he could photograph the trail of a swiftly moving electron, was a Scottish physicist, C. T. R. Wilson (1869–), who invented the "cloud chamber" for this purpose. The track of the electron can be seen on the photographs in the mist of water vapor suddenly condensed in the tiny chamber. An American physicist and Nobel prize winner, Robert A. Millikan (1868–), professor at the University of Chicago (1910–21) and since at the California Institute of Technology, is credited with being the first to isolate the electron and measure its charge.

Today the intra-atomic world is known to be peopled with far more characters than the simple electrons discovered by Thomson. It includes protons, photons, neutrons, deutrons—and only tomorrow's scientific assemblies can reveal what else.

English was the language in which Thomson wrote his "Recollections and Reflections," quoted here. It was published in 1936 by George Bell & Sons, Ltd., London.

THE DISCOVERY OF THE ELECTRON

THE RESEARCH which led to the discovery of the electron began with an attempt to explain the discrepancy between the behavior of cathode rays under magnetic and electric forces. Magnetic forces deflect the rays in just the same ways as they would a negatively electrified particle moving in the direction of the rays.

A Faraday cylinder placed out of the normal path of a thin beam of cathode rays does not receive any charge of electricity, but it receives a copious negative one when the beam is deflected by a magnet into the cylinder. This would seem to be conclusive evidence that the rays carried a charge of negative electricity had not Hertz found that when they were exposed to an electric force they were not deflected at all. From this he came to the conclusion that they were not charged particles. He took the view, which was held by the majority of German physicists, that they were flexible electric currents flowing through the ether, the negative electricity flowing out of the cathode and the positive into it, and that they were acted upon by magnetic forces in accordance with the laws discovered by Ampère for the forces exerted on electric currents.

Such currents would give a charge of negative electricity to bodies against which they struck. They would be deflected by a magnet in accordance with Ampère's laws. They would not be deflected by electric forces. These are just the properties which the cathode rays were for a long time thought to possess. . . .

My first attempt to deflect a beam of cathode rays was to pass it between two parallel metal plates fastened inside the discharge tube, and to produce an electric field between the plates. This failed to produce any lasting deflection. I could, however, detect a slight flicker in the beam when the electric force was first applied. This gave the clue to what I think is the explanation of the absence of the electric deflection of the rays. If there is any gas between the plates it will be ionized by the cathode rays when they pass through it, and thus produce a supply of both positively and negatively electrified particles. The positively charged plate will attract to itself negatively electrified particles which will neutralize, in the space between the plates, the effect of its own positive electrification. Similarly, the effect of the negatively electrified plate will be neutralized by the positively electrified particles it attracts. Thus charging up the plates will not produce an electric force between them; the momentary flicker was due to the neutralization of the plates not being instantaneous.

The absence of deflection on this view is due to the presence of gas— to the pressure being too high—thus the thing to do was to get a much higher vacuum. This was more easily said than done. The technique of producing high vacua in those days was in an elementary stage. The necessity of getting rid of gas condensed on the walls of the discharge tube, and on the metal of the electrodes by prolonged baking, was not realized. As this gas was liberated when the discharge passed through the tube, the vacuum deteriorated rapidly during the discharge, and the pumps then available were not fast enough to keep pace with this liberation. However, after running the discharge through the tube day after day without introducing fresh gas, the gas on the walls and electrodes got driven off and it was possible to get a much better vacuum. The deflection of the cathode rays by electric forces became quite marked, and its direction indicated that the particles forming the cathode rays were negatively electrified.

This result removed the discrepancy between the effects of magnetic and electric forces on the cathode particles; it did much more than this: it provided a method of measuring v the velocity of these particles, and also m/e, where m is the mass of a particle and e its electric charge. . . .

These experiments were of an exploratory nature; the apparatus was of a simple character and not designed to get the most accurate numerical results. It was sufficient, however, to prove that e/m for the cathode ray particles was of the order 10^7, whereas the smallest value hitherto found was 10^4 for the atom of hydrogen in electrolysis. So that if e were the same as the charge of electricity carried by an atom of hydrogen—as was subsequently proved to be the case—m, the mass of the cathode-ray particle, could not be greater than one thousandth part of the mass of an atom of hydrogen, the smallest mass hitherto recognized. It was also proved that the mass of these particles did not depend upon the kind of gas in the discharge tube. These results were so surprising that it seemed more important to make a general survey of the subject than to endeavor to improve the determination of the exact value of the ratio of the mass of the particle to the mass of the hydrogen atom. . . .

I next tested electrified particles which had been produced by methods in which no electric force had been applied to their source. It is known that metals when exposed to ultraviolet light give off negative electricity, and that metallic and carbon filaments do so when incandescent. I measured, by methods based on similar principles to those used for cathode rays, the values of e/m for the carriers of negative electricity in these cases, and found that it was the same as for cathode rays.

After long consideration of the experiments it seemed to me that there was no escape from the following conclusions:

(1) That atoms are not indivisible, for negatively electrified particles can be torn from them by the action of electrical forces, impact of rapidly moving atoms, ultraviolet light or heat.

(2) That these particles are all of the same mass, and carry the same charge of negative electricity from whatever kind of atom they may be derived, and are a constituent of all atoms.

(3) That the mass of these particles is less than one thousandth part of the mass of an atom of hydrogen.

I at first called these particles corpuscles, but they are now called by the more appropriate name "electrons." I made the first announcement of the existence of these corpuscles in a Friday Evening Discourse at the Royal Institution on April 29, 1897. . . .

At first there were very few who believed in the existence of these bodies smaller than atoms. I was even told long afterward by a distinguished physicist who had been present at my lecture at the Royal Institution that he thought I had been "pulling their legs." I was not surprised at this, as I had myself come to this explanation of my experiments with great reluctance, and it was only after I was convinced that the experiment left no escape from it that I published my belief in the existence of bodies smaller than atoms.

The Modern Concept of Matter

ERNEST RUTHERFORD (1871–1937)

WHAT DOES an atom look like? An electron? Science cannot give you a picture, but it can give you an idea. The man who first enunciated the idea that an atom could be compared with the solar system, having a nucleus analogous to the sun and electrons revolving about it like planets, was Sir Ernest Rutherford, a native of New Zealand, who (with Soddy) at McGill University in Montreal, began early investigations of that strange phenomenon of intra-atomic radioactivity. As he insists in the compact essay on the structure of matter, here quoted in full, written in 1927 when he was president of the British Association for the Advancement of Science, the analogy between the solar system and the atom cannot be pressed too far.

In twentieth-century science, truth of a proposition can be demonstrated only by writing an equation. In the nineteenth century, and indeed back to the time of Galileo, it was sufficient to make a diagram or a model; before that, to draw a picture. Early science was pictorial, expressible like the drawings of Vesalius in images of objects of nature; middle or "classical" science (1543–1895) was diagrammatic, delineating mechanical forces by geometric lines and figures, such as we find in diagrams of Newton or even the "thermodynamic surfaces" modeled in wood and clay by Gibbs and Maxwell. Modern science is mathematical;

invisible truths reside in the niceties of equations, transformations, and other mathematical operations with which modern scientists like Einstein and other exponents of the higher physics are skilled in deploying. To put it another way, the emphasis in early science was on man's eye; in classical science, on his muscles; in modern science, on his cranium. Though they can tell us much about the behavior of electrons and the other atomic entities that go to make up what common sense designates as solid matter, neither Rutherford nor any other modern scientist has been able to picture the atomic system accurately except in terms of mathematics.

Rutherford's was an especially fruitful scientific career. From McGill he went to the University of Manchester (England); thence to Cambridge, where from 1919 he was director of the Cavendish Laboratory. His experiments in radioactivity led him to some of the early efforts at atom smashing, later more effectively carried out by E. O. Lawrence and others. He succeeded in disintegrating the nucleus of the nitrogen atom with alpha particles from radium, an important step in transformation of the elements. It is interesting that the title of his last book, published the year he died, should have been "The Newer Alchemy."

English was the language in which Rutherford wrote. The quoted passage on the electrical structure of matter was contributed to a series of "Popular Research Narratives," collected by the Engineering Foundation, New York, and for it done into a book by the Williams & Wilkins Company (Baltimore, 1928).

THE ELECTRICAL STRUCTURE OF MATTER

ALL MEN deal with matter in the gross and our bodies are constructed of it. Mysteries of matter, therefore, have a fascination for thoughtful laymen as well as scientists and technologists. The atom has long been familiar as the ultimate unit of matter.

While the vaguest ideas were held as to the possible structure of atoms, there was a general belief among the more philosophically minded that the atoms could not be regarded as simple, unconnected units. For the clarifying of these somewhat vague ideas, the proof in 1897 of the independent existence of the electron as a mobile electrified unit of mass, minute compared with that of the lightest atom, was of extraordinary importance.

Our whole conception of the atom was revolutionized by the study of radioactivity. The discovery of radium provided the experimenter with powerful sources of radiation specially suitable for examining the nature of the characteristic radiations emitted by the radioactive bodies in general. The wonderful succession of changes that occur in uranium, more than thirty in number, was soon disclosed.

It was early surmised that electricity was atomic in nature. This view was confirmed and extended by a study of the charges of electricity carried by electrons. Skillful experiments by physicists added to the knowledge of the subject. One of the main difficulties has been the uncertainty as to the relative part played by positive and negative electricity in the structure of the atom. The electron has a negative charge of one fundamental unit, while the charged hydrogen atom has a charge of one positive unit. There is the strongest evidence that the atoms of matter are built up of these two electrical units.

It may be of interest to try to visualize the conception of the atom we have so far reached by taking for illustration the heaviest atom, uranium. At the center of the atom is a minute nucleus surrounded by a swirling group of 92 electrons, all in motion in definite orbits, and occupying but by no means filling a volume very large compared with that of the nucleus. Some of the electrons describe nearly circular orbits round the nucleus; others, orbits of a more elliptical shape whose axes rotate rapidly round the nucleus. The motion of the electrons in the different groups is not necessarily confined to a definite region of the atom, but the electrons of one group may penetrate deeply into the region mainly occupied by another group, thus giving a type of interconnection or coupling between the various groups. The maximum speed of any electron depends on the closeness of the approach to the nucleus, but the outermost electron will have a minimum speed of more than 600 miles per second, while the innermost K electrons have an average speed of more than 90,000 miles per second, or half the speed of light.

The nucleus atom has often been likened to a solar system where the sun corresponds to the nucleus and the planets to the electrons. The analogy, however, must not be pressed too far. Suppose, for example, we imagine that some large and swift celestial visitor traverses and escapes from our solar system without any catastrophe to itself or the planets. There will inevitably result permanent changes in the lengths of the month and year, and our system will never return to its original state. Contrast this with the effect of shooting an electron through the electronic structure of the atom. The motion of many of the electrons will be disturbed by its passage, and in special cases an electron may be

removed from its orbit and hurled out of its atomic system. In a short
time another electron will fall into the vacant place from one of the
outer groups, and this vacant place in turn will be filled up, and so on
until the atom is again reorganized. In all cases the final state of the
electronic system is the same as in the beginning.

The Philosophic Foundations of Modern Science

HENRI POINCARÉ (1854-1912)

JULES HENRI POINCARÉ, French mathematician and philosopher, was the
cousin of Raymond Poincaré, President of the Republic of France during World War I. From 1881 Henri Poincaré was a professor at the
University of Paris, holding chairs in such abstruse subjects as physical
mechanics, mathematical physics, calculus of probabilities, and celestial
mechanics. With icy logic, tempered by a gentle style, he applied one
of the keenest analytical minds of all time to the problems of mathematics, physics—including electromagnetism—and astronomy. He
showed that mathematics was human, as may be read here. He was the
philosopher par excellence of modern science.

What Francis Bacon did for the development of experimental science
in the seventeenth century, Poincaré accomplished for the acceptance
of mathematical science in the twentieth century. More than any other
man, he cleared away the intellectual underbrush which might have
tangled and impeded twentieth-century scientific advances. He made it
respectable to introduce into serious scientific thinking the subject of
epistemology ("science of knowledge"), long a fugitive from philosophy
and theology. The state of science in Bacon's time made it desirable to
banish speculative philosophy from scientific experiment. In Poincaré's
and our own time the further development of scientific thought demanded the reintroduction of philosophic concepts, particularly that
branch of philosophy (that is, epistemology) which raises the question,
How sure can we be of what we know? Poincaré cleared the way for
Einstein, Planck, and other twentieth-century higher physicists. Without Poincaré it is doubtful whether the scientific world would have so
quickly accepted the revolutionary new concepts of relativity, quantum,
wave mechanics—or even genetics and psychoanalysis.

French was the language in which Poincaré wrote with the beauty, clarity, and simplicity exemplified in his highly personal essay on "Mathematical Creation," quoted here in full. The essay, in an authorized English translation by George Bruce Halsted, is to be found in the volume truly titled "The Foundations of Science" (New York and Garrison, New York: The Science Press, 1913).

MATHEMATICAL CREATION

THE GENESIS of mathematical creation is a problem which should intensely interest the psychologist. It is the activity in which the human mind seems to take least from the outside world, in which it acts or seems to act only of itself and on itself, so that in studying the procedure of geometric thought we may hope to reach what is most essential in man's mind.

This has long been appreciated, and some time back the journal called *"L'enseignement mathématique,"* edited by Laisant and Fehr, began an investigation of the mental habits and methods of work of different mathematicians. I had finished the main outlines of this article when the results of that inquiry were published, so I have hardly been able to utilize them and shall confine myself to saying that the majority of witnesses confirm my conclusions; I do not say all, for when the appeal is to universal suffrage unanimity is not to be hoped.

A first fact should surprise us, or rather would surprise us if we were not so used to it. How does it happen there are people who do not understand mathematics? If mathematics invokes only the rules of logic, such as are accepted by all normal minds; if its evidence is based on principles common to all men, and that none could deny without being mad, how does it come about that so many persons are here refractory?

That not everyone can invent is nowise mysterious. That not everyone can retain a demonstration once learned may also pass. But that not everyone can understand mathematical reasoning when explained appears very surprising when we think of it. And yet those who can follow this reasoning only with difficulty are in the majority: that is undeniable, and will surely not be gainsaid by the experience of secondary school teachers.

And further: how is error possible in mathematics? A sane mind should not be guilty of a logical fallacy, and yet there are very fine minds who do not trip in brief reasoning such as occurs in the ordinary doings of life, and who are incapable of following or repeating without error the mathematical demonstrations which are longer, but which after all are only an accumulation of brief reasonings wholly analogous to those they make so easily. Need we add that mathematicians themselves are not infallible?

The answer seems to me evident. Imagine a long series of syllogisms, and that the conclusions of the first serve as premises of the following: we shall be able to catch each of these syllogisms, and it is not in passing from premises to conclusion that we are in danger of deceiving ourselves. But between the moment in which we first meet a proposition as conclusion of one syllogism and that in which we re-encounter it as premise of another syllogism occasionally some time will elapse, several links of the chain will have unrolled; so it may happen that we have forgotten it, or, worse, that we have forgotten its meaning. So it may happen that we replace it by a slightly different proposition, or that, while retaining the same enunciation, we attribute to it a slightly different meaning, and thus it is that we are exposed to error.

Often the mathematician uses a rule. Naturally he begins by demonstrating this rule; and at the time when this proof is fresh in his memory he understands perfectly its meaning and its bearing, and he is in no danger of changing it. But subsequently he trusts his memory and afterward only applies it in a mechanical way; and then if his memory fails him, he may apply it all wrong. Thus it is, to take a simple example, that we sometimes make slips in calculation because we have forgotten our multiplication table.

According to this, the special aptitude for mathematics would be due only to a very sure memory or to a prodigious force of attention. It would be a power like that of the whist player who remembers the cards played; or, to go up a step, like that of the chess player who can visualize a great number of combinations and hold them in his memory. Every good mathematician ought to be a good chess player, and inversely; likewise he should be a good computer. Of course that sometimes happens; thus Gauss was at the same time a geometer of genius and a very precocious and accurate computer.

But there are exceptions; or rather I err; I cannot call them exceptions without the exceptions being more than the rule. Gauss it is, on the contrary, who was an exception. As for myself, I must confess, I am absolutely incapable even of adding without mistakes. In the same way I should be but a poor chess player; I would perceive that by a certain play I should expose myself to a certain danger; I would pass in review several other plays, rejecting them for other reasons, and then finally I should make the move first examined, having meantime forgotten the danger I had foreseen.

In a word, my memory is not bad, but it would be insufficient to make me a good chess player. Why, then, does it not fail me in a difficult piece of mathematical reasoning where most chess players would lose themselves? Evidently because it is guided by the general march of the reasoning. A mathematical demonstration is not a simple juxtaposition of syllogisms, it is syllogisms *placed in a certain order,* and the order in which these elements are placed is much more important than the elements themselves. If I have the feeling, the intuition, so to speak, of this order, so as to perceive at a glance the reasoning as a whole, I need no longer fear lest I forget one of the elements, for each of them will take its allotted place in the array, and that without any effort of memory on my part.

It seems to me then, in repeating a reasoning learned, that I could have invented it. This is often only an illusion; but even then, even if I am not so gifted as to create it by myself, I myself reinvent it in so far as I repeat it.

We know that this feeling, this intuition of mathematical order, that makes us divine hidden harmonies and relations, cannot be possessed by everyone. Some will not have either this delicate feeling so difficult to define, or a strength of memory and attention beyond the ordinary, and then they will be absolutely incapable of understanding higher mathematics. Such are the majority. Others will have this feeling only in a slight degree, but they will be gifted with an uncommon memory and a great power of attention. They will learn by heart the details one after another; they can understand mathematics and sometimes make applications, but they cannot create. Others, finally, will possess in a less or greater degree the special intuition referred to, and then not only can they understand mathematics even if their memory is nothing extraordinary, but they may become creators and try to invent with more or less success according as this intuition is more or less developed in them.

In fact, what is mathematical creation? It does not consist in making new combinations with mathematical entities already known. Anyone could do that, but the combinations so made would be infinite in number and most of them absolutely without interest. To create consists precisely in not making useless combinations and in making those which are useful and which are only a small minority. Invention is discernment, choice.

How to make this choice I have before explained; the mathematical facts worthy of being studied are those which, by their analogy with other facts, are capable of leading us to the knowledge of a mathematical law just as experimental facts lead us to the knowledge of a physical law. They are those which reveal to us unsuspected kinship between other facts, long known, but wrongly believed to be strangers to one another.

Among chosen combinations the most fertile will often be those formed of elements drawn from domains which are far apart. Not that I mean as sufficing for invention the bringing together of objects as disparate as possible; most combinations so formed would be entirely sterile. But certain among them, very rare, are the most fruitful of all.

To invent, I have said, is to choose; but the word is perhaps not wholly exact. It makes one think of a purchaser before whom are displayed a large number of samples, and who examines them, one after the other, to make a choice. Here the samples would be so numerous that a whole lifetime would not suffice to examine them. This is not the actual state of things. The sterile combinations do not even present themselves to the mind of the inventor. Never in the field of his consciousness do combinations appear that are not really useful, except some that he rejects but which have to some extent the characteristics of useful combinations. All goes on as if the inventor were an examiner for the second degree who would only have to question the candidates who had passed a previous examination.

But what I have hitherto said is what may be observed or inferred in reading the writings of the geometers, reading reflectively.

It is time to penetrate deeper and to see what goes on in the very soul of the mathematician. For this, I believe, I can do best by recalling memories of my own. But I shall limit myself to telling how I wrote my first memoir on Fuchsian functions. I beg the reader's pardon; I am about to use some technical expressions, but they need not frighten him, for he is not obliged to understand them. I shall say, for example, that I have found the demonstration of such a theorem under such circumstances. This theorem will have a barbarous name, unfamiliar to many, but that is unimportant; what is of interest for the psychologist is not the theorem but the circumstances.

For fifteen days I strove to prove that there could not be any functions like those I have since called Fuchsian functions. I was then very ignorant; every day I seated myself at my worktable, stayed an hour or two, tried a great number of combinations, and reached no results. One evening, contrary to my custom, I drank black coffee and could not sleep. Ideas rose in crowds; I felt them collide until pairs interlocked, so to speak, making a stable combination. By the next morning I had established the existence of a class of Fuchsian functions, those which come from the hypergeometric series; I had only to write out the results, which took but a few hours.

Then I wanted to represent these functions by the quotient of two series; this idea was perfectly conscious and deliberate, the analogy with elliptic functions guided me. I asked myself what properties these series must have if they existed, and I succeeded without difficulty in forming the series I have called theta-Fuchsian.

Just at this time I left Caen, where I was then living, to go on a geologic excursion under the auspices of the school of mines. The changes of travel made me forget my mathematical work. Having reached Coutances, we entered an omnibus to go some place or other. At the moment when I put my foot on the step the idea came to me, with out anything in my former thoughts seeming to have paved the way for it, that the transformations I had used to define the Fuchsian functions were identical with those of non-Euclidean geometry. I did not verify the idea; I should not have had time, as, upon taking my seat in the omnibus, I went on with a conversation already commenced, but I felt a perfect certainty. On my return to Caen, for conscience' sake I verified the result at my leisure.

Then I turned my attention to the study of some arithmetical questions apparently without much success and without a suspicion of any connection with my preceding researches. Disgusted with my failure, I went to spend a few days at the seaside, and thought of something else. One morning, walking on the bluff, the idea came to me, with just the same characteristics of brevity, suddenness, and immediate certainty, that the arithmetic transformations of indeterminate ternary quadratic forms were identical with those of non-Euclidean geometry.

Returned to Caen, I meditated on this result and deduced the consequences. The example of quadratic forms showed me that there were Fuchsian groups other than those corresponding to the hypergeometric series; I saw that I could apply to them the theory of theta-Fuchsian series and that consequently there existed Fuchsian functions other than those from the hypergeometric series, the ones I then knew. Naturally I set myself to form all these functions. I made a systematic attack upon them and carried all the outworks, one after another. There was one, however, that still held out, whose fall would involve that of the whole place. But all my efforts only served at first the better to show me the difficulty, which indeed was something. All this work was perfectly conscious.

Thereupon I left for Mont Valérien, where I was to go through my military service; so I was very differently occupied. One day, going along the street, the solution of the difficulty which had stopped me suddenly appeared to me. I did not try to go deep into it immediately, and only after my service did I again take up the question. I had all the elements and had only to arrange them and put them together. So I wrote out my final memoir at a single stroke and without difficulty.

I shall limit myself to this single example; it is useless to multiply them. In regard to my other researches I would have to say analogous things, and the observations of other mathematicians given in *"L'enseignement mathématique"* would only confirm them.

Most striking at first is this appearance of sudden illumination, a manifest sign of long, unconscious prior work. The role of this unconscious work in mathematical invention appears to me incontestable, and traces of it would be found in other cases where it is less evident. Often when one works at a hard question, nothing good is accomplished at the first attack. Then one takes a rest, longer or shorter, and sits down anew to the work. During the first half-hour, as before, nothing is found, and then all of a sudden the decisive idea presents itself to the mind. It might be said that the conscious work has been more fruitful because it has been interrupted and the rest has given back to the mind its force and freshness. But it is more probable that this rest has been filled out with unconscious work and that the result of this work has afterward revealed itself to the geometer just as in the cases I have cited; only the revelation, instead of coming during a walk or journey, has happened during a period of conscious work, but independently of this work which plays at most a role of excitant, as if it were the goad stimulating the results already reached during rest, but remaining unconscious, to assume the conscious form.

There is another remark to be made about the conditions of this unconscious work: it is possible, and of a certainty it is only fruitful, if it is on the one hand preceded and on the other hand followed by a period of conscious work. These sudden inspirations (and the examples already cited sufficiently prove this) never happen except after some days of voluntary effort which has appeared absolutely fruitless and whence nothing good seems to have come, where the way taken seems totally astray. These efforts then have not been as sterile as one thinks; they have set agoing the unconscious machine and without them it would not have moved and would have produced nothing.

The need for the second period of conscious work, after the inspiration, is still easier to understand. It is necessary to put in shape the results of this inspiration, to deduce from them the immediate consequences, to arrange them, to word the demonstrations, but above all is verification necessary. I have spoken of the feeling of absolute certitude accompanying the inspiration; in the cases cited this feeling was no deceiver, nor is it usually. But do not think this a rule without exception; often this feeling deceives us without being any the less vivid, and we only find it out when we seek to put on foot the demonstration. I have especially noticed this fact in regard to ideas coming to me in the morning or evening in bed while in a semi-hypnagogic state.

Such are the realities; now for the thoughts they force upon us. The unconscious, or, as we say, the subliminal self plays an important role in mathematical creation; this follows from what we have said. But usually the subliminal self is considered as purely automatic. Now we have seen that mathematical work is not simply mechanical, that it could not be done by a machine, however perfect. It is not merely a question of applying rules, of making the most combinations possible according to certain fixed laws. The combinations so obtained would be exceedingly numerous, useless, and cumbersome. The true work of the inventor consists in choosing among these combinations so as to eliminate the useless ones or rather to avoid the trouble of making them, and the rules which must guide this choice are extremely fine and delicate. It is almost impossible to state them precisely; they are felt rather than formulated. Under these conditions, how imagine a sieve capable of applying them mechanically?

A first hypothesis now presents itself: the subliminal self is in no way inferior to the conscious self; it is not purely automatic; it is capable of discernment; it has tact, delicacy; it knows how to choose, to divine. What do I say? It knows better how to divine than the conscious self, since it succeeds where that has failed. In a word, is not the subliminal self superior to the conscious self? You recognize the full importance of this question. Boutroux in a recent lecture has shown how it came up on a very different occasion, and what consequences would follow an affirmative answer.

Is this affirmative answer forced upon us by the facts I have just given?

I confess that, for my part, I should hate to accept it. Re-examine the facts then and see if they are not compatible with another explanation.

It is certain that the combinations which present themselves to the mind in a sort of sudden illumination, after an unconscious working somewhat prolonged, are generally useful and fertile combinations, which seem the result of a first impression. Does it follow that the sub-liminal self, having divined by a delicate intuition that these combinations would be useful, has formed only these, or has it rather formed many others which were lacking in interest and have remained unconscious?

In this second way of looking at it, all the combinations would be formed in consequence of the automatism of the subliminal self, but only the interesting ones would break into the domain of consciousness. And this is still very mysterious. What is the cause that, among the thousand products of our unconscious activity, some are called to pass the threshold, while others remain below? Is it a simple chance which confers this privilege? Evidently not; among all the stimuli of our senses, for example, only the most intense fix our attention, unless it has been drawn to them by other causes. More generally the privileged unconscious phenomena, those susceptible of becoming conscious, are those which, directly or indirectly, affect most profoundly our emotional sensibility.

It may be surprising to see emotional sensibility invoked à propos of mathematical demonstrations which, it would seem, can interest only the intellect. This would be to forget the feeling of mathematical beauty, of the harmony of numbers and forms, of geometric elegance. This is a true aesthetic feeling that all real mathematicians know, and surely it belongs to emotional sensibility.

Now, what are the mathematic entities to which we attribute this character of beauty and elegance, and which are capable of developing in us a sort of aesthetic emotion? They are those whose elements are harmoniously disposed so that the mind without effort can embrace their totality while realizing the details. This harmony is at once a satisfaction of our aesthetic needs and an aid to the mind, sustaining and guiding. And at the same time, in putting under our eyes a well-ordered whole, it makes us foresee a mathematical law. Now, as we have said above, the only mathematical facts worthy of fixing our attention and capable of being useful are those which can teach us a mathematical law. So that we reach the following conclusions: The useful combinations are precisely the most beautiful. I mean those best able to charm this special sensibility that all mathematicians know, but of which the profane are so ignorant as often to be tempted to smile at it.

What happens then? Among the great numbers of combinations blindly formed by the subliminal self, almost all are without interest and without utility; but just for that reason they are also without effect upon the aesthetic sensibility. Consciousness will never know them; only certain ones are harmonious, and, consequently, at once useful and beautiful. They will be capable of touching this special sensibility of the geometer of which I have just spoken, and which, once aroused, will call our attention to them, and thus give them occasion to become conscious.

This is only a hypothesis, and yet here is an observation which may confirm it: when a sudden illumination seizes upon the mind of the mathematician, it usually happens that it does not deceive him, but it also sometimes happens, as I have said, that it does not stand the test of verification; well, we almost always notice that this false idea, had it been true, would have gratified our natural feeling for mathematical elegance.

Thus it is this special aesthetic sensibility which plays the role of the delicate sieve of which I spoke, and that sufficiently explains why the one lacking it will never be a real creator.

Yet all the difficulties have not disappeared. The conscious self is narrowly limited, and as for the subliminal self we know not its limitations, and this is why we are not too reluctant in supposing that it has been able in a short time to make more different combinations than the whole life of a conscious being could encompass. Yet these limitations exist. Is it likely that it is able to form all the possible combinations, whose number would frighten the imagination? Nevertheless, that would seem necessary, because if it produces only a small part of these combinations, and if it makes them at random, there would be small chance that the *good,* the one we should choose, would be found among them.

Perhaps we ought to seek the explanation in that preliminary period of conscious work which always precedes all fruitful unconscious labor. Permit me a rough comparison. Figure the future elements of our combinations as something like the hooked atoms of Epicurus. During the complete repose of the mind, these atoms are motionless; they are, so to speak, hooked to the wall; so this complete rest may be indefinitely prolonged without the atoms meeting, and consequently without any combination between them.

On the other hand, during a period of apparent rest and unconscious work, certain of them are detached from the wall and put in motion. They flash in every direction through the space (I was about to say the room) where they are enclosed, as would, for example, a swarm of gnats or, if you prefer a more learned comparison, like the molecules of gas in the kinematic theory of gases. Then their mutual impacts may produce new combinations.

What is the role of the preliminary conscious work? It is evidently to mobilize certain of these atoms, to unhook them from the wall and put them in swing. We think we have done no good, because we have moved these elements a thousand different ways in seeking to assemble them, and have found no satisfactory aggregate. But, after this shaking up imposed upon them by our will, these atoms do not return to their primitive rest. They freely continue their dance.

Now, our will did not choose them at random; it pursued a perfectly determined aim. The mobilized atoms are therefore not any atoms whatsoever; they are those from which we might reasonably expect the desired solution. Then the mobilized atoms undergo impacts which make them enter into combinations among themselves or with other atoms at rest which they struck against in their course. Again I beg pardon; my comparison is very rough, but I scarcely know how otherwise to make my thought understood.

However it may be, the only combinations that have a chance of forming are those where at least one of the elements is one of those atoms freely chosen by our will. Now, it is evidently among these that is found what I called the *good combination*. Perhaps this is a way of lessening the paradoxical in the original hypothesis.

Another observation. It never happens that the unconscious work gives us the result of a somewhat long calculation *all made,* where we have only to apply fixed rules. We might think the wholly automatic subliminal self particularly apt for this sort of work, which is in a way exclusively mechanical. It seems that thinking in the evening upon the factors of a multiplication we might hope to find the product ready made upon our awakening, or again that an algebraic calculation, for example a verification, would be made unconsciously. Nothing of the sort, as observation proves. All one may hope from these inspirations, fruits of unconscious work, is a point of departure for such calculations. As for the calculations themselves, they must be made in the second period of conscious work, that which follows the inspiration, that in which one verifies the results of this inspiration and deduces their consequences. The rules of these calculations are strict and complicated. They require discipline, attention, will, and therefore consciousness. In the subliminal self, on the contrary, reigns what I should call liberty, if we might give this name to the simple absence of discipline and to the disorder born of chance. Only, this disorder itself permits unexpected combinations.

I shall make a last remark: when above I made certain personal observations, I spoke of a night of excitement when I worked in spite of myself. Such cases are frequent, and it is not necessary that the abnormal cerebral activity be caused by a physical excitant as in that mentioned. It seems, in such cases, that one is present at his own unconscious work, made partially perceptible to the overexcited consciousness, yet without having changed its nature. Then we vaguely comprehend what distinguishes the two mechanisms or, if you wish, the working methods of the two egos. And the psychologic observations I have been able thus to make seem to me to confirm in their general outlines the views I have given.

Surely they have need of it, for they are and remain in spite of all very hypothetical: the interest of the questions is so great that I do not repent of having submitted them to the reader.

The Theory of Relativity

ALBERT EINSTEIN (1879-   )

THOUGH HE HAS contributed to many other branches of modern theoretical physics—developing, for example, the laws of photoelectric effects on which the "electric eye" operates—the name of Albert Einstein is inseparably linked with the theory of relativity, one of the greatest scientific concepts of the twentieth century. The original, or "special," theory of relativity was enunciated in 1905, while the brilliant German-born physicist was working in the Swiss Patent Office. The "general" theory was announced eleven years later, in 1916, by which time the distinguished Professor Einstein was director of the Kaiser Wilhelm Physical Institute, in Berlin. An astronomical verification of the validity of the theory of relativity—namely, observation of the calculated deviation of the planet Mercury—was accomplished by British astronomers, notably Eddington, from observations of an eclipse of the sun in 1919. In 1922 Einstein was awarded the 1921 Nobel prize in physics.

Albert Einstein has gone through more changes in citizenship status than most men: from German, to Swiss, to German, to American. He came to the United States in 1933 and joined the Princeton Institute for Advanced Study. In 1934 the Nazi government of Germany abrogated his German citizenship and confiscated his property.

Much abstruse mathematics underlies the rigorous proof of the theory of relativity, but the important basic concepts, as related here, can be grasped by the ordinary intelligent person. The so-called "non-Euclidean geometry" is perhaps a stumbling block more in name than in fact. Great mathematicians of the nineteenth century, including Karl Friedrich Gauss (1777–1855), the "prince of mathematicians," director of the astronomical observatory at Göttingen; János Bolyai (1802–60), a young Hungarian officer whom Gauss described as a "geometer of genius of the first rank"; Nikolai Lobachevski (1793–1856), a Russian mathematician, professor at Kazan; Georg Friedrich Riemann (1826–66), a German; and others had all conclusively demonstrated that perfectly rigid and logical systems of geometry could be built without assuming Euclid's unprovable postulate that through a point not on it one and only one line can be drawn which is parallel to the line. The case for non-Euclidean geometry was succinctly stated by Poincaré, trail blazer for Einstein, in these words: "Axioms of geometry are only definitions in disguise. That being so, what ought one to think of this question: Is the Euclidean geometry true? The question is nonsense. One might as well ask whether the metric system is true and the old measures false."

German was the language in which Einstein himself, in 1916, wrote a popular exposition of "Relativity, the Special and the General Theory," here abridged from an original text of approximately 35,000 words. The authorized English translation, by Robert W. Lawson, was first published by Methuen & Co., London, in 1920, and ran through ten editions in a decade. The text here is from the tenth edition (1931). A "Key to Vocabulary" has been provided to assist the reader with this selection.

KEY TO VOCABULARY

WE SHALL NOT attempt to "explain" Einstein. In the following co-ordinated extracts from his own popular exposition of the special and general theories of relativity you will discover that he can explain himself far better than those who try to explain him. Most important, you will discover that his ideas are nothing to be afraid of. In condensing his discussion (simply by leaving out many parts) to a fraction of the original book, we have gone even farther than he did in omitting the mathematical language of theoretical physics. To have attempted the inclusion of the mathematical language (symbols, formulae, equations) would be as discouraging to the average reader—and as unintelligible—as to have printed the text in the German language in which it was originally written.

Einstein is not trying to do anything different from the great physical and mathematical scientists who have already been met in this volume: Copernicus, Galileo, Descartes, Newton, Faraday, and Maxwell. Like them, he looked at the world and the various glorious phenomena of nature, both on and off this rapidly spinning terrestrial globe—the propagation of light, the action of gravity, the motion of the stars—and asked himself, "What is the simplest explanation that we can find as to how the universe is put together and how it operates?" The simplest explanation found to date is the general theory of relativity. Such difficulty as there may be in understanding the theory stems principally from the fact that the simplest explanation is first and best expressed in an unfamiliar language: mathematics. In expounding relativity in mere prose, we lose some appreciation of the "sublime poetry" of the mathematical original, just as the melody and cadence of a poem in an unfamiliar language, say ancient Hebrew, is likely to be lost when we translate it into English. However, as anyone who has read the King James Bible versions of the Psalms of David understands with joy, the disappointment inherent in literal translation from one language to another is made to vanish when the translator gives a version of his subject which is faithful in spirit and thought, if not in language, to the original.

Einstein himself has authorized several popular versions, in English, German, and other languages, of his essentially mathematical theory. Indeed, he says that he has "spared himself no pains in his endeavor to present the main ideas in the simplest and most intelligible form." Why bother with these ideas? asks an uninformed reader. No reason at all, we may reply, except that they happen to offer the best answer to date as to what makes the world tick. Only the dullest clod has never asked himself that question in one form or another.

The shocking thing about the introduction of the theory of relativity into the realm of scientific and philosophic thought was that most scientists, and even more philosophers and political economists, thought at the time that they really knew—that Newton and Maxwell had told them once and for all. Like Zola in the famous Dreyfus case, Einstein—with the mathematical apparatus of the theory of relativity—insisted on re-opening a case that the authorities most concerned—in one case the French generals; in the other, the classical physicists—were more than willing to consider closed. The main questions that Einstein exploded into the arena of scientific thought revolved about the legal point (how Francis Bacon would have loved it!), "Let us reconsider the evidence on which our supposed knowledge of the ways of the universe—especially the Newtonian laws of gravity—is based."

"It seems to us," said Einstein and his followers in effect, "that we ought to say how long our yardsticks are before we attempt to measure the distance between ourselves and the end of the universe. And we ought to agree about the corresponding numbers on the faces of our clocks before we try to tell each other what time it is. Furthermore, in the world of physical reality at least (if not in the world of thought) we must always remember that we cannot transmit signals to one another—or from one star to another—at speeds greater than the velocity of light. And finally we must realize that no one has ever *proved,* although almost everyone since Euclid has agreed to assume, that a straight line is the shortest path between two points."

The words which you will have to watch most carefully in the following passage by Einstein are **these:**

Plane geometry is the **Euclidean geometry** of the Greeks, set down in thirteen books of "Elements" at Alexandria in 300 B.C. (circa) by **Euclid,** and still studied. It is based on the assumptions or axioms, which nobody bothered to question seriously until the middle of the nineteenth century, that equal quantities added, subtracted, multiplied, or divided by equal quantities remain equal; that a point is defined as having only **position,** not extension; that a moving point generates a **plane** (or flat surface, such as would be inhabited by citizens of "Flatland"); that a moving plane generates a solid (which we conventionally define as having three **dimensions,** length, breadth, and thickness, even though it exists only in the mind of the geometrician and not in the tangible, **physical universe** of which our earth and all its striving inhabitants are a part); that through a given point only one **straight line** can be drawn parallel to a given straight line. **Non-Euclidean geometry,** developed by Lobachevski and Riemann in the nineteenth century, demonstrated that it is possible to set up a **logical** system of drawing imaginary figures in the minds of mathematicians without assuming the postulate of parallels laid down by Euclid.

Classical mechanics, the science of **bodies** in **motion,** developed chiefly by Newton and Galileo in the sixteenth and seventeenth centuries, employed the straight-line geometry of Euclid and assumed in its arguments the then-convincing but still-unproved **theories** and **hypotheses**—especially in establishing the so-called "laws" of **gravitation**—that **time** and **space** (by measuring which they thought to establish absolute values for **distance** and **events** at a distance) were always independent of each other and **infinite,** which—fuzzily—meant greater than any assignable quantity. The theory of **relativity** implies that space is curved and **finite,** does have a limited volume even though, like the surface of a perfectly round **sphere,** it has no boundaries. Classical mechanics thought in terms of **rigid bodies of reference** throughout the universe, **clocks** and **measuring rods** whose speed and length did not change when they were moved at speeds approximating the enormous **velocity** of the **propagation of light** (as they actually would do), of unchanged **orbits** or pathways for planets and **fixed stars,** of actions occurring **in vacuo** (i.e., in a vacuum theoretically void of every **material** particle of **matter)** at a **uniform,** unchanging rate **instantaneously** or **simultaneously** in the same instant of time. These **quasi-Euclidean** (based on Euclid) classical physicists forgot about themselves as **observers,** a habit of thinking uprooted by the theory of relativity, whose mathematical **transformations** (changing, like a hair-do, the shape but not the quantity) make use of a **system of co-ordinates** (whereby magnitudes, such as distance from the equator, can be used to show position) that regards the universe in which we live as a **continuum,** meaning simply that its fundamental and common characteristics, as discerned by the observer, are continuous and selfsame.

If you will pay attention to the use of the key words, you will find that Einstein explains the theory of relativity quite plainly.

A POPULAR EXPOSITION BY THE FOUNDER HIMSELF

IN YOUR SCHOOLDAYS most of you who read this book made acquaintance with the noble building of Euclid's geometry, and you remember—perhaps with more respect than love—the magnificent structure, on the lofty staircase of which you were chased about for uncounted hours by conscientious teachers. By reason of your past experience, you would certainly regard everyone with disdain who should pronounce even the most out-of-the-way proposition of this science to be untrue. But perhaps this feeling of proud certainty would leave you immediately if someone were to ask you: "What, then, do you mean by the assertion that these propositions are true?" Let us proceed to give this question a little consideration.

Geometry sets out from certain conceptions such as "plane," "point," and "straight line," with which we are able to associate more or less definite ideas, and from certain simple propositions (axioms) which, in virtue of these ideas, we are inclined to accept as "true." Then, on the basis of a logical process, the justification of which we feel ourselves compelled to admit, all remaining propositions are shown to follow from these axioms, i.e., they are proven.

A proposition is then correct ("true") when it has been derived in the recognized manner from the axioms. The question of the "truth" of the individual geometrical propositions is thus reduced to one of the "truth" of the axioms. Now it has long been known that the last question is not only unanswerable by the methods of geometry, but that it is in itself entirely without meaning. We cannot ask whether it is true that only one straight line goes through two points. We can only say that Euclidean geometry deals with things called "straight lines," to each of which is ascribed the property of being uniquely determined by two points situated on it. The concept "true" does not tally with the assertions of pure geometry, because by the word "true" we are eventually in the habit of designating always the correspondence with a "real" object; geometry, however, is not concerned with the relation of the ideas involved in it to objects of experience, but only with the logical connection of these ideas among themselves.

Every description of the scene of an event or of the position of an object in space is based on the specification of the point on a rigid body (body of reference) with which that event or object coincides. This applies not only to scientific description, but also to everyday life. If I analyze the place specification "Times Square, New York,"[1] I arrive at the following result. The earth is the rigid body to which the specification of place refers; "Times Square, New York," is a well-defined point, to which a name has been assigned, and with which the event coincides in space.[2]

[1] We have chosen this as being more familiar to the American reader than the "Potsdamer Platz, Berlin," which is referred to in the original.

[2] It is not necessary here to investigate further the significance of the expression "coincidence in space." This conception is sufficiently obvious to ensure that differences of opinion are scarcely likely to arise as to its applicability in practice.

This primitive method of place specification deals only with places on the surface of rigid bodies, and is dependent on the existence of points on this surface which are distinguishable from each other. But we can free ourselves from both of these limitations without altering the nature of our specification of position. If, for instance, a cloud is hovering over Times Square, then we can determine its position relative to the surface of the earth by erecting a pole perpendicularly on the Square, so that it reaches the cloud. The length of the pole measured with the standard measuring rod, combined with the specification of the position of the foot of the pole, supplies us with a complete place specification. On the basis of this illustration, we are able to see the manner in which a refinement of the conception of position has been developed.

We thus obtain the following result: Every description of events in space involves the use of a rigid body to which such events have to be referred. The resulting relationship takes for granted that the laws of Euclidean geometry hold for "distances," the "distance" being represented physically by means of the convention of two marks on a rigid body.

"The purpose of mechanics is to describe how bodies change their position in space with time." I should load my conscience with grave sins against the sacred spirit of lucidity were I to formulate the aims of mechanics in this way, without serious reflection and detailed explanations. Let us proceed to disclose these sins.

It is not clear what is to be understood here by "position" and "space." I stand at the window of a railway carriage which is traveling uniformly, and drop a stone on the embankment, without throwing it. Then, disregarding the influence of the air resistance, I see the stone descend in a straight line. A pedestrian who observes the misdeed from the footpath notices that the stone falls to earth in a parabolic curve. I now ask: Do the "positions" traversed by the stone lie "in reality" on a straight line or on a parabola? Moreover, what is meant here by motion "in space"? From the considerations of the previous section the answer is self-evident. In the first place, we entirely shun the vague word "space," of which, we must honestly acknowledge, we cannot form the slightest conception, and we replace it by "motion relative to a practically rigid body of reference." The positions relative to the body of reference (railway carriage or embankment) have already been defined in detail in the preceding section. If instead of "body of reference" we insert "system of coordinates," which is a useful idea for mathematical description, we are in a position to say: The stone traverses a straight line relative to a system of co-ordinates rigidly attached to the carriage, but relative to a system of co-ordinates rigidly attached to the ground (embankment) it describes a parabola. With the aid of this example it is clearly seen that there is no such thing as an independently existing trajectory (literally, "path-curve"[3]), but only a trajectory relative to a particular body of reference.

In order to have a *complete* description of the motion we must specify how the body alters its position *with time;* i.e., for every point on the trajectory it must be stated at what time the body is situated there. These data must be supplemented by such a definition of time that, in virtue of this definition, these time values can be regarded essentially as magnitudes (results of measurements) capable of observation. If we take our stand on the ground of classical mechanics, we can satisfy this requirement for our illustration in the following manner. We imagine two clocks of identical construction; the man at the railway-carriage window is holding one of them, and the man on the footpath the other. Each of the observers determines the position on his own reference body occupied by the stone at each tick of the clock he is holding in his hand. In this connection we have not taken account of the inaccuracy involved by the finiteness of the velocity of propagation of light. With this and with a second difficulty prevailing here we shall have to deal in detail later.

As long as one was convinced that all natural phenomena were capable of representation with the help of classical mechanics, there was no need to doubt the validity of this principle of relativity. But in view of the more recent development of electrodynamics and optics it became more and more evident that classical mechanics affords an insufficient foundation for the physical description of all natural phenomena. At this juncture the question of the validity of the principle of relativity became ripe for discussion, and it did not appear impossible that the answer to this question might be in the negative.

Now in virtue of its motion in an orbit round the sun, our earth is comparable with a railway carriage traveling with a velocity of about 30 kilometers per second. If the principle of relativity were not valid we should therefore expect that the direction of motion of the earth at any moment would enter into the laws of nature, and also that physical systems in their behavior would be dependent on the orientation in space with respect to the earth.

However, the most careful observations have never revealed such

[3]That is, a curve along which the body moves.

anisotropic properties in terrestrial physical space, i.e., a physical non-equivalence of different directions. This is very powerful argument in favor of the principle of relativity.

There is hardly a simpler law in physics than that according to which light is propagated in empty space. Every child at school knows, or believes he knows, that this propagation takes place in straight lines with a velocity $c=300,000$ km./sec. At all events we know with great exactness that this velocity is the same for all colors, because if this were not the case, the minimum of emission would not be observed simultaneously for different colors during the eclipse of a fixed star by its dark neighbor. By means of similar considerations based on observations of double stars, the Dutch astronomer De Sitter was also able to show that the velocity of propagation of light cannot depend on the velocity of motion of the body emitting the light. The assumption that this velocity of propagation is dependent on the direction "in space" is in itself improbable.

At this juncture the theory of relativity entered the arena. As a result of an analysis of the physical conceptions of time and space, it became evident that *in reality there is not the least incompatibility between the principle of relativity and the law of propagation of light,* and that by systematically holding fast to both these laws a logically rigid theory could be arrived at. This theory has been called the *special theory of relativity* to distinguish it from the extended theory, with which we shall deal later.

Lightning has struck the rails on our railway embankment at two places A and B far distant from each other. I make the additional assertion that these two lightning flashes occurred simultaneously. If I ask you whether there is sense in this statement, you will answer my question with a decided "Yes." But if I now approach you with the request to explain to me the sense of the statement more precisely, you find after some consideration that the answer to this question is not so easy as it appears at first sight.

Are two events (e.g., the two strokes of lightning A and B) which are simultaneous *with reference to the railway embankment* also simultaneous *relatively to the train?* We shall show directly that the answer must be in the negative.

When we say that the lightning strokes A and B are simultaneous with respect to the embankment, we mean: the rays of light emitted at the places A and B, where the lightning occurs, meet each other at the mid-point M of the length A→B of the embankment. But the events A and B also correspond to positions A and B on the train. Let M′ be the mid-point of the distance A→B on the traveling train. Just when the flashes[4] of lightning occur, this point M' naturally coincides with the point M, but it moves toward the right [in a diagram] with the velocity v of the train. If an observer sitting in the position M' in the train did not possess this velocity, then he would remain permanently at M, and the light rays emitted by the flashes of lightning A and B would reach him simultaneously, i.e., they would meet just where he is situated. Now in reality (considered with reference to the railway embankment) he is hastening toward the beam of light coming from B, whilst he is riding on ahead of the beam of light coming from A. Hence the observer will see the beam of light emitted from B earlier than he will see that emitted from A. Observers who take the railway train as their reference body must therefore come to the conclusion that the lightning flash B took place earlier than the lightning flash A. We thus arrive at the important result:

Events which are simultaneous with reference to the embankment are not simultaneous with respect to the train, and vice versa (relativity of simultaneity).

Our train of thought in the foregoing pages can be epitomized in the following manner. Experience has led to the conviction that, on the one hand, the principle of relativity holds true, and that on the other hand the velocity of transmission of light *in vacuo* has to be considered equal to a constant c. By uniting these two postulates we obtained the law of transformation for the rectangular co-ordinates $x, y, z,$ and the time t of the events which constitute the processes of nature. In this connection we did not obtain the Galilei transformation, but, differing from classical mechanics, the *Lorentz transformation*. General laws of nature are co-variant with respect to Lorentz transformations.

It is clear from our previous considerations that the (special) theory of relativity has grown out of electrodynamics and optics. In these fields it has not appreciably altered the predictions of theory, but it has considerably simplified the theoretical structure, i.e., the derivation of laws, and—what is incomparably more important—it has considerably reduced the number of independent hypotheses forming the basis of theory. The special theory of relativity has rendered the Maxwell-Lorentz theory so plausible that the latter would have been generally accepted by physicists even if experiment had decided less unequivocally in its favor.

Classical mechanics required to be modified before it could come into line with the demands of the special theory of relativity. For the main part, however, this modification affects only the laws for rapid motions,

[4]As judged from the embankment.

in which the velocities of matter v are not very small as compared with the velocity of light. We have experience of such rapid motions only in the case of electrons and ions; for other motions the variations from the laws of classical mechanics are too small to make themselves evident in practice. We shall not consider the motion of stars until we come to speak of the general theory of relativity.

Let me add a final remark of a fundamental nature. The success of the Faraday-Maxwell interpretation of electromagnetic action at a distance resulted in physicists becoming convinced that there are no such things as instantaneous actions at a distance (not involving an intermediary medium) of the type of Newton's law of gravitation. According to the theory of relativity, action at a distance with the velocity of light always takes the place of instantaneous action at a distance or of action at a distance with an infinite velocity of transmission.

The non-mathematician is seized by a mysterious shuddering when he hears of "four-dimensional" things, by a feeling not unlike that awakened by thoughts of the occult. And yet there is no more commonplace statement than that the world in which we live is a four-dimensional space-time continuum.

That we have not been accustomed to regard the world in this sense as a four-dimensional continuum is due to the fact that in physics, before the advent of the theory of relativity, time played a different and more independent role, as compared with the space co-ordinates. It is for this reason that we have been in the habit of treating time as an independent continuum. As a matter of fact, according to classical mechanics, time is absolute, i.e., it is independent of the position and the condition of motion of the system of co-ordinates.

Since the introduction of the special principle of relativity has been justified, every intellect which strives after generalization must feel the temptation to venture the step toward the general principle of relativity. But a simple and apparently quite reliable consideration seems to suggest that, for the present at any rate, there is little hope of success in such an attempt. Let us imagine ourselves transferred to our old friend the railway carriage, which is traveling at a uniform rate. As long as it is moving uniformly, the occupant of the carriage is not sensible of its motion, and it is for this reason that he can without reluctance interpret the facts of the case as indicating that the carriage is at rest but the embankment in motion. Moreover, according to the special principle of relativity, this interpretation is quite justified also from a physical point of view.

If the motion of the carriage is now changed into a non-uniform motion, as for instance by a powerful application of the brakes, then the occupant of the carriage experiences a correspondingly powerful jerk forward. The retarded motion is manifested in the mechanical behavior of bodies relative to the person in the railway carriage. The mechanical behavior is different from that of the case previously considered, and for this reason it would appear to be impossible that the same mechanical laws hold relatively to the non-uniformly moving carriage, as hold with reference to the carriage when at rest or in uniform motion.

"If we pick up a stone and then let it go, why does it fall to the ground?" The usual answer to this question is: "Because it is attracted by the earth." Modern physics formulates the answer rather differently.

The action of the earth on the stone takes place indirectly. The earth produces in its surroundings a gravitational field, which acts on the stone and produces its motion of fall.

In contrast to electric and magnetic fields, the gravitational field exhibits a most remarkable property, which is of fundamental importance for what follows. Bodies which are moving under the sole influence of a gravitational field receive an acceleration, *which does not in the least depend either on the material or on the physical state of the body*. For instance, a piece of lead and a piece of wood fall in exactly the same manner in a gravitational field (*in vacuo*) when they start off from rest or with the same initial velocity.

We obtain a new result of fundamental importance when we carry out the analogous consideration for a ray of light. We conclude *that, in general, rays of light are propagated curvilinearly in gravitational fields*. In two respects this result is of great importance.

In the first place, it can be compared with the reality. Although a detailed examination of the question shows that the curvature of light rays required by the general theory of relativity is only exceedingly small for the gravitational fields at our disposal in practice, its estimated magnitude for light rays passing the sun at grazing incidence is nevertheless 1.7 seconds of arc. This ought to manifest itself in the following way. As seen from the earth, certain fixed stars appear to be in the neighborhood of the sun, and are thus capable of observation during total eclipse of the sun. At such times these stars ought to appear to be displaced outward from the sun by an amount indicated above, as compared with their apparent position in the sky when the sun is situated at another part of the heavens. The examination of the correctness or otherwise of this deduction is a problem of the greatest importance, the early solution of which is to be expected of astronomers.[5]

[To establish a relationship between time and space in the physical world it is necessary to consider the behavior of the clocks and measuring rods with which we might measure them. The problem of accurate and meaningful measurement turns out to be especially complicated when the timepieces and measuring rods are moving rapidly—say rotating at the speed of light—from the point of view of the observer. Hence it becomes necessary to specify the position of objects and events in the physical world by means of a mathematical system which does not depend on the rigid-body geometry of Euclid for definition of length or the straight-line co-ordinate system established by Descartes (Cartesian co-ordinates) for marking their position. Fortunately, the great mathematician, Gauss, had worked out his own system of co-ordinates (Gaussian co-ordinates) by which positions (that is, the distances between points) can be established by saying in effect that they are to be found at the intersections of two or more named curves. Since the four-dimensional space-time continuum of relativity is not rigidly Euclidean in character, it is extremely convenient to use Gaussian co-ordinates instead of a rigid body of reference to determine the time and place of an event or object in nature.]

The following statement corresponds to the fundamental idea of the general principle of relativity: *"All Gaussian co-ordinate systems are essentially equivalent for the formulation of the general laws of nature."*

In gravitational fields there are no such things as rigid bodies with Euclidean properties; thus the fictitious rigid body of reference is of no avail in the general theory of relativity. The motion of clocks is also influenced by gravitational fields, and in such a way that a physical definition of time which is made directly with the aid of clocks has by no means the same degree of plausibility as in the special theory of relativity.

For this reason non-rigid reference bodies are used, which are as a whole not only moving in any way whatsoever, but which also suffer alterations in form *ad lib,* during their motion. Clocks, for which the law of motion is of any kind, however irregular, serve for the definition of time. We have to imagine each of these clocks fixed at a point on the non-rigid reference body. These clocks satisfy only the one condition,

[5]By means of the star photographs of two expeditions equipped by a Joint Committee of the Royal and Royal Astronomical Societies, the existence of the deflection of light demanded by theory was first confirmed during the solar eclipse of May 29, 1919.

that the "readings" which are observed simultaneously on adjacent clocks (in space) differ from each other by an indefinitely small amount.

If we confine the application of the theory to the case where the gravitational fields can be regarded as being weak, and in which all masses move with respect to the co-ordinate system with velocities which are small compared with the velocity of light, we then obtain as a first approximation the Newtonian theory. Thus the latter theory is obtained here without any particular assumption, whereas Newton had to introduce the hypothesis that the force of attraction between mutually attracting material points is inversely proportional to the square of the distance between them. If we increase the accuracy of the calculation, deviations from the theory of Newton make their appearance, practically all of which must nevertheless escape the test of observation owing to their smallness.

We must draw attention here to one of these deviations. According to Newton's theory, a planet moves round the sun in an ellipse, which would permanently maintain its position with respect to the fixed stars, if we could disregard the motion of the fixed stars themselves and the action of the other planets under consideration. Thus, if we correct the observed motion of the planets for these two influences, and if Newton's theory be strictly correct, we ought to obtain for the orbit of the planet an ellipse, which is fixed with reference to the fixed stars. This deduction, which can be tested with great accuracy, has been confirmed for all the planets save one, with the precision that is capable of being obtained by the delicacy of observation attainable at the present time. The sole exception is Mercury, the planet which lies nearest the sun. Since the time of Leverrier, it has been known that the ellipse corresponding to the orbit of Mercury, after it has been corrected for the influences mentioned above, is not stationary with respect to the fixed stars, but that it rotates exceedingly slowly in the plane of the orbit and in the sense of the orbital motion. The value obtained for this rotary movement of the orbital ellipse was forty-three seconds of arc per century, an amount ensured to be correct to within a few seconds of arc. This effect can be explained by means of classical mechanics only on the assumption of hypotheses which have little probability, and which were devised solely for this purpose.

On the basis of the general theory of relativity, it is found that the ellipse of every planet round the sun must necessarily rotate in the manner indicated above; that for all the planets, with the exception of Mercury, this rotation is too small to be detected with the delicacy of observation possible at the present time; but that in the case of Mercury it must amount to forty-three seconds of arc per century, a result which is strictly in agreement with observation.

If we ponder over the question as to how the universe, considered as a whole, is to be regarded, the first answer that suggests itself to us is surely this: As regards space (and time) the universe is infinite. There are stars everywhere, so that the density of matter, although very variable in detail, is nevertheless on the average everywhere the same. In other words: However far we might travel through space, we should find everywhere an attenuated swarm of fixed stars of approximately the same kind of density.

This view is not in harmony with the theory of Newton. The latter theory rather requires that the universe should have a kind of center in which the density of the stars is a maximum, and that as we proceed outward from this center the group density of the stars should diminish, until finally, at great distances, it is succeeded by an infinite region of emptiness. This stellar universe ought to be a finite island in the infinite ocean of space.

This conception is in itself not very satisfactory. It is less satisfactory because it leads to the result that the light emitted by the stars and also individual stars of the stellar system are perpetually passing out into infinite space, never to return, and without ever again coming into interaction with other objects of nature. Such a finite material universe would be destined to become gradually but systematically impoverished.

But speculations on the structure of the universe also move in quite another direction. The development of non-Euclidean geometry led to the recognition of the fact that we can cast doubt on the *infiniteness* of our space without coming into conflict with the laws of thought or with experience (Riemann, Helmholtz).

In the first place, we imagine an existence in two-dimensional space. Flat beings with flat implements, and in particular flat rigid measuring rods, are free to move in a *plane*. For them nothing exists outside of this plane: that which they observe to happen to themselves and to their flat "things" is the all-inclusive reality of their plane. In particular, the constructions of plane Euclidean geometry can be carried out by means of the rods. In contrast to ours, the universe of these beings is two-dimensional; but, like ours, it extends to infinity. In their universe there is room for an infinite number of identical squares made up of rods, i.e., its volume (surface) is infinite. If these beings say their universe is "plane," there is sense in the statement, because they mean that they can perform the constructions of plane Euclidean geometry with their rods. In this connection the individual rods always represent the same distance, independently of their position.

Let us consider now a second two-dimensional existence, but this time on a spherical surface instead of on a plane. The flat beings with their measuring rods and other objects fit exactly on this surface and they are unable to leave it. Their whole universe of observation extends exclusively over the surface of the sphere. Are these beings able to regard the geometry of their universe as being plane geometry and their rods withal as the realization of "distance"? They cannot do this. For if they attempt to realize a straight line, they will obtain a curve, which we "three-dimensional beings" designate as a great circle, i.e., a self-contained line of definite finite length, which can be measured up by means of a measuring rod. Similarly, this universe has a finite area that can be compared with the area of a square constructed with rods. The great charm resulting from this consideration lies in the recognition of the fact that *the universe of these beings is finite and yet has no limits.*

But the spherical-surface beings do not need to go on a world tour in order to perceive that they are not living in a Euclidean universe. They can convince themselves of this on every part of their "world," provided they do not use too small a piece of it.

To this two-dimensional sphere universe there is a three-dimensional analogy, namely, the three-dimensional spherical space which was discovered by Riemann. Its points are likewise all equivalent. It possesses a finite volume, which is determined by its "radius."

According to the general theory of relativity, the geometrical properties of space are not independent, but they are determined by matter. Thus we can draw conclusions about the geometrical structure of the universe only if we base our considerations on the state of the matter as being something that is known. We know from experience that, for a suitably chosen co-ordinate system, the velocities of the stars are small as compared with the velocity of transmission of light. We can thus as a rough approximation arrive at a conclusion as to the nature of the universe as a whole if we treat the matter as being at rest.

We already know from our previous discussion that the behavior of measuring rods and clocks is influenced by gravitational fields, i.e., by the distribution of matter. This in itself is sufficient to exclude the possibility of the exact validity of Euclidean geometry in our universe. But it is conceivable that our universe differs only slightly from a Euclidean one, and this notion seems all the more probable, since calculations show that the metrics of surrounding space is influenced only to an exceedingly small extent by masses even of the magnitude of our sun. We might imagine that, as regards geometry, our universe behaves analogously to a surface which is irregularly curved in its individual parts, but which nowhere departs appreciably from a plane: something like the rippled surface of a lake. Such a universe might fittingly be called a quasi-Euclidean universe. As regards its space it would be infinite. But calculation shows that in a quasi-Euclidean universe the average density of matter would necessarily be nil. Thus such a universe could not be inhabited by matter everywhere; it would present to us that unsatisfactory picture which we portrayed.

If we are to have in the universe an average density of matter which differs from zero, however small may be that difference, then the universe cannot be quasi-Euclidean. On the contrary, the results of calculation indicate that if matter be distributed uniformly, the universe would necessarily be spherical (or elliptical). Since in reality the detailed distribution of matter is not uniform, the real universe will deviate in individual parts from the spherical, i.e., the universe will be quasi-spherical. But it will be necessarily finite. In fact, the theory [of relativity] supplies us with a simple connection between the space expanse of the universe and the average density of matter in it.

Quantum: "Bullets of Energy"

MAX PLANCK (1858–   )

QUANTUM? It was originally a Latin adverb that asked the common question, "How much?"—or sometimes answered it, "So much." Nowadays—since 1900 in fact—it has come to stand for "so much energy." Especially in the miniscule world of the atom and the electron, physicists have found it most convenient and helpful to determine what was going on by measuring and calculating the changes in energy; in other words they have "quantized" their equations. It is not uncommon to describe things in terms of their energy—which is capacity for work or destruction. We speak of a 60-horsepower automobile or a "blockbuster" bomb. It was astonishing to discover that energy changes in the atomic world can be successfully measured, even though the energy changes there concerned are so small that they would not disturb a fly.

The father of the quantum theory, Max Planck, then professor of physics at the University of Berlin, hardly guessed what a lusty theory he was siring when, on December 14, 1900, he communicated to the German Physical Society a paper which contained this remarkable statement: "Radiant heat is not a continuous flow and indefinitely divisible. It must be defined as a discontinuous mass made up of units all of which are similar to one another." Those units are now identified as "quanta" of action. Crudely speaking, such a quantum is the smallest coin of energy that nature mints; it is the one-cent piece of the atomic world; nothing smaller—no fractions of a cent—change hands or atoms. Furthermore all energy changes can be (sometimes must be) expressed in units of quantum, just as if war expenditures were to be written in pennies.

In the very decade when the atom itself was turning out to be more and more divisible into electrons, protons, and the like, it was comforting, to say the least, to discover something that appeared not "indefinitely divisible": the quantum of action. Nature's "preference for the particulate"—one of the great scientific generalizations—was not to be abolished. Planck was actually studying black-body radiation when he fell upon the quantum theory. Through a spectroscope he observed the effects of a beam of radiation escaping from a hollow body, or cavity, heated up to incandescence. In flat contradiction to principles of physics then held true, Planck observed that the radiation was not flowing out of the hole in the hot body continuously like water from a fire hose but rather was being spit out in tiny "parcels," "bundles," or "quanta" like bullets from a machine gun.

But Planck's work went further. In order to determine quantum measurements, which were of course figured by mathematical equations, he had to calculate a certain constant to fit these frequency equations. Its value, he found, was 6.55×10^{-27} and it turned out to be a universal constant. Now called "Planck's constant," it is signified by the letter h. The importance of this finding has been expressed by a distinguished Dutch scientist, H. A. Lorentz, who said in 1925:

"We have now advanced so far that this [Planck's] constant not only furnishes the basis for explaining the intensity of radiation and the wave length for which it represents a maximum, but also for interpreting the quantitative relations existing in several other cases among the many physical quantities it determines. I shall mention only a few; namely, the specific heat of solids, the photochemical effects of light, the orbits of electrons in the atom, the wave lengths of the lines of the spectrum, the frequency of the Roentgen rays which are produced by the impact of electrons of given velocity, the velocity with which gas molecules can rotate, and also the distances between the particles which make up a crystal. It is no exaggeration to say that in our picture of nature nowadays it is the quantum conditions that hold matter together and prevent it from completely losing its energy by radiation. It is convincingly clear that we are here dealing with real relations because the values of h as derived from the different phenomena always agree, and these values differ only by slight shades from the number which Planck computed twenty-five years ago on the experimental data then available."[1]

Max Planck was one of the most honored and respected men of science in pre-Nazi Germany. Native of Kiel, he studied at Munich and Berlin; taught at Kiel and Berlin; became permanent secretary of the Prussian Academy of Science; received a (1919) Nobel prize in 1920; was elevated in 1930 to the highest academic post in Germany, presidency of the Kaiser Wilhelm Society for the Advancement of Science.

German was the language in which Max Planck delivered his 7,000-word Nobel Prize Address before the Royal Swedish Academy of Sciences in Stockholm on June 2, 1920. The English translation, from which the excerpts are taken, was made by H. T. Clarke and L. Silberstein and published by the Clarendon Press (of the Oxford University Press) at Oxford, England, in 1922.

"THE ORIGIN AND DEVELOPMENT OF THE QUANTUM THEORY"

WHEN I RECALL the days of twenty years ago, when the conception of the physical quantum of "action" was first beginning to disentangle itself from the surrounding mass of available experimental facts, and when I look back upon the long and tortuous road which finally led to its disclosure, this development strikes me at times as a new illustration of Goethe's saying that "man errs, so long as he is striving." And all the mental effort of an assiduous investigator must indeed appear vain and hopeless if he does not occasionally run across striking facts which form incontrovertible proof of the truth he seeks, and show him that after all he has moved at least one step nearer to his objective. The pursuit of a

[1] *"Die Naturwissenschaft"* 35:1,008, 1925 (Quoted by J. A. Murphy in the Introduction to "Where Is Science Going," by Max Planck [New York: W. W. Norton & Company, Inc., 1932]).

goal, the brightness of which is undimmed by initial failure, is an indispensable condition, though by no means a guarantee, of final success.

In my own case such a goal has been for many years the solution of the question of the distribution of energy in the normal spectrum of radiant heat. . . .

Since this whole problem deals with a universal law of nature, and since I was then, as today, pervaded with a view that the more general and natural a law is the simpler it is (although the question as to which formulation is to be regarded as the simpler cannot always be definitely and unambiguously decided), I believed for the time that the basis of the law of the distribution of energy could be expressed by the theorem that the value of R is proportional to the energy. But in view of the results of new measurements this conception soon proved untenable. . . .

Two simple limits were established by direct observation for the function R: for small energies proportionality to the energy, for large energies proportionality to the square of the energy. Nothing therefore seemed simpler than to put in the general case R equal to the sum of a term proportional to the first power and another proportional to the square of the energy, so that the first term is relevant for small energies and the second for large energies; and thus was found a new radiation formula which up to the present has withstood experimental examination fairly satisfactorily. Nevertheless it cannot be regarded as having been experimentally confirmed with final accuracy, and a renewed test would be most desirable.

But even if this radiation formula should prove to be absolutely accurate it would after all be only an interpolation formula found by happy guesswork, and would thus leave one rather unsatisfied. I was, therefore, from the day of its origination, occupied with the task of giving it a real physical meaning, and this question led me, along Boltzmann's line of thought, to the consideration of the relation between entropy and probability; until after some weeks of the most intense work of my life clearness began to dawn upon me, and an unexpected view revealed itself in the distance. . . .

To work out these probability considerations the knowledge of two universal constants is required, each of which has an independent meaning, so that the evaluation of these constants from the radiation law could serve as an *a posteriori* test whether the whole process is merely a mathematical artifice or has a true physical meaning. The first constant is of a somewhat formal nature; it is connected with the definition of temperature. . . .

Much less simple than that of the first was the interpretation of the second universal constant of the radiation law, which, as the product of energy and time (amounting on a first calculation to 6.55×10^{-27} erg. sec.) I called the elementary quantum of action. While this constant was absolutely indispensable to the attainment of a correct expression for entropy—for only with its aid could be determined the magnitude of the "elementary region" or "range" of probability, necessary for the statistical treatment of the problem—it obstinately withstood all attempts at fitting it, in any suitable form, into the frame of the classical theory. So long as it could be regarded as infinitely small, that is to say, for large values of energy or long periods of time, all went well; but in the general case a difficulty arose at some point or other which became the more pronounced the weaker and the more rapid the oscillations. The failure of all attempts to bridge this gap soon placed one before the dilemma: either the quantum of action was only a fictitious magnitude, and, therefore, the entire deduction from the radiation law was illusory and a mere juggling with formulae, or there is at the bottom of this method of deriving the radiation law some true physical concept. If the latter were the case, the quantum would have to play a fundamental role in physics, heralding the advent of a new state of things, destined, perhaps, to transform completely our physical concepts which since the introduction of the infinitesimal calculus by Leibnitz and Newton have been founded upon the assumption of the continuity of all causal chains of events.

Experience has decided for the second alternative.

"Electrons Move in Stationary Orbits"

NIELS BOHR (1885–)

A SCRUPULOUS DANE, Niels Bohr, professor of physics at the University of Copenhagen from 1916, and head of its Institute for Theoretical Physics from 1920, had the honor of being the first to piece together again acceptably the picture—or, better, the mathematical structure—of the atom that had been torn apart by the new discoveries in radioactivity, electronics, and quantum. The simple atomic model proposed by Rutherford did not satisfy the new energy concepts arising out of

Planck's quantum theory, with its emphasis on the discontinuity of energy changes. Nor did the old classical ideas of mechanics and dynamics worked out by Kepler and Newton to describe the vast expanse of the solar system and stars beyond seem to be capable of describing usefully and accurately the changes that went on in the miniature solar system of the atom. Bohr proposed the fruitful theory that if one wanted to regard the ever-changing atomic structure as a nucleus around which electrons revolved in "planetary" orbits, he must further assume that the orbits of the electrons have a few stationary states and that radiation is emitted only during the passage of the electron from an orbit of higher energy to one of lower energy. Thus was the quantum theory wed to atomic structure.

By analogy to the astronomical world, there would be a tremendous explosion of energy in the solar system if a planet, say Mars or the Earth, should suddenly jump from its present orbit down to the smaller orbit of Venus. The scale on which these atomic-energy changes actually take place can be better realized if one visualizes this fact: if a drop of water were magnified to the size of the earth, each molecule in it would be no larger than a football. And the atoms, of course, are much smaller than the molecules.

Bohr's ingenious concept of the atom arose from studies in spectroscopy, a subject which has become of first-rank scientific and industrial importance. X-ray spectroscopy is an important tool of metallurgy, used to test the purity and structure of metals. Pioneers in the development of optical spectroscopy and spectrum analysis, which has uncovered such important facts as the chemical composition of the sun and such new-at-the-time (1860) elements as cesium and rubidium, were Joseph von Fraunhofer (1787-1826), after whom "Fraunhofer's lines"—dark lines in the spectrum—are named; R. W. Bunsen (1811-99), professor at Heidelberg, who invented the Bunsen burner common to every chemical laboratory; and Gustav Kirchhoff (1824-87), another German physicist, who demonstrated that radiations are absorbed by vapors of the same substances that give them off. Essentially a spectroscope is nothing more than a prism, such as Newton used to split the colors of white light, to which are attached a pair of telescopes. The arrangement is such that the spectrum of colors produced by the prism may be studied in detail through a slit and the location of the dark lines plotted.

Further connecting the classical ideas of mechanics, which dealt in terms of motions of bodies through space, and the energy changes of atomic quanta, Bohr also developed the "correspondence principle."

As may be read here, theories developed in the study of sound helped him out. Just as Helmholtz had pointed out that shrieks, squeaks, and musical chords could be reduced to combinations of simple vibrations, or harmonic oscillations, so Bohr demonstrated that the silent oscillations of tiny atomic resonators might be usefully analyzed into simpler motions that would fulfill many of the postulates of classical mechanics and electrodynamics. Bohr was awarded the 1922 Nobel prize in physics.

Danish was the language in which Niels Bohr addressed the Physical Society of Copenhagen "On the Spectrum of Hydrogen" on December 20, 1913. In this essay, printed in the *"Fysisk Tidsskrift"* (Vol. 12, p. 97, 1914), he suggests the fundamental assumptions upon which the "Bohr atom," with its stationary orbits for electrons, is imaginatively constructed. The English translation, made by Dr. A. D. Udden of the University of Pennsylvania, was published in 1922 by the Cambridge University Press under the title "The Theory of Spectra and Atomic Constitution—Three Essays" by Niels Bohr.

Danish was also the language in which Bohr discussed the "correspondence principle" before a joint meeting of the Physical and Chemical societies of Copenhagen, October 18, 1921, in an address entitled, "The Structure of the Atom and the Physical and Chemical Properties of the Elements." It was first printed in the *Fysisk Tidsskrift* (Vol. 19, p. 153, 1921); slightly revised and enlarged for inclusion in the Cambridge University Press volume noted.

THE SPECTRUM OF HYDROGEN

HYDROGEN POSSESSES not only the smallest atomic weight of all the elements, but it also occupies a peculiar position both with regard to its physical and its chemical properties. One of the points where this becomes particularly apparent is the hydrogen line spectrum.

The spectrum of hydrogen observed in an ordinary Geissler tube consists of a series of lines, the strongest of which lies at the red end of the spectrum, while the others extend out into the ultra-violet, the distance between the various lines, as well as their intensities, constantly decreasing. In the ultraviolet the series converges to a limit. . . .

We shall now consider the second part of the foundation on which we shall build, namely, the conclusions arrived at from experiments with the rays emitted by radioactive substances. I have previously here in the Physical Society had the opportunity of speaking of the scattering of α rays in passing through thin plates, and to mention how Rutherford (1911) has proposed a theory for the structure of the atom in order to explain the remarkable and unexpected results of these experiments. I shall, therefore, only remind you that the characteristic feature of Rutherford's theory is the assumption of the existence of a positively charged nucleus inside the atom. A number of electrons are supposed to revolve in closed orbits around the nucleus, the number of these electrons being sufficient to neutralize the positive charge of the nucleus. The dimensions of the nucleus are supposed to be very small in comparison with the dimensions of the orbits of the electrons, and almost the entire mass of the atom is supposed to be concentrated in the nucleus. . . .

Let us now assume that a hydrogen atom simply consists of an electron revolving around a nucleus of equal and opposite charge, and of a mass which is very large in comparison with that of the electron. It is evident that this assumption may explain the peculiar position already referred to which hydrogen occupies among the elements, but it appears at the outset completely hopeless to attempt to explain anything at all of the special properties of hydrogen, still less its line spectrum, on the basis of considerations relating to such a simple system.

Let us assume for the sake of brevity that the mass of the nucleus is infinitely large in proportion to that of the electron, and that the velocity of the electron is very small in comparison with that of light. If we now temporarily disregard the energy radiation, which, according to the ordinary electrodynamics, will accompany the accelerated motion of the electron, the latter in accordance with Kepler's first law will describe an ellipse with the nucleus in one of the foci.

These expressions are extremely simple and they show that the magnitude of the frequency of revolution as well as the length of the major axis depend only on W, the work which must be added to the system in order to remove the electron to an infinite distance from the nucleus; and are independent of the eccentricity of the orbit. By varying W we may obtain all possible values for the frequency of revolution and the major axis of the ellipse. This condition shows, however, that it is not possible to employ Kepler's formula directly in calculating the orbit of the electron in a hydrogen atom.

For this it will be necessary to assume that the orbit of the electron cannot take on all values, and in any event the line spectrum clearly indicates that the oscillations of the electron cannot vary continuously between wide limits. The impossibility of making any progress with a simple system like the one considered here might have been foretold from a consideration of the dimensions involved.

It can be seen that it is impossible to employ Rutherford's atomic model so long as we confine ourselves exclusively to the ordinary electrodynamics. But this is nothing more than might have been expected. As I have mentioned, we may consider it to be an established fact that it is impossible to obtain a satisfactory explanation of the experiments on temperature radiation with the aid of electrodynamics, no matter what atomic model be employed. The fact that the deficiencies of the atomic model we are considering stand out so plainly is therefore perhaps no serious drawback; even though the defects of other atomic models are much better concealed they must nevertheless be present and will be just as serious.

QUANTUM THEORY OF SPECTRA

Let us now try to overcome these difficulties by applying Planck's theory to the problem.

In assuming Planck's theory we have manifestly acknowledged the inadequacy of the ordinary electrodynamics and have definitely parted with the coherent group of ideas on which the latter theory is based. In fact in taking such a step we cannot expect that all cases of disagreement between the theoretical conceptions hitherto employed and experiment will be removed by the use of Planck's assumption regarding the quantum of the energy momentarily present in an oscillating system. We stand here almost entirely on virgin ground, and upon introducing new assumptions we need only take care not to get into contradiction with experiment. Time will have to show to what extent this can be avoided; but the safest way is, of course, to make as few assumptions as possible.

With this in mind let us first examine the experiments on temperature radiation. The subject of direct observation is the distribution of radiant energy over oscillations of the various wave lengths. Even though we may assume that this energy comes from systems of oscillating particles, we know little or nothing about these systems. No one has ever seen a Planck's resonator, nor indeed even measured its frequency of oscillation; we can observe only the period of oscillation of the radiation which is emitted. It is therefore very convenient that it is possible to show that to obtain the laws of temperature radiation it is not necessary to make any assumptions about the systems which emit the radiation except that the amount of energy emitted each time shall be equal to $h\nu$, where h is Planck's constant and ν is the frequency of the radiation.

During the emission of the radiation the system may be regarded as passing from one state to another; in order to introduce a name for these states we shall call them "stationary" states, simply indicating thereby that they form some kind of waiting places between which occurs the emission of the energy corresponding to the various spectral lines. . . .

Under ordinary circumstances a hydrogen atom will probably exist only in the state corresponding to $n=1$. For this state W will have its greatest value and, consequently, the atom will have emitted the largest amount of energy possible; this will therefore represent the most stable state of the atom from which the system cannot be transferred except by adding energy to it from without.

I shall not tire you any further with more details; I hope to return to these questions here in the Physical Society, and to show how, on the basis of the underlying ideas, it is possible to develop a theory for the structure of atoms and molecules.

THE CORRESPONDENCE PRINCIPLE

So far as the principles of the quantum theory are concerned, the point which has been emphasized hitherto is the radical departure of these principles from our usual conceptions of mechanical and electrodynamical phenomena. As I have attempted to show in recent years, it appears possible, however, to adopt a point of view which suggests that the quantum theory may, nevertheless, be regarded as a rational generalization of our ordinary conceptions. As may be seen from the postulates of the quantum theory, and particularly the frequency relation, a direct connection between the spectra and the motion of the kind required by the classical dynamics is excluded, but at the same time the form of these postulates leads us to another relation of a remarkable nature.

Let us consider an electrodynamic system and inquire into the nature of the radiation which would result from the motion of the system on the basis of the ordinary conceptions. We imagine the motion to be decomposed into purely harmonic oscillations, and the radiation is assumed to consist of the simultaneous emission of series of electromagnetic waves possessing the same frequency as these harmonic components and intensities which depend upon the amplitudes of the components.

An investigation of the formal basis of the quantum theory shows us now that it is possible to trace the question of the origin of the radiation processes which accompany the various transitions back to an investigation of the various harmonic components, which appear in the motion of the atom. The possibility that a particular transition shall occur may be regarded as being due to the presence of a definitely assignable "corresponding" component in the motion. This principle of correspondence at the same time throws light upon a question mentioned several times previously, namely, the relation between the number of quantum numbers, which must be used to describe the stationary states of an atom, and the types to which the orbits of the electrons belong. The classification of these types can be based very simply on a decomposition of the motion into its harmonic components. Time does not permit me to consider this question any further, and I shall confine myself to a statement of some simple conclusions, which the correspondence principle permits us to draw concerning the occurrence of transitions between various pairs of stationary states. These conclusions are of decisive importance in the subsequent argument. . . .

Before I leave the interpretation of the chemical properties by means of this atomic model I should like to remind you once again of the fundamental principles which we have used. The whole theory has evolved from an investigation of the way in which electrons can be captured by an atom. The formation of an atom was held to consist in the successive binding of electrons, this binding resulting in radiation according to the quantum theory. According to the fundamental postulates of the theory this binding takes place in stages by transitions between stationary states accompanied by emission of radiation. For the problem of the stability of the atom the essential problem is at what stage such a process comes to an end. As regards this point the postulates give no direct information, but here the correspondence principle is brought in. Even though it has been possible to penetrate considerably further at many points than the time has permitted me to indicate to you, still it has not yet been possible to follow in detail all stages in the formation of the atoms. We cannot say, for instance, that a given table of the atomic constitution of the inert gases may in every detail be considered as the unambiguous result of applying the correspondence principle. On the other hand, it appears that our considerations already place the empirical data in a light which scarcely permits of an essentially different interpretation of the properties of the elements based upon the postulates of the quantum theory. This applies not only to the

series spectra and the close relationship of these to the chemical properties of the elements, but also to the X-ray spectra, the consideration of
which leads us into an investigation of interatomic processes of an entirely different character. As we have already mentioned, it is necessary
to assume that the emission of the latter spectra is connected with processes which may be described as a reorganization of the completely
formed atom after a disturbance produced in the interior of the atom
by the action of external forces.

"Matter and Light: The New Physics"

LOUIS DE BROGLIE (1892–   )

UNTIL THE ADVENT of the brothers Maurice (1875–   ) and Louis Victor,
both distinguished physicists, the noble French family of De Broglie,
originating in Piedmont, was more famous for its soldiers, statesmen,
and politicians than for its scientists. The first Prince de Broglie, Victor
Maurice, was marshal of France under Louis XIV; another De Broglie,
Victor Claude was president of the Constituent Assembly of 1791; and,
though favoring the French Revolution, was guillotined in Paris; Jacques
Victor Albert, the grandfather of the present generation of De Broglie
scientists, was once Premier of France.

Louis de Broglie became professor of physics at the University of
Paris in 1932, a few years after he had been honored with the 1929 Nobel
prize in physics. In a formal address on this occasion he explained, as
may be read in the passage quoted here, how simply he came on the
concept of wave mechanics, resolving a dilemma of science that has
been casting its shadow since the time of Huygens and Newton: the
true nature of light. Such considerations have particularly led scientific
thought back into the realm of philosophy and discussions of ultimate
realities. No mean epistemologist, De Broglie has very neatly, in the
ethical terms of defining an "honest man," raised and partially answered
the Platonic question—which almost no nineteenth-century scientist
would for a moment have considered worth discussing—How real is
scientific truth?

French is the language of the original Nobel prize address on "The

Undulatory Aspects of the Electron," delivered by De Broglie in Stockholm on December 12, 1929. Both pieces are from a collection of his works, published in 1937, in French, under the title *"Matière et Lumière";* and in 1939 in English translation by W. H. Johnston, under the title, "Matter and Light: The New Physics" (New York: W. W. Norton & Company, Inc.).

WAVE MECHANICS: THE UNDULATORY ASPECTS OF THE ELECTRON

ONCE AGAIN it had become necessary to assume two contradictory theories of light, in terms of waves, and of corpuscles, respectively; while it was impossible to understand why, among the infinite number of paths which an electron ought to be able to follow in the atom according to classical ideas, there was only a restricted number which it could pursue in fact. Such were the problems facing physicists at the time when I returned to my studies.

When I began to consider these difficulties I was chiefly struck by two facts. On the one hand the quantum theory of light cannot be considered satisfactory, since it defines the energy of a light corpuscle by the equation $W = h\nu$, containing the frequency ν. Now a purely corpuscular theory contains nothing that enables us to define a frequency; for this reason alone, therefore, we are compelled, in the case of light, to introduce the idea of a corpuscle and that of periodicity simultaneously.

On the other hand, determination of the stable motion of electrons in the atom introduces integers; and up to this point the only phenomena involving integers in physics were those of interference and of normal modes of vibration. This fact suggested to me the idea that electrons too could not be regarded simply as corpuscles, but that periodicity must be assigned to them also.

In this way, then, I obtained the following general idea, in accordance with which I pursued my investigations: that it is necessary in the case of matter, as well as of radiation generally and of light in particular, to introduce the idea of the corpuscle and of the wave simultaneously; or, in other words, in the one case as well as in the other, we must assume the existence of corpuscles accompanied by waves. But corpuscles and waves cannot be independent of each other: in Bohr's terms, they are two complementary aspects of reality: and it must consequently be possible to establish a certain parallelism between the motion of a corpuscle and the propagation of its associated wave. The first object at which to aim, therefore, was to establish the existence of this parallelism.

With this in view, I began by considering the simplest case: that of an isolated corpuscle, i.e., one removed from all external influence; with this we wish to associate a wave. . . .

We thus find that in order to describe the properties of matter, as well as those of light, we must employ waves and corpuscles simultaneously. We can no longer imagine the electron as being just a minute corpuscle of electricity: we must associate a wave with it. And this wave is not just a fiction: its length can be measured and its interferences calculated in advance. In fact a whole group of phenomena was in this way predicted before being actually discovered. It is, therefore, on this idea of the dualism in nature between waves and corpuscles, expressed in a more or less abstract form, that the entire recent development of theoretical physics has been built up, and that its immediate future development appears likely to be erected.

WHO CAN DEFINE AN HONEST MAN?

Without continuing indefinitely the list of examples drawn from modern physics, let us at once assume the philosophical point of view and ask the following question: May it not be universally true that the concepts produced by the human mind, when formulated in a slightly vague form, are roughly valid for reality, but that when extreme precision is aimed at, they become ideal forms whose real content tends to vanish away? It seems to me that such is, in fact, the case, and that innumerable examples can be found in all spheres, particularly in those of psychology and ethics, as well as of everyday life.

Let us take an example from the ethical field and consider the concept of an honest man. Let us begin with a somewhat vague definition; let us say that an honest man is a man of great probity, who always tends to do what he considers his duty and to resist all temptations drawing him in the opposite direction. We shall find around us—for we must not be too pessimistic—a certain number of people who fulfill this definition. But if we were to insist that the crown of honesty is to be awarded only to a man who never, in any circumstances, at any mo-

ment of his life, experienced the slightest temptation to disobey his conscience, then no doubt we shall find a striking diminution—since human
nature is full of frailty—in the number of men to whom our definition
will apply. The more precise and rigid the concept becomes . . .
the more restricted becomes its sphere of application. Like the plane
monochromatic wave, absolute virtue, if defined with too exacting a
precision, is an idealization the probability of whose full realization
tends to vanish away.

Examples of this kind are, it should be repeated, innumerable. In
the psychological, ethical, and social spheres an uncompromisingly rigid
definition or argument often leads away from, rather than toward,
reality. It is true that the facts tend to assume a certain order within
the framework supplied by our reason; but it is no more than a tendency,
and the facts invariably overflow if the framework is too exactly defined.

Thus in the region of the inexact sciences of human conduct the
strictness of the definitions varies inversely as their applicability to the
world of reality. But now the question arises whether we have any right
to compare this fact with those encountered during the development
of modern physics. Admittedly we are dealing with nothing more than
an analogy whose applicability must not be overstressed; yet I believe
that it is less superficial than might at first be thought. Whenever we
wish to describe facts, whether of a psychological or an ethical nature,
or belonging to the sphere of the physical or natural sciences, we are
inevitably dealing with a reality which is always infinitely complex and
full of an infinity of shades on the one hand, and on the other with our
understanding, which forms concepts which are always more or less
rigid and abstract. A confrontation between reality and understanding
is inevitable, and as far-reaching a reconciliation as possible, desirable.
It is certain that our concepts are capable of adaptation to reality to a
considerable extent, provided that we allow them a certain margin of indeterminateness: if it were otherwise, no argument relating to real facts
could be effected on the basis of any order of ideas. What is more doubtful is whether such a correspondence can be maintained to the end, if
we insist on eliminating the margin of indeterminateness and on effecting extreme precision in our concepts. Even in the most exact of all the
natural sciences, in physics, the need for margins of indeterminateness
has repeatedly become apparent—a fact which, it seems to us, is worthy
of the attention of philosophers, since it may throw a new and illuminating light on the way in which the idealizations formed by our reason
become adaptable to reality.

"Science and the Human Temperament"

ERWIN SCHROEDINGER (1887–   )

IN 1921, Erwin Schroedinger, then professor of mathematical physics at the University of Zurich, propounded the theory of wave mechanics and published an equation which, according to Max Planck, "has provided the basis of modern quantum mechanics, in which it seems to play the same part as do the equations established by Newton, Lagrange, and Hamilton in classical mechanics." In so doing Schroedinger developed a subtler meaning for Hamilton's equations. His ideas, he says, grew most immediately out of De Broglie's theories of electron waves.

Schroedinger was born in Vienna, Austria; studied at the Physical Institute of the University of Vienna; taught at Zurich; and in 1926 took Planck's chair of theoretical physics in the University of Berlin. He left Germany in 1933 to become a temporary professor at the University of Oxford, England, and in the same year was awarded the Nobel prize in physics (with Paul Dirac). In addition to his work on wave mechanics and the quantum theory, he has made important contributions to the theory of color and has also investigated radium.

German was the language in which Schroedinger delivered his Nobel prize address on "The Fundamentals of Wave Mechanics" in Stockholm on December 12, 1933. The excerpts here given are from an English translation made by Dr. James Murphy and W. H. Johnston, and published in "Science and the Human Temperament" (New York: W. W. Norton & Company, Inc., 1935).

THE FUNDAMENTAL IDEA OF WAVE MECHANICS

WHEN A RAY of light passes through an optical instrument, such as a telescope or a photographic lens, it undergoes a change of direction as it strikes each refractive or reflective surface. We can describe the path of the light ray once we know the two simple laws which govern the change of direction. One of these is the law of refraction, which was discovered by Snell about three hundred years ago; and the other is the law of reflection, which was known to Archimedes nearly two thousand years before. . . .

From a much more general point of view, Fermat summed up the whole career of a light ray. In passing through media of varying optical densities light is propagated at correspondingly varying speeds, and the path which it follows is such as would have to be chosen by the light if it had the purpose of arriving within the shortest possible time at the destination which it actually reaches. (Here it may be remarked, in parentheses, that any two points along the path of the light ray can be chosen as the points of departure and arrival respectively.) Any deviation from the path which the ray has actually chosen would mean a delay. This is Fermat's famous principle of least time. In one admirably concise statement it defines the whole career of a ray of light, including also the more general case where the nature of the medium does not change suddenly but alters gradually from point to point. The atmosphere surrounding our earth is an example of this. When a ray of light, coming from outside, enters the earth's atmosphere, the ray travels more slowly as it penetrates into deeper and increasingly denser layers. And although the difference in the speed of propagation is extremely small, yet under these circumstances Fermat's principle demands that the ray of light must bend earthward. . . .

Thus Fermat's principle directly appears as the *trivial quintessence* of the wave theory. Hence it was a very remarkable event when Hamilton one day made the theoretical discovery that the orbit of a mass point moving in a field of force (for instance, of a stone thrown in the gravitational field of the earth or of some planet in its course around the sun) is governed by a very similar general principle, which thenceforth bore the name of the discoverer and made him famous. Although Hamilton's principle does not precisely consist in the statement that the mass point chooses the quickest way, yet it states something so similar—that is to say, it is so closely analogous to the principle of minimum light time— that one is faced with a puzzle. It seemed as if nature had effected exactly the same thing twice, but in two very different ways—once, in the case of light, through a fairly transparent wave mechanism, and on the other occasion, in the case of mass points, by methods which were utterly mysterious, unless one was prepared to believe in some underlying undulatory character in the second case also. But at first sight this idea seemed impossible. . . .

The way out of the difficulty was actually (though unexpectedly) found in the possibility I have already mentioned, namely, that in the

Hamiltonian principle we might also assume the manifestation of a "wave mechanism," which we supposed to lie at the basis of events in point mechanics, just as we have been long accustomed to acknowledge it in the phenomena of light and in the governing principle enunciated by Fermat. . . .

Let us now return from optics to mechanics and try to develop the analogy fully. The optical parallel of the old mechanics is the method of dealing with isolated rays of light, which are supposed not to influence one another. The new wave mechanics has its parallel in the undulatory theory of light. The advantage of changing from the old concept to the new must obviously consist in clearer insight into diffraction phenomena, or rather into something that is strictly analogous to the diffraction of light, although ordinarily even less significant; for otherwise the old mechanics could not have been accepted as satisfactory for so long a time. But it is not difficult to conjecture the conditions in which the neglected phenomenon must become very prominent, entirely dominate the mechanical process, and present problems that are insoluble under the old concept. This occurs inevitably whenever the entire mechanical system is comparable in its extension with the wave lengths of "material waves," which play the same role in mechanical processes as light waves do in optics.

That is the reason why, in the tiny system of the atom, the old concept is bound to fail. In mechanical phenomena on a large scale it will retain its validity as an excellent approximation, but it must be replaced by the new concept if we wish to deal with the fine interplay which takes place within regions of the order of magnitude of only one or a few wave lengths.

I would describe the present state of our knowledge as follows: The light ray, or track of the particle, corresponds to a longitudinal continuity of the propagating process (that is to say, in the direction of the spreading); the wave front, on the other hand, to a transverse one (that is to say, perpendicular to the direction of spreading). Both continuities are undoubtedly real.

The Higher Physics Are Indeterminate: One Can't Say "For Sure"

WERNER HEISENBERG (1901–　　)

Ah, what a dusty answer gets the soul
When hot for certainties in this our life!—GEORGE MEREDITH

SCIENTISTS as well as poets are now pretty well agreed that some of the questions which thought and experiment throw up to the subtlety of nature will always be fobbed off with dusty answers. The higher physics are indeterminate; one can't say "for sure"; science does not offer any final, complete answers—a by-product of the new concepts of quantum, relativity, and wave mechanics. When the epistemological conflict in scientific thinking was at its height a young German physicist, Werner Heisenberg, still in his twenties, came forward with mathematical proof of the assertion that there are inevitable limits to the accuracy of scientific knowledge; specifically, that, labor as he might, no scientist will ever be able to specify exactly both the position and velocity of an electron at the same instant. For proving this supremely negative assertion, called the uncertainty principle, comparable to such other negative scientific proofs as the impossibility of squaring the circle with ruler and compass or inventing a "perpetual-motion machine," Heisenberg was awarded the 1932 Nobel prize for physics. His work has included the development of quantum mechanics, investigation of atomic structure, and the Zeeman effect. In 1927 he was appointed professor of theoretical physics at the University of Leipzig.

German was the language in which Heisenberg composed a series of lectures delivered at the University of Chicago in 1929. The English translations, quoted here, were made by Carl Eckart and Frank C. Hoyt, of the department of physics of the University of Chicago, and published in July 1930 by the University of Chicago Press, under the title, "The Physical Principles of the Quantum Theory."

THE UNCERTAINTY PRINCIPLE

ALTHOUGH the theory of relativity makes the greatest of demands on the ability for abstract thought, still it fulfills the traditional requirements of science insofar as it permits a division of the world into subject and object (observer and observed) and hence a clear formulation of the law of causality. This is the very point at which the difficulties of the quantum theory begin. In atomic physics the concepts "clock" and "measuring rod" need no immediate consideration, for there is a large field of phenomena in which $1/c$ is negligible. The concepts "space-time coincidence" and "observation," on the other hand, do require a thorough revision.

Particularly characteristic of the discussions to follow is the interaction between observer and object; in classical physical theories it has always been assumed either that this interaction is negligibly small, or else that its effect can be eliminated from the result by calculations based on "control" experiments. This assumption is not permissible in atomic physics; the interaction between observer and object causes uncontrollable and large changes in the system being observed, because of the discontinuous changes characteristic of atomic processes. The immediate consequence of this circumstance is that in general every experiment performed to determine some numerical quantity renders the knowledge of others illusory, since the uncontrollable perturbation of the observed system alters the values of previously determined quantities. If this perturbation be followed in its quantitative details, it appears that in many cases it is impossible to obtain an exact determination of the simultaneous values of two variables, but rather that there is a lower limit to the accuracy with which they can be known.

The starting point of the critique of the relativity theory was the postulate that there is no signal velocity greater than that of light. In a similar manner this lower limit to the accuracy with which certain variables can be known simultaneously may be postulated as a law of nature (in the form of the so-called uncertainty relations). . . .

From experiments it is seen that both matter and radiation possess a remarkable duality of character, as they sometimes exhibit the properties of waves, at other times those of particles. Now it is obvious that a thing cannot be a form of wave motion and composed of particles at the same time—the two concepts are too different.

It is not surprising that our language should be incapable of describing the processes occurring within the atoms, for, as has been remarked, it was invented to describe the experiences of daily life, and these consist only of processes involving exceedingly large numbers of atoms. Furthermore, it is very difficult to modify our language so that it will be able to describe these atomic processes, for words can only describe things of which we can form mental pictures, and this ability, too, is a result of daily experience.

Fortunately mathematics is not subject to this limitation, and it has been possible to invent a mathematical scheme—the quantum theory—which seems entirely adequate for the treatment of atomic processes; for visualization, however, we must content ourselves with two incomplete analogies—the wave picture and the corpuscular picture. The simultaneous applicability of both pictures is thus a natural criterion to determine how far each analogy may be "pushed" and forms an obvious starting point for the critique of the concepts which have entered atomic theories in the course of their development, for, obviously, uncritical deduction of consequences from both will lead to contradictions. In this way one obtains the limitations of the concept of a particle by considering the concept of a wave. As N. Bohr has shown, this is the basis of a very simple derivation of the uncertainty relations between co-ordinate and momentum of a particle. In the same manner one may derive the limitations of the concept of a wave by comparison with the concept of a particle. . . .

The concepts of velocity, energy, et cetera, have been developed from simple experiments with common objects, in which the mechanical behavior of macroscopic bodies can be described by the use of such words. These same concepts have then been carried over to the electron, since in certain fundamental experiments electrons show a mechanical behavior like that of the objects of common experience. Since it is known, however, that this similarity exists only in a certain limited region of phenomena, the applicability of the corpuscular theory must be limited in a corresponding way. According to Bohr, this restriction may be deduced from the principle that the processes of atomic physics can be visualized equally well in terms of waves or particles. . . .

The velocity of the electron corresponds to that of the wave packet, but this latter cannot be exactly defined, because of the diffusion which takes place. This indeterminateness is to be considered as an essential characteristic of the electron, and not as evidence of the inapplicability of the wave picture. . . .

The uncertainty relation specifies the limits within which the particle picture can be applied. Any use of the words "position" and "velocity" with an accuracy exceeding that given by equation $\triangle x \triangle p > h$ is just as meaningless as the use of words whose sense is not defined.

The uncertainty principle refers to the degree of indeterminateness in the possible present knowledge of the simultaneous values of various quantities with which the quantum theory deals; it does not restrict, for example, the exactness of a position measurement alone or a velocity measurement alone. Thus suppose that the velocity of a free electron is precisely known, while the position is completely unknown. Then the principle states that every subsequent observation of the position will alter the momentum by an unknown and undeterminable amount such that after carrying out the experiment our knowledge of the electronic motion is restricted by the uncertainty relation. This may be expressed in concise and general terms by saying that every experiment destroys some of the knowledge of the system which was obtained by previous experiments. This formulation makes it clear that the uncertainty relation does not refer to the past; if the velocity of the electron is at first known and the position then exactly measured, the position for times previous to the measurement may be calculated. Then for these past times $\triangle p \triangle q$ is smaller than the usual limiting value, but this knowledge of the past is of a purely speculative character, since it can never (because of the unknown change in momentum caused by the position measurement) be used as an initial condition in any calculation of the future progress of the electron and thus cannot be subjected to experimental verification. It is a matter of personal belief whether such a calculation concerning the past history of the electron can be ascribed any physical reality or not.

Atom-Smashing Brings True the Alchemist's Dream

ERNEST O. LAWRENCE (1901–   )

AN AMERICAN physicist at the University of California, Ernest O. Lawrence is representative of the twentieth-century experimental physicists who, profiting by the long and winding course of mathematical and theoretical physics that made possible their success, finally brought true the alchemist's dream of transmutation of the elements. For inventing the cyclotron (1931), one of the most practical machines for smashing the atom, and for other researches on the structure of the atom, on transmutation of certain elements, on artificial radioactivity (cf. Curie), and on the application of radiation to biology and medicine, Lawrence was awarded the 1939 Nobel prize in physics. With the massive cyclotron, here described in the words of its inventor, it has been possible to manufacture such artificial elements as "radio-phosphorus," "radio-sodium," and "radio-iron," which, fed to experimental animals, have permitted tracing the "tagged atoms" through the body.

Here we close the saga of the atom and our story of the physical sciences, begun almost two thousand years ago with the vague but not altogether incorrect ideas of Democritus and Lucretius about atoms swerving in the void. But it would be a foolish man who thought we did not have oceans more of knowledge to cross before the fuller story of the atom is revealed. Indeed, scientists stand only at the threshold of the new science of nuclear physics and chemistry; the amount of subatomic energy that exists in a single teacup of water is astounding. It remains for scientists who have shown that the atoms make the world to demonstrate whether they can remake it.

English was the language in which Lawrence delivered the lecture from which the passages quoted here have been taken. It was published in "Science in Progress" (New Haven: Yale University Press, 1939).

ATOMS, NEW AND OLD

THE ESSENTIAL IDEAS of Rutherford and Bohr on the structure of matter are now firmly established. There is an abundance of evidence that an atom consists of a nebulous cloud of electrons whirling about a very dense, positively charged nucleus. Indeed, our assurance that this is so rivals our confidence that the planets revolve about the sun!

The number and configuration of the electrons determine the ordinary chemical and physical properties of the atom, and it might be thought that the nucleus is relatively unimportant, particularly as it is such a small region. But this is by no means the case; the nucleus really plays a dominant role in atomic structure.

THE NUCLEUS

The nucleus consists of a closely packed group of neutrons and protons, elementary building blocks of nature, which weigh something like two thousand times as much as the electrons. Thus, more than 99.99 per cent of the atom's mass is contained in the nucleus, and since mass is a manifestation of energy, it follows that practically all of the atom's energy also resides there. Moreover, the protons are positively charged particles, and the number of protons in the nucleus equals the number of electrons outside, for the atom as a whole is electrically neutral. Therefore, since it is the number of electrons outside that determines the chemical and physical properties of the atom, it follows that the nuclear charge determines the place of the atom in the Periodic Table. On the other hand, the number of neutrons in the nucleus does not affect the number or configuration of the extranuclear electrons and hence does not have much to do with the chemistry of the atom; but the neutrons in the nucleus do contribute to the atom's weight, and hence we have isotopes of many of the elements—atoms of equal nuclear charge but differing in number of nuclear neutrons. . . .

Neutrons and protons are exceedingly small particles. At the present time we know so little about their properties that we are content to speak of them as elementary particles, spherical in shape and having radii of the order of magnitude of 10^{-13} cm. As regards the structure of nuclei, we know little more than that they consist of neutrons and protons sticking together in much the same way as water molecules form a water droplet. Someday, doubtless, we shall have very definite and detailed ideas about nuclear structure, but for the present we know little more than that neutrons and protons can be put into nuclei and that they come out also. Whether the elementary particles fuse together to form a new form of nuclear matter or whether they retain their identity in the nucleus is a question that has no answer at this time. In any case, it is known that the nuclear particles are so closely aggregated that the volume of the nucleus is about what one would expect if the neutrons and protons were tiny spheres in contact. Thus, even for the heavier elements, the nuclei may be regarded as spheres with radii of approximately 10^{-12} cm.

TRANSMUTATION

The Rutherford-Bohr theory of the atom reduced the age-old problem of alchemy—the transmutation of the elements—to very simple terms. For, since the number of protons in the nucleus determined the number of electrons outside and hence the place of the atom in the Periodic Table, it was clear that the conversion of one element into another was simply the problem of changing the number of protons in the atomic nucleus.

Rutherford considered how it might be possible to knock out one or more protons from the nucleus of an atom. He realized that it would be necessary to bombard the atomic nucleus with nuclear particles of great energy; for he had already established the fact that nuclear matter is held together by very strong forces and that the nucleus is surrounded by a great wall of electrical potential due to the nuclear charge. He had also shown that the alpha particles emitted from radium consist of swiftly moving nuclei of helium, and accordingly it was clear that they were promising projectiles for the nuclear bombardment.

Just before the Great War, in 1914, Rutherford carried out his first experiments on transmutation by alpha-particle bombardment and obtained some encouraging results, but war duties made it necessary to suspend the experiments until 1919. In that year he returned to the laboratory and was not long in establishing, beyond any doubt, the conversion of nitrogen into oxygen. He bombarded nitrogen gas with the alpha particles from a strong radioactive source and observed the emission of swiftly moving protons from the bombarded nitrogen. His observations led him to the logical conclusion that a small fraction of the alpha particles passing through the nitrogen gas collided with nitrogen nuclei, and, although they stuck to the nucleus, they generally collided with such energy as to knock out a proton with terrific energy. At that time the existence of the neutron had not been recognized (the nucleus was thought to contain protons and electrons), but in recent years it has been established that often in such nuclear collisions neutrons as well as protons are knocked out. Rutherford's interpretation of his observations, which is the classical nuclear reaction, marks the beginning of a new science which may well be called nuclear chemistry, the science of the reactions of nuclei.

ATOMIC PROJECTILES

Rutherford's experiments were clearly but a fragmentary glimpse into a region of the atom of inconceivable richness, and they brought to the forefront the need for atomic projectiles of various kinds and in vastly greater numbers for the further exploration of the nuclear domain. As a result, many laboratories over the world undertook the development of methods of accelerating atoms to very high speeds for purposes of nuclear research, and it was not long before atomic projectiles of many kinds were available to carry forward the attack.

From the moment the problem of accelerating atoms to high speeds was proposed, it was clear that the only practical way would be to form ions of the atoms in a rarefied gaseous atmosphere within a vacuum tube and cause them to be accelerated in the electric field between electrodes at a suitable difference of potential. Indeed, the kinetic energies of atomic projectiles have from the beginning been given in terms of the energy they would have if they were singly charged positive ions falling through a given potential difference. Thus we speak of a million-volt proton as one which has the kinetic energy that it would have as the result of passing through a vacuum tube from one electrode to another at a difference of potential of one million volts. The alpha particles emitted from radium have a kinetic energy of approximately eight million volts, and it was presumed from early experiments with these atomic projectiles that particles of energies of several million volts would be needed for nuclear investigations. Thus it became clear that a straightforward method of accelerating atoms to energies sufficient to bring about nuclear reactions would be to apply millions of volts to the electrodes of vacuum tubes and to cause the ions to pass from one electrode to the other. Accordingly, many laboratories undertook the development of means of generating very high voltages and vacuum tubes of sufficient ruggedness to withstand these great electrical potentials.

THE CYCLOTRON, OR ATOM-SMASHER

One method of accelerating particles might be termed the method of resonance or of multiple acceleration. A child in a swing knows that a high swing velocity can be achieved by one big push, corresponding to the single acceleration of ions by application of high voltage, or by a succession of small pushes, properly timed with the swing action, corresponding to the resonance method of accelerating ions by repeated application of low voltages. One type of apparatus that uses this resonance principle involves both a magnetic field and an oscillating electric field; and, because the ions spiral around as they are accelerated, the apparatus has come to be called the "cyclotron."

The most prominent feature of the cyclotron is a giant electromagnet. The one in the Radiation Laboratory at the University of California weighs about eighty tons. With this apparatus deuterons have been accelerated to energies of nearly eight million volts and alpha particles to nearly sixteen million volts. . . .

It is perhaps well to indicate briefly the principle of the cyclotron. The ions are accelerated in the vacuum chamber between the poles of the magnet. The function of the magnetic field is to cause the ions to spiral around with constant angular velocity. Within the chamber there are two semicircular hollow electrodes, between which is applied a high-frequency potential difference. The pillbox-shaped chamber, with cover removed, exposes the accelerating electrodes, called "dees." The ions circulate around from within one dee to within the other, and, as they cross the diametrical region, they gain increments of kinetic energy corresponding to the potential difference. Inasmuch as the angular velocity of the ions is determined by the magnetic field alone, they can be made to spiral around in synchronism with the oscillating electric field, thus gaining successive increments of velocity. As they are speeded up, the ions travel on ever widening spirals, finally emerging at the periphery of the apparatus, where they may be withdrawn by a deflecting electrostatic field and directed to a target for bombarding purposes.

It is sometimes desired to bring the swiftly moving ions out of the vacuum into the air; and this can be readily done, as they have enough energy to penetrate a thin metal window, usually of platinum. A beam of deuterons emerging through such a window passes for some distance through the air before losing its energy, and excites the molecules of the air to the emission of visible light, appearing as a bright lavender-colored glow. This may be shown in a photograph where a six-million-volt beam of deuterons emerges from the window, producing a luminosity through the air for a distance of about thirty centimeters. For most purposes it is not necessary to bring the accelerated ions out of the vacuum chamber, since the targets to be bombarded can be placed conveniently within the vacuum. On the other hand, it is sometimes more convenient to have the beam come out into the air; for example, when it is desired to render a salt crystal radioactive. This can be done simply by holding the salt crystal in the beam in the air for a short while. For some purposes it is desirable to withdraw the beam entirely away from the vacuum chamber, and this can be done by attaching a suitable vacuum-tube extension.

The Future of Atomic Energy: The Equivalence of Mass and Energy

One of the consequences of Einstein's theory of relativity, first enunciated in 1905, was the discovery that matter is one form of energy. As the relativity theory grew in favor, the validity of the mass-energy relation became more apparent, but until direct experimental verification was forthcoming Einstein's great deduction could not be regarded as an established law of nature.

Now that it is an established fact that matter can be destroyed and converted into energy, let us consider for a moment what this means. At the outset one is impressed with the tremendous store of energy tied up in the form of matter. For example, a simple calculation according to the relativity theory shows that a glass of water, if completely destroyed and converted into useful energy, would yield more than a billion kilowatt hours, enough energy to supply a city with light and power for quite a time. It is a highly practical question, therefore, to inquire whether it is possible to tap this almost inexhaustible supply of fuel.

The source of the sun's energy has long been a great mystery, for there is good evidence that it has been blazing at its present brilliance for billions of years. Fuel for this eternal fire could be of no ordinary sort, and astronomers and physicists now believe that conditions within the sun are such that nuclear reactions are taking place on an extensive scale with the destruction of matter and conversion into radiant energy. Thus the sun is gradually through the ages losing its mass. Slowly its very substance is radiating into space.

But whether it will be possible to release subatomic energy on a practical and profitable basis for industrial purposes, whether perhaps it will be possible to realize conditions on the earth similar to those in the sun, are questions which, of course, interest the engineer. Indeed, they are questions of interest to everyone, and accordingly this has been a subject for much popular discussion and speculation. The fact is, at this time, that although we now know that matter can be converted into energy we are aware of no greater prospect of destroying nuclear matter for power purposes than of cooling the ocean to freezing temperatures and extracting the heat for profitable work. Certain considerations bearing on the second law of thermodynamics appear to govern the availability of energy in the hearts of atoms as in the Atlantic Ocean itself. The establishment of the great principle of mass-energy equivalence is, however, a keystone in the development of physical theory.

Anthropology Seeks the Origin of Man

HENRY FAIRFIELD OSBORN (1857–1935)

MANKIND CAME LATE to the serious study of its beginnings. The search among fossils for the "missing link," if there be one, between modern man and his remote ancestors started in the late nineteenth century. Drawing on the work of earlier natural historians, such as Buffon, Lamarck, and Darwin; of geologists, such as Lyell; of paleontologists, like Cuvier; of archeologists, like Sir John Lubbock and Boucher de Perthes; of physical and cultural anthropologists; spurred on by a three-weeks' guided tour through the upper Paleolithic caverns of southern France and Spain, where the pictures of animals made by men who lived twenty-five thousand years ago remain to be seen, a Connecticut-born Yankee, Henry Fairfield Osborn, undertook in 1915 to reconstruct in considerable detail the prehistoric life of the human race. Eminent paleontologist, author of "The Age of Mammals," Osborn was (from 1890) professor of zoology at Columbia and (from 1891) curator of vertebrate paleontology at the American Museum of Natural History in New York.

The passages here selected from "Men of the Old Stone Age" deal chiefly with *modern* man's (*Homo sapiens'*) immediate predecessor, the Neanderthal man (merely *Homo*), so called because the first-studied fossil remains (skullcap and bones) of this fellow were discovered at Neanderthal, near Düsseldorf, in Germany. He lived in the glacial and postglacial stages of Europe, when the great mammals—like the woolly rhinoceros—were dying out, at the dawn of industry, art, and truly "human" intelligence. Though not as large as ours, the Neanderthal's brain showed considerable improvement in size over his "ancestors": the Piltdown, or "dawn," man (*Eoanthropus*), whose remains were discovered at Piltdown, Sussex, in 1911; and the still remoter Java, or "ape," man (*Pithecanthropus erectus*), the finding of whose skullcap and leg-bone on the Trinil River in Java in 1891 created a great sensation in an evolution-conscious world.

English in the original, the 550-page "Men of the Old Stone Age" was published in 1915 by Charles Scribner's Sons, New York.

"MEN OF THE OLD STONE AGE"

THE ANTICIPATION of nature by Lucretius in his philosophical poem, *"De Rerum Natura,"* accords in a broad and remarkable way with our present knowledge of the prehistory of man:

> Things throughout proceed
> In firm, undevious order, and maintain,
> To nature true, their fixt generic stamp.
> Yet man's first sons, as o'er the fields they trod,
> Reared from the hardy earth, were hardier far;
> Strong built with ampler bones, with muscles nerved
> Broad and substantial; to the power of heat,
> Of cold, of varying viands, and disease,
> Each hour superior; the wild lives of beasts
> Leading, while many a luster o'er them rolled.
> Nor crooked plowshare knew they, nor to drive,
> Deep through the soil, the rich-returning spade;
> Nor how the tender seedling to replant,
> Nor from the fruit tree prune the withered branch. . . .
>
> Nor knew they yet the crackling blaze t' excite,
> Or clothe their limbs with furs, or savage hides.
> But groves concealed them, woods, and hollow hills;
> And, when rude rains or bitter blasts o'erpowered,
> Low bushy shrubs their squalid members wrapped.
> And in their keen rapidity of hand
> And foot confiding, oft the savage train
> With missile stones they hunted, or the force
> Of clubs enormous; many a tribe they felled,
> Yet some in caves shunned, cautious; where, at night,
> Thronged they, like bristly swine; their naked limbs
> With herbs and leaves entwining. Nought of fear
> Urged them to quit the darkness, and recall
> With clamorous cries the sunshine and the day:
> But sound they sunk in deep, oblivious sleep,
> Till o'er the mountains blushed the roseate dawn. . . .
>
> This ne'er distressed them, but the fear alone,
> Some ruthless monster might their dreams molest,

The foamy boar, or lion, from their caves
Drive them aghast beneath the midnight shade,
And seize their leaf-wrought couches for themselves. . . .

Yet then scarce more of mortal race than now
Left the sweet luster of the liquid day.
Some doubtless, oft the prowling monsters gaunt
Grasped in their jaws, abrupt; whence, through the groves,
The woods, the mountains, they vociferous groaned,
Destined thus living to a living tomb. . . .

Yet when, at length, rude huts they first devised,
And fires, and garments; and, in union sweet,
Man wedded woman, the pure joys indulged
Of chaste connubial love, and children rose,
The rough barbarians softened. The warm hearth
Their frames so melted they no more could bear,
As erst, th' uncovered skies; the nuptial bed
Broke their wild vigor, and the fond caress
Of prattling children from the bosom chased
Their stern ferocious manners.

This is a picture of many phases in the life of primitive man: his powerful frame, his ignorance of agriculture, his dependence on the fruits and animal products of the earth, his discovery of fire and of clothing, his chase of wild beasts with clubs and missile stones, his repair to caverns, his contests with the lion and the boar, his invention of rude huts and dwellings, the softening of his nature through the sweet influence of family life and of children, all these are veritable stages in our prehistoric development. The influence of Greek thought is also reflected in the satires of Horace, and the Greek conception of the natural history of man, voiced by Aeschylus as early as the fifth century B.C., prevailed widely before the Christian Era, when it gradually gave way to the Mosaic conception of special creation, which spread all over western Europe.

As the idea of the natural history of man again arose, during the sixteenth and seventeenth centuries, it came not so much from previous sources as from the dawning science of comparative anatomy. From the year 1597, when a Portuguese sailor's account of an animal resembling the chimpanzee was embodied in Filippo Pigafetta's "Description of the Kingdom of the Congo," the many points of likeness between the anthropoid apes and man were treated both in satire and caricature and in serious anatomical comparison as evidence of kinship.

The first French evolutionist, Buffon, observed in 1749: "The first truth that makes itself apparent on serious study of nature is one that man may perhaps find humiliating; it is this—that he, too, must take his place in the ranks of animals, being, as he is, an animal in every material point." Buffon's convictions were held in check by clerical and official influences, yet from his study of the orang in 1766 we can entertain no doubt of his belief that men and apes are descended from common ancestors. . . .

We now reach a prolonged and important stage in the prehistory of Europe, namely, the period of the fourth glaciation, of the final development of the Neanderthal race of man, of the Mousterian industry, of the beginnings of cave life, of the chase of the reindeer, and its use for food and clothing.

In all Europe the Acheulean industry appears to have come to a close during a period of arid climate, warm in some parts of western Europe and cool or even cold in others. The seasonal variations may well have been extreme, as on the steppes of southern Russia, where exceedingly hot summers may be followed by intensely cold winters, with high winds and snowstorms destructive of life.

It is this seasonal alternation, as well as the recurrence, either seasonal or secular, of milder climate, which explains the survival or return of the Asiatic fauna even after the close of the Acheulean industry and when the Mousterian industry was well advanced.

From deposits found at Grimaldi, in the Grotte des Enfants and in the Grotte du Prince, it has long been said that men of early Mousterian times lived contemporary with the hippopotamus, the straight-tusked elephant, and Merck's rhinoceros in the genial climate of the Mediterranean Riviera. More recently the same animals have been found as far north as the Somme Valley in the "river drifts" of Montières-les-Amiens. Here, again, we find remains of the hippopotamus, the straight-tusked elephant, and its companion, Merck's rhinoceros, in Mousterian deposits, a surprising discovery, because it had always been supposed that a cold climatic period had set in all over western Europe even before the close of the Acheulean culture. But there is also evidence of a temperate climate still prevailing in the Thames Valley in the period of the Mousterian "floors." Again, along the Vézère Valley, Dordogne, we find that at the station of La Micoque, where the industry marks the transition between late Acheulean and early Mousterian times, Merck's rhinoceros is found in the lowest layers associated with remains of the moose (*Alces*).

There is evidence that Merck's rhinoceros and the straight-tusked elephant lingered in western Europe during the whole period of the early development of the Mousterian industry. As observed above, these animals were hardier than the southern mammoth, which was the first of the Asiatic mammals to disappear, soon to be followed by its companion, the hippopotamus. Even after the advent of the closely associated tundra pair, the woolly mammoth and the woolly rhinoceros, Merck's rhinoceros persists, as, for example, in the deposits of Rixdorf, near Berlin, where this ancient type occurs in the same deposits with the woolly mammoth, the woolly rhinoceros, the reindeer, and the musk ox, as well as with the forest forms, the moose, stag, wolf, and forest horse. The extreme northern latitude of this deposit explains the absence of the straight-tusked elephant, which may at the time have been living farther to the south.

The same mingling of south and north Asiatic mammals is found at Steinhim, in the valley of the Murr, some degrees to the west and south of Rixdorf, not far from Göttingen, where we find Merck's rhinoceros and the straight-tusked elephant in association with the woolly mammoth, the woolly rhinoceros, the giant deer, and the reindeer.

Thus the Neanderthal races were entering the Mousterian stage of culture during the close of the third interglacial stage and during the early period of the advance of the ice fields from the great center in Scandinavia and the Alps. As these ice fields slowly approached each other from the north and from the south a very great period of time must have elapsed during which all the south Asiatic mammals abandoned western Europe or became extinct, with the exception of the lions and hyenas, which became well fitted to the very severe climate that prevailed over Europe during the fourth glaciation, and even during the long postglacial stage which ensued.

The large carnivora readily become thoroughly adapted to cold climates, as they subsist on animal life wherever it may be found; tigers of the same stock as those of India have been found as far north as the river Lena, in latitude 52° 25′, where the climate is colder than that of Petrograd or of Stockholm, while the lion throve in the cold atmosphere of the upper Atlas range. Thus the cave lion (*Felis leo spelaea*) and the cave hyena (*H. crocuta spelaea*) doubtless evolved an undercoating of fur as well as an overcoating of long hair, like the tundra mammals. In size the lion of this period in France often equaled and sometimes surpassed its existing relatives, the African and west Asiatic lion; it frequently figures in the art of the Upper Palaeolithic artists and survived in western Europe to the very close of Upper Palaeolithic times. . . .

CUSTOMS OF THE CHASE AND OF CAVE LIFE

We have only indirect means of knowing the courage and activity of the Neanderthals in the chase, through the bones of animals hunted for food which are found intermingled with the flints around their ancient hearths. These include in the early Mousterian hearths, as we have seen, bones of the bison, the wild cattle, and the horse, which are followed at Combe-Capelle by the first appearance of the bones of the reindeer. The bones of the bison and of the wild horse are both utilized in the bone anvils of the closing Mousterian culture at La Quina.

What we believe to be the period of the great mammalian life of the region of the upper Danube is found in the Mousterian levels of the grotto of Sirgenstein, from which it would appear that the Neanderthals hunted the mammoth, the rhinoceros, the wild horse, bison, and cattle, and the giant deer as well as the reindeer. We should keep in mind, however, that when these caves were for a time deserted the beasts of prey returned, and so it often happens that the succeeding layers afford proofs of alternate occupation by man and by beasts of prey of sufficient size to bring in the larger kinds of game, while owls may be responsible for the deposits of the lemming, as in the "lower rodent layer."

Obermaier has given careful study to the vicissitudes of cave life in Mousterian times. Long before these caves were inhabited by man they served as lairs or refuges for the cave bear and cave hyena, as well as for many birds of prey. For example, the cave of Echenoz-la-Moline, on the upper waters of the Saône, contained the remains of over eight hundred skeletons of the cave bear, and no doubt it cost the Neanderthals many a hard-fought battle before the beasts were driven out and man possessed himself of the grotto. Fire may have been the means employed.

It has been questioned whether the caves were not unhealthy dwelling places, but it must be remembered that, except in certain caverns which had natural openings through the roof for the exit of smoke, there was no true cave life, but rather a grotto life, which centered around the entrance of the cave. The smallest cave, this author observes, was considerably larger and better ventilated than the small, smoky cabins of some of the European peasants or the snow huts of the Eskimo. The most serious obstacle was the prevailing dampness, which varied periodically in the caverns, so that dry seasons were succeeded by abundant moisture seeping through the limestone roof and down the side walls. At such times the caverns were probably uninhabitable, and in the bones of both men and beasts many instances have been observed of diseased swellings and of inflammation of the vertebrae, such as are caused by extreme dampness.

The compensating advantages were the shelter offered from the rain and cold, a constant temperature at moderate distances from the entrance, and also the fact that the caves were very easily defensible, because the entrance was generally small and the approach often steep and difficult; a high stone wall across the opening would have made the defense still easier, and a flaming firebrand would have prevented the approach of bears and other beasts of prey. On account of this shelter from the weather and wild beasts the grottoes and the larger openings of the caverns were certainly crowded with the Mousterian flint workers during the inclement seasons of the year.

Yet the greater part of the life of the Neanderthals was undoubtedly passed in the open and in the chase. Throughout Mousterian times the commonest game consisted of the wild horse, wild ox, and reindeer. Both flesh and pelts were ultilized, and the marrow was sought by splitting all the larger bones. Thus frequently we find in the hearths the remains of the mammoth, the woolly rhinoceros, the giant deer, the cave bear, and the brown bear. From these beasts of prey the Neanderthal hunters obtained pelts and perhaps also fat for torches used to light the caverns; there is no proof of the invention of the lamp at this period.

The work of the women undoubtedly consisted of preparing the meals and making the pelts into covers and clothing. Whenever possible this would be done in the daylight outside of the grottoes, but in chilly, rainy weather, or the bitter cold of winter, the whole tribe would seek refuge in the grotto, gathering around the fire hearths fed with wood; odd corners would serve as storehouses for fuel or dried meat, preserved against the days when extreme cold and blinding snow forbade the hunters to venture forth.

It appears that the game was dismembered where it fell and the best parts removed. The skull was split open for the brain; the long bones were preserved for the marrow; thus the bones of the flank and shoulder of game occur frequently in cave deposits, while the ribs and vertebrae are rare.

The pitfall may have been part of the hunting craft known to the

Neanderthals. The chase was pursued with spears or darts fitted with flint points, also by means of "throwing stones," which are found in great numbers in the upper Mousterian levels of La Quina, in the Wolf Cave of Yonne, Les Cottés, and various places in Spain. If one imagines, as is quite possible, that the throwing stone was placed in a leather sling or in the cleft end of a stick, or fastened to a long leather thong, one can readily see it would prove a very effective weapon.

The methods of chase by the Neanderthals are, nevertheless, somewhat of a mystery. There was a very decided disparity between the size and effectiveness of their weapons and the strength and resistance of the animals which they pursued. None of the very heavy implements of Acheulean times was preserved; the dart and spear heads are not greatly improved, certainly they could not penetrate the thick hides of the larger arctic tundra mammals, heavily protected with hair and wool; the chase even of the horses, wild cattle, and reindeer was apparently without the aid of the bow and arrow and prior to the invention of the barbed arrow or lance head.

"The Life of the Bee": Sociology of the Insect World

MAURICE MAETERLINCK (1862–   )

"THE FINEST PROSE that has ever been used to describe the subject matter of science" is the tribute paid by the distinguished American naturalist and littérateur, Donald Culross Peattie, to the passages quoted here from the scientific work of "the beekeeper of Oostacker," Maurice Maeterlinck. Many may be amazed to discover that the great Belgian poet, dramatist, and essayist, author of the immortal play, "The Blue Bird," and the only man quoted in this volume who won the Nobel prize (1911) for *literature*, also enjoys a high and legitimate reputation in one of the oldest fields of scientific endeavor: natural history. He summates a tradition of apt description of natural phenomena beginning in antiquity with Aristotle and Pliny and carried through the centuries, in the writings of such men as Gesner, Goethe, Gilbert White, Alexander von Humboldt, Charles Darwin, Alfred Russel Wallace, Hugh Miller,

John Powell, W. H. Hudson, and others too numerous to quote, persistently inspiring even to the present day.

As a natural historian, Maeterlinck not only proved himself thoroughly conversant with the classics of his subject, the works of Réaumur and the blind François Huber, but also demonstrated that he was a practical apiarist. "The Life of the Bee" is as packed with useful information on beekeeping as it is illumined with brilliant figures of speech and potent prose. The scientific writing of Maeterlinck gives the lie direct to a misapprehension on the part of writers and scientists in this age of specialization; namely, that science and literature are disparate subjects. Granted that they are separate disciplines, each of which must be mastered, they are no different in this respect from mathematics and biology, both of which advance under the banner of science. At the level of their highest impact upon the course of human life and thought —as the increasing interest in scientific epistemology betokens—both science and literature own the same purpose, fill the same need: the truest possible description of the ultimate reality of things.

In this respect at least it is believed that every great scientist quoted in this volume has likewise proved himself a great writer; and many, indeed, must be accredited also as masters of literary style. It is hoped that their example will prove an inspiration to the present generation of professional scientists and writers. And in this endeavor no better model can be offered than Maeterlinck's "Life of the Bee."

Maeterlinck left his native town of Ghent for Paris in 1896. There he came under the influence of the French symbolists and wrote some of his most celebrated works. At present—since 1940—he lives in the United States.

French is the language in which Maeterlinck wrote "The Life of the Bee" in 1901. The English translation, by Alfred Sutro, was published by Dodd, Mead & Company, Inc., New York.

THE SPIRIT OF THE HIVE

WE WILL NOW, so as to draw more closely to nature, consider the different episodes of the swarm as they come to pass in an ordinary hive, which is ten or twenty times more populous than an observation one, and leaves the bees entirely free and untrammeled.

Here, then, they have shaken off the torpor of winter. The queen started laying again in the very first days of February, and the workers have flocked to the willows and nut trees, gorse and violets, anemones and lungworts. Then spring invades the earth, and cellar and stream with honey and pollen, while each day beholds the birth of thousands of bees. The overgrown males now all sally forth from their cells and disport themselves on the combs; and so crowded does the too prosperous city become that hundreds of belated workers, coming back from the flowers toward evening, will vainly seek shelter within and will be forced to spend the night on the threshold, where they will be decimated by the cold.

Restlessness seizes the people, and the old queen begins to stir. She feels that a new destiny is being prepared. She has religiously fulfilled her duty as a good creatress; and from this duty done there result only tribulation and sorrow. An invincible power menaces her tranquillity; she will soon be forced to quit this city of hers, where she has reigned. But this city is her work, it is she herself. She is not its queen in the sense in which men use the word. She issues no orders; she obeys, as meekly as the humblest of her subjects, the masked power, sovereignly wise, that for the present, and till we attempt to locate it, we will term the "spirit of the hive." But she is the unique organ of love; she is the mother of the city. She founded it amid uncertainty and poverty. She has peopled it with her own substance; and all who move within its walls—workers, males, larvae, nymphs, and the young princesses whose approaching birth will hasten her own departure, one of them being already designed as her successor by the "spirit of the hive"—all these have issued from her flanks.

What is this "spirit of the hive"—where does it reside? It is not like the special instinct that teaches the bird to construct its well-planned nest and then seek other skies when the day for migration returns. Nor is it a kind of mechanical habit of the race, or blind craving for life, that will fling the bees upon any wild hazard the moment an unforeseen event shall derange the accustomed order of phenomena. On the contrary, be the event never so masterful, the "spirit of the hive" still will follow it, step by step, like an alert and quick-witted slave, who is able to derive advantage even from his master's most dangerous orders.

It disposes pitilessly of the wealth and the happiness, the liberty and life, of all this winged people; and yet with discretion, as though governed itself by some great duty. It regulates day by day the number of births and contrives that these shall strictly accord with the number of flowers that brighten the countryside. It decrees the queen's deposition or warns her that she must depart; it compels her to bring her own rivals into the world, and rears them royally, protecting them from their mother's political hatred. So, too, in accordance with the generosity of the flowers, the age of the spring, and the probable dangers of the nuptial flight will it permit or forbid the first-born of the virgin princesses to slay in their cradles her younger sisters, who are singing the song of the queens.

At other times, when the season wanes, and flowery hours grow shorter, it will command the workers themselves to slaughter the whole imperial brood, that the era of revolutions may close, and work become the sole object of all. The "spirit of the hive" is prudent and thrifty, but by no means parsimonious. And thus, aware, it would seem, that nature's laws are somewhat wild and extravagant in all that pertains to love, it tolerates, during summer days of abundance, the embarrassing presence in the hive of three or four hundred males, from whose ranks the queen about to be born shall select her lover; three or four hundred foolish, clumsy, useless, noisy creatures, who are pretentious, gluttonous, dirty, coarse, totally and scandalously idle, insatiable, and enormous.

But after the queen's impregnation, when flowers begin to close sooner and open later, the spirit one morning will coldly decree the simultaneous and general massacre of every male. It regulates the workers' labors, with due regard to their age; it allots their task to the nurses who tend the nymphs and the larvae, the ladies of honor who wait on the queen and never allow her out of their sight; the house bees who air, refresh, or heat the hive by fanning their wings, and hasten the evaporation of the honey that may be too highly charged with water; the architects, masons, waxworkers, and sculptors who form the chain and construct the combs; the foragers who sally forth to the flowers in search of the nectar that turns into honey, of the pollen that feeds the nymphs and the larvae, the propolis that welds and strengthens the buildings of the city, or the water and salt required by the youth of the nation.

Its orders have gone to the chemists who ensure the preservation of the honey by letting a drop of formic acid fall in from the end of their sting; to the capsule makers who seal down the cells when the treasure is ripe, to the sweepers who maintain public places and streets most irreproachably clean, to the bearers whose duty it is to remove the corpses; and to the amazons of the guard who keep watch on the threshold by night and by day, question comers and goers, recognize the novices who return from their very first flight, scare away vagabonds, marauders, and loiterers, expel all intruders, attack redoubtable foes in a body, and, if need be, barricade the entrance.

Finally, it is the spirit of the hive that fixes the hour of the great annual sacrifice to the genius of the race: the hour, that is, of the swarm; when we find a whole people, who have attained the topmost pinnacle of prosperity and power, suddenly abandoning to the generation to come their wealth and their palaces, their homes and the fruits of their labor; themselves content to encounter the hardships and perils of a new and distant country. This act, be it conscious or not, undoubtedly passes the limits of human morality. Its result will sometimes be ruin, but poverty always; and the thrice-happy city is scattered abroad in obedience to a law superior to its own happiness. Where has this law been decreed, which, as we soon shall find, is by no means as blind and inevitable as one might believe? Where, in what assembly, what council, what intellectual and moral sphere, does this spirit reside to whom all must submit, itself being vassal to an heroic duty, to an intelligence whose eyes are persistently fixed on the future?

It comes to pass with the bees as with most of the things in this world; we remark some few of their habits; we say they do this, they work in such and such fashion, their queens are born thus, their workers are virgin, they swarm at a certain time. And then we imagine we know them, and ask nothing more. We watch them hasten from flower to flower, we see the constant agitation within the hive; their life seems very simple to us, and bounded, like every life, by the instinctive cares of reproduction and nourishment. But let the eye draw near and endeavor to see; and at once the least phenomenon of all becomes overpoweringly complex; we are confronted by the enigma of intellect, of destiny, will, aim, means, causes; the incomprehensible organization of the most insignificant act of life.

THE YOUNG QUEENS

THESE MEASURES concern the care of the youthful queens who still lie immured in their waxen prisons. Let us assume that the "spirit of the hive" has pronounced against the dispatch of a second swarm. Two courses still remain open. The bees may permit the first-born of the royal virgins, the one whose birth we have witnessed, to destroy her sister enemies; or they may elect to wait till she has performed the perilous ceremony known as the "nuptial flight," whereon the nation's future depends. The immediate massacre will be authorized often, and often denied; but in the latter case it is, of course, not easy for us to pronounce whether the bees' decision be due to a desire for a second swarm or to their recognition of the dangers attending the nuptial flight; for it will happen at times that, on account of the weather unexpectedly becoming less favorable, or for some other reason we cannot divine, they will suddenly change their mind, renounce the cast that they had decreed, and destroy the royal progeny they had so carefully preserved.

But at present we will suppose that they have determined to dispense with a second swarm, and that they accept the risks of the nuptial flight. Our young queen hastens toward the large cradles, urged on by her great desire, and the guard make way before her. Listening only to her furious jealousy, she will fling herself onto the first cell she comes across, madly strip off the wax with her teeth and claws, tear away the cocoon that carpets the cell, and divest the sleeping princess of every covering. If her rival should be already recognizable, the queen will turn so that her sting may enter the capsule, and will frantically stab it with her venomous weapon until the victim perish. She then becomes calmer, appeased by the death that puts a term to the hatred of every creature; she withdraws her sting, hurries to the adjoining cell, attacks it and opens it, passing it by should she find in it only an imperfect larva or nymph; nor does she pause till, at last, exhausted and breathless, her claws and teeth glide harmless over the waxen walls.

The bees that surround her have calmly watched her fury, have stood by, inactive, moving only to leave her path clear; but no sooner has a cell been pierced and laid waste than they eagerly flock to it, drag out the corpse of the ravished nymph or the still living larva, and thrust it forth from the hive, thereupon gorging themselves with the precious royal jelly that adheres to the sides of the cell. And finally, when the queen has become too weak to persist in her passion, they will themselves complete the massacre of the innocents; and the sovereign race, and their dwellings, will all disappear.

This is the terrible hour of the hive; the only occasion, with that of the more justifiable execution of the drones, when the workers suffer discord and death to be busy among them; and here, as often in nature, it is the favored of love who attract to themselves the most extraordinary shafts of violent death.

It will happen at times that two queens will be hatched simultaneously, the occurrence being rare, however, for the bees take special care to prevent it. But whenever this does take place, the deadly combat will begin the moment they emerge from their cradles; and of this combat Huber was the first to remark an extraordinary feature. Each time it would seem that the queens, in their passes, present their chitinous cuirasses to each other in such a fashion that the drawing of the sting would prove mutually fatal; one might almost believe that, even as a god or goddess was wont to interpose in the combats of the "Iliad," so a god or a goddess, the divinity of the race, perhaps, interposes here; and the two warriors, stricken with simultaneous terror, divide and fly, to meet shortly after and separate again should the double disaster once more menace the future of their people; till at last one of them shall succeed in surprising her clumsier or less wary rival, and in killing her without risk to herself. For the law of the race has called for one sacrifice only.

The cradles having thus been destroyed and the rivals all slain, the young queen is accepted by her people; but she will not truly reign over them, or be treated as was her mother before her, until the nuptial flight be accomplished; for until she be impregnated the bees will hold her but lightly and render most passing homage. Her history, however, will rarely be as uneventful as this, for the bees will not often renounce their desire for a second swarm.

In that case, as before, quick with the same desires, the queen will approach the royal cells; but instead of meeting with docile servants who second her efforts, she will find her path blocked by a numerous and hostile guard. In her fury, and urged on by her fixed idea, she will endeavor to force her way through or to outflank them; but everywhere sentinels are posted to protect the sleeping princesses. She persists, she returns to the charge, to be repulsed with ever increasing severity, to be somewhat roughly handled even, until at last she begins vaguely to understand that these little inflexible workers stand for a law before which that law must bend whereby she is inspired.

And at last she goes, and wanders from comb to comb, her unsatisfied wrath finding vent in a war song, or angry complaint, that every bee-keeper knows; resembling somewhat the note of a distant trumpet of silver; so intense in its passionate feebleness as to be clearly audible, in the evening especially, two or three yards from the double walls of the most carefully enclosed hive.

Upon the workers this royal cry has a magical effect. It terrifies them, it induces a kind of respectful stupor; and when the queen sends it forth, as she halts in front of the cells whose approach is denied her, the guardians who have but this moment been hustling her, pushing her back, will at once desist and wait, with bent head, till the cry shall have ceased to resound. Indeed, some believe that it is thanks to the prestige of this cry, which the Sphinx Atropos imitates, that the latter is able to enter the hive and gorge itself with honey, without the least molestation on the part of the bees.

For two or three days, sometimes even for five, this indignant lament will be heard, this challenge that the queen addresses to her well-protected rivals. And as these in their turn develop, in their turn grow anxious to see the light, they too set to work to gnaw the lids of their cells. A mighty disorder would now appear to threaten the republic. But the genius of the hive, at the time that it formed its decision, was able to foretell every consequence that might ensue; and the guardians have had their instructions: they know exactly what must be done, hour by hour, to meet the attacks of a foiled instinct and conduct two opposite forces to a successful issue. They are fully aware that if the young queens should escape who now clamor for birth they would fall into the hands of their elder sister, by this time irresistible, who would destroy them one by one. The workers, therefore, will pile on fresh layers of wax in proportion as the prisoner reduces, from within, the walls of her tower; and the impatient princess will ardently persist in her labor, little suspecting that she has to deal with an enchanted obstacle that rises ever afresh from its ruin. She hears the war cry of her rival; and, already aware of her royal duty and destiny, although she has not yet looked upon life, nor knows what a hive may be, she answers the challenge from within the depths of her prison. But her cry is different; it is stifled and hollow, for it has to traverse the walls of a tomb; and, when night is falling, and noises are hushed, and high over all there reigns the silence of the stars, the apiarist who nears these marvelous cities and stands, questioning, at their entrance, recognizes and understands the dialogue that is passing between the wandering queen and the virgins in prison.

A Key to the Riddle of Heredity

GREGOR MENDEL (1822–84)

WOULD you have known better?

On February 8 and March 8, 1865, the members of the Natural History Society of Brunn, Austria, provincial amateurs in science, listened patiently while the quiet, mathematically minded abbot of the local monastery, Königskloster, read to the meeting a long (20,000 words), figure-ridden paper summarizing the results of an experiment in the crossbreeding or hybridization of common edible garden peas. The work had taken Mendel eight painstaking years in the monastery garden. The difficult paper, with new words like "dominant" and "recessive" characteristics, was duly published in the Society's proceedings, distributed to gather dust in scientific libraries all over the world, including thirty or more American libraries. It was forgotten while the earnest, peasant-born Silesian abbot, fulfilling his extensive clerical duties, tried with another plant—unhappily chosen—and failed to repeat his earlier experiment. Mendel died in 1884, unknown to the great world.

Meanwhile biological scientists were struggling uncomfortably with the problems of heredity struck off from Darwin's theory of evolution. August Weismann (1834–1914), German biologist, was arguing brilliantly for the continuity of the germ plasm, locating the physical basis of heredity in the chromosomes and denying the possibility of passing on to one's offspring any characteristics acquired from environment. But no one could arrive at a simple, experimentally verifiable law, principle, theory, or mechanism that permitted following the subtly complicated course of heredity.

Then suddenly, just at the turn of the century, Mendel's lost paper was rediscovered almost simultaneously by Hugo de Vries (1848–1935), in Holland, Karl Correns (1864–1933) in Germany, and Erich Tschermak (1871–   ) in Austria; promptly translated and championed by William Bateson (1861–1926), pioneer geneticist in England. Mendel's experiments could be repeated, his arithmetic ratios verified, and the once sickly science of genetics struck firm roots in human understanding. The fundamental Mendelian ratio, as you can discover in the portions of his now famous paper given here, is 3 to 1; that is, in the generation bred from hybrids, *three* out of four will display the dominant and *one* the recessive characteristics, whether length of stalk or color of hair.

German is the language of Mendel's original paper. The English translation was made by the Royal Horticultural Society of London with minor revisions by Bateson. It is used with permission of the Council of the Society. The original paper was published in the *"Verh. naturf. Ver. in Brunn," Abhandlung iv. 1865* ("Proceedings of the Natural History Society of Brunn," Vol. IV, 1865), actually issued in 1866.

EXPERIMENTS IN PLANT HYBRIDIZATION—THE "LOST PAPER"

EXPERIENCE of artificial fertilization, such as is effected with ornamental plants in order to obtain new variations in color, has led to the experiments which will here be discussed. The striking regularity with which the same hybrid forms always reappeared whenever fertilization took place between the same species induced further experiments to be undertaken, the object of which was to follow up the developments of the hybrids in their progeny.

To this object numerous careful observers, such as Kölreuter, Gärtner, Herbert, Lecoq, Wichura, and others, have devoted a part of their lives with inexhaustible perseverance. Gärtner especially, in his work "The Production of Hybrids in the Vegetable Kingdom," has recorded very valuable observations; and quite recently Wichura published the results of some profound investigations into the hybrids of the willow. That, so far, no generally applicable law governing the formation and development of hybrids has been successfully formulated can hardly be wondered at by anyone who is acquainted with the extent of the task and can appreciate the difficulties with which experiments of this class have to contend. A final decision can only be arrived at when we shall have before us the results of detailed experiments made on plants belonging to the most diverse orders.

Those who survey the work done in this department will arrive at the conviction that, among all the numerous experiments made, not one has been carried out to such an extent and in such a way as to make it possible to determine the number of different forms under which the offspring of hybrids appear, or to arrange these forms with certainty according to their separate generations, or definitely to ascertain their statistical relations.

It requires indeed some courage to undertake a labor of such far-reaching extent; this appears, however, to be the only right way by which we can finally reach the solution of a question, the importance of which cannot be overestimated in connection with the history of the evolution of organic forms.

The paper now presented records the results of such a detailed experiment. This experiment was practically confined to a small plant group and is now, after eight years' pursuit, concluded in all essentials. Whether the plan upon which the separate experiments were conducted and carried out was the best suited to attain the desired end is left to the friendly decision of the reader.

SELECTION OF THE EXPERIMENTAL PLANTS

The value and utility of any experiment are determined by the fitness of the material to the purpose for which it is used, and thus in the case before us it cannot be immaterial what plants are subjected to experiment and in what manner such experiments are conducted.

The selection of the plant group which shall serve for experiments of this kind must be made with all possible care if it be desired to avoid from the outset every risk of questionable results.

The experimental plants must necessarily—

1. Possess constant differentiating characters.

2. The hybrids of such plants must, during the flowering period, be protected from the influence of all foreign pollen or be easily capable of such protection.

The hybrids and their offspring should suffer no marked disturbance in their fertility in the successive generations.

Accidental impregnation by foreign pollen, if it occurred during the experiments and were not recognized, would lead to entirely erroneous conclusions. Reduced fertility or entire sterility of certain forms, such as occurs in the offspring of many hybrids, would render the experiments very difficult or entirely frustrate them. In order to discover the relations in which the hybrid forms stand toward each other and also toward their progenitors, it appears to be necessary that all members of the series developed in each successive generation should be, without exception, subjected to observation.

At the very outset special attention was devoted to the *Leguminosae* on account of their peculiar floral structure. Experiments which were made with several members of this family led to the result that the genus *Pisum* was found to possess the necessary qualifications.

Some thoroughly distinct forms of this genus possess characters which are constant, and easily and certainly recognizable, and when their hybrids are mutually crossed they yield perfectly fertile progeny. Furthermore, a disturbance through foreign pollen cannot easily occur, since the fertilizing organs are closely packed inside the keel and the anther bursts within the bud, so that the stigma becomes covered with pollen even before the flower opens. This circumstance is of special importance. As additional advantages worth mentioning, there may be cited the easy culture of these plants in the open ground and in pots, and also their relatively short period of growth. Artificial fertilization is certainly a somewhat elaborate process, but nearly always succeeds. For this purpose the bud is opened before it is perfectly developed, the keel is removed, and each stamen carefully extracted by means of forceps, after which the stigma can at once be dusted over with the foreign pollen.

In all, thirty-four more or less distinct varieties of peas were obtained from several seedsmen and subjected to a two-years' trial. In the case of one variety there were noticed, among a larger number of plants all alike, a few forms which were markedly different. These, however, did not vary in the following year, and agreed entirely with another variety obtained from the same seedsman; the seeds were therefore doubtless merely accidentally mixed. All the other varieties yielded perfectly constant and similar offspring; at any rate, no essential difference was observed during two trial years. For fertilization twenty-two of these were selected and cultivated during the whole period of the experiments. They remained constant without any exception.

Their systematic classification is difficult and uncertain. If we adopt the strictest definition of a species, according to which only those individuals belong to a species which under precisely the same circumstances display precisely similar characters, no two of these varieties could be referred to one species. According to the opinion of experts, however, the majority belong to the species *Pisum sativum;* while the rest are regarded and classed, some as subspecies of *P. sativum,* and some as independent species, such as *P. quadratum, P. saccharatum,* and *P. umbellatum.* The positions, however, which may be assigned to them in a classificatory system are quite immaterial for the purposes of the experiments in question. It has so far been found to be just as impossible to draw a sharp line between the hybrids of species and varieties as between species and varieties themselves.

DIVISION AND ARRANGEMENT OF THE EXPERIMENTS

If two plants which differ constantly in one or several characters be crossed, numerous experiments have demonstrated that the common characters are transmitted unchanged to the hybrids and their progeny; but each pair of differentiating characters, on the other hand, unite in the hybrid to form a new character, which in the progeny of the hybrid is usually variable. The object of the experiment was to observe these variations in the case of each pair of differentiating characters, and to deduce the law according to which they appear in the successive generations. The experiment resolves itself, therefore, into just as many separate experiments as there are constantly differentiating characters presented in the experimental plants.

The various forms of peas selected for crossing showed differences in the length and color of the stem; in the size and form of the leaves; in the position, color, and size of the flowers; in the length of the flower stalk; in the color, form, and size of the pods; in the form and size of the seeds; and in the color of the seed coats and of the albumen [cotyledons]. Some of the characters noted do not permit of a sharp and certain separation, since the difference is of a "more or less" nature, which is often difficult to define. Such characters could not be utilized for the separate experiments; these could only be applied to characters which stand out clearly and definitely in the plants. Lastly, the result must show whether they, in their entirety, observe a regular behavior in their hybrid unions, and whether from these facts any conclusion can be come to regarding those characters which possess a subordinate significance in the type. . . .

THE FORMS OF THE HYBRIDS

Experiments which in previous years were made with ornamental plants have already afforded evidence that the hybrids, as a rule, are not exactly intermediate between the parental species. With some of the more striking characters—those, for instance, which relate to the form and size of the leaves, the pubescence of the several parts, et cetera—the intermediate, indeed, is nearly always to be seen; in other cases, however, one of the two parental characters is so preponderant that it was difficult, or quite impossible, to detect the other in the hybrid.

This is precisely the case with pea hybrids. In the case of each of the seven crosses the hybrid character resembles that of one of the parental forms so closely that the other either escapes observation completely or cannot be detected with certainty. This circumstance is of great importance in the determination and classification of the forms under which the offspring of the hybrids appear. Henceforth in this paper those characters which are transmitted entirely, or almost unchanged in the hybridization, and therefore in themselves constitute the characters of the hybrid, are termed *dominant,* and those which become latent in the process *recessive.* The expression "recessive" has been chosen because the characters thereby designated withdraw or entirely disappear in the hybrids, but nevertheless reappear unchanged in their progeny, as will be demonstrated later on. . . .

THE FIRST GENERATION [BRED] FROM THE HYBRIDS

In this generation there reappear, together with the dominant characters, also the recessive ones with their peculiarities fully developed, and this occurs in the definitely expressed average proportion of three to one, so that among each four plants of this generation three display the dominant character and one the recessive. This relates without exception to all the characters which were investigated in the experiments. The angular wrinkled form of the seed, the green color of the albumen, the white color of the seed coats and the flowers, the constrictions of the pods, the yellow color of the unripe pod, of the stalk, of the calyx, and of the leaf venation, the umbel-like form of the inflorescence, and the dwarfed stem, all reappear in the numerical proportion given, without any essential alteration. *Transitional forms were not observed in any experiment. . . .*

If now the results of the whole of the experiments be brought together, there is found, as between the number of forms with the dominant and recessive characters, an average ratio of 2.98 to 1, or 3 to 1.

The dominant character can have here a double signification—viz., that of a parental character, or a hybrid character. In which of the two significations it appears in each separate case can only be determined by the following generation. As a parental character it must pass over unchanged to the whole of the offspring; as a hybrid character, on the other hand, it must maintain the same behavior as in the first generation.

The Second Generation [Bred] from the Hybrids

Those forms which in the first generation exhibit the recessive character do not further vary in the second generation as regards this character; they remain constant in their offspring.

It is otherwise with those which possess the dominant character in the first generation [bred from the hybrids]. Of these two thirds yield offspring which display the dominant and recessive characters in the proportion of 3 to 1, and thereby show exactly the same ratio as the hybrid forms, while only *one* third remains with the dominant character constant. . . .

In each of these experiments a certain number of the plants came constant with the dominant character. For the determination of the proportion in which the separation of the forms with the constantly persistent character results, the two first experiments are of especial importance, since in these a larger number of plants can be compared. The ratios 1.93 to 1 and 2.13 to 1 gave together almost exactly the average ratio of 2 to 1. The sixth experiment gave a quite concordant result; in the others the ratio varies more or less, as was only to be expected in view of the smaller number of a hundred trial plants. Experiment 5, which shows the greatest departure, was repeated, and then, in lieu of the ratio of 60 and 40, that of 65 and 35 resulted. *The average ratio of 2 to 1 appears, therefore, as fixed with certainty.* It is therefore demonstrated that, of those forms which possess the dominant character in the first generation, two thirds have the hybrid character, while one third remains constant with the dominant character.

The ratio of 3 to 1, in accordance with which the distribution of the dominant and recessive characters results in the first generation, resolves itself therefore in all experiments into the ratio of 2 to 1 to 1 if the dominant character be differentiated according to its significance as a hybrid character or as a parental one. Since the members of the first generation spring directly from the seed of the hybrids, *it is now clear that the hybrids form seeds having one or other of the two differentiating characters, and of these one half develop again the hybrid form, while the other half yield plants which remain constant and receive the dominant or the recessive characters [respectively] in equal numbers. . . .*

If we endeavor to collate in a brief form the results arrived at, we find that those differentiating characters, which admit of easy and certain recognition in the experimental plants, all behave exactly alike in their hybrid associations. The offspring of the hybrids of each pair of differentiating characters are, one half, hybrid again, while the other half are constant in equal proportions having the characters of the seed and pollen parents respectively. If several differentiating characters are combined by cross-fertilization in a hybrid, the resulting offspring form the terms of a combination series in which the combination series for each pair of differentiating characters are united.

The uniformity of behavior shown by the whole of the characters submitted to experiment permits, and fully justifies, the acceptance of the principle that a similar relation exists in the other characters which appear less sharply defined in plants, and therefore could not be included in the separate experiments. An experiment with peduncles of different lengths gave on the whole a fairly satisfactory result, although the differentiation and serial arrangement of the forms could not be effected with that certainty which is indispensable for correct experiment.

THE REPRODUCTIVE CELLS OF THE HYBRIDS

The results of the previously described experiments led to further experiments, the results of which appear fitted to afford some conclusions as regards the composition of the egg and pollen cells of hybrids. . . .

Experimentally, therefore, the theory is confirmed that *pea hybrids form egg and pollen cells which, in their constitution, represent in equal numbers all constant forms which result from the combination of the characters united in fertilization.*

The New Science of Genetics

THOMAS HUNT MORGAN (1866-   )

Pursued pleasantly out of doors with garden peas (Mendel) and rose-bushes (De Vries), the science of genetics—offshoot of evolution—was moved inside laboratory walls with the introduction of the delightfully rapid-breeding fruit fly as the prime experimental material. With its help the mechanism of heredity has been more and more completely eluci-dated and elaborated in terms of *mutation* and *genes,* the carriers of inheritable characteristics.

An American from Kentucky, Thomas Hunt Morgan, was one of the pioneers in this research, and he received the Nobel prize (1933) for it. Morgan was professor of zoology at Columbia from 1904 to 1928; since then director of the Kerckhoff Laboratories of Biological Sciences at the California Institute of Technology. Though author of many books and articles, nowhere has he spoken more clearly, comprehensively, and in-terestingly of his fundamental work and interests than in the following passages from "A Critique of the Theory of Evolution," a book made from a series of lectures delivered at Princeton University in 1916.

English, and informal, in the original, this 200-page book was pub-lished the same year by the Princeton University Press.

"A CRITIQUE OF THE THEORY OF EVOLUTION" IN THE LIGHT OF MENDEL'S DISCOVERY

Why do biologists throughout the world today agree that Mendel's discovery is one of first rank?

A great deal might be said in this connection. What is essential may be said in a few words. Biology had been, and is still, largely a descrip-tive and speculative science. Mendel showed by experimental proof that heredity could be explained by a simple mechanism. His discovery has been exceedingly fruitful.

Science begins with naïve, often mystic conceptions of its problems. It reaches its goal whenever it can replace its early guessing by verifiable hypotheses and predictable results. This is what Mendel's law did for heredity. . . .

Within the last five or six years, from a common wild species of fly, the fruit fly, *Drosophila ampelophila,* which we have brought into the laboratory, have arisen over a hundred and twenty-five new types whose origin is completely known. Let me call attention to a few of the more interesting of these types and their modes of inheritance, comparing them with wild types in order to show that the kinds of inheritance found in domesticated races occur also in wild types. The results will show beyond dispute that the characters of wild types are inherited in precisely the same way as are the characters of the mutant types—a fact that is not generally appreciated except by students of genetics, although it is of the most far-reaching significance for the theory of evolution.

A mutant appeared in which the eye color of the female was different from that of the male. The eye color of the mutant female is a dark eosin color, that of the male yellowish eosin. From the beginning this difference was as marked as it is today. Breeding experiments show that eosin eye color differs from the red color of the eye of the wild fly by a single mutant factor. Here then at a single step a type appeared that was sexually dimorphic.

Zoologists know that sexual dimorphism is not uncommon in wild species of animals, and Darwin proposed the theory of sexual selection to account for the difference between the sexes. He assumed that the male preferred certain kinds of females differing from himself in a particular character, and thus in time through sexual selection the sexes came to differ from each other. . . .

THE FACTORIAL THEORY OF HEREDITY AND THE COMPOSITION OF THE GERM PLASM

The discovery that Mendel made with edible peas concerning heredity has been found to apply everywhere throughout the plant and animal kingdoms—to flowering plants, to insects, snails, crustacea, fishes, amphibians, birds, and mammals (including man).

There must be something that these widely separated groups of plants and animals have in common—some simple mechanism perhaps—to give such definite and orderly series of results. There is, in fact, a mechanism, possessed alike by animals and plants, that fulfills every requirement of Mendel's principles.

THE CELLULAR BASIS OF ORGANIC EVOLUTION AND HEREDITY

In order to appreciate the full force of the evidence, let me first pass rapidly in review a few familiar historical facts that preceded the discovery of the mechanism in question.

Throughout the greater part of the last century, while students of evolution and of heredity were engaged in what I may call the more general, or, shall I say, the grosser aspects of the subject, there existed another group of students who were engaged in working out the minute structure of the material basis of the living organism. They found that organs such as the brain, the heart, the liver, the lungs, the kidneys, et cetera, are not themselves the units of structure, but that all these organs can be reduced to a simpler unit that repeats itself a thousandfold in every organ. We call this unit a cell.

The egg is a cell, and the spermatozoon is a cell. The act of fertilization is the union of two cells. Simple as the process of fertilization appears to us today, its discovery swept aside a vast amount of mystical speculation concerning the role of the male and of the female in the act of procreation.

Within the cell a new microcosm was revealed. Every cell was found to contain a spherical body called the nucleus. Within the nucleus is a network of fibers, a sap fills the interstices of the network. The network resolves itself into a definite number of threads at each division of the cell. These threads we call chromosomes. Each species of animals and plants possesses a characteristic number of these threads which have a definite size and sometimes a specific shape and even characteristic granules at different levels. Beyond this point our strongest microscopes fail to penetrate. Observation has reached, for the time being, its limit.

The story is taken up at this point by a new set of students who have worked in an entirely different field. Certain observations and experiments that we have not time to consider now led a number of biologists to conclude that the chromosomes are the bearers of the hereditary units. If so, there should be many such units carried by *each* chromosome, for the number of chromosomes is limited while the number of independently inherited characters is large. In *Drosophila* it has been demonstrated not only that there are exactly as many groups of characters that are inherited together as there are pairs of chromosomes, but even that it is possible to locate one of these groups in a particular chromosome and to state the *relative position* there of the factors for the characters. If the validity of this evidence is accepted, the study of the cell leads us finally in a mechanical, but not in a chemical sense, to the ultimate units about which the whole process of the transmission of the hereditary factors centers.

But before plunging into this somewhat technical matter (that is difficult only because it is unfamiliar), certain facts which are familiar for the most part should be recalled, because on these turns the whole of the subsequent story.

The thousands of cells that make up the cell state that we call an animal or plant come from the fertilized egg. An hour or two after fertilization the egg divides into two cells. Then each half divides again. Each quarter next divides. The process continues until a large number of cells is formed and out of these organs mold themselves.

At every division of the cell the chromosomes also divide. Half of these have come from the mother, half from the father. Every cell contains, therefore, the sum total of all the chromosomes, and if these are the bearers of the hereditary qualities, every cell in the body, whatever its function, has a common inheritance.

At an early stage in the development of the animal certain cells are set apart to form the organs of reproduction. In some animals these cells can be identified early in the cleavage.

The reproductive cells are at first like all the other cells in the body in that they contain a full complement of chromosomes, half paternal and half maternal in origin. They divide as do the other cells of the body for a long time. At each division each chromosome splits lengthwise and its halves migrate to opposite poles of the spindle.

But there comes a time when a new process appears in the germ cells. It is essentially the same in the egg and in the sperm cells. The discovery of this process we owe to the laborious researches of many workers in many countries. The list of their names is long, and I shall not even attempt to repeat it. The chromosomes come together in pairs. Each maternal chromosome mates with a paternal chromosome of the same kind.

Then follow two rapid divisions. At one of the divisions the double chromosomes separate so that each resulting cell comes to contain some maternal and some paternal chromosomes, i.e., one or the other member of each pair. At the other division each chromosome simply splits as in ordinary cell division.

The upshot of the process is that the ripe eggs and the ripe spermatozoa come to contain only half the total number of chromosomes.

When the eggs are fertilized the whole number of chromosomes is
restored again.

THE MECHANISM OF MENDELIAN HEREDITY DISCOVERED IN THE BEHAVIOR OF THE CHROMOSOMES

If the factors in heredity are carried in the chromosomes and if the
chromosomes are definite structures, we should anticipate that there
should be as many *groups* of characters as there are kinds of chromosomes. In only one case has a sufficient number of characters been studied
to show whether there is any correspondence between the number of
hereditary groups of characters and the number of chromosomes. In the
fruit fly, *Drosophila ampelophila,* we have found about a hundred and
twenty-five characters that are inherited in a perfectly definite way. . . .

If the factors for these characters are carried by the chromosomes, then
we should expect that those factors that are carried by the same chromosomes would be inherited together, provided the chromosomes are definite structures in the cell.

In the chromosome group of *Drosophila* there are four pairs of chromosomes, three of nearly the same size and one much smaller. Not only is
there agreement between the number of hereditary groups and the number of the chromosomes, but even the size relations are the same, for
there are three great groups of characters and three pairs of large chromosomes, and one small group of characters and one pair of small chromosomes. . . .

CONCLUSIONS

I have passed in review a long series of researches as to the nature of
the hereditary material. We have in consequence of this work arrived
within sight of a result that seemed a few years ago far beyond our reach.
The mechanism of heredity has, I think, been discovered—discovered
not by a flash of intuition but as the result of patient and careful study
of the evidence itself.

With the discovery of this mechanism I venture the opinion that the
problem of heredity has been solved. We know how the factors carried
by the parents are sorted out to the germ cells. The explanation does not
pretend to state how factors arise or how they influence the development
of the embryo. But these have never been an integral part of the doctrine

of heredity. The problems which they present must be worked out in their own field. So, I repeat, the mechanism of the chromosomes offers a satisfactory solution of the traditional problem of heredity.

Psychoanalysis

SIGMUND FREUD (1856-1939)

THE DISCOVERY of X rays in 1895 made it possible to "see" inside the human body. That same year a young Austrian physician specializing in neurology, Sigmund Freud, published a work, "Studies in Hysteria," which gave the first hint of a revolutionary technique for delving deeper into the human mind and emotions than anyone before had ever succeeded in doing. The new technique—psychoanalysis—opened floodgates of words. Its very basis was words—simply letting the neurotic patient talk. It put new words into the everyday vocabulary: "repression," "subconscious," and "libido." It sparked up a whole new school of literature; many millions of words were poured into "stream of consciousness" writing, the kind of literature of which James Joyce's "Ulysses" is the prototype. First and foremost, however, psychoanalysis evoked words of protest because it mentioned unmentionables. The father of psychoanalysis is now dead, the novelty of his teachings worn off, the overenthusiasm of his earlier disciples quenched, and the trend in modern psychiatry away from psychoanalytic techniques toward psychosomatic medicine (in which the interaction between mind and body is given greater emphasis). Nevertheless, the techniques of psychoanalysis remain important in the history of science for revealing much that was unknown of the true and queer composition of the human mind.

Freud, born in Moravia, studied at Vienna and under Charcot in Paris, where he first observed the use of hypnotism (a heritage from discredited mesmerism) seriously employed in the treatment of mental ailments. Discarding hypnotism, which gave only the clue, he developed psychoanalysis. He was professor of neuropathology at the University of Vienna from 1902 to 1938, when the Nazis drove him out. Dealing primarily in words, Freud was a voluminous writer. Nowhere, however, does he give a clearer, more coherent account of the fundamentals of psychoanalysis than in the series of lectures delivered at the University of Vienna in the winter sessions of 1915–17. It is from these lectures that the passages given here are quoted.

German was the language in which Freud wrote and lectured. The authorized English translations of his Vienna lectures, made by Joan Riviere, were published under the title, "A General Introduction to Psychoanalysis," by the Liveright Publishing Corporation in 1934.

AN INTRODUCTION TO PSYCHOANALYSIS

I DO NOT KNOW what knowledge any of you may already have of psychoanalysis, either from reading or from hearsay.

One thing, at least, I may presuppose that you know—namely, that psychoanalysis is a method of medical treatment for those suffering from nervous disorders; and I can give you at once an illustration of the way in which psychoanalytic procedure differs from, and often even reverses, what is customary in other branches of medicine. Usually, when we introduce a patient to a new form of treatment, we minimize its difficulties and give him confident assurances of its success. This is, in my opinion, perfectly justifiable, for we thereby increase the probability of success. But when we undertake to treat a neurotic psychoanalytically we proceed otherwise. We explain to him the difficulties of the method, its long·duration, the trials and sacrifices which will be required of him; and, as to the result, we tell him that we can make no definite promises, that success depends upon his endeavors, upon his understanding, his adaptability, and his perseverance. . . .

In psychoanalytic treatment nothing happens but an exchange of words between the patient and the physician. The patient talks, tells of his past experiences and present impressions, complains, and expresses his wishes and his emotions. The physician listens, attempts to direct the patient's thought processes, reminds him, forces his attention in certain directions, gives him explanations, and observes the reactions of understanding or denial thus evoked. The patient's unenlightened relatives—people of a kind to be impressed only by something visible and tangible, preferably by the sort of "action" that may be seen at a cinema—never omit to express their doubts of how "mere talk can possibly cure anybody." Their reasoning is, of course, as illogical as it is inconsistent. For they are the same people who are always convinced that the sufferings of neurotics are purely "in their own imagination." Words and magic were in the beginning one and the same thing, and even today words retain much of their magical power. By words one of us can give to another the greatest happiness or bring about utter despair; by words the teacher imparts his knowledge to the student; by words the orator sweeps his audience with him and determines its judgments and decisions. Words call forth emotions and are universally the means by which we influence our fellow creatures. Therefore let us not despise the use of words in psychotherapy. . . .

There are two tenets of psychoanalysis which offend the whole world and excite its resentment; the one conflicts with intellectual, the other with moral and aesthetic prejudices. Let us not underestimate these prejudices; they are powerful things, residues of valuable, even necessary, stages in human evolution. They are maintained by emotional forces, and the fight against them is a hard one.

The first of these displeasing propositions of psychoanalysis is this: that mental processes are essentially unconscious, and that those which are conscious are merely isolated acts and parts of the whole psychic entity. Now I must ask you to remember that, on the contrary, we are accustomed to identify the mental with the conscious. Consciousness appears to us as positively the characteristic that defines mental life, and we regard psychology as the study of the content of consciousness. This even appears so evident that any contradiction of it seems obvious nonsense to us, and yet it is impossible for psychoanalysis to avoid this contradiction, or to accept the identity between the conscious and the psychic. The psychoanalytical definition of the mind is that it comprises processes of the nature of feeling, thinking, and wishing, and it maintains that there are such things as unconscious thinking and unconscious wishing. But in doing so psychoanalysis has forfeited at the outset the sympathy of the sober and scientifically minded, and incurred the suspicion of being a fantastic cult occupied with dark and unfathomable mysteries. You yourselves must find it difficult to understand why I should stigmatize an abstract proposition, such as "The psychic is the conscious," as a prejudice; nor can you guess yet what evolutionary process could have led to the denial of the unconscious, if it does indeed exist, nor what advantage could have been achieved by this denial. It seems like an empty wrangle over words to argue whether mental life is to be regarded as coextensive with consciousness or whether it may be said to stretch beyond this limit, and yet I can assure you that the acceptance of unconscious mental processes represents a decisive step toward a new orientation in the world and in science.

As little can you suspect how close is the connection between this first bold step on the part of psychoanalysis and the second to which I am now coming. For this next proposition, which we put forward as one of the discoveries of psychoanalysis, consists in the assertion that impulses, which can only be described as sexual in both the narrower and the wider sense, play a peculiarly large part, never before sufficiently appreciated, in the causation of nervous and mental disorders. Nay, more, that these sexual impulses have contributed invaluably to the highest cultural, artistic, and social achievements of the human mind.

In my opinion it is the aversion from this conclusion of psychoanalytic investigation that is the most significant source of the opposition it has encountered. Are you curious to know how we ourselves account for this? We believe that civilization has been built up, under the pressure of the struggle for existence, by sacrifices in gratification of the primitive impulses, and that it is to a great extent forever being re-created, as each individual, successively joining the community, repeats the sacrifice of his instinctive pleasures for the common good. The sexual are among the most important of the instinctive forces thus utilized: they are in this way sublimated, that is to say, their energy is turned aside from its sexual goal and diverted toward other ends, no longer sexual and socially more valuable.

But the structure thus built up is insecure, for the sexual impulses are with difficulty controlled; in each individual who takes up his part in the work of civilization there is a danger that a rebellion of the sexual impulses may occur, against this diversion of their energy. Society can conceive of no more powerful menace to its culture than would arise from the liberation of the sexual impulses and a return of them to their original goal. Therefore society dislikes this sensitive place in its development being touched upon; that the power of the sexual instinct should be recognized, and the significance of the individual's sexual life revealed, is very far from its interests; with a view to discipline it has rather taken the course of diverting attention away from this whole field. For this reason the revelations of psychoanalysis are not tolerated by it, and it would greatly prefer to brand them as aesthetically offensive, morally reprehensible, or dangerous. But since such objections are not valid arguments against conclusions which claim to represent the objective results of scientific investigation, the opposition must be translated into intellectual terms before it can be expressed. It is a characteristic of human nature to be inclined to regard anything which is disagreeable as untrue, and then without much difficulty to find arguments against it. So society pronounces the unacceptable to be untrue, disputes the results of psychoanalysis with logical and concrete arguments, arising, however, in affective sources, and clings to them with all the strength of prejudice against every attempt at refutation.

SLIP OF THE TONGUE: THE PSYCHOLOGY OF ERRORS

WE SHALL now begin, not with postulates, but with an investigation. For this purpose we shall select certain phenomena which are very frequent, very familiar and much overlooked, and which have nothing to do with illness, since they may be observed in every healthy person. I refer to the errors that everyone commits: as when anyone wishes to say a certain thing but uses the wrong word ("slip of the tongue"); or when the same sort of mistake is made in writing ("slip of the pen"); in which case one may or may not notice it; or when anyone reads in print or writing something other than what is actually before him ("misreading"); or when anyone mishears what is said to him, naturally when there is no question of any disease of the auditory sense organ. Another series of such phenomena are those based on forgetting something temporarily, though not permanently; as, for instance, when anyone cannot think of a name which he knows quite well and is always able to recognize whenever he sees it; or when anyone forgets to carry out some intention, which he afterward remembers, and has therefore forgotten only for a certain time. This element of transitoriness is lacking in a third class, of which mislaying things so that they cannot be found is an example. This is a kind of forgetfulness which we regard differently from the usual kind; one is amazed or annoyed at it, instead of finding it comprehensible. . . .

If I diverge into the field of other kinds of errors I can give you a wide selection of examples of such circumstantial evidence.

If anyone forgets an otherwise familiar proper name and has difficulty in retaining it in his memory—even with an effort—it is not hard to guess that he has something against the owner of the name and does not like to think of him; consider in the light of this the following notes on the mental situation in which an error of this kind was made.

A Mr. Y. fell in love with a lady, who did not return the feeling and shortly after married a Mr. X. Although Mr. Y. had already known Mr. X. for some time, and even had business relations with him, he forgets his name over and over again, so that he frequently has to ask someone the man's name when it is necessary to write to him.[1] Obviously Mr. Y. wants to obliterate all knowledge of his fortunate rival. "Never thought of shall he be."

Another example: a lady inquires of a doctor about a common acquaintance, calling her by her maiden name. She has forgotten the married name. She admits that she strongly objected to the marriage and dislikes the husband intensely.[2] . . .

Perhaps the idea has also come to you that in these examples mistakes seem to have replaced the omens or portents of the ancients. And indeed, certain kinds of portents were nothing but errors, for instance, when anyone stumbled or fell down. . . .

Every one of us who can look back over a fairly long experience of life would probably say that he might have spared himself many disappointments and painful surprises if he had had the courage and resolution to interpret as omens the little mistakes which he noticed in his intercourse with others, and to regard them as signs of tendencies still in the background. For the most part one does not dare to do this; one has an impression that one would become superstitious again by a circuitous scientific path. And then, not all omens come true, and our theories will show you how it is that they need not all come true. . . .

Here is a simple example of this which I observed myself. Once in the beautiful Dolomites I met two Viennese ladies who were starting for a walking tour. I accompanied them part of the way and we discussed the pleasures, but also the trials, of this way of life. One of the ladies admitted that spending the day like this entailed much discomfort. "It certainly is very unpleasant to tramp all day in the sun till one's blouse . . . and things are soaked through." In this sentence she had to overcome a slight hesitation at one point. Then she continued: "But then, when one gets *nach Hose* and can change . . ." (*Hose* means *drawers:* the lady meant to say *nach Hause,* which means *home*). We did not analyze this slip, but I am sure you will easily understand it. The lady's intention had been to enumerate a more complete list of her clothes, "blouse, chemise, and drawers." From motives of propriety, mention of the drawers (*Hose*) was omitted; but in the next sentence, the content of which is quite independent, the unuttered word came to light as a distortion of the word it resembled in sound, *home* (*Hause*). . . .

[1] From C. G. Jung.
[2] From A. A. Brill.

My interpretation includes the assumption that tendencies of which a speaker knows nothing can express themselves through him and that I can deduce them from various indications. You hesitate before a conclusion so novel and so pregnant with consequences. . . .

Let us pause a moment on mechanisms of a slip of the tongue. Fortunately this common element is unmistakable. In the first two groups the interfering tendency is admitted by the speaker; in the first there is the additional fact that it showed itself immediately before the slip. But in both cases *it has been forced back. The speaker had determined not to convert the idea into speech and then it happens that he makes a slip of the tongue; that is to say, the tendency which is debarred from expression asserts itself against his will and gains utterance, either by altering the expression of the intention permitted by him, or by mingling with it, or actually by setting itself in place of it.* This, then, is the mechanism of a slip of the tongue. . . .

INTERPRETATION OF DREAMS: THE PSYCHOLOGY OF THE UNCONSCIOUS

ONE DAY the discovery was made that the symptoms of disease in certain nervous patients have meaning.[3] It was upon this discovery that the psychoanalytic method of treatment was based. In this treatment it happened that patients in speaking of their symptoms also mentioned their dreams, whereupon the suspicion arose that these dreams, too, had meaning. . . .

For the present we will leave the "meaning" of the dream out of question and try instead, by starting from the common element in dreams, to clear a path to a better understanding of their nature. From the relationship of dreams to sleep we have drawn the conclusion that dreams are the reaction to a stimulus disturbing sleep. As we have heard, this is also the single point at which exact experimental psychology can come to our aid; it affords proof of the fact that stimuli brought to bear during sleep make their appearance in dreams. . . .

The striking feature about dreams produced under experimental conditions will perhaps become still clearer to us in "stimulus" dreams. We have an account of a clever observer, Hildebrandt, of reactions to the sound of an alarm clock. . . .

Now for example: "I see a kitchen maid with dozens of piled-up

[3] By Joseph Breuer, in the years 1880–82.

plates going along the passage to the dining room. It seems to me that the pyramid of china in her arms is in danger of overbalancing. I call out a warning: 'Take care, your whole load will fall to the ground.' Of course I receive the usual answer: that they are accustomed to carrying china in that way, and so on; meanwhile I follow her as she goes with anxious looks. I thought so—the next thing is a stumble on the threshold, the crockery falls, crashing and clattering in a hundred pieces on the ground. But—I soon become aware that that interminably prolonged sound is no real crash, but a regular ringing—and this ringing is due merely to the alarm clock, as I realize at last on awakening."

Such dreams are very pretty, perfectly sensible, and by no means so incoherent as dreams usually are. We have no quarrel with them on those grounds. The thing common to them all is that in each case the situation arises from a noise, which the dreamer on waking recognizes as that of the alarm clock. Hence we see here how a dream is produced, but we find out something more. In the dream there is no recognition of the clock, which does not even appear in it, but for the noise of the clock another noise is substituted; the stimulus which disturbs sleep is interpreted, but interpreted differently in each instance. Now why is this? There is no answer; it appears to be mere caprice. But to understand the dream we should be able to account for its choice of just this noise and no other to interpret the stimulus given by the alarm clock. . . .

Now, transferring our conception from the single element to the dream as a whole, it follows that the latter is the distorted substitute for something else, something unconscious, and that the task of dream interpretation is to discover these unconscious thoughts. Hence are derived three important rules which should be observed in the work of dream interpretation:

1. We are not to trouble about the surface meaning of the dream, whether it be reasonable or absurd, clear or confused; in no case does it constitute the unconscious thoughts we are seeking.

2. We are to confine our work to calling up substitute ideas for every element and not to ponder over them and try to see whether they contain something which fits in, nor to trouble ourselves about how far they are taking us from the dream element.

3. We must wait until the hidden unconscious thoughts which we are seeking appear of their own accord.

Now we understand also how entirely indifferent it is whether we remember much or little of our dreams, above all whether we remember them accurately or not. The dream as remembered is not the real thing at all, but *a distorted substitute* which, by calling up other substitute ideas, provides us with a means of approaching the thought proper, of bringing into consciousness the unconscious thoughts underlying the dream. If our recollection was at fault, all that has happened is that a further distortion of the substitute has taken place, and this distortion itself cannot be without motivation. . . .

Here is an example of death symbolism in dreams: *The dreamer was crossing a very high, steep, iron bridge, with two people whose names he knew, but forgot on waking. Suddenly both of them had vanished and he saw a ghostly man in a cap and an overall. He asked him whether he were the telegraph messenger. . . . "No." Or the coachman? . . . "No." He then went on,* and in the dream had a feeling of great dread; on waking, he followed it up with the fantasy that the iron bridge suddenly broke and that he fell into the abyss.

When stress is laid upon the fact that people in a dream are unknown to the dreamer, or that he has forgotten their names, they are, as a rule, persons with whom he is intimately connected. The dreamer was one of a family of three children; if he had ever wished for the death of the other two, it would be only just that he should be visited with the fear of death. With reference to the telegraph messenger, he remarked that they always bring bad news. From his uniform, the man in the dream might have been a lamplighter, who also puts out the lights, as the spirit of death extinguishes the torch of life. With the coachman he associated Uhland's poem of the voyage of King Karl, and recalled a dangerous sail on a lake with two companions, when he played the part of the king in the poem. The iron bridge suggested to him a recent accident, also the stupid saying: "Life is a suspension bridge."

The following may be regarded as another example of a death dream: *An unknown gentleman was leaving a black-edged visiting card on the dreamer. . . .*

Let us start afresh from our conclusion that, under the influence of the censorship, the dream work translates the latent dream thoughts into another form. These thoughts are of the same nature as the familiar, conscious thoughts of waking life; the new form in which they are expressed is, owing to many peculiar characteristics, incomprehensible to us. . . .

A more profound study of the dream work must lead to valuable conclusions about the initial stages of our intellectual development, of which at present little is known. I hope it will be so, but so far this task has not been attempted. The era to which the dream work takes us back is "primitive" in a twofold sense: in the first place, it means the early days of the *individual*—his childhood—and, secondly, insofar as each individual repeats in some abbreviated fashion during childhood the whole course of the development of the human race, the reference is *phylogenetic*. . . .

You are all familiar from actual experience with the peculiar *amnesia of childhood* to which we are subject. I mean that the first years of life, up to the age of five, six, or eight, have not left the same traces in memory as our later experiences. True, we come across individuals who can boast of continuous recollection from early infancy to the present time, but it is incomparably more common for the opposite, a blank in memory, to be found. In my opinion this has not aroused sufficient surprise. At two years old the child can speak well and soon shows his capacity for adapting himself to complicated mental situations, and, moreover, says things which he himself has forgotten when they are repeated to him years later. And yet memory is more efficient in early years, being less overburdened than it is later. . . .

It is a regular task in psychoanalytic treatment to fill in the blank in infantile memories, and insofar as the treatment is successful to any extent at all (very frequently, therefore) we are enabled to bring to light the content of those early years long buried in oblivion. These impressions have never really been forgotten but were only inaccessible and latent, having become part of the unconscious. But sometimes it happens that they emerge spontaneously from the unconscious, and it is in connection with dreams that this happens. It is clear that the dream life knows the way back to these latent, infantile experiences. . . .

This knowledge has a bearing on another of the problems which up to the present have proved insoluble. You will remember the astonishment caused by our discovery that dreams have their origin in actively evil or in excessive sexual desires, which have made both the dream censorship and dream distortion necessary. Supposing now that we have interpreted a dream of this sort, and the circumstances are specially favorable in that the dreamer does not quarrel with the interpretation itself, he does nevertheless invariably ask how any such wish could come into his mind, since it seems quite foreign to him and he is conscious of desiring the exact opposite. We need have no hesitation in pointing out to him the origin of the wish he repudiates: these evil impulses may be traced to the past, often indeed to a past which is not so very far away. It may be demonstrated that he once knew and was conscious of them, even if this is no longer so. A woman who had a dream meaning that she wished to see her only daughter (then seventeen years old) lying dead found, with our help, that at one time she actually had cherished this death wish. The child was the offspring of an unhappy marriage, which ended in the speedy separation of husband and wife. Once when the child was as yet unborn the mother, in an access of rage after a violent scene with her husband, beat her body with her clenched fists in order to kill the baby in her womb. How many mothers who today love their children tenderly, perhaps with excessive tenderness, yet conceived them unwillingly and wished that the life within them might not develop further; and have indeed turned this wish into various actions, fortunately of a harmless kind. The later death wish against beloved persons, which appears so puzzling, thus dates from the early days of the relationship to them.

A father, whose dream when interpreted shows that he wished for the death of his eldest and favorite child, is in the same way obliged to recall that there was a time when this wish was not unknown to him. The man, whose marriage had proved a disappointment, often thought when the child was still an infant that if the little creature who meant nothing to him were to die he would again be free and would make better use of his freedom. A large number of similar impulses of hate are to be traced to a similar source; they are recollections of something belonging to the past, something which was once in consciousness and played its part in mental life. . . .

There is nothing to wonder at therefore if the dreams of a great number of people bring to light the wish for the removal of their parents, especially of the parent whose sex is the same as the dreamer's. We may assume that the wish exists in waking life as well, sometimes even in consciousness if it can disguise itself behind another motive. . . . It is but rarely that hostility reigns alone—far more often it yields to more tender feelings which finally suppress it, when it has to wait in abeyance till a dream shows it, as it were, in isolation. That which the dream shows in a form magnified by this very isolation resumes its true proportions when our interpretation has assigned to it its proper place in relation to the rest of the dreamer's life. (H. Sachs.) But we also find this death wish where there is no basis for it in real life and where the adult would never have to confess to entertaining it in his waking life. The reason for this is that the deepest and most common motive for estrangement, especially between parent and child of the same sex, came into play in the earliest years of childhood.

I refer to that rivalry of affections in which sexual elements are plainly emphasized. The son, when quite a little child, already begins to develop a peculiar tenderness toward his mother, whom he looks upon as his own property, regarding his father in the light of a rival who disputes this sole possession of his; similarly the little daughter sees in her mother someone who disturbs her tender relations to her father and occupies a place which she feels she herself could very well fill. Observation shows us how far back these sentiments date, sentiments which we describe by the term *Oedipus complex,* because in the Oedipus myth the two extreme forms of the wishes arising from the situation of the son—the wish to kill the father and to marry the mother—are realized in an only slightly modified form. I do not assert that the Oedipus complex exhausts all the possible relations which may exist between parents and children; these relations may well be a great deal more complicated. Again, this complex may be more or less strongly developed, or it may even become inverted, but it is a regular and very important factor in the mental life of the child; we are more in danger of underestimating than of overestimating its influence and that of the developments which may follow from it. Moreover, the parents themselves frequently stimulate the children to react with an Oedipus complex, for parents are often guided in their preferences by the difference in sex of their children, so that the father favors the daughter and the mother the son; or else, where conjugal love has grown cold, the child may be taken as a substitute for the love object which has ceased to attract.

It cannot be said that the world has shown great gratitude to psychoanalytic research for the discovery of the Oedipus complex; on the contrary, the idea has excited the most violent opposition. . . .

Now you will be impatiently waiting to hear what this terrible Oedipus complex comprises. The name tells you: you all know the Greek myth of King Oedipus, whose destiny it was to slay his father and to wed his mother, who did all in his power to avoid the fate prophesied by the oracle, and who in self-punishment blinded himself when he discovered that in ignorance he had committed both these crimes. I trust that many of you have yourselves experienced the profound effect of the tragic drama fashioned by Sophocles from this story. The Attic poet's work portrays the gradual discovery of the deed of Oedipus, long since accomplished, and brings it slowly to light by skillfully prolonged inquiry, constantly fed by new evidence; it has thus a certain resemblance to the course of a psychoanalysis. In the dialogue the deluded mother-wife, Jocasta, resists the continuation of the inquiry; she points out that many people in their dreams have mated with their mothers, but that dreams are of no account. To us dreams are of much account, especially typical dreams which occur in many people; we have no doubt that the dream Jocasta speaks of is intimately related to the shocking and terrible story of the myth.

It is surprising that Sophocles' tragedy does not call forth indignant remonstrance in its audience. . . . For at bottom it is an immoral play; it sets aside the individual's responsibility to social law and displays divine forces ordaining the crime and rendering powerless the moral instincts of the human being which would guard him against the crime. . . . The poet's words seem to mean: "In vain do you deny that you are accountable, in vain do you proclaim how you have striven against these evil designs. You are guilty, nevertheless; for you could not stifle them; they still survive unconsciously in you." And psychological truth is contained in this; even though man has repressed his evil desires into his unconscious and would then gladly say to himself that he is no longer answerable for them, he is yet compelled to feel his responsibility in the form of a sense of guilt for which he can discern no foundation.

There is no possible doubt that one of the most important sources of the sense of guilt which so often torments neurotic people is to be found in the Oedipus complex. More than this: in 1913, under the title of *Totem und Tabu,* I published a study of the earliest forms of religion and morality in which I expressed a suspicion that perhaps the sense of guilt of mankind as a whole, which is the ultimate source of religion and morality, was acquired in the beginnings of history through the Oedipus complex. . . .

ANXIETY: "THE THEORY OF NEUROSIS IS PSYCHO-ANALYSIS ITSELF"

THE INTRODUCTION to psychoanalysis lies in the study of errors and of dreams; the theory of neurosis is psychoanalysis itself. . . .

In the *traumatic neuroses,* especially in those arising from the terrors of war, we are particularly impressed by a self-seeking, egoistic motive, a straining toward protection and self-interest; this alone perhaps could not produce the disease, but it gives its support to the latter and maintains it once it has been formed. This tendency aims at protecting the ego from the dangers which led by their imminence to the outbreak of illness; nor does it permit of recovery until a repetition of the dangers appears to be no longer possible, or until some gain in compensation for the danger undergone has been received.

The ego takes a similar interest in the origin and maintenance of all the other forms of neurosis; we have said already that the symptom is supported by the ego because one side of it offers a satisfaction to the repressing ego tendency. More than this, a solution of the conflict by a symptom formation is the most convenient one, most in accordance with the pleasure principle; for it undoubtedly spares the ego a severe and painful piece of internal labor. There are indeed cases in which the physician himself must admit that the solution of a conflict by a neurosis is the one most harmless and most tolerable socially. . . .

Now let us turn to neurotic anxiety; what are the special manifestations and conditions found in the anxiety of nervous persons? There is a great deal to be described here. First of all, we find a general apprehensiveness in them, a "free-floating" anxiety, as we call it, ready to attach itself to any thought which is at all appropriate, affecting judgments, inducing expectations, lying in wait for any opportunity to find a justification for itself. We call this condition *"expectant dread"* or "anxious expectation." People who are tormented with this kind of anxiety always anticipate the worst of all possible outcomes, interpret every chance happening as an evil omen, and exploit every uncertainty to mean the worst. The tendency to this kind of expectation of evil is found as a character trait in many people who cannot be described as ill in any other way, and we call them "overanxious" or pessimistic; but a marked degree of expectant dread is an invariable accompaniment of the nervous disorder which I have called anxiety neurosis and include among the actual neuroses.

In contrast to this type of anxiety, a second form of it is found to be much more circumscribed in the mind and attached to definite objects and situations. This is the anxiety of the extraordinarily various and often very peculiar phobias. Stanley Hall, the distinguished American psychologist, has recently taken the trouble to designate a whole series of these phobias by gorgeous Greek titles; they sound like the ten plagues of Egypt, except that there are far more than ten of them. Just listen to the things that can become the object or content of a phobia: darkness, open air, open spaces, cats, spiders, caterpillars, snakes, mice, thunder, sharp points, blood, enclosed places, crowds, loneliness, crossing bridges, traveling by land or sea, and so on. . . .

What is foreign to us in these phobias is not so much their content as

their intensity. The anxiety accompanying a phobia is positively inde-
scribable! And we sometimes get the impression that neurotics are not
really at all fearful of those things which can, under certain conditions,
arouse anxiety in us and which they call by the same names. . . .

The difference between nervous health and nervous illness (neurosis)
is narrowed down, therefore, to a practical distinction and is determined
by the practical result—how far the person concerned remains capable
of a sufficient degree of capacity for enjoyment and active achievement
in life. The difference can probably be traced back to the proportion
of the energy which has remained free relative to that of the energy
which has been bound by repression, i.e., it is a quantitative and not a
qualitative difference. I do not need to remind you that this view provides a theoretical basis for our conviction that the neuroses are essentially amenable to cure, in spite of their being based on a constitutional
disposition.

The Philosophy of a Beloved Physician

WILLIAM OSLER (1849–1919)

"THERE WERE indeed many Oslers: the physician, the professor, the
scholar, the author, the bibliophile, the historian, the philanthropist, the
friend and companion for young or old," declared Harvey Cushing,
his biographer, of the beloved physician, Sir William Osler, whose charm
of personality and wealth of scientific and classical learning epitomized
for the twentieth century all that was noblest in the long tradition of
medical history. "Probably no physician while living has been so much
quoted or so much written about," continues Cushing. During his sixteen years' service as professor of medicine at Johns Hopkins Medical
School during its "golden—or heroic—age," "Osler became recognized,
one may say without exaggeration, as the most eminent and widely influential physician of his time. . . . Few so eminent and so industrious
come in turn to be so widely beloved for their own sake." Here was a
man, his successor at Hopkins tells us, who had "a light springing step,
a kindly glance, a bright word" for everyone he met, who "entered the
sickroom with a song and an epigram, an air of gaiety, an atmosphere
that lifted the invalid out of his ills," whose joyful visits made "half a

ward forget the symptoms that it *fancied* were important," who spoke ill of no man, who "truly loved his fellow . . . and was loved by all." A master of psychotherapy, Osler could quickly and effectively "soothe the heartache of any pessimistic brother."

A consummate literary stylist, nurtured on the Greek Testament and Sir Thomas Browne's *"Religio Medici,"* which were constantly at his bedside, and a keen physician, whose cheerful presence before patients and students never betrayed the long and weary hours of pathological studies in the charnel house, Osler spoke and felt strongly of the necessity of wedding "the old humanities" and "the new sciences." His own prolific writing—there are 730 titles in his bibliography—constantly proved the possibility of this mating. Most notable of his books is the textbook, "The Principles and Practice of Medicine," originally composed at Hopkins in 1891–92, now in its 14th revised edition. "Read—nay, devoured—by countless medical students and graduates," said Cushing, this textbook remains "probably the most used and most useful book in medicine." Indirectly—see "William Henry Welch and the Heroic Age of American Medicine," by Simon and James T. Flexner—Osler's book touched off the surge of medical philanthropy that has supported many of the recent great advances in medicine.

Osler was born at Bond Head, in Ontario, Canada, the eighth of nine children. After graduating from Trinity College, Toronto, he studied medicine at McGill, in Montreal, spent two years in Europe, and returned in 1874 to become—at the age of twenty-five—professor of the Institutes of Medicine at McGill. In 1884 he moved to Philadelphia to the University of Pennsylvania; five years later to Johns Hopkins in Baltimore, where he was one of the famous "four doctors" (along with Welch, Howard Kelly, and William Halsted) who revolutionized medical education in the United States. In 1904 following a grievously misquoted farewell address (falsely headlined, "Chloroform Men over Sixty"), Osler went to England to become regius professor of physic, at Oxford, the most honored post in medicine that the British Empire could bestow.

English was the language in which Osler expounded "A Way of Life," a reflection of his own philosophy of life, for the benefit of "fellow students"—the young men of Yale University assembled on April 20, 1913, to hear the Silliman lecture. The essay has been republished separately and in many collections of Osler's essays.

"A WAY OF LIFE"

EVERY MAN has a philosophy of life in thought, in word, or in deed, worked out in himself unconsciously. In possession of the very best, he may not know of its existence; with the very worst he may pride himself as a paragon. As it grows with the growth it cannot be taught to the young in formal lectures. What have bright eyes, red blood, quick breath, and taut muscles to do with philosophy? Did not the great Stagirite say that young men were unfit students of it—they will hear as though they heard not, and to no profit. Why, then, should I trouble you? Because I have a message that may be helpful.

It is not philosophical, nor is it strictly moral or religious, one or other of which I was told my address should be, and yet in a way it is all three. It is the oldest and the freshest, the simplest and the most useful; so simple indeed is it that some of you may turn away disappointed as was Naaman the Syrian when told to go wash in Jordan and be clean. You know those composite tools, to be bought for fifty cents, with one handle to fit a score or more of instruments. The workmanship is usually bad, so bad, as a rule, that you will not find an example in any good carpenter's shop; but the boy has one, the chauffeur slips one into his box, and the sailor one into his kit, and there is one in the odds-and-ends drawer of the pantry of every well-regulated family. It is simply a handy thing about the house, to help over the many little difficulties of the day. Of this sort of philosophy I wish to make you a present—a handle to fit your life tools. Whether the workmanship is Sheffield or shoddy, this helve will fit anything from a hatchet to a corkscrew.

My message is but a word, *a way,* an easy expression of the experience of a plain man whose life has never been worried by any philosophy higher than that of the shepherd in "As You Like It." I wish to point out a path in which the wayfaring man, though a fool, cannot err; not a system to be worked out painfully, only to be discarded, not a formal scheme, simply a habit as easy—or as hard!—to adopt as any other habit, good or bad.

A few years ago a Christmas card went the rounds, with the legend "Life is just one 'derned' thing after another," which, in more refined language, is the same as saying "Life is a habit," a succession of actions that become more or less automatic. This great truth, which lies at the basis of all actions, muscular or psychic, is the keystone of the teaching of Aristotle, to whom the formation of habits was the basis of moral excellence. "In a word, habits of any kind are the result of actions of the same kind; and so what we have to do is to give a certain character to these particular actions" ("Ethics").

Lift a seven-months'-old baby to his feet—see him tumble on his nose. Do the same at twelve months—he walks. At two years he runs. The muscles and the nervous system have acquired the habit. One trial after another, one failure after another, has given him power. Put your finger in a baby's mouth, and he sucks away in blissful anticipation of a response to a mammalian habit millions of years old. And we can deliberately train parts of our body to perform complicated actions with unerring accuracy. Watch that musician playing a difficult piece. Batteries, commutators, multipliers, switches, wires innumerable control those nimble fingers, the machinery of which may be set in motion as automatically as in a pianola, the player all the time chatting as if he had nothing to do in controlling the apparatus—habit again, the gradual acquisition of power by long practice and at the expense of many mistakes. The same great law reaches through mental and moral states. "Character," which partakes of both, in Plutarch's words, is "long-standing habit."

Now the way of life that I preach is a habit to be acquired gradually by long and steady repetition. It is the practice of living for the day only, and for the day's work, *life in day-tight compartments.* "Ah," I hear you say, "that is an easy matter, simple as Elisha's advice!" Not as I shall urge it, in words which fail to express the depth of my feelings as to its value. I started life in the best of all environments—in a parsonage, one of nine children. A man who has filled chairs in four universities, has written a successful book and has been asked to lecture at Yale is supposed popularly to have brains of a special quality. A few of my intimate friends really know the truth about me, as I know it! Mine —in good faith I say it—are of the most mediocre character. But what about those professorships, et cetera? Just habit, a way of life, an outcome of the day's work, the vital importance of which I wish to impress upon you with all the force at my command.

Dr. Johnson remarked upon the trifling circumstances by which men's lives are influenced, "not by an ascendant planet, a predominating humor, but by the first book which they read, some early conversation which they have heard, or some accident which excited ardor and enthusiasm." This was my case in two particulars. I was diverted to the Trinity College School, then at Weston, Ontario, by a paragraph in the circular stating that the senior boys would go into the drawing room in the evenings, and learn to sing and dance—vocal and pedal accomplishments for which I was never designed; but like Saul seeking his asses, I found something more valuable, a man of the White of Selborne type, who knew nature, and who knew how to get boys interested in it. The other happened in the summer of 1871, when I was attending the Montreal General Hospital. Much worried as to the future, partly about the final examination, I picked up a volume of Carlyle, and on the page I opened there was the familiar sentence: *"Our main business is not to see what lies dimly at a distance, but to do what lies clearly at hand."* A commonplace sentiment enough, but it hit and stuck and helped, and was the starting point of a habit that has enabled me to utilize to the full the single talent entrusted to me. . . .

The load of tomorrow, added to that of yesterday, carried today makes the strongest falter. Shut off the future as tightly as the past. No dreams, no visions, no delicious fantasies, no castles in the air, with which, as the old song so truly says, "hearts are broken, heads are turned." To youth, we are told, belongs the future, but the wretched tomorrow that so plagues some of us has no certainty, except through today. Who can tell what a day may bring forth? Though its uncertainty is a proverb, a man may carry its secret in the hollow of his hand. Make a pilgrimage to Hades with Ulysses, draw the magic circle, perform the rites, and then ask Tiresias the question. I have had the answer from his own lips. The future is today—there is no tomorrow! The day of a man's salvation is *now*—the life of the present, of today, lived earnestly, intently, without a forward-looking thought, is the only insurance for the future. Let the limit of your horizon be a twenty-four-hour circle. On the title page of one of the great books of science, the *"Discours de la Méthode"* of Descartes (1637), is a vignette showing a man digging in a garden with his face toward the earth, on which rays of light are streaming from the heavens; above him is the legend *"Fac et Spera."* 'Tis a good attitude and a good motto. Look heavenward, if you wish, but never to the horizon—that way danger lies. Truth is not there, happiness is not there, certainty is not there, but the falsehoods, the frauds, the quackeries, the *ignes fatui* which have deceived each generation—all beckon from the horizon and lure the men not content to look for the truth and happiness that tumble out at their feet. Once while at college, climb a mountaintop and get a general outlook of the land, and make it the occasion perhaps of that careful examination of yourself, that inquisition which Descartes urges every man to hold once in a lifetime—not oftener.

Waste of energy, mental distress, nervous worries dog the steps of a man who is anxious about the future. Shut close, then, the great fore and aft bulkheads, and prepare to cultivate the habit of a life of day-tight compartments. Do not be discouraged—like every other habit, the acquisition takes time, and the way is one you must find for yourselves. I can only give general directions and encouragement, in the hope that while the green years are on your heads you may have the courage to persist.

Now for the day itself! What first? Be your own daysman and sigh not with Job for any mysterious intermediary, but prepare to lay your own firm hand upon the helm. Get into touch with the finite, and grasp in full enjoyment that sense of capacity in a machine working smoothly. Join the whole creation of animate things in a deep, heartfelt joy that you are alive, that you see the sun, that you are in this glorious earth which nature has made so beautiful, and which is yours to conquer and to enjoy. Realize, in the words of Browning, that "There's a world of capability for joy spread round about us, meant for us, inviting us."

What are the morning sensations—for they control the day? Some of us are congenitally unhappy during the early hours; but the young man who feels on awakening that life is a burden or a bore has been neglecting his machine, driving it too hard, stoking the engine too much, or not cleaning out the ashes and clinkers. Or he has been too much with the Lady Nicotine, or fooling with Bacchus, or, worst of all, with the younger Aphrodite—all "messengers of strong prevailment in unhardened youth." To have a sweet outlook on life you must have a clean body. As I look on the clear-cut, alert, earnest features, and the lithe, active forms of our college men, I sometimes wonder whether or not Socrates and Plato would find the race improved. I am sure they would love to look on such a gathering as this. Make their ideal yours —the fair mind in the fair body. The one cannot be sweet and clean without the other, and you must realize, with Rabbi Ben Ezra, the great truth that flesh and soul are mutually helpful. The morning outlook—which really makes the day—is largely a question of a clean machine—of physical morality in the wide sense of the term. *"C'est l'estomac qui fait les heureux,"* as Voltaire says; no dyspeptic can have a sane outlook on life; and a man whose bodily functions are impaired has a lowered moral resistance. To keep the body fit is a help in keeping the mind pure, and the sensations of the first few hours of the day are the best test of its normal state. The clean tongue, the clear head, and the bright eye are birthrights of each day. Just as the late Professor Marsh would diagnose an unknown animal from a single bone, so can the day be predicted from the first waking hour. The start is everything, as you well know, and to make a good start you must feel fit.

In the young, sensations of morning slackness come most often from lack of control of the two primal instincts—biologic habits—the one concerned with the preservation of the individual, the other with the continuance of the species. Yale students should by this time be models of dietetic propriety, but youth does not always reck the rede of the teacher; and I dare say that here, as elsewhere, careless habits of eating are responsible for much mental disability. My own rule of life has been to cut out unsparingly any article of diet that had the bad taste to disagree with me, or to indicate in any way that it had abused the temporary hospitality of the lodging which I had provided. To drink, nowadays, but few students become addicted, but in every large body of men a few are to be found whose incapacity for the day results from the morning clogging of nocturnally flushed tissues. As moderation is very hard to reach, and as it has been abundantly shown that the best of mental and physical work may be done without alcohol in any form, the safest rule for the young man is that which I am sure most of you follow—abstinence. . . .

The other primal instinct is the heavy burden of the flesh which nature puts on all of us to ensure a continuation of the species. To drive Plato's team taxes the energies of the best of us. One of the horses is a raging, untamed devil, who can only be brought into subjection by hard fighting and severe training. This much you all know as men: once the bit is between his teeth the black steed Passion will take the white horse Reason with you and the chariot rattling over the rocks to perdition. . . .

Listen to the words of a master in Israel, William James: "Neither the nature nor the amount of our work is accountable for the frequency and severity of our breakdowns, but their cause lies rather in those absurd feelings of hurry and having no time, in that breathlessness and tension, that anxiety of feature and that solicitude of results, that lack of inner harmony and ease, in short, by which the work with us is apt to be accompanied, and from which a European who would do the same work would, nine out of ten times, be free." *Es bildet ein Talent sich in der Stille,* but it need not be for all day. A few hours out of the sixteen will suffice, only let them be hours of daily dedication—in routine, in order, and in system, and day by day you will gain in power over the mental mechanism, just as the child does over the spinal marrow in walking, or the musician over the nerve centers. Aristotle somewhere says that the student who wins out in the fight must be slow in his movements, with voice deep, and slow speech, and he will not be worried over trifles which make people speak in shrill tones and use rapid movements. Shut close in hour-tight compartments, with the mind directed intensely upon the subject in hand, you will acquire the capacity to do more and more, you will get into training; and once the mental habit is established, you are safe for life.

Concentration is an art of slow acquisition, but little by little the mind is accustomed to habits of slow eating and careful digestion, by which alone you escape the "mental dyspepsy" so graphically described by Lowell in the "Fable for Critics." Do not worry your brains about that bugbear Efficiency, which, sought consciously and with effort, is just one of those elusive qualities very apt to be missed. The man's college output is never to be gauged at sight; all the world's coarse thumb and finger may fail to plumb his most effective work, the casting of the mental machinery of self-education, the true preparation for a field larger than the college campus. Four or five hours daily—it is not much to ask; but one day must tell another, one week certify another, one month bear witness to another of the same story, and you will acquire a habit by which the one-talent man will earn a high interest, and by which the ten-talent man may at least save his capital.

Steady work of this sort gives a man a sane outlook on the world. No corrective so valuable to the weariness, the fever, and the fret that are so apt to wring the heart of the young. This is the talisman, as George Herbert says,

> The famous stone
> That turneth all to gold,

and with which, to the eternally recurring question, What is life? you answer, I do not think—I act it; the only philosophy that brings you in contact with its real values and enables you to grasp its hidden meaning. . . .

The quiet life in day-tight compartments will help you to bear your own and others' burdens with a light heart. Pay no heed to the Batrachians who sit croaking idly by the stream. Life is a straight, plain business, and the way is clear, blazed for you by generations of strong men, into whose labors you enter and whose ideals must be your inspiration. In my mind's eye I can see you twenty years hence—resolute-eyed, broad-headed, smooth-faced men who are in the world to make a success of life; but to whichever of the two great types you belong, whether controlled by emotion or by reason, you will need the leaven of their spirit, the only leaven potent enough to avert that only too common Nemesis to which the Psalmist refers: "He gave them their heart's desire, but sent leanness withal into their souls."

The Wisdom of the Body: Studies in Physiology

WALTER B. CANNON (1871-   )

THE PROGRESS of science has brought mankind closer to control over its ills than over its emotions. Many infectious and deficiency diseases have been conquered in the past few decades. We have sulfa drugs and penicillin to combat many infections; insulin to control diabetes; plasma to avert shock; arsphenamines to cure syphilis; vitamins and potent endocrine preparations, some synthetic, to prevent and relieve deficiency diseases. But we still have misery and vice, war and destruction, outcroppings of uncontrolled baser human drives. Whatever opinions one may hold as to the role of science in the future improvement of mankind, it is certain that we can profit by more exact knowledge of the reactions of the body under conditions of emotional excitation. Studies of this sort, beginning with physiology and ranging on—in interpretation—to psychology, sociology, and ethics, were made at the Harvard Physiological Laboratories, especially between 1911 and 1915. The results of these studies, more provocative than definitive, have been summarized by Walter B. Cannon, who (from 1906) was the George Higginson professor of physiology at Harvard. A native of Wisconsin, Cannon studied at Harvard and joined its faculty in 1899, a year before receiving his M.D. degree. A lieutenant colonel in the Medical Corps during World War I, he was president of the Medical Research Society of the American Red Cross in France in 1917–18. In 1939 he was president of the American Association for the Advancement of Science.

English is the original language of "Bodily Changes in Pain, Hunger, Fear and Rage," from whose second edition (1929) the passages quoted here are taken. The book was originally published in 1920 by D. Appleton & Company, New York.

"BODILY CHANGES IN PAIN, HUNGER, FEAR AND RAGE"

FEAR, RAGE, and pain, and the pangs of hunger are all primitive experiences which human beings share with the lower animals. These experiences are properly classed as among the most powerful that determine the action of men and beasts. A knowledge of the conditions which attend these experiences, therefore, is of general and fundamental importance in the interpretation of behavior.

There are, of course, many surface manifestations of excitement. The contraction of blood vessels with resulting pallor, the pouring out of "cold sweat," the stopping of saliva flow so that the "tongue cleaves to the roof of the mouth," the dilation of the pupils, the rising of the hairs, the rapid beating of the heart, the hurried respiration, the trembling and twitching of the muscles, especially those about the lips—all these bodily changes are well-recognized accompaniments of pain and great emotional disturbance, such as horror, anger, and deep disgust. But these disturbances of the even routine of life, which have been commonly noted, are mainly superficial and therefore readily observable. Even the increased rapidity of the heartbeat is noted at the surface in the pulsing of the arteries. There are, however, other organs, hidden deep in the body, which do not reveal so obviously as the structures near or in the skin the disturbances of action which attend states of intense feeling. Special methods must be used to determine whether these deep-lying organs also are included in the complex of an emotional agitation.

Lying anterior to each kidney is a small body—the adrenal gland. It is composed of an external portion or cortex, and a central portion or medulla. From the medulla can be extracted a substance, called variously suprarenin, adrenin, epinephrin, or "adrenalin," which, in extraordinarily minute amounts, affects the structures innervated by the sympathetic division of the autonomic system precisely as if they were receiving nervous impulses. For example, when adrenin is injected into the blood, it will cause pupils to dilate, hairs to stand erect, blood vessels to be constricted, the activities of the alimentary canal to be inhibited, and sugar to be liberated from the liver. These effects are not produced by action of the substance on the central nervous system, but by direct action on the organ itself. And the effects occur even after the structures have been removed from the body and kept alive artificially.

The adrenals are glands of internal secretion, i.e., like the thyroid, parathyroid, and pituitary glands, for example; they have no connection with the surface of the body, and they give out into the blood the material which they elaborate.

The phenomena of a great emotional disturbance in an animal indicate that sympathetic impulses dominate the viscera. When, for example, a cat becomes frightened, the pupil dilates, the activities of the stomach and intestines are inhibited, the heart beats rapidly, the hairs of the back and tail stand erect—from one end of the animal to the other there are abundant signs of nervous discharges along sympathetic courses. Do not the adrenal glands share in this widespread subjugation of the viscera to sympathetic control?

This question, whether the common excitements of an animal's life might be capable of evoking a discharge of adrenin, was taken up by D. de la Paz and myself in 1910. We made use of the natural enmity between two laboratory animals, the dog and the cat, to pursue our experiments. In these experiments the cat, fastened in a comfortable holder, was placed near a barking dog. Some cats when thus treated showed almost no signs of fear; others, with scarcely a movement of defense, presented the typical picture. In favorable cases the excitement was allowed to prevail for five or ten minutes, and in a few cases longer. Samples of blood were taken within a few minutes before and after the period.

All these considerations, taken with the proof that sympathetic impulses increase secretion of the adrenal glands, and taken also with the evidence that, during such emotional excitement as was employed in these experiments, signs of sympathetic discharges appeared throughout the animal from the dilated pupil of the eye to the standing hairs of the tail tip, led us to the conclusions that the characteristic action of adrenin on intestinal muscle was in fact, in our experiments, due to secretion of the adrenal glands, and that that secretion is increased in great emotion.

THE INCREASE OF BLOOD SUGAR IN PAIN AND GREAT EMOTION

Sugar is the form in which carbohydrate material is transported in organisms; starch is the storage form. In the bodies of animals that have been well fed the liver contains an abundance of glycogen or "animal starch," which may be called upon in times of need. At such times the glycogen is changed and set free in the blood as sugar. Ordinarily there is a small percentage of sugar in the blood—from 0.06 to 0.1 per cent. When only this small amount is present the kidneys are capable of preventing its escape in any noteworthy amount. If the percentage rises to the neighborhood of 0.18 per cent, however, the sugar passes over the obstacle set up by the kidneys, and is readily demonstrable in the urine by ordinary tests. This condition of "glycosuria," therefore, may properly be considered, in certain circumstances, as evidence of increased sugar in the blood. The injection of adrenin can liberate sugar from the liver to such an extent that glycosuria results. Does the adrenal secretion discharged in pain and strong emotional excitement play a role in producing glycosuria under such conditions?

In clinical literature scattered suggestions are to be found that conditions giving rise to emotional states may be the occasion also of more or less permanent glycosuria. Great grief and prolonged anxiety during a momentous crisis have been regarded as causes of individual instances of diabetes, and anger or fright has been followed by an increase in the sugar excreted by persons who already have the disease. Kleen cites the instance of a German officer whose diabetes and whose Iron Cross for valor both came from a stressful experience in the Franco-Prussian War. The onset of the disease in a man directly after his wife was discovered in adultery is described by Naunyn; and this author also mentions two cases in his own practice—one started during the bombardment of Strasbourg (1870), the other started a few days after a companion had shot himself. . . .

The results noted in lower animals have been confirmed in human beings. One of my former students, W. G. Smillie, found that four of nine medical students, all normally without sugar in their urine, had glycosuria after a hard examination, and only one of the nine had glycosuria after an easier examination. The tests, which were positive with Fehling's solution . . . were made on the first urine passed after the examination. Furthermore, C. H. Fiske and I examined the urine of twenty-five members of the Harvard University football squad immediately after the final and most exciting contest of the season of 1913, and found sugar in twelve cases. Five of these positive cases were among substitutes not called upon to enter the game. The only excited spectator of the Harvard victory whose urine was examined also had a marked glycosuria, which on the following day had disappeared.

Other tests made on students before and after important scholastic examinations have been published by Folin, Denis, and Smillie. Of thirty-four second-year medical students tested, one had sugar before the examination as well as afterward. Of the remaining thirty-three, six, or 18 per cent, had small but unmistakable traces of sugar in the urine passed directly following the ordeal. A similar study was made on second-year students at a women's college. Of thirty-six students who had no sugar in the urine on the day before, six, or 17 per cent, eliminated sugar with the urine passed immediately after the examination.

From the foregoing results it is reasonable to conclude that just as in the cat, dog, and rabbit, so also in man, emotional excitement produces temporary increase of blood sugar.

THE UTILITY OF THE BODILY CHANGES IN PAIN AND GREAT EMOTION

We now turn from a consideration of the data secured in our experiments to an interpretation of the data. One of the most important lessons of experience is learning to distinguish between the facts of observation and the inferences drawn from those facts. The facts may remain unquestioned; the explanation, however, may be changed by additional facts or through the influence of more extensive views. Having given this warning, I propose to discuss the bearings of the results reported in the earlier chapters.

Our inquiry thus far has revealed that the adrenin secreted in times of stress has all the effects in the body that are produced by injected adrenin. It co-operates with sympathetic nerve impulses in calling forth stored carbohydrate from the liver, thus flooding the blood with sugar; it helps in distributing the blood to the heart, lungs, central nervous system, and limbs, while taking it away from the inhibited organs of the abdomen; it quickly abolishes the effects of muscular fatigue; and it renders the blood more rapidly coagulable. These remarkable facts are, furthermore, associated with some of the most primitive experiences in the life of higher organisms, experiences common to all, both man and beast—the elemental experiences of pain and fear and rage that come suddenly in critical emergencies. What is the significance of these profound bodily alterations? What are the emergency functions of the sympathico-adrenal system?

THE REFLEX NATURE OF BODILY RESPONSES IN PAIN AND THE MAJOR EMOTIONS, AND THE USEFUL CHARACTER OF REFLEXES

The most significant feature of these bodily reactions in pain and in the presence of emotion-provoking objects is that they are of the nature

of reflexes—they are not willed movements, indeed they are often dis-
tressingly beyond the control of the will. The pattern of the reaction, in
these as in other reflexes, is deeply inwrought in the workings of the
nervous system, and when the appropriate occasion arises, typical organic
responses are evoked through inherent automatisms.

It has long been recognized that the most characteristic feature of
reflexes is their "purposive" nature, or their utility either in preserving
the welfare of the organism or in safeguarding it against injury. The
reflexes of sucking, swallowing, vomiting, and coughing, for instance,
need only to be mentioned to indicate the variety of ways in which
reflexes favor the continuance of existence. When, therefore, these automatic responses accompanying pain and fear and rage—the increased
discharge of adrenin and sugar—are under consideration, it is reasonable
to inquire first as to their utility.

Numerous ingenious suggestions have been offered to account for the
more obvious changes accompanying emotional states—as, for example,
the terrifying aspect produced by the bristling of the hair and by the
uncovering of the teeth in an access of rage. The most widely applicable
explanation proposed for these spontaneous reactions is that during the
long course of racial experience they have been developed for quick
service in the struggle for existence. . . .

"Reservoirs of Power"

That the major emotions have an energizing effect has been commonly
recognized. Darwin testified to having heard, "as a proof of the exciting
nature of anger, that a man when excessively jaded will sometimes invent
imaginary offenses and put himself into a passion, unconsciously, for the
sake of reinvigorating himself; and," Darwin continues, "since hearing
this remark, I have occasionally recognized its full truth." Under the
impulse of fear, also, men have been known to achieve extraordinary feats
of running and leaping. McDougall cites the instance of an athlete who,
when pursued as a boy by a savage animal, leaped over a wall which he
could not again "clear" until he attained his full stature and strength.
The exploit of John Colter, as reported by a contemporary, exemplifies
vividly the reinforcing effects of great excitement. In Montana, in 1808,
Colter and a companion were seized by Indians. Colter was stripped
naked; his companion, who resisted, was killed and hacked in pieces. The
chief then made signs to Colter to go away across the prairie. When he
had gone a short distance he saw the younger men casting aside every-

thing but their weapons and making ready for a chase. "Now he knew their object. He was to run a race, of which the prize was to be his own life and scalp. Off he started with the speed of the wind. The war whoop immediately arose; and looking back, he saw a large company of young warriors, with spears, in rapid pursuit. He ran with all the speed that nature, excited to the utmost, could give; fear and hope lent a supernatural vigor to his limbs, and the rapidity of his flight astonished himself." After nearly three miles his strength began to wane. He stopped and looked back. Only one of his pursuers was near. The Indian rushed toward him, attempted to cast his spear, and fell headlong. Colter seized the spear, killed his enemy, and again set out, "with renewed strength, feeling, as he said to me, as if he had not run a mile."

The very unusual abilities, both physical and mental, which men have exhibited in times of stress were dealt with from the psychological point of view by William James in one of his last essays. He suggested that in every person there are "reservoirs of power" which are not ordinarily called upon, but which are nevertheless ready to pour forth streams of energy if only the occasion presents itself. These figurative expressions of the psychologist receive definite and concrete exemplification, so far as the physical exhibitions of power are concerned, in the highly serviceable bodily changes which have been described.

It would doubtless be incorrect to attempt to account for all the increased strength and tireless endurance, which may be experienced in periods of great excitement, on the basis of abundant supplies provided then for muscular contraction, and a special secretion for avoiding or abolishing the depressive influences of fatigue. Tremors, muscular twitchings, the assumption of characteristic attitudes, all indicate that there is an immensely augmented activity of the nervous system—an activity that discharges powerfully even into parts not directly concerned in struggle, as, for example, into the muscles of the voice, causing peculiar cries or warning notes; into the muscles of the ears, drawing them back or causing them to stand erect, and into the small muscles about the lips, tightening them and revealing the teeth. The typical appearances of human beings, as well as lower animals, when in the grip of such deeply agitating emotions as fear and rage, are so well recognized as to constitute a primitive and common means of judging the nature of the experience through which the organism is passing. This "pattern" response of the nervous system to an emotion-provoking object or situation is probably capable of bringing into action a much greater number of neurones in the central nervous system than are likely to be concerned in even a supreme act of volition. The nervous impulses delivered to the muscles, furthermore, operate upon organs well supplied with energy-yielding material and well fortified by rapidly circulating blood and by secreted adrenin, against quick loss of power because of accumulating waste. Under such circumstances of excitement the performance of extraordinary feats of strength or endurance is natural enough. . . .

THE FIERCE EMOTIONS AND STRUGGLES OF BATTLE

Throughout the discussion of the probable significance of the bodily changes in pain and great emotion the value of these changes in the struggle of conflict or escape was emphasized. In human beings as well as in lower animals the wildest passions are aroused when the necessities of combat become urgent. One needs only to glance at the history of war-fare to observe that when the primitive emotions of anger and hatred are permitted full sway men who have been considerate and thoughtful of their fellows and their fellows' rights suddenly may turn into infuriated savages, slaughtering innocent women and children, mutilating the wounded, burning, ravaging, and looting, with all the wild fervor of demons. It is in such excesses of emotional turbulence that the most astonishing instances of prolonged exertion and incredible endurance are to be found. . . .

THE DESIRABILITY OF PRESERVING THE MARTIAL VIRTUES

Although there is increasing opposition to the display of the fighting emotions and instincts in war, nevertheless the admirable moral and physical qualities, claimed by the militarists to be the unique products of war, are too valuable to be lost. As McDougall has indicated, when the life of ideas becomes richer, and the means we take to overcome obstructions to our efforts more refined and complex, the instinct to fight ceases to express itself in its crude natural manner, save when most intensely excited, and becomes rather a source of increased energy of action toward the end set by any other instinct; the energy of its impulses adds itself to and reinforces that of other impulses and so helps us to overcome our difficulties. In this lies its great value for civilized man. A man devoid of the pugnacious instinct would not only be incapable of anger but would lack this great source of reserve energy which is called into play in most of us by any difficulty in our path.

Thus the very efficiency of a war against war, as well as struggle against other evils that beset civilized society, rests on the preservation and use of aggressive feeling and the instinct to attack. From this point of view the insistence by the militarists that we must accept human nature as we find it, and that the attempt to change it is foolish, seems a more justifiable attitude than that of the pacifists who belittle the fighting qualities and urge that changing them is a relatively simple process. We should not wish them changed. Even if in the war against war a means should be established of securing international justice, and if through co-operative action the decrees of justice were enforced, so that the occasions which would arouse belligerent emotions and instincts were much reduced, there would still remain the need of recognizing their elemental character and their possible usefulness to society. What is needed is not a suppression of these capacities to feel and act, but their diversion into other channels where they may have satisfactory expression.

Moral Substitutes for Warfare

"We must make new energies and hardihoods continue the manliness to which the military mind so faithfully clings. Martial virtues must be the enduring cement; intrepidity, contempt of softness, surrender of private interest, obedience to command, must still remain the rock upon which states are built." Thus wrote William James in proposing a "moral equivalent for war." This, he suggested, should consist of such required service in the hard and difficult occupations as would take the childishness and superciliousness out of our youth and give them soberer ideas and healthier sympathies with their fellow men. He conceived that by proper direction of its education a people should become as proud of the attainment by the nation of superiority in any ideal respect as it would be if the nation were victorious in war. "The martial type of character," he declared, "can be bred without war. Strenuous honor and disinterestedness abound elsewhere. Priests and medical men are in a fashion educated to it, and we should all feel some degree of it imperative if we were conscious of our work as an obligatory service to the state. We should be owned, as soldiers are by the army, and our pride would rise accordingly. We could be poor, then, without humiliation, as army officers now are. The only thing needed henceforth is to inflame the civic temper as past history has inflamed the military temper."

Similar ideas have been expressed by others. It has been pointed out that the great war of mankind is that against pain, disease, poverty, and sin; that the real heroes are not those who squander human strength and courage in fighting one another, but those who fight for man against these his eternal foes. War of man against man, in this view, becomes dissension in the ranks, permitting the common enemies to strike their most telling blows.

These moral considerations, however, are apart from the main intent of our discussion. Our earlier inquiry confirmed the belief that the fighting emotions are firmly rooted in our natures, and showed that these emotions are intimately associated with provisions for physical exertion.

The History of Surgery, Amusingly Summarized

HARVEY CUSHING (1869–1939)

BEFORE CUSHING the brain of the living human being was *terra incognita* —an unknown land—to the surgeon. Today successful neurosurgery is a commonplace. Cushing himself removed more than two thousand brain tumors. More than that, his influence established centers of neurosurgical teaching and practice throughout the world; there is even a Harvey Cushing Society for the exchange of information on neurology. While still a young man, practicing surgery at Johns Hopkins Hospital after graduation from Yale (1891), the Harvard Medical School and an internship at the Massachusetts General Hospital, Cushing was advised by his chief, Halsted, against undertaking the unpromising new specialty which he eventually conquered. The work was slow and painstaking, it had many ramifications, and it led to developments in medicine far removed from the techniques of surgery. For example, when in 1909 Cushing operated to remove from the base of the brain a diseased pituitary gland causing acromegaly (gigantism), his work set in train new developments in endocrinology which demonstrated that the "enigmatic organ," the pituitary body, was no mere vestigial affair but a "master gland" of the whole endocrine system.

Harvey Cushing was born in Cleveland, Ohio, to a New England family in which three generations of doctors had preceded him. After leaving Hopkins to study in Europe with Kocher and Kronecker in Switzerland and Sherrington in England, Cushing was appointed to the faculty of the Harvard Medical School and became surgeon in chief at the Peter Bent Brigham Hospital. In World War I he rose to become senior consultant in neurologic surgery to the British and American armies. In 1933 he left Boston to become Sterling professor of neurology at the Yale Medical School.

Cushing was as distinguished with his pen as with his scalpel. In 1925 he was awarded the Pulitzer prize for his imperishable biography: "The Life of Sir William Osler." Like Osler, Cushing himself was a historian of medicine, a bibliophile, a wit, and a demon for work. He contributed over two hundred and fifty articles and books to lay and medical literature, including "The Pituitary Body and Its Disorders" and "From a Surgeon's Journal—1915–18." He collected a magnificent medical library (now at Yale) and owned the most complete assemblage of the works of Vesalius. The essay here selected to represent Cushing's work again emphasizes the fact that men of science can also be men of letters. This pleasant summary of the history of surgery, its wisdom coated with wit, its learning mocked with pseudo references, may bring especial pleasure to those who have followed in these pages the history of medical science's long and continuing struggle against the forces of death. This intrepid work continues. On the occasion of his seventieth birthday, when a celebration in his honor had been arranged, Cushing closed his own acknowledgment of the tribute with these words:

"In closing, may I quote a verse from the Talmud which is mindful of the first aphorism of Hippocrates but is none the worse for that:

" 'The day is short and work is great. The reward is also great and The Master praises. It is not incumbent on thee to complete the work, but thou must not therefore cease from it.' "

English was the language in which Cushing addressed the Boston Surgical Society, on May 3, 1933, on the topic of *"Homo Chirurgicus."* The occasion was the award to him of the Bigelow Medal "for contributions to the advancement of surgery." The address was published and is reprinted from "The New England Journal of Medicine" (208:18, 922–29, May 4, 1933).

HOMO CHIRURGICUS: THE SURGEON

BIOLOGICALLY SPEAKING, the chirurgeon is a peculiar animal of comparatively recent era with a pair of hands terminating in ten more or less highly specialized digits. It has been generally assumed that they were his most distinguishing feature and from a paleontological standpoint the only satisfactory explanation for the appearance of his species.

Through them—his hands—by the natural course of selective evolution out of *Homo eoanthropus* of the Pliocene (exemplified by the Piltdown man), through *Homo medicus ordinarius et generalis* of whom (or which) fossiliferous specimens are numerous in the early Pleistocene deposits, and then by way of *Homo medicus internus* (an interglacial form), he had arrived and been set apart among Paleolithic cave dwellers as *Homo chirurgicus, superbus et supremus*—proving the truth of the Darwinian theory.

While this, for all practical purposes, would seem incontrovertible and as near the scientific truth as one might expect to arrive in this fallen world, it has proved annoying rather than gratifying to *Homo medicus internus,* whose present postglacial [sometimes called human] representative looks upon himself as the last word, as he says: "Produce the facts."

Now this Baconian idea—long used and at times abused even by what are known as biometricians and astrophysicists—of first assembling the facts, has suddenly struck the popular fancy and nowadays if you are not "factual" you are as nothing. Whether you have got at the true facts, rather than misleading ones, and whether you can interpret them properly or more easily twist them to your own way of thinking, and what you are going to do with them even then doesn't much matter. And since *H. medicus internus* has raised this question of Who's Who-est among medical *Homos,* let us, between friends, get at the facts—he his, we ours.

This was not so simple as it promised at first to be, for *H. medicus* promptly insisted on enlarging the scope of the inquiry to include not only Who's Who, but How's How, and Why's Why. It was quite impossible to comply with this demand for several reasons. To drag personalities into a scientific discussion would lead no one could tell where, and it was almost certain to get into the papers. Should this happen, it was no less certain to attract the attention of *Homo sociologicus,* a primitive fact-finding mammal whose contemporary flora and fauna (to quote from Professor G. Elliot Smith) "indicate a favorable forest environment where food was plentiful and safety was assured by concealment or flight rather than by combat with weapons."[1]

Still, as we say, facts must be faced, and to assemble our own before *H. medicus* assembled his, the first thing to do unquestionably was to make a factual study of those appendages most essential to *H. chirurgicus,*

[1] The claim put forth by *H. sociologicus* of his descent from *Homo pithecanthropus,* the early ape man, is, to be sure, only his wish to believe; others are inclined to trace the species back to the lemur, for in the study of an example and comparing it with the walrus, Wolfgang Goethe, in a factual mood during his early youth, first discovered the intermaxillary bone.

viz., his hands. There, surely, would lie the secret of his selective peculiarities—his pre-eminence. In short, as has been often said: "Hands make the man." Hence we will begin with ourselves, work back through the sculptor, artist, musician, cabinetmaker, blacksmith, bricklayer, until we come finally to *H. medicus* and others unhandy. It will be a long and expensive study, but what of that? We will enlist the interest of one or more of the foundations in the problem.

The methods to be pursued having thus been formulated, as opportunity has offered, beginning with the most clever and distinguished of the species from evenly distributed parts of the country, chirurgeons, one by one, over the course of the past seven years have been lured, under one pretext or another, into the well-known shop of the late Signor Caproni. He, Signor Caproni, having previously been let into the conspiracy, while the lurer was about his pretended errand in the back of the shop, would politely show the unsuspecting victim his latest works in plaster—the Winged Victory, the Discobolus, and this or that Venus—and then would suddenly say: "Your hand, signor, what a marvelous hand! Allow me to take a cast of it to preserve for future generations: it will take but a moment."

It was of course highly essential that no one should surmise the scientific purport of what was being assembled, least of all *H. medicus,* lest spurious, non-surgical, even female hands be surreptitiously added to the collection. Needless to say, all precautions were taken in this regard and the type groupings *per 1000* of the population, which will be found in the tables of the Appendix (Note particularly Table 161), may be looked upon as mathematically correct. With this secretly acquired and painstakingly assorted material before us, it has been possible quietly to study, analyze, and make graphs of some of the more famous and characteristic hands of *H. chirurgicus* ever submitted to intensive research, coupled at the same time with what is known as "an exhaustive perusal of the literature." (Cf. Bibliography, 419–456.)

At the outset it was somewhat disconcerting to find that there were an unsuspected number of manumetric subspecies. However, it was soon realized that they could be divided into certain major groups: viz., (1) big hands, (2) little hands, (3) fat hands, (4) skinny hands, (5) muscular hands, and (6) those which showed a definite affinity for feminine hands. These six principal groups having thus been satisfactorily classified, the next step was to subdivide them in correspondence with the several chirurgical specialties which have acquired their own lingo and issue weekly "Transactions" in the vernacular. Easily recognized were the following digital types: (a) long, (b) stubby, (c) tapering, (d) bulbous, and finally, (e) crooked—these last having been discarded from the study to be dealt with separately in a privately printed monograph now going through the press and promised for October (Barnum, Bailey and Saunders, Inc., Pub's., N. Y. and Phila.).

Properly to interpret the data thus assembled, the aid of *Homo mathematicus* was solicited at this point, and he by the employment of those processes understandable only to his species succeeded, for the first time in the history of science, in plotting on a single graph the five variables representing each and every digit. This of itself was said to be a brilliant achievement fully justifying the entire research as was promptly reported in the "Science News Letter" for August 12, 1928, pp. 19–21.

However, as is so often the case, the calculations were unconvincing from the double standpoint of astrology and alchemy, and consequently some more dependable method had to be sought. Fortunately at this juncture it was proposed, by a recent undergraduate student of tutorial grade, that if samples were taken from each hand in the collection and subjected to biochemical study, it might be possible by the phosphotase determinations to detect an enzyme, a pleuriglandular hormone, or even to precipitate a crystalline base that was common to all.

This clever suggestion was immediately acted upon. Under sterile precautions, biopsy specimens were removed, quickly refrigerated, and transferred in suitable containers to the laboratory of *H. biochemicus,* who, though otherwise engaged, kindly allowed one of his most trustworthy lady technicians (candidate for a Ph.D.) to make the determinations. To cut a long story short, she finally reported that, with variations so slight they could be excluded, the ash of all surgeons' hands is basically the same, being composed of $CaSO_4 . 2H_2O$, or what in the arts is known as parisian gypsum of surprising chemical purity. Therefore, as Euclidian geometers and Humanists would say: *"Quod erat demonstrandum."*

Now this investigation might have been pursued further by a similar comparative analysis of the hands of *Homo medicus,* but to his species the same exact and precise methods were inapplicable. In the first place, he could not be lured into Signor Caproni's shop, even under the pretense of viewing this or that Venus—he saw plenty of 'em on ward rounds. In the second place, this control study seemed scarcely necessary for both Cuvier and Othniel Charles Marsh, after much grubbing in the tertiary gravel, had made it clear that *H. medicus* is five-toed and represents the ancient, and hitherto unrecorded, primitive form of Eocene man; whereas *H. chirurgicus* in the early quatenary had developed a splint bone, which has had much to do with his selective superiority. There indeed is abundant evidence to show that from times most remote he has found it useful in his trade of immobilizing fractures.

Obviously with factual data of this convincing sort in our possession, a control study was a mere waste of time, for the deductions could be drawn by any laboratory technician familiar with a slide rule and accustomed to measuring intake and output in mgm. per cent. While *H. medicus* was obliged to admit the truth of this argument, he nevertheless proceeded to issue a minority report in which it was asserted, on anthropological grounds, that a doer with his hands is a retrocessive type compared with a thinker with his brains. He demanded consequently that comparative measurements be made of the intracranial volume of the two species; for in this way, and in this way only, could the true index of encephalic superiority be determined.

Though the vote was close, this disturbing proposal was blackballed on the third ballot after it had been pointed out that even though the frontal cortex of *H. medicus* may in certain instances be larger and show deeper sulci, not to speak of its gyrations, *H. chirurgicus* has a magnificently developed prerolandic motor area which takes up just as much room. Furthermore, should one progress in the usual fashion from morphology to the study of function, there is abundant experimental evidence to show that both species exhibit no determinable alteration of behavior when completely deprived of their frontal lobes; but should, on the other hand, the motor area be removed from *H. chirurgicus,* he is as nothing, whereas *H. medicus* gets along just as well as before. So again: Q.E.D.

Now in the passage of geological time *Homo chirurgicus,* who formerly was content to nibble at, and occasionally to lop off, the external parts of the body under the direction of *H. medicus internus,* has gradually become more internal than *H. internus* himself. Indeed, as a "looker in" on slight provocation he can scarcely be excelled by *Homo pathologicus*—a subspecies of doer, of whom mention has not heretofore been made, though he is a very important check on *H. chirurgicus* during his occasional recurring periods of aerophagic self-inflation.

Naturally enough, *H. chirurgicus* first began by looking in at what *H. poeticus* has called the windows of the soul. This was harmless enough and easy enough, for the blinds are rarely drawn. He started as a mere window washer but it wasn't long before he began to see things his digits impelled him to remove—an imprisoned eyelash, a cinder from the communal fireplace. He even learned to evert the upper blind in his search for these foreign bodies, and it was not long before he saw something opaque and white behind the glass which was impeding his view of what lay beyond. So he set to work to fashion a tool with which he could manage to pry it out. His fame spread so rapidly that all those who experienced any difficulty in seeing through their windows from inside began coming to him in increasing numbers and he learned much as he went along that was new and unrecorded. So he set it down in manuscript and disciples of the new learning wore a path to his cave, and finally, not long after his invention of the lorgnette, he emerged as *H. chirurgicus* (*subspec.*) *ophthalmicus,* the first, capable of leading an independent existence, to bud off from the parent chirurgical stock.

But it was not for long that he was the only separatist. Certain representatives of *H. chirurgicus* soon began peering into holes that had neither windows nor shutters—notably noses, mouths, and ears, for they also were accessible, convenient, and required no time-consuming removal of garments. Long before the advent of *H. c.* (*subspec.*) *ophthalmicus,* a buccal claim to which he had acquired legal rights, had already been staked out by *Homo dentarius,* a maverick with no ancestral relation even to *H. medicus generalis*—or if he had, it was so long ago it's been forgotten when. Though his digits have not been fully studied, a brief note regarding them will be found in Appendix 14, where mention is made of the prehistoric traces of his highly ingenious inlays on the incisors of Assyrian pundits in the Stone Age.

Until recent times *H. dentarius* lived somewhat apart and was reached by taking the stairs, but ever since he carved out of lignum vitae a double set of ivory dentures for the Father of his Country (now in the National Museum—i.e., the dentures), his social importance has begun to be more fully appreciated. He has moved his place of business to the first floor front and is no longer just an occasional puller and filler and rubber dammer as of old.

H. medicus internus, who dislikes all orifices and has never been known to go farther than to look at the protruded tongue and classify its coats, has begun to show such regard for *H. dentarius* that should you happen to have an obscure rheumatic ache you will first lose your impacted wisdoms and subsequently all others you have left—at one sitting under gas—unless you are unusually strong-minded. With this medical backing *H. dentarius* has driven *H. chirurgicus* almost wholly out of the mouth, stopping, like the Japanese in Manchukuo, only at the Great Wall of the fauces. And though he has been temporarily obliged to go off the gold standard, his exports and imports are well balanced, and should you desire to have your maxilla or mandible artistically exchanged for something else, he's your man.

All this has proved highly embarrassing to *H. chirurgicus (subspec.) laryngologicus,* who must cross Manchukuo to get at what he wants south of the wall. He still holds claim to the nose and its accessories but you can't easily set a snare for the tonsils through the nostrils, much less view the vocal cords and explore the bronchial tubes for inhaled peanuts. Like enough any day *H. dentarius* will claim he's a bandit and on a pretended foray go south of the wall himself and remain there. And what, pray, would the League of Ethics and Discipline have to say to this? The tonsils certainly have in the past shown no capacity for self-determination.

Then there is *H. c. (subspec.) otologicus,* who has acquired distinction as an expert looker in at the ears. This side-door work is usually done from outside, but it is well known that when *Homo naso-laryngologicus* is not around *H. otologicus* uses his private front-door openings and goes right through the house to put his blowpipe in the kitchen entrance of the *Ductus eustachii.* He can do this blindfolded by the sense of feel, which shows he's been there fairly often.

He also has an advantage over all other lookers in because he isn't obliged to work in the mid-line, and being ambidextrous can take his choice, east or west. And though he scarcely ventures so far from home as does his nose-dwelling colleague who spends his vacations fishing for diaper pins in the southern oesophagus, he too drills and quarries deeply and sometimes has even been known actually to insert his thumb in the *Encephalon* and say, "What a good boy am I."

One peculiarity that has often been observed regarding both *H. otologicus* and *H. laryngologicus* is the fact that, not content with puttering in their small portals of entry, they must also show their expertness by peering at the same time through a small hole in a mirror, which must be a very difficult thing to learn. It is supposed to be a relic of the days when they had to wear something over their faces to conceal the expression of surprise when they hooked something they could land. Certain Arabic authorities dealing with early folkways have, to be sure, given a different explanation of the custom. (Cf. Appendix 39.)

And there are other hole-and-corner subspecies of *H. chirurgicus,* of whose ways less is known, for their expeditionary base is so far south it is necessary to cross the Equator to get there. Some of the early explorers were often unheard from for years and the accounts of their thrilling experiences, now found in only a few libraries, were privately printed either in Spanish or Portuguese—the male and female languages spoken in those remote parts of the microcosmos. To be sure, it is now possible for these venturesome spirits to keep in touch with civilization by wireless and the loud-speaker, but from all accounts, in view of the poorly charted coast and its beacons far between, one must be an exceptionally good mariner to reach his destination, more often than not by blind reckoning.

It is in the memory of living *Homos* that one of these southerly disposed workers, while looking for the New Atlantis, lost his bearings during an equinoctial hurricane and landed by mistake on the Isle of Omphalos [this was a navel expedition] which lies approximately halfway between the Pole Star and the Southern Cross, toward which he was supposed to be headed. The rediscovery of this barren atoll offered a rare opportunity for a new specialty, not to be lost; and while certain ruins and inscriptions made it evident that some medical viking by the name of S. Cabot, M.D., had been there before, the newcomer's priority was established in that beautifully illustrated preliminary account of the expedition published anonymously with colored plates in the Transactions of the National Geographical Society for August 1896 (now out of print and a *rarissime* of collectors).

It was shown in this treatise that the *Omphalos* (as it is now called for short) can be so easily and perfectly removed *in toto* that the subject afterward might well be mistaken for Adam—or for Eve (as the case might be). An additional advantage lay in the fact that all subsequent temptation to utilize the region for the induction of hypnotic reveries, as commonly practiced in the Orient, would thereby be permanently removed.

The United Tropical Debuttonizing Company, Inc., with its main offices in Miami was promptly organized with several retired naval officers on the board. Stock was issued and by a successful advertising campaign what promised to be a very profitable business was launched. As is well known, with the outbreak of the Spanish War and the taking over of all naval operations by the government, the popularity of the procedure waned and the company went into forced liquidation. In his detailed description of this episode in the "History of Our Times," Mark Sullivan points out that the only present reminder of it is the game of "Button-Button," which was set to music and was once as popular as "Sweet Adeline" and "Casey at the Bat."

While this was the last hope of *H. c.* (*subspec.*) *gynaecologicus* to establish a colony so far from his home base, the *Omphalos* is not, and never was, truly an orifice, whatever else one may say of it—and that is not much. Hence this form of beautification, along with face lifting and other plastic arts which flourished during the mauve period, has always been regarded by all true lookers in as something of which the less said the better—at least until the ladies have left the table.

As will have been gathered from the lamentable episode of the U. T. D. Co. and its dissolution, *H. c. (subspec.) gynaecologicus* was no timid coastwise mariner. In the course of his long search for the Northwest Passage by repeated soundings and palpatings, he had already established colonies throughout the lower venter; and it was a race to see whether he or *H. c. (subspec.) urologicus,* a rough and ready deep-sea fisherman, would be the first to reach the upper tidal basin and make a forced landing on the rockbound coast of the calyces—which is the Norwegian for fjord. And when they did finally arrive there neck and neck, it was found impossible in the dark, even after turning on the X ray, to tell which calyx was the female of the species; and the matter is still in the hands of a board of arbitration for decision.

Now it was becoming all too apparent to *H. chirurgicus* that these *(subspec.)* hole-and-corner chirurgeons, who instead of just looking in were daring to penetrate, by air, land, or water routes, into the ever deeper recesses of the body, would soon meet in *medias res,* as it is called, and unless he bestirred himself, or in sporting parlance "beat them to it," there would be nothing left for him but the arms, the legs, the neck, and the back.

Even in these widely separated outlying districts there was trouble brewing. A fellow called *H. orthopaedicus,* who was clever with weights and pulleys and claimed to be a natural-born bonesetter had suddenly discovered the possibilities of doing business with the skeleton. There was no special menace in this for *H. chirurgicus,* who, while perfectly aware of the skeleton, had shown no particular hankering for it. Anyone who would cart it away could have it for nothing so far as he was concerned.

But things began to take on a different aspect when *H. orthopaedicus* began to fool with the joints, claiming they were the hinges of the skeleton and went with it. In fact, in the sacroiliac hinterland—a three-day journey from Erewhon—he discovered a joint which he could put in and out with a click, and though painful it became a popular resort in spite of the distance from home. Beginning with this obscure region back of the beyond, it was not long before he claimed complete supervision over the extremities "and all that in them is," including bones, joints, muscles, and nerves.

While *H. orthopaedicus* never pretended to be much of a looker in, he soon entered into business cahoots with a foreigner called *H. roentgenologicus,* a homuncule whom *H. chirurgicus* had befriended, put up at his club, and introduced to the best people when he first arrived bearing German letters of introduction. But *H. roentgenologicus* had an evil eye which enabled him to look in almost anywhere without the necessity of having his own hole or being obliged to make one. While this peculiar gift was embarrassing to certain prudish people, it slowly came to be realized both by *H. orthopaedicus* and *H. medicus* that a power so unusual might be very useful to them, and these three are now inseparable; they rotate in the same seats at the symphony and play a threesome together every Sunday morning.

It can be readily understood that *H. chirurgicus generalis* had begun to feel distinctly uneasy in regard to all these permanent squatters on the badlands of his ancestral preserves, which he had often shot over but never attempted seriously to cultivate. It was shortly after the appearance on the scene of *H. roentgenologicus,* and while the attention of the world was focused on the aforementioned renal dispute between *H. urologicus* and *H. gynaecologicus,* that he roused himself and determined to do a little exploratory looking in on his own account.

Shortly before this time there had been rumors of popular discontent in a little explored and scarcely known region lying southeast of the *Omphalos* and vaguely indicated in the geographies as the *Fossa iliaca dextra.* Over this region *H. obstetricus,* a distant cousin of *H. gynaecologicus,* had claimed a quasi mandate ever since July 12, 102 B.C., when, during that chance encounter on the Via Linea Alba, he had the presence of mind to say: "Mr. Julius Caesar, I believe." This claim *H. chirurgicus* had always regarded as a form of cisalpine gaul, particularly as *H. obstetricus* had rarely been there since and had engaged *H. medicus* superficially to patrol the region from time to time and act as his general factotum. So it proved a simple matter, by the distribution of some purgative propaganda, to stir up a revolution in the *Fossa* and to make this a justifiable cause of chirurgical intervention.

While a full account of this episode will also be found in an Appendix, it may suffice to say here that *H. chirurgicus,* having once forced his way in during a midwinter campaign (since known as "the attack *à froid*") and having consolidated and quieted this area by drastic measures, soon found himself obliged, owing to unsettled conditions in the neighborhood, to extend the campaign in order to protect his flanks.

The successful storming of that ancient icteric fortress, the *Ductus communis choledochus,* after a prolonged siege ending in a surprise attack by way of the gall bladder occurred, if one may believe the historian Sudhoff, in the last decade of the nineteenth century A.D. Then in turn, one after the other, fell the pylorus, the spleen, the pancreas, and other strongholds (too numerous to mention even by their colloquial names) that lay scattered here and there in that vast and turbulent continent south of the great *Diaphragma*—more generally speaking, between wind and water. The Thirty Years' War, which lasted almost an equal length of time, was as nothing in comparison with this; and though after each successive bombardment the hospitals were put on emergency-expansion basis, and the chirurgical teams worked on sixteen-hour shifts, it was a war to end all wars and worth the price. " 'Twas indeed a famous victory," quoth little Peterkin.

Ever since those hectic days when history was being rapidly made, the great terrain so successfully wrested from *H. medicus* has been held by right of occupation. This does not mean that it has remained entirely pacified, for what are known as recurrent attacks are frequent and are likely to keep up for some time. In view of the rebellious, not to say inflammatory, nature of the inhabitants, egged on by that secret revolutionary body, the Society of Internal Secretions, which instigated a succession of anti-peristaltic movements, one perhaps could scarcely expect that law and order would everywhere prevail even under the obviously beneficent rule of *H. chirurgicus.*

The chief source of recurrent trouble has lain in the fact that when the treaty of peace was signed *H. medicus* was permitted to retain what is commonly known as a Polish corridor. This has given him a southern outlet to the Adriatic, where he has built up so profitable an export trade in diuretics, nitrates, and other saline products, the traffic of *H. c.* (*subspec.*) *urologicus* has been nearly ruined and he now ekes out a miserable existence wholly under water, diving for oysters and pearls. It is entirely due to this lack of political foresight, as Walter Lippmann has pointed out, that *H. medicus* thus manages to balance his budget and even to pay an income tax, which just now is unusual for medical *Homos* of any sort or class.

Warned by these troubles on the Italian border and to protect himself against a possible rear attack from the hepatic area over which *H. medicus* has continued to maintain a certain authority, *H. chirurgicus* has been obliged for military reasons to storm the wind-swept heights above the diaphragm. Under the pretense of once more opening up the ancient drains from the pleura for sanitary purposes, a mobile force known as the T.E.F., heavily armed with modern osteoclasts, was dispatched in caterpillar cars along the old Via Mammillaria used by the Roman legions as the more direct approach to the upper pectoral border. Arrived there and before any effective opposition could be organized, a large portion of the thoracic wall was blasted away and an advance guard wearing gas masks entered through the breach, quickly set up a positive-pressure chamber, and securely entrenched themselves within.

From this point of vantage frequent raids have been made by the T.E.F. up and down the mediastinal pathways in the course of which so much plunder has been removed it has been necessary for the engineers, at great expense and labor, to collapse the entire easterly wall of the thorax, almost obliterating their very base of operations.

All this was quite contrary to the intentions of *H. chirurgicus generalis* and orders were consequently issued from his headquarters in the R.I.F. for the recall of the expedition. Whereupon with their osteotomes the T.E.F. severed all lines of communication with the outer world by dividing both phrenics and set up an independent satrapy of their own under the name of *H. c. (subspec.) thoracicus* with the insolent slogan: "*Venimus, Vidimus, Vicimus.*"

It has been rumored that in some of their forays for the capture of clots in the pulmonary arteries they have occasionally met *H. c. (subspec.) naso-laryngologicus* on one of his peanutting expeditions from the north. He has usually retreated after a brief scrimmage, being unaccustomed to the sound of heavy artillery, preferring to leave the question of his mandate to the League of Organs.

Meanwhile, not satisfied with paralyzing that international boundary, the *Diaphragma, H. c. (subspec.) thoracicus,* with complete disregard for others, while executing some of his more complicated maneuvers along the *Chordae tendineae,* has had the effrontery from time to time actually to stop the heart. All this has been simply incredible to *H. medicus internus,* who has been listening to the fracas from behind the scapula through his binaural stethoscope, and he says: "What *are* we coming to?"

Nor is this the end, for something almost worse than this, I hesitate to say, has happened well within the Arctic Circle, in what formerly was a sort of No Man's Land, sparsely inhabited by aimless and harmless Eskimos known as *H. psychologicus sive psychiatricus.* From certain crania found embedded in the ice it has been learned that even in the days of the hairy mastodon certain preglacial and Stone Age representatives of *H. chirurgicus* had practiced there what was known as trepanning, by scratching holes with a piece of flint in the heads of those who harbored evil spirits—or thought they did—and were willing to take the chance. *H. psychiatricus,* at all events, had probably given the diagnosis up by that time, or he may indeed have actually referred the case, and suggested splitting the fee, thus originating an intolerable custom it's been difficult to eradicate. But this, of course, is only a guess and we must stick to what is factual.

And the facts of this sorry case are that even before *H. c. (subspec.) intrathoracicus* broke loose from the control of *H. chirurgicus,* an expeditionary force equipped with two-handed weapons of powerful biting type had embarked on sledges for the far north where they have permanently ensconced themselves in their artificially lighted igloos under the banner of *H. c. (subspec.) neurochirurgicus.*

They were a motley crew at best, miners and sappers, donors and suckers, embryogenic differentiators with their freezers, fixers, and cutters, orderlies and disorderlies—one of them a top sergeant who had seen service in several wars and knew all about motor-driven battering rams no calvarium could resist. What manner of mischief they may be up to is scarcely known even to their nearest neighbors, the lookers in at nose, ears, and eyes, and it's perhaps just as well to forget about them and to let them frappé in their own frigid clime.

The rumor has been circulated that they have already split into three political parties, central, spinal, and peripheral. The last, having communistic tendencies, sit on the left and so continuously utter their peculiar party cry of "Sympathico-tonus, rah, rah, rah!" it is exceedingly difficult for the temporary presiding officer, who happens to be a conservative centralist, to keep any semblance of order—much less to get any business done.

Now *H. chirurgicus generalis* lives in hope that he is at last done with all these separatist movements on the part of his subalterns, for he is busy enough in more temperate, not to say tropical, zones holding *H. medicus generalis* at bay. For the latter has made a powerful ally of that very *Homo, H. biochemicus,* who generally shuns intercourse with others, feeling that he has lost caste since the tutorial student induced him to have that historic study of chirurgeons' hands made in his laboratory.

There is a constant threat that through this political alliance much hardly won territory in the venter may be lost; for should the local anesthetic used in the outlying regions happen to wear off, a revolution might be fomented which could easily spread and get out of hand.

Should this occur, *H. chirurgicus* might be driven back to make a last desperate stand behind the *Fossa iliaca dextra,* which in all these years has been so thoroughly emptied and drained it no longer affords so good a protection as it once did.

From this brief historical sketch it might be gathered that all this shifting of boundaries is something peculiar to our own turbulent times. History, however, but repeats itself and the rising sun sees no occurrence it has not seen before—as someone seems already to have said better and more briefly. In the remote dawn of recorded time, as long before Hippocrates practiced his art in the Temple of Cos as we practice ours after him, an unknown Theban scribe sat himself down in the upper valley of the Nile to make in cursive hieroglyphs a copy, for someone, of a papyrus roll which, to judge from its terms and phraseology, may already have been a thousand or two years old.

The original text may well enough have been contemporary with, possibly even written by, that deified Egyptian, the venerable Imhotep, medical adviser of the Pharaoh and much else besides. That would be some five thousand years ago, taking us back to the days when the pyramid of Gizeh was in process of erection—alongside of which our most ambitious structures of steel and concrete of the present day are as pigmies.

So in a world already old, and with civilization at its unmistakable peak, the scribe on his twelve carefully united sheets of well-chosen papyrus, partly in ink which was black, partly for rubrics in ink which was red, began to copy line by line the text of a medical document whose antiquity is such as to make the Hippocratic codices seem almost a product of our own times.

Why and for whom the copy was being made, and why the transcription was left incomplete, ending as it did in the middle of a sentence, is as unknown as are the names both of author and transmitter. But there is enough of it to show that the original was written by an observer who at that early time, fifty centuries ago, had broken away from the superstitions which even to this day encumber the progress of medicine.

He has set down what observation and experience had taught him, probably much of it in time of war, for he was a surgeon and his treatise, which was illustrated by fifty-eight case reports, dealt principally with wounds. In a truly scientific spirit, after a brief statement of each case, he gives the history, the results of his examination, and by an inductive process proceeds to his diagnostic conclusion and the recommendations for treatment should intervention of any sort be advisable. Nor does he hesitate to include the sixteen cases unfavorable for therapeutic measures, and he specifically points out when natural processes should be allowed to run their course without meddling.

The treatise begins methodically, in true scholastic fashion, with the description of the head, goes on to the thorax and then to the spine and dorsal region, where the copy comes to its abrupt end; but had it gone farther, the venter, the pelvis, and the extremities would have followed in turn. This downward progression from head to foot has been the classical method of presentation ever since that time, and heaven only knows for how long a time before. Toward the close of what we absurdly call the Middle Ages and reckon as long ago, it was the method followed by William of Salicet, by Lanfranco, by Henri de Mondeville, by Guy de Chauliac; and in a recent textbook by a certain *Homo* yclept Homans from our very midst it was still being followed.

How much of this was the obvious method and how much of it merely tradition is impossible now to say, for the roots of tradition lie deep in all of us and while we go through the motions of periodically freeing ourselves from its presumed shackles, we only imagine that we wholly succeed. Records based on observation have an enduring value that transcends all our social philosophies and the doer merely does over again—always a little better, we would like to believe—what someone has done before and someone else before him.

From the beginning when men have quarreled, they have armed themselves with the nearest thing at hand—a chance club or a boulder; and the most vulnerable thing to hit, if one could, has always been the head. Were the blow not fatal, some third party learned to bind it up; and when men fought in groups and wounds were many, learning came faster for those already adept, and so the chirurgeon emerges.

Unlike the priest-physician, the chirurgeons may well enough from the first have been reckoned as combatants who, like Podalarius and Machaon, happened at the same time to possess some measure of skill in the treatment of wounds. But the wars of which Homer sang bred pestilential diseases even as they do today. Then as now it was not all dressing of wounds. While the gods were being propitiated, camps had to be drained, pure water and proper food provided, the diseased segregated and evacuated. We may flatter ourselves on knowing more, but the general problem was, is, and always will be the same. And after the lapse of a few centuries—much less fifty—what, pray, will be thought of us, now so proud of our vaunted accomplishments?

Both physic and surgery arose from the necessities of life, and whether the surgeon arrived already differentiated or was a physician turned specialist is less important than the fact that he was always a better surgeon if he was a good deal of both. In his special line, observation and reasoning were born of realities and, as he was often called upon in emergencies, causes and results were usually self-evident. He has had less inclination and scant time to speculate on the phenomena of disease and to philosophize about the bearing of the four elements—fire, air, earth, and water—on symptoms that were hot or cold or dry or moist, and on the relation of these to phlegm, blood, yellow or black bile, not to speak of the complexions. He probably couldn't see what all these doctrines had to do with the practical business of setting a fracture any more than his modern prototype cares to bother his head with prolactin, folliculin, intermedin and prolan B, to mention a very few of our present-day humors, which so markedly affect the temperaments and complexions of our patients.

But these ruminations are too serious for an occasion such as this, and the topic is scarcely a safe one for an *H. chirurgicus* to handle even with his rubber gloves. Even from a chirurgical operation, to withdraw may sometimes be the better part of valor. It was my intention to carry the session through under novocaine, but I see signs of restlessness and rather than put you fully to sleep it is perhaps wiser to postpone the rest for a second sitting—should you survive and be willing, of which there is considerable doubt.

So while "closing up" I may add that the only reason for harking back to Imhotep was to point out that even in his remote time *H. medicus* had the same richly convoluted frontal cortex he now has and *H. chirurgicus* showed the same propensity to fly off into numerous forms of specialization because of his expansive prerolandic gyrus. And should Imhotep return to us, one could guarantee that he would adjust himself in short order to all our newfangled devices and rituals and at the same time hold in reserve a good deal to teach us in the bargain.

And finally, while adjusting the dressing and pinning the binder as comfortably as I may, it is unnecessary to remind you that as a class we chirurgeons often do things better with our hands, when our heads and hearts are not allowed wholly to govern our actions. For if I had permitted you to know, during the course of this operation, what was really in the back of my head and what lay deep in my heart to say to you, you would have judged me to be a sentimentalist rather than the eminently practical person which every *Homo chirurgicus* outwardly feigns to be.

A Sense of Nature

DONALD CULROSS PEATTIE (1898–)

In the end as in the beginning, scientist and poet alike stand in awe before the inscrutable subtleties of nature, forever defying a final explanation. An able American botanist and author, Donald Culross Peattie, in two brief passages from his "Almanac for Moderns" has phrased the spirit of eternal quest that permeates the heart of science and offers a fitting epilogue to the original words of great scientists from antiquity to the present—and beyond.

Peattie was born in the Middle West—Chicago; studied in the East—Harvard; worked at plant research in the South—Miami; resides in the West—California. Among the better known of his twenty-five published books are "Singing in the Wilderness," "Flowering Earth," "Green Laurels," and "The Road of a Naturalist."

English is the language of "An Almanac for Moderns," published by G. P. Putnam's Sons, New York, in 1939.

THE BEST OF LIFE

June First

Now this is the best of life, that a man should have children who promise fair, and a loving wife, and that he should know what his work is, and own a sense of nature. This sense is nothing less than a feeling for reality. I do not mean the reality intended by cantankerous and disagreeable people, who are so fond of calling upon others to face the unpleasant. They enjoy referring to the sores and cuts of life, to the power of evil, to their own disappointments and failures and the abysmal depths to which human nature can sink.

But all these things—war and money and cruelty—are passing illusions. These are the unquenchable realities—the power of the expanding seed to break a stone, the strength that sustains men to die for others, the shortness of life that makes it so precious, all futurity hungering in us, that makes woman taste so sweet.

NO FINALITY

January Twentieth

THE ROLE of biology today, like the role of every other science, is simply to describe, and when it explains it does not mean that it arrives at finality; it only means that some descriptions are so charged with significance that they expose the relationship of cause and effect. It may be an ingrained trait of the human mind to look for a first great cause of all natural phenomena such as some poets and some mechanistically disposed scientists believe in, but it is a far nobler thing to be able to suspend your judgment—for your whole lifetime, if necessary; to observe without the will to believe some particular thing or the intention of proving some preconceived belief.

That is the stand that every honest modern man, scientist or otherwise, must take, and mechanists and vitalists alike ought to be found assembled on that hill, lifting up their arms to heaven and praising truth.

SELECTED READINGS[1]

IN THE HISTORY OF SCIENCE

BELL, E. T. *Men of Mathematics*. New York: Simon & Schuster, Inc., 1937.

BOAS, FRANZ. *The Mind of Primitive Man*. Revised edition. New York: The Macmillan Company, 1938.

CAJORI, FLORIAN. *History of Mathematics*. 2nd edition. New York: The Macmillan Company, 1919.

——. *History of Physics*. Revised edition. New York: The Macmillan Company, 1929.

CORNER, G. W. *Anatomy* (Vol. 3 of Clio Medica). New York: Paul B. Hoeber, Inc.—Harper & Brothers, 1930.

CROWTHER, J. G. *British Scientists of the Nineteenth Century*. London: George Routledge & Sons, Ltd., 1936.

DAMPIER-WHETHAM, SIR W. C. *A History of Science*. Cambridge University Press, 1929.

DARROW, FLOYD L. *Masters of Science and Invention*. New York: Harcourt, Brace & Company, 1923.

DRACHMAN, J. M. *Studies in the Literature of Natural Science*. New York: 1930.

FARRINGTON, B. *Science in Antiquity*. London: Thornton Butterworth, Ltd., 1936.

FINDLAY, A. *A Hundred Years of Chemistry*. London and New York: The Macmillan Company, 1937.

GARRISON, FIELDING H. *Introduction to the History of Medicine*. 4th edition. Philadelphia: W. B. Saunders Co., 1929.

GUMPERT, MARTIN. *Trail Blazers of Science*. New York: Funk & Wagnalls Company, 1936.

HARVEY-GIBSON, R. J. *Two Thousand Years of Science*. New York, 1929.

HOGBEN, LANCELOT. *Science for the Citizen*. 2nd edition. New York: Alfred A. Knopf, 1938.

MOTTELAY, P. F. *Bibliographical History of Electricity and Magnetism*. London: J. B. Lippincott Company, 1922.

[1]Though this bibliography is far from exhaustive, it includes only books published in the last quarter century (since 1919).

MUMFORD, LEWIS. *Technics and Civilization*. New York: Harcourt, Brace & Company, 1934.

PARTINGTON, J. R. *Short History of Chemistry*. London and New York: The Macmillan Company, 1937.

PEATTIE, DONALD C. *Green Laurels, The Lives and Achievements of the Great Naturalists*. New York: Simon & Schuster, Inc., 1936.

RÁDL, E. *The History of Biological Theories*. Translated by E. J. Hatfield. London: Oxford University Press, 1930.

RIESMAN, DAVID. *The Story of Medicine in the Middle Ages*. New York: Paul B. Hoeber, Inc.—Harper & Brothers, 1935.

SARTON, GEORGE. *Introduction to the History of Science*. Baltimore: Williams & Wilkins Company, 1927.

SEDGWICK, W. T., and TYLER, H. W. *A Short History of Science,* revised by H. W. Tyler and R. P. Bigelow. Revised edition. New York: The Macmillan Company, 1939.

SHRYOCK, R. H. *The Development of Modern Medicine*. Philadelphia: University of Pennsylvania Press, 1936.

SINGER, CHARLES. *A Short History of Biology*. London: Oxford University Press, 1931.

SMITH, DAVID E. *History of Mathematics*. Boston: Ginn & Company, 1923–25.

THORNDIKE, LYNN. *History of Magic and Experimental Science During the First Thirteen Centuries of Our Era*. New York: The Macmillan Company, 1923–34.

TRATTNER, E. R. *Architects of Ideas*. New York: Carrick & Evans, Inc., 1938.

VAN LOON, HENDRIK. *The Story of Inventions*. Garden City: Garden City Publishing Company, Inc., 1934.

WOLF, A. *History of Science, Technology and Philosophy in the Sixteenth and Seventeenth Centuries*. New York: The Macmillan Company, 1935.

———. *History of Science, Technology and Philosophy in the Eighteenth Century*. New York: The Macmillan Company, 1939.

SOURCE BOOKS (ANTHOLOGIES)

BEEBE, WILLIAM (editor). *The Book of Naturalists, An Anthology of the Best Natural History*. New York: Alfred A. Knopf, 1944.

CLENDENING, LOGAN (compiler). *Source Book of Medical History*. New York and London: Paul B. Hoeber, Inc.—Harper & Brothers, 1942.

CULLIMORE, ALLAN R. (editor). *Through Engineering Eyes, Science Selections from Literature*. (Re-edited by Frank A. Grammer and James H. Pitman.) New York and Chicago: Pitman Publishing Corporation, 1941.

DAMPIER-WHETHAM, SIR W. C., and WHETHAM, MARGARET D. (arrangers). *Cambridge Readings in the Literature of Science*. New York: The Macmillan Company, 1924.

ELIOT, CHARLES W. (editor). *Harvard Classics* (Vol. 38, Scientific Papers). New York, 1897.

FULTON, JOHN F. (editor). *Selected Readings in the History of Physiology*. Springfield (Illinois): Charles C Thomas, 1930.

KNICKERBOCKER, W. S. (editor). *Classics of Modern Science (Copernicus to Pasteur)*. New York: Alfred A. Knopf, 1927.

LAW, FREDERICK HOUK (editor). *Science in Literature, A Collection of Literary Scientific Essays*. New York and London: Harper & Brothers, 1929.

LONG, E. R. (editor). *Selected Reading in Pathology from Hippocrates to Virchow*. Springfield (Illinois): Charles C Thomas, 1929.

MAGIE, WILLIAM FRANCIS (editor). *A Source Book in Physics*. New York and London: McGraw-Hill Book Company, Inc., 1935.

MAJOR, RALPH H. (editor). *Classic Descriptions of Disease*. Springfield (Illinois): Charles C Thomas, 1932.

MATHER, KIRTLEY F., and MASON, SHIRLEY L. (editors). *A Source Book in Geology*. New York and London: McGraw-Hill Book Company, Inc., 1939.

SHAPLEY, HARLOW, and HOWARTH, HELEN E. (editors). *A Source Book in Astronomy*. New York and London: McGraw-Hill Book Company, Inc., 1929.

———, RAPPORT, SAMUEL, and WRIGHT, HELEN (editors). *A Treasury of Science*. New York and London: Harper & Brothers, 1943.

SMITH, DAVID EUGENE (editor). *A Source Book in Mathematics*. New York and London: McGraw-Hill Book Company, Inc., 1929.

THOMS, HERBERT (editor). *Classical Contributions to Obstetrics and Gynecology*. Springfield (Illinois): Charles C Thomas, 1935.

WILLIUS, F. A., and KEYS, T. E. (editors). *Cardiac Classics*. St. Louis: The C. V. Mosby Company, 1941.

PERIODICALS

Bulletin of Johns Hopkins University Institute of the History of Medicine. Baltimore.

Isis, the official journal of the History of Science Society. Boston.

Medical Classics. Baltimore.

Proceedings of the Section of the History of Medicine of the Royal Society of Medicine. London.

Acknowledgments

We wish to thank our publishers for their gracious co-operation and enthusiastic interest in helping us prepare this book for publication, often under difficult conditions. We are grateful to Donald Elder for his early and unflagging editorial interest in this work; to Mrs. John Tebbel and Miss Ethel Ryan for accurately and pleasantly carrying through a perfectly stupendous copy-editing job; and to Mrs. Christine Pollard for aiding us in the complicated business of getting copyright clearances. To various members of the staff at the New York Public Library, Columbia University Libraries, and the University of Minnesota Library we also wish to extend our thanks.

The editors wish to express their thanks to the following authors, publishers, or holders of copyright for permission to reprint the selections listed below:

John Bale Medical Publications Limited—for extracts from "Roentgen and the Early History of the Roentgen Rays," by William Conrad Roentgen, translated by Otto Glaser.

G. Bell & Sons, Ltd.—for extracts from "Recollections and Reflections," by Sir J. J. Thomson.

Cambridge University Press—for extracts from "The Theory of Spectra and Atomic Constitution," by Niels Bohr, translated by Dr. A. D. Udden; and from "The Works of Archimedes," translated by Sir Thomas Heath, Sc.D.

W. B. Cannon, M.D.—for extracts from his book, "Bodily Changes in Pain, Hunger, Fear and Rage."

The Clarendon Press—for extracts from "The Works of Aristotle: Historia Animalium," edited by J. A. Smith and W. D. Ross; and from "The Origin and Development of the Quantum Theory," by Max Planck, translated by H. T. Clarke and L. Silberstein.

Columbia University Press—for extracts from "The Black Death and Men of Learning," by Anna Montgomery Campbell; from "Three Copernican Treatises," translated by Edward Rosen, 1939; and from "The Physical Treatises of Pascal," translated by I. H. B. and A. G. H. Spiers, 1937.

E. P. Dutton & Co., Inc.—for extracts from "Greek Medicine," translated by A. J. Brock, M.D.; from "On the Nature of Things," by Lucretius, translated by W. E. Leonard; from "A Discourse on Method," by René Descartes, translated by John Veitch, permission also from J. M. Dent & Sons, Ltd.; for extracts from "The Philosophical Works of Francis Bacon," edited by John M. Robertson, reprinted from texts and translations by Ellis and Spedding, with permission also from George Routledge & Sons, Ltd.; and extracts from "Memories of My Life," by Francis Galton, with special permission from the executors of Francis Galton and Methuen & Co., Ltd.

Dodd, Mead & Company, Inc.—for extracts from "The Life of the Bee," by Maurice Maeterlinck, copyright 1901, by Dodd, Mead & Company, with permission also from George Allen & Unwin Ltd.

Thomas P. Fleming—for his translation of "Letter from an Editor," by Conrad Gesner.

Charles Griffin & Co., Ltd.—for an extract from "Magnetism and Electricity," by William Gilbert, translated by P. Fleury Mottelay, 1893.

Harvard University Press—for extracts from "Vitruvius: The Ten Books on Architecture," translated by Morris Hicky Morgan, 1914.

Paul B. Hoeber, Inc.—for "Prevention of Rabies," by Dorothy Clendening, from "Source Book of Medical History," edited by Logan Clendening; and for extracts from "Life and Times of Ambroise Paré," by Francis R. Packard.

The Johns Hopkins Press—for "The Hippocratic Oath," translated by Ludwig Edelstein, from Supplement No. 1 to the "Bulletin of the History of Medicine," edited by Henry E. Sigerist.

Liveright Publishing Corporation—for extracts from "A General Introduction to Psychoanalysis," by Professor Sigmund Freud, translated by Joan Riviere, with permission also from George Allen & Unwin Ltd.

Longmans, Green and Co., Inc.—for extracts from "Lamarck: The Founder of Evolution: His Life and Work," translated by Alpheus S. Packard; from "On the Sensations of Tone," by Hermann L. F. von Helmholtz, M.D., translated by Alexander J. Ellis; and for "The Training of Nurses," by Florence Nightingale, from "Quain's Dictionary of Medicine," 1894 edition.

The Macmillan Company—for extracts from "The Autobiography of Benvenuto Cellini," translated by John Addington Symonds; from "Treatise on Light," by Christian Huygens, translated by Sylvanus P. Thompson, published in England by Macmillan & Co., Ltd.; from "Sedgwick's Principles of Sanitary Science and Public Health," revised by Samuel C. Prescott and Murray P. Horwood; from "The Miscellaneous Papers of Heinrich Hertz," translated by D. E. Jones and G. A. Schott, published in England by Macmillan & Co., Ltd.; from "The Theory of Spectra and Atomic Constitution," by Niels Bohr, translated by Dr. A. D. Udden; and from "The Works of Archimedes," edited by Sir Thomas Heath, Sc.D.

Massachusetts General Hospital—for extracts from "The Semicentennial of Anesthesia: The Account of an Eyewitness," by Washington Ayer.

McGraw-Hill Book Company, Inc.—for extracts from "A Source Book in Physics," edited by William Francis Magie.

"The New England Journal of Medicine"—for *Homo Chirurgicus*," by Harvey Cushing, M.D.

Northwestern University Studies—for extract from "Dialogues Concerning Two New Sciences," by Galileo Galilei, translated by Henry Crew and Alfonso de Salvio.

W. W. Norton & Company, Inc.—for extracts from "Matter and Light: The New Physics," by Louis de Broglie, with special permission from the author and George Allen & Unwin Ltd.; from "Science and the Human Temperament," by Erwin Schroedinger, translated by Dr. James Murphy and W. H. Johnston, with permission also from George Allen & Unwin Ltd.; and from "Where Is Science Going?" by Max Planck, translated by Dr. James Murphy.

Princeton University Press—for extracts from "A Critique of the Theory of Evolution," by Thomas Hunt Morgan.

G. P. Putnam's Sons—for extracts from "The Interpretation of the Atom," by Frederick Soddy, M.A., with permission also from John Murray, London; and for extracts from "An Almanac for Moderns," by Donald Culross Peattie, with permission also from George Allen & Unwin Ltd.

Ray Society, London—for extracts from "Critica Botanica of Linnaeus," translated by Sir Arthur Hort, revised by M. L. Green, B.A., F.L.S.

Reynal & Hitchcock, Inc.—for extracts from "The Notebooks of Leonardo da Vinci," translated by Edward MacCurdy, permission also from Jonathan Cape Limited.

Royal Horticultural Society, London—for an extract from "Experiments in Plant Hybridization," by Gregor Mendel.

The Royal Society of Medicine—for extracts from the Preface of Andreas Vesalius to *De Humani Corporis Fabrica*," 1543, translated by B. Farrington.

The Science Press—for "Mathematical Creation," from "The Foundations of Science," by H. Poincaré, authorized translation by George Bruce Halsted.

Charles Scribner's Sons—for extracts from "Men of the Old Stone Age," by Henry Fairfield Osborn.

Peter Smith—extract from "Relativity: The Special and the General Theory," by Albert Einstein, Ph.D., authorized translation by Robert W. Lawson, D.Sc., permission also from Methuen & Co., Ltd.

University of California Press—for extract from Motte's translation of Newton's *Principia*," edited by Florian Cajori.

University of Chicago Press—for extracts from "The Physical Principles of the Quantum Theory," by Werner Heisenberg, translated by Carl Eckart and Frank C. Hoyt.

University of Pennsylvania Press—for extracts from "The *Opus Majus* of Roger Bacon," translated by Robert Belle Burke.

Vassar College—for "The Discovery of Radium," a speech by Marie Curie.

Estate of Arthur Edward Waite—for extract from "Hermetic and Alchemical Writings of Paracelsus," translated by Arthur Edward Waite, 1894.

Ward Ritchie Press—for extract from "The Sinister Shepherd," by Girolamo Fracastoro, translated by Dr. William Van Wyck, with special permission from Dr. Van Wyck.

Bernhard Wolf Weinberger—for extract from "The Surgeon-Dentist," by Pierre Fauchard, translated by Bernhard Wolf Weinberger.

The Williams & Wilkins Company—for an extract from "Popular Research Narratives," Vol. II, by Sir Ernest Rutherford.

Yale University Press—for extracts from "Atoms, New and Old," from "Science in Progress," edited by George Baitsell.

Index